LONGMAN STUDY GUIDES

GCSE

Chemistry

Mark McElroy
John Sadler

LONGMAN STUDY GUIDES

SERIES EDITORS: **Geoff Black and Stuart Wall**

Titles available

Biology
Business Studies
Chemistry
Design and Technology
Economics
English
English Literature
French
Geography
German
Information Technology
Mathematics
Mathematics: Higher Level
Music
Physics
Psychology
Religious Studies
Science
Sociology
Spanish
World History

Addison Wesley Longman Ltd,
Edinburgh Gate, Harlow,
Essex CM20 2JE, England
and Associated Companies throughout the world.

First published 1988
Third edition 1997

ISBN 0582–30482–2

British Library Cataloguing-in-Publication Data
A catalogue record for this book is available from the British Library.

Set by 16 in 9.75/12pt Sabon
Produced by Longman Singapore Publishers Pte Ltd
Printed in Singapore

CONTENTS

EDITORS' PREFACE

Longman Study Guides have been written by the people who set and mark the exams—the examiners. Examiners are aware that, due to lack of practice and poor preparation, some students achieve only the lowest grades: they are not able to effectively show the examiner what they know. These books give excellent advice about exam practice and preparation, and organising a structured revision programme, all of which are essential for examination success. Remember: the examiners are looking for opportunities to *give* you marks, not take them away!

Longman Study Guides are designed to be used throughout the course. The self-contained chapters can be read in any order appropriate to the stage you have reached in your course. The examiner guides you through the essential parts of each topic, making helpful comments throughout.

We believe that this book, and the series as a whole, will help you establish and build your basic knowledge and examination technique skills. For additional help with exam practice and revision techniques, we have published a series called **Longman Exam Practice Kits**, which are available from all good bookshops, or direct from Addison Wesley Longman.

GEOFF BLACK AND STUART WALL

AUTHORS' PREFACE

This book has been prepared as a complete guide for all students studying for GCSE: Key Stage 4 and to help those wanting more information on chemistry aspects of Double Science or preparing for a separate GCSE in Science: Chemistry. It can be used either as a revision guide or as a textbook to supplement the work you do at school, college or home. The book does not contain experiments for you to do; these will be provided by your teacher. The book will not replace your teacher, but we hope that it will provide a valuable aid.

The authors are chief examiners in GCSE Chemistry and this enables them to pass on useful advice and tips which should be directly beneficial to the student.

The authors' aims are to ensure that you get the best possible grade from your work; their experience in teaching, setting examination papers and marking question papers, together with your own hard work, should help to improve your chances of success.

MARK McELROY AND JOHN SADLER

INFORMATION ABOUT THIS BOOK

The first two chapters give valuable information about how to prepare for a GCSE course in Chemistry, including information about techniques for revision, examinations, coursework and practicals, and details about examination board syllabuses. You should use the contents page and index to help you identify the sections you require at any one time. At the start of each chapter there is a topic chart which you should use to identify whether topics in that chapter are covered by your examination board; the chart can also be used to check your study and revision progress over the two years.

There is a chapter on the chemical industry and its place in society. This should be helpful not only to students but also to parents and to teachers starting out on their careers in chemistry.

In each chapter there are examination questions for you to practise what you have just learned. Answers have been supplied to all the questions set in the book. Do not look at the answers until you have attempted to answer the questions yourself. You should compare your answers with the answers supplied and, if need be, learn from any mistakes you may have made.

At the end of each chapter there is a summary box which briefly identifies the key points about topics covered in the chapter. You should check that you know and understand more fully each of the key points listed.

ACKNOWLEDGEMENTS

We are indebted to the following Examination Groups for permission to reproduce questions which have appeared in the examination papers. Whilst permission has been granted to reproduce their questions, the answers, or hints on answers, are solely the responsibility of the authors and have not been provided by a Group.

EDEXCEL Foundation (London)
Midland Examining Group (MEG)
Northern Examinations and Assessment Board (NEAB)
Southern Examining Group (SEG)
University of Cambridge Local Examinations Syndicate (UCLES)
Welsh Joint Committee (WJEC)
Northern Ireland Council for Curriculum, Examinations and Assessment (NICCEA)

We record our thanks to Stuart Wall and Geoff Black, from whom we have received a great deal of help and guidance and whose comments have led to improvements on the original manuscript.

We also thank Elizabeth Hayes for her suggestion on how to revise for examinations.

Finally, we must thank our families for their patience and their encouragement during the preparation of this book.

Chapter 1

Revision, examinations and coursework

GETTING STARTED

The National Curriculum

Since you have chosen to study Chemistry, then you must also take Biology and Physics in order to fulfil the requirements of the National Curriculum. This book has been designed to help you with your studies. It contains all the relevant information that you will need.

This chapter gives you ideas on how to revise; how to prepare yourself for the examination, and how to carry out an investigation for the coursework you must perform. Chemistry is not an easy subject but it is a very enjoyable one. Do not be afraid of the chemicals; everything is quite safe provided you carry out instructions carefully and follow the safety rules supplied by your teacher.

As you study chemistry more and more, you will become confident in your abilities. You will develop a sense of curiosity and inventiveness and hopefully acquire an open and critical mind. You will manage to solve problems more readily. As you look around you, you will become aware of the benefits and harm caused by chemists. You will appreciate the need for control of pollution and realize that chemists influence our everyday lives. Chemists are always looking for ways to improve industry and the environment. We hope that this book will help you in your studies and start you on the road to being a successful chemist.

TOPIC CHART

LONDON	MEG	NEAB	NICCEA	SEG	WJEC	IGCSE	TOPIC	STUDY	REVISION 1	REVISION 2
✓	✓	✓	✓	✓	✓	✓	Advice about revision			
✓	✓	✓	✓	✓	✓	✓	Advice about the examination			
✓	✓	✓	✓	✓	✓	✓	Types of questions			
✓	✓	✓	✓	✓	✓	✓	Mathematical requirements			
✓	✓	✓	✓	✓	✓	✓	Coursework			
✓	✓	✓	✓	✓	✓	✓	Using your practical skills			

Advice about revision

Here are some hints for committing information to long-term memory. You must try and get the information into your long-term memory in order that you can reproduce answers more easily on the day of the examination. Long-term memory depends on rehearsal and repetition. You may be surprised to learn that, for most students, 80 per cent of a lesson is forgotten by the next day! Brief but constant review over a 21-day period will ensure that you can recall material months later. Avoiding last-minute revision panic will help reduce examination anxiety and enable you to answer questions effectively.

Following a schedule will help information become part of your knowledge store, helping you to remember it as easily as you remember your home address! A suggested schedule is given in Table 1.1.

Additional points:

1. Post-It stickers can be used to keep track of your review schedule.
2. Use colours for underlining and highlighting to aid memory.

Table 1.1 Revision schedule

Time after lesson	Time spent	Procedure
Same day	5 minutes	Review lesson notes, clarify information if necessary, and highlight key facts and concepts.
One day	10 minutes	Review notes, briefly write out key points without reference to original; use a different colour pen to underline any points you missed.
Seven days	30 minutes	Reconstruct key points in revision format. Store in revision file.
Twenty-one days	30 minutes	Reproduce revision notes without reference to original scheme; compare and review. Highlight any points missed.
Three-month intervals until examinations.	10–30 minutes	Study and duplicate review notes on topics.

3. Much of memory is visual. Consider the layout of your notes, use space and symbols to make them easy to read and attractive to the eye.

At the end of each chapter there is a **summary box**. This has been designed to help you revise. You should work through the summary notes regularly until you are certain that you understand a topic completely. If you do have problems with a topic, ask a friend or your teacher to explain it to you. Also, do help other people who are having problems. Working together is another way that helps you (and your friend) to commit information to your long-term memory.

Advice about the examination

Remember that:

- The exams are written carefully by experienced teachers.
- They want you to show what you know, understand and can do.
- The examiners do not have to fail a certain number of candidates for each examination. They have standards for each grade; you will get the grade for the standard you reach.

The day before the examination:

- Get ready, collect all the equipment you will need and a spare for each. Do not rely on old pen cartridges or old calculator batteries.
- Have a relaxing day and a good night's sleep.
- Do not cram, last-minute revision may confuse you.
- Double check that you have correct details of where and when the examination will take place.

The day of the examination

- Arrive at the examination room early and try to relax.
- Once in the room, listen carefully to everything the invigilator says, they have important instructions to give you.
- If you do not understand the instructions—ask.
- Use all the time you are given to answer the question paper. You do not get extra marks for finishing early and you may lose marks by rushing.
- Pace yourself, plan your time.

For all the written examinations

- Read the instructions carefully, particularly the rubric. (The rubric tells you, among other things, how many questions you should answer.)
- Make sure you write in the information requested, such as your name, candidate number, centre number, the name of the paper, on all the answer sheets you hand in.

- Calculate how much time you can spend on each question; allow for reading the question, planning your answer, writing it and reading it over.

For short answers or structured written papers

- Make sure you know how many questions you have to answer and whether the paper has sections (these details will be shown on the front sheet of the question paper).
- Make sure you answer the compulsory questions first and the correct number of questions overall.
- Underline the key words in the question to help you keep to the point in your answer.
- Do not waste time by repeating the question in your answer.
- Look for instruction words in the question such as **describe** and **explain**. These tell you the type of answer to give.

Instruction words

Here are some instruction words: ask your teacher if you find any others in past papers or the syllabuses.

List/name	Give a number of points or facts required rather than sentences. No explanation is needed.
State	Give a brief answer, with little or no explanation.
Describe	Give a full account of the main points of the topic, using diagrams where appropriate. The marks for the question will indicate how much detail you should include.
Outline	Briefly give all the essential points.
Compare/contrast	Point out similarities and differences, advantages and disadvantages of the items mentioned in the question.
Define	Give the exact meaning of a term, principle or procedure.
Explain	Give the reasons for.
Sketch	Do a simple free-hand drawing that shows correct proportions and important details.
Suggest	Implies that there is no one correct answer. You should use your overall knowledge of the subject.

Other hints

- If you start to dry up on one question, leave space and move on. You are likely to gain more marks on the next question than you will by struggling on with the present one.
- If you feel your answer is incomplete, leave sufficient space below it so that you can come back to it later and keep it all together.
- With structured questions answer all the parts because each part does carry marks.
- Write down the answers the examiner has asked for, not all the things you can possibly tell the examiner on the subject; for example, if you were asked to list three items, list *three*. You will not get extra marks for listing more.
- Help your examiner by numbering your answers clearly. Show all your working. If you make a mistake, do not rub it out, simply cross it through.
- Make your sketches and drawings good-sized. Label them clearly and include all essential points.
- If you start to run out of time, write short, accurate notes instead of sentences.
- If you have time, read through your answers and check any calculations you have made.

Types of questions

There are no multiple choice questions in Chemistry. Questions are targeted at specific levels, either foundation level or higher level. In this book we have indicated the level of the question by using an **F** to indicate a foundation-level question and an **H** to indicate a higher-level question.

Structured questions

In these questions you will be asked very clearly for the answer the examiner is expecting. There is usually a *theme* in a structured question. The number of marks for each section is in brackets; you should write your answers to these questions in the spaces provided on the question paper using blue or black biro (ink tends to smudge). DO NOT USE OTHER COLOURED BIROS—examiners mark in red and they use other colours for checking papers.

An example of a structured question is:

The compound calcium carbonate occurs in nature as marble.

(a) **Name two other forms of calcium carbonate which occur in nature.** (2)
(b) **Write down the chemical formula of calcium carbonate.** (1)
(c) **Carbon dioxide can be detected using an aqueous solution of a calcium compound:**
  (i) **Write down the common name of the aqueous solution of the calcium compound which is used to test for carbon dioxide.** (1)
  (ii) **What is the chemical name for this compound?** (1)

Essay questions

The higher-level papers for chemistry tend to have essay questions. These questions usually draw on knowledge from various parts of the course. Make a plan of your essay and write neatly and legibly. There is no need to write pages; an essay that is short and to the point will gain as many marks as a long-winded answer. Essay questions are written either on the question paper or on paper supplied to you. Again, if your answers are to be written on the examination question paper, use a biro.

Explain why the following cause pollution of our environment; (a) the discharge of acid waste into the rivers, (b) the incomplete combustion of petrol in car engines.

Note that the question is about pollution—but you do not have to write everything you know about pollution. Part (a) has nothing to do with acid rain, so don't waste time writing about it. Part (b) is about the incomplete combustion of petrol, so there is no need to mention lead compounds in petrol. In other words, **you must read the question.**

Mathematical requirements

Some of the questions in chemistry require some mathematics. The mathematical skills required will be those that you have learnt from your studies in your National Curriculum Mathematics course. The following list is not exhaustive but will act as a guide to the skills that you will require.

'Some useful mathematical skills.'

- whole numbers; odd, even
- estimation/approximation to obtain reasonable answers
- the four rules applied to whole numbers and decimal fractions
- measures of weight, length, area, volume and capacity in current terms
- time: 24-hour and 12-hour clock
- reading of clocks and dials
- use of tables and charts
- interpretation and use of graphs in practical situations
- drawing graphs from given data
- simple solid figures
- collection, classification and tabulation of statistical data
- reading, interpretation and drawing simple inference from tables and statistical diagrams
- construction of bar charts and pictograms
- whole numbers: prime, square
- factors, multiples, idea of square root
- directed numbers in a practical situation
- vulgar and decimal fractions and percentages; equivalence between these forms
- cases; conversion from vulgar to decimal fraction with the help of a calculator
- scales, including map scales
- elementary ideas and applications of common measures of rate
- efficient use of a pocket calculator; application of appropriate checks of accuracy

Table 1.2

Quantity	Base unit	Symbol
Electric current	ampere	A
Length	metre	m
Mass	kilogram	kg
Temperature	kelvin Celsius Centigrade	K °C
Energy (heat)	joule	J
Volume	litre or cubic decimetre	l or dm^3

Table 1.3

Multiple	Prefix	Symbol
10^6	mega	M
10^3	kilo	k
10^{-2}	centi	c
10^{-3}	milli	m
10^{-6}	micro	μ
10^{-9}	nano	n
10^{-12}	pico	p

Data books

A candidates' data book is available for use in some examinations. It contains data that you are not expected to remember. You should make sure that you are familiar with this booklet prior to the examination.

Units

You should be familiar with the units and prefixes listed in Tables 1.2 and 1.3.

Thus, kilometres would be represented by km, millilitres by ml and microseconds by μs.

You will be allowed to use a calculator.

Graphs

Most graphs that you draw in chemistry will be *straight lines*. The only *exceptions* are likely to be rate graphs (plotting mass or volume against time). Examples of *straight-line* graphs are:

(a) plotting mass of one element against another (to find formulae);
(b) electrolysis (plotting mass or volume against time);
(c) precipitation reactions (plotting mass precipitated against volume or mass added);
(d) plotting heat combustion of various hydrocarbons against number of carbon atoms.

With the more difficult papers you have to select your own scale for your graph. Make sure that your graph almost fills the graph paper. On other papers, the scales will be given to you. Make sure you understand the scale used.

Diagrams

It is difficult to draw diagrams clearly and accurately and you should practise. Diagrams (see Fig. 1.1) should be two-dimensional and you should *not* draw the bench, the stands used for holding the apparatus or people. The diagram must represent *real* apparatus. The

Fig. 1.1

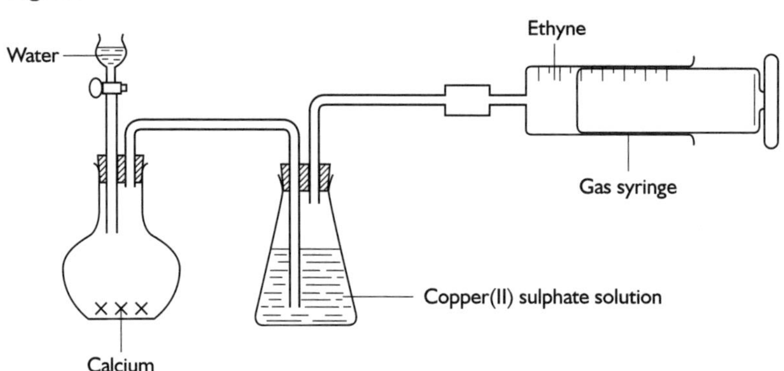

'A clear, well-labelled diagram is important.'

apparatus should be labelled in pencil using *full names* of chemicals (i.e. not formulae). Unless you are collecting a gas in a syringe, make sure the apparatus is not completely sealed (it would blow up!). An example of a question requiring a diagram is:

> **When water is added to calcium dicarbide, calcium hydroxide and the gas ethyne are formed. Ethyne contains impurities which can be removed by passing the gas through aqueous copper(II) sulphate solution. Ethyne is insoluble in water. Draw a labelled diagram of the apparatus you would use to prepare and collect pure ethyne.**

Note that in this diagram a tap funnel has been used to prevent gas from escaping; the gas will bubble through copper(II) sulphate solution; there are corks in both flasks; the tubes are seen to pass through the corks; the gas is collected in a gas syringe (it could have been collected over water); lines are used for labelling (not arrows); the names of chemicals are written in full.

Study the other diagrams in this book; we have been very careful to make them accurate.

Coursework

Throughout the years of taking your GCSE examination in chemistry your coursework will be assessed by your teacher. You will get used to your teacher coming round the class with a clip-board in his or her hand. If you are having problems, do not hesitate to ask your teacher. It is better to do this than to score no marks in the assessment! In practical work always wear goggles and tie back long hair. Try to work tidily and logically. Do *not* start your experiment until you have understood what you are doing. Do not let your partner do all the work—*you* must become competent as well as him or her.

Assessment of spelling, punctuation and grammar

All the examining boards will award up to three marks for spelling, punctuation and grammar for *coursework only*. The performance criteria are the same for all the boards.

Threshold performance (1 mark)	Candidates spell, punctuate and use the rules of grammar with reasonable accuracy; they use a limited range of specialist terms appropriately.
Intermediate performance (2 marks)	Candidates spell, punctuate and use the rules of grammar with considerable accuracy; they use a good range of specialist terms with facility.
High performance (3 marks)	Candidates spell, punctuate and use the rules of grammar with almost faultless accuracy, deploying a range of grammatical constructions; they use a wide range of specialist terms adeptly and with precision.

Using your practical skills

The experimental work described so far forms the basis of the internally assessed practical content of your GCSE course. Coursework will be worth 25 per cent of your final mark. The courses are designed to allow you to show your ability in a range of experimental skills. You will be able to demonstrate that you can do the following.

P Plan experimental procedures
You will be expected to suggest ideas to investigate. You could carry out preliminary ideas before making a plan on how to carry out the investigation. Decide on the observations and measurements you are going to take and decide how you will control key variables. Finally, decide on the apparatus and equipment that you are going to use, but above all make sure that your experiment is safe. Your teacher will certainly help you here.

O Obtain evidence
Using the apparatus and ideas in planning, you will carry out the investigation making observations and measurements with care and accuracy. Make sure that your observations are relevant, and if necessary repeat observations and measurements. Record all your results in an orderly and appropriate manner.

A Analyse evidence and draw conclusions
You must present both your qualitative and quantitative work clearly, using graphs if appropriate. You should look for trends or patterns in your results. Make sure that your conclusions are valid and that your numerical results have an appropriate degree of accuracy. (If you have weighed chemicals to one decimal point of accuracy, you must not give conclusions containing several decimal points!) Finally, you must decide whether your results support your initial idea when planning and explain any conclusions to the best of your ability.

E Evaluate evidence
Once you have finished the investigation you should consider whether you collected sufficient evidence and the right evidence. You must look at the results carefully to see whether there are any anomalies and reject them. Finally, you might like to make suggestions to improve the methods you have used and to suggest further ideas for investigation.

Remember that you are also assessed on spelling, punctuation and grammar.

To gain marks in your coursework you must have carried out at least two pieces of work to cover all four skill areas and at least one of the skill area marks must have been obtained from a *whole investigation*; i.e. a piece of work which covered all four skill areas. Your teacher will make sure that you have performed at least the minimum amount of two pieces of work.

Putting these criteria into practice

You may be asked to suggest your own investigation. However, it is more likely that you will be given one to investigate. Consider the following:

You are asked to design and carry out an investigation to test the efficiency of three kettle-fur removing solutions, which are acids. You are told that kettle-fur is a form of calcium carbonate. You are also given the following equation as a guide to how these chemical solutions act:

fur remover + fur → solution + carbon dioxide

Planning experimental procedures

(a) First you must understand the problem and the information you have been given. It would help if you could try a preliminary experiment with one of the fur-removers and a little fur—mix them in a test tube. If this is not possible, you will see from the equation that a gas will be given off in the process of fur-removal.

So, measuring the gas given off might be an idea to pursue.

(b) Now you must interpret the meaning of 'efficiency'. Does most efficient mean fastest removal? Or does it mean removal of the most fur with the least fur-remover? You could decide to investigate one or both of these interpretations depending on the time available or your knowledge of chemistry.

Both can, in fact, be investigated using the same apparatus, so you must now choose that. Since the gas given off tells you that the fur-remover is working, the speed of the process is measured by the rate of evolution of gas. You now need to:

(i) choose a vessel to put the fur-remover and kettle-fur into;
(ii) choose a means of measuring the volume of gas given off;
(iii) choose how to measure the rate at which the gas is given off.

(c) There are variables to identify and control in this investigation. They are:

- Temperature—the fur-remover may be used at any temperature between room temperature and the boiling point of water simply by switching on the kettle with the solution inside. Would fur-removal be more efficient at higher or lower temperatures? We can find out.
- Concentration of the fur-removing solution—it could be used 'from-the-bottle' but could also be diluted. So different dilutions could be investigated.
- State of the kettle-fur—are you given some genuine kettle-fur or are you given calcium carbonate (its chemical equivalent?). The fur-removers must each be tested against the same type of calcium carbonate for a fair comparison. If no genuine kettle-fur is available, calcium carbonate in a lump or in a powdered form can be chosen. If powdered, the sample must come from the same source each time. If lumps, the size must be the same for each experiment.

(d) The method of carrying out the investigation must be planned.

A fair comparison could be made by choosing room temperature, fur-remover straight from the bottle and three equal masses of the same-sized lumps of calcium carbonate (usually in the form of marble chippings).

If we take the suggestion in the box above we will need a thermometer, a measuring cylinder, a chemical balance, a supply of marble chippings all of the same size, a vessel to carry out the reaction in and a stop-clock.

Obtaining evidence

(a) Decide first what results you will be recording. You will need to measure the volume of the carbon dioxide gas collected in the gas syringe, say, every minute. You should record the temperatures of the fur-removers to ensure that all are the same.

(b) Next decide how your results will be recorded. In this investigation the gas volumes are best recorded in a table with two columns. One column is for time in minutes, the other column is for gas volume in cm^3.

(c) Now carry out the investigation. Put a weighed sample of the marble chippings into the flask. Add, say, $10\,cm^3$ of one fur-remover and quickly stopper the flask. Start the stop-clock as the flask is stoppered. Record the volume of gas in the gas syringe every minute until the reaction stops and the reading becomes constant. Repeat the experiment to see whether the results are consistent.

(d) Repeat the whole experiment using each of the other two fur-removers.

Analysing evidence and drawing conclusions

(a) The results as recorded—six tables—are difficult to interpret as they stand. They become easier to understand if they are plotted on a graph. Any set of results with two variables can be plotted on a graph.

(b) Graphs show trends and patterns more clearly than tables.

Usually, the *independent variable* (the one whose values are chosen by the investigator—in this case time) is plotted along the horizontal or x-axis. The *dependent variable* (so-called because the volume of gas depends on the times chosen to make the measurement) is plotted vertically on the y-axis.

The type of graph you will get is shown in Fig. 1.2.

(c) This set of graphs can be interpreted as follows.

The fur-removers are A, B and C.

The steeper the graph, the faster the gas is given off. The faster the gas is given off, the faster the marble chippings (kettle-fur) is reacting and so dissolving.

Fig. 1.2

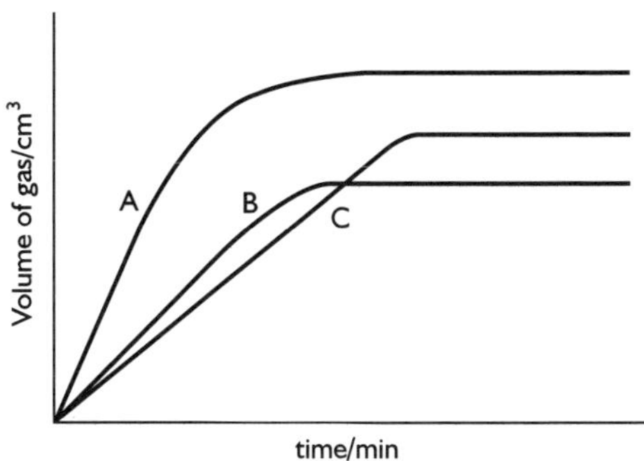

Clearly the order of rate of dissolving marble chippings (removing kettle-fur) is

A > B > C
(fastest) (slowest)

In terms of speed of removal as a measure of efficiency, A is the most efficient and C the least efficient.

Another feature of the graph needs interpretation, however. Fur-remover A gave off more gas than the other two for the same volume used. What does this mean? The gas was not only produced faster but there was more of it. More gas means more marble dissolved. So the fur-removed which produces most gas will also remove most fur.

The graphs can now be interpreted in the second way to indicate that A removes more fur than C which removes more fur than B. So efficiency measured by the amount of fur removed gives the order

A > C > B
(dissolves most fur) (dissolves least fur)

Evaluating evidence

The combined efficiency rating gives A more efficient than B or C, since it is both faster at removing fur and also removes more of it for a given volume of the solution used. No overall decision can be made about B and C since each is better than the other in either speed of action or mass of fur removed per unit volume of solution used.

(a) What suggestions can be made for improving the investigation?

It might be found that some of the carbon dioxide gas escapes before the bung can be placed in the flask. The way to overcome this is to place the fur-removing solution in a small test tube and hang it in the flask by a thread. Then the bung can be inserted taking care not to tip out the solution. Once the bung is on, the flask can be tilted to tip the solution out onto the marble chippings. This method has the added advantage of allowing a free hand to start the stop-clock.

(b) Extending the investigation.

(i) The investigations could be carried out at higher temperatures such as those that could be achieved in a kettle. A water bath would be used for obtaining temperatures up to about 80°C.

(ii) The fur-removers could be used at different concentrations. However, because these would be more dilute than the original, it is unlikely—though not entirely impossible—that the order of speed-efficiency would change.

Safety in the laboratory

In planned investigations like the one described above there are safety matters to consider.

(i) You should find out the hazards of all the chemicals you will be using and discover the safest way to use them. Always wear eye protection when carrying out experiments with chemicals.

(ii) Always support your apparatus where possible, to free your hands for carrying out the experiments.

(iii) Be extra attentive if heating is involved. Be aware what a mishap might do and where your fellow students are working so that an accident will not harm them too.
(iv) Be as tidy as possible. Do not have books or personal belongings in the area where you are carrying out your experiment. Mop up liquid and solid spills as soon as they occur. Do not leave unclamped pieces of apparatus where it can be easily knocked off the bench onto the floor or into a sink.
(v) Do not rush; think about each operation and stop if you cease to understand what you are doing. Consult a teacher if you get into difficulties.
(vi) If an accident does occur seek your teacher's help immediately.

Experimental chemistry is usually interesting, sometimes exciting, rarely dull. The more you know of chemistry and its principles, the more delight you will find in practical work. Experimental work is the heart of chemistry. Whether qualified chemists are preparing substances, analysing them or researching new compounds, they are doing the sort of investigations that you will do at school or college. If you enjoy chemistry and succeed at it you may be joining them one day.

And finally Remember that doing your best is not about luck. Success in examinations is based on sound knowledge, revision skills and thorough preparation.

EXAMINATION GROUP ADDRESSES

London
EDEXCEL Foundation
Stewart House, 32 Russell Square, London, WC1B 5DN
Tel: 0171 331 4000
Fax: 0171 631 3369

MEG
Midland Examining Group
1 Hills Road, Cambridge, CB1 2EU
Tel: 01223 553311
Fax: 01223 460278

NEAB
Northern Examinations and Assessment Board
Devas Street, Manchester, M15 6EX
Tel: 0161 953 1180
Fax: 0161 273 7572

NICCEA
Northern Ireland Council for Curriculum, Examinations and Assessment
29 Clarendon Road, Belfast, BT1 3BG
Tel: 01232 261200
Fax: 01232 261234

SEG
Southern Examining Group
Stag Hill House, Guildford, GU2 5XJ
Tel: 01483 506505
Fax: 01483 300152

WJEC
Welsh Joint Education Committee
245 Western Road, Cardiff, CF5 2YX
Tel: 01222 561231
Fax: 01222 571234

IGCSE
International General Certificate of Secondary Education
University of Cambridge Local Examinations Syndicate
1 Hills Road, Cambridge, CB1 2EU
Tel: 01223 553311
Fax: 01223 460278

When contacting the examination Groups you will need to ask for the Publications Department and request an order form to be sent to you. On the order form indicate exactly which syllabus you are studying and be prepared to send a cheque or postal order with your order.

Chapter 2

Syllabus detail

GETTING STARTED

All chemistry syllabuses at GCSE involve components of various types. The word component is used instead of examination papers so that coursework can be included in the assessment. Essay papers test your ability to develop arguments or to give details of a topic. You might be asked to explain or work with materials in the absence of any prescribed or suggested pattern of answering. Structured questions test the breadth of your knowledge and are usually based on a theme. They give a guidance as to the type of answer expected and there is also an indication of the length of answer required. Short-answer questions are usually 'free standing' and require either one word or a short sentence.

The coursework is very important, so make sure that you keep up to date with your work and do not leave everything until the last minute. You must try and be well organized and work systematically.

The grade you will be awarded in chemistry represents your overall performance in the different components. Your ultimate goal should be to obtain the grade which represents your achievements.

WHAT YOU NEED TO KNOW

Syllabuses

Whenever you study a subject, you and your teacher will follow a syllabus. Your teacher will ask you questions to check that you are gaining a knowledge of the basic facts, patterns, principles and theories of chemistry. The chemistry syllabus you follow will depend upon your school, but all the syllabuses will have a large amount of common material. This is because all schools must follow the National Curriculum.

One of the topics you will have studied in science during your schooling is Materials and their Properties. This is essentially chemistry. During this topic you look at the properties of materials; look for patterns; understand the importance of making new substances; and make predictions. The topic is broken down into three sections. We have used these three sections in this book to help you see the pattern of your study. The three sections are:

- classifying materials
- changing materials
- patterns of behaviour

These sections are further sub-divided and we have, as far as possible, used these for the headings of the various chapters. Sometimes, where the topic is very short or where we have covered the topic elsewhere, you will notice that there does not appear to be a chapter on that topic. We can assure you that the topic is covered. You should use the index at the back of this book to find out the section you require.

Content

All the syllabuses will have the following content; this is the content for Foundation level. (You will find the extra content for the Higher level at the end of this section.) You must make sure that you know and understand all the facts and principles in the following list.

Classifying materials

Atomic structure

(a) That solids, liquids and gases are all composed of particles
(b) That atoms consist of nuclei and electrons
(c) The charges and relative masses of protons, neutrons and electrons
(d) About mass number, atomic number and isotopes
(e) About a model of the way electrons are arranged in atoms
(f) That the reactions of elements depend upon the arrangement of electrons in their atoms

Bonding

(g) That new substances are formed when atoms combine
(h) That chemical bonding can be explained in terms of the transfer or sharing of electrons
(i) How ions are formed when atoms gain or lose electrons
(j) That ionic lattices are held together by the attraction between oppositely charged ions
(k) That covalent bonds are formed when atoms share electrons
(l) That substances with covalent bonds may form simple molecular structures or giant structures
(m) The physical properties of some substances with giant structures and some with simple molecular structures

Changing materials

Useful products from oil

(a) How oil deposits are formed
(b) That crude oil is a mixture of substances, most of which are hydrocarbons, which can be separated by fractional distillation
(c) The use as fuels of some of the products from crude oil distillation
(d) The products of burning hydrocarbons
(e) That there are different groups of hydrocarbons

(f) That alkanes are saturated hydrocarbons, and alkenes are unsaturated hydrocarbons containing one double covalent bond between the carbon atoms
(g) That hydrocarbon molecules can be cracked to form smaller molecules, including alkenes
(h) That addition polymers can be made from alkenes formed during cracking
(i) Some uses of addition polymers

Useful products from metal ores and rocks

(j) That metal ores are found in the Earth
(k) That the way a particular metal is extracted from its ore is related to its reactivity
(l) An example of how a reactive metal can be extracted by electrolysis
(m) An example of how a less reactive metal can be extracted by reduction with carbon or carbon monoxide
(n) An example of how a metal can be purified by electrolysis
(o) That a variety of useful substances can be made from rocks and minerals

Useful products from air

(p) How nitrogen can be converted to ammonia in industry
(q) How nitrogenous fertilizers are manufactured, and their effects on plant growth and the environment

Representing reactions

(r) How to represent chemical reactions by word equations
(s) How to represent reactions, including electrolytic reactions, by balanced equations using chemical symbols

Quantitative chemistry

(t) How to use chemical equations to predict reacting quantities
(u) How to determine the formula of simple compounds from reacting masses

Changes to the atmosphere

(v) How to use chemical eqautions to predict reacting quantities
(w) How the carbon cycle helps to maintain atmospheric composition

Geological changes

(x) How igneous rocks are formed by the cooling of magma, sedimentary rocks by the deposition and consolidation of sediments, and metamorphic rocks by the action of heat and pressure on existing rocks
(y) How the sequence of, and evidence for, these processes is obtained from the rock record
(z) How plate tectonic processes are involved in the formation, deformation and recycling of rocks.

Patterns of behaviour

The periodic table

(a) That the periodic table shows all elements, arranged in order of ascending atomic number
(b) The connection between the arrangement of outer electrons and the position of an element in the periodic table
(c) That elements in the same group of the periodic table have similar properties
(d) That there is a gradual change in the properties of the elements from the top to the bottom of a group
(e) The properties and uses of the noble gases

(f) The properties and reactions of the alkali metals
(g) The properties, reactions and uses of simple compounds of the alkali metals
(h) The properties, reactions and uses of the halogens
(i) The properties, reactions and uses of simple compounds of the halogens
(j) Similarities between transition metals and characteristic properties of their compounds
(k) Some uses of transition metals

Rates of reactions

(l) That there is a great variation in the rate at which different reactions take place
(m) How the rates of reactions can be altered by varying temperature or concentration, or by changing the surface area of a solid reactant, or by adding a catalyst
(n) That reactions can occur when particles collide
(o) That the rates of many reactions can be increased by increasing the frequency or energy of collisions between particles

Reactions involving enzymes

(p) How the rates of enzyme-catalysed reactions vary with temperature
(q) The use of enzymes in the baking, brewing and dairy industries

Reversible reactions

(r) That some reactions are reversible
(s) How the yield of products from reversible reactions depends on the conditions
(t) That some manufacturing processes are based on reversible reactions

Energy transfer in reactions

(u) That changes of temperature often accompany reactions
(v) That reactions can be exothermic or endothermic
(w) That making and breaking chemical bonds in chemical reactions involves energy transfers.

Higher level

MEG, NEAB and NICCEA have added extra areas of study to the National Curriculum topics. (Topics marked with * are MEG only, † SEG only and § NICCEA only.) The topics include:

- metallic bonding
- ideal gas equation§
- preparation of salts
- reversible reactions (*not* NICCEA)
- tests for ions*
- chemicals from the sea*
- vegetable oils; isomerism; alcohols and carboxylic acids
- half equations for electrolysis
- extraction of titanium†; manufacture of steel; manufacture of sulphuric acid
- calculations involving gases; titrations and electrolysis
- reversible reactions

SEG has additional content in each of the three main classifications. They are:

Classifying materials
- alloys
- allotropy
- covalent compounds

Changing materials
- limestone, chalk and marble
- hardness of water
- contact process

- hydrocarbons
- compounds from natural products

Patterns of behaviour

- calcium and magnesium
- sulphur
- electrolysis
- reacting quantities of solution

For **London** there are three additional topic areas:

- Chemistry in the Laboratory
- Chemistry in Industry
- Chemistry and the Environment

WJEC has extension material in the following content areas:

- group II
- bonding and structure
- acids, bases and salts; identification of ions
- chemical calculations including volumetric
- metal corrosion
- air—the fire triangle
- contact process
- ethanol and thermoplastics

MEG offers two other Chemistry syllabuses: Salters and Nuffield.

Different syllabuses

If you are studying at home, you will probably want a copy of the syllabus. If this is not available from your school or college, find out the **syllabus** that you are studying and write for a copy to the appropriate Examining Group (these are given on page 10, remembering to enclose the cost of the syllabus and postage. If you are at a state maintained school you must also take the examination in Biology and Physics.

The syllabuses contain all the information that you will need to know about your examination, including details on how many papers you will have to take and the time allowed for each paper.

The new syllabuses are similar in lay-out to previous syllabuses. They all have **aims, assessment objectives, subject content, scheme of assessment, weightings and grade descriptions.**

Aims

Aims describe the **reasons** for studying chemistry and many of the aims are reflected in the Assessment Objectives and in the Scheme of Assessment. An example of an aim is '*to stimulate pupils' curiosity, interest and enjoyment in chemistry and encourage them to undertake further studies*'. Many aims, such as the example quoted, CANNOT be readily assessed.

Assessment objectives

These are the **objectives** you *will be tested on* in the examination. They are divided into groups such as Scientific Investigations and Knowledge and Understanding of Chemistry. Included in the latter is the ability to **communicate, handle data, evaluate** and **solve problems**. When an examination paper is written it must include questions testing the assessment objectives. Remember that the examination is trying to find out what you *know* about chemistry (not what you do not know). You may have heard the phrase '**positive achievement**'; this means demonstrating what you know, understand and can do in a subject such as chemistry.

Subject content

The **subject content** will contain all the content from Attainment Target 3 on the National Curriculum for Science (Materials and Their Properties).

Scheme of assessment

It is very important to note that awards outside the targeted range will not be available. Thus, if you enter for the foundation tier the grades available are G–C and for the higher tier grades D–A*. If you receive less than the minimum mark for grade D on the higher tier you will be ungraded and recorded as U.

If you think that you are likely to attain grade D or below on the Higher tier, you should seriously consider entering for the Foundation tier.

Weightings

The weighting of the papers is really for the benefit of the examiners. It is used to ensure that the examination papers cover all the skills required in chemistry and give a good coverage of the syllabus. There is also a weighting of the questions within each paper which will give you an idea of how to allocate your time. If a question has twice as many marks as another question it is worth spending more time on that question.

Spelling, punctuation and grammar (SPAG)

In the Coursework component 5 per cent of the total marks are given for the use of spelling, punctuation and grammar. The marks awarded will be based on your performance in the paper as a whole.

To gain maximum marks for SPAG you must be able to:

- spell, punctuate and use rules of grammar with sufficient accuracy to convey meaning;
- record and store information in an appropriate form;
- use and understand information gained from various sources;
- communicate ideas to others;
- summarize and organize information in order to communicate adequately;
- use appropriate language to explain the results of observations in a variety of contexts.

Nature of assessment

Table 2.1 outlines the combinations of examination papers and coursework required by the different examination groups. (Please check with the latest version of your examination group's syllabus as these requirements sometimes change.) Sc 1 and Sc 3 refer to the National Curriculum attainment target. Sc 1 describes the practical requirements and Sc 3 is the attainment target 'Materials and Their Properties'. 'Extn' refers to the extension materials in each syllabus.

Grade descriptors

The following grade descriptions will give you a general idea of the standard required to achieve a grade A, C or F. You might be able to work out the grade you might get from seeing whether or not you are able to reach the standard required for each grade.

Grade A

You will be able to:

- Use scientific knowledge and understanding to select an appropriate strategy for a task, identifying the key factors to be considered and making predictions where appropriate; you will be able to select a method of presenting data appropriate to the task; you will be able to use information from a range of sources where it is appropriate to do so; you will be able to identify and explain anomalous observations on measurements and the salient features of graphs; you will be able to use your scientific knowledge and understanding to draw conclusions from your evidence and identify shortcomings in the evidence.
- Decide on the level of precision needed in measurements and use a range of apparatus with precision and skill; you will make appropriate precise measurements; make systematic observations in qualitative work and decide on the observations that are relevant to the task in hand.
- Recall a wide range of knowledge from all areas of the syllabus.
- Use detailed scientific knowledge and understanding in a range of applications relating to scientific systems or phenomena: for example, you would routinely use a balanced

Table 2.1

Group	Tier	Component number	Type of assess-ment	AT	Grades available	Duration (minutes)	Percentage weighting
LONDON							
	Foundation	1F	Written	Sc 3	G–C	90	50%
	Foundation	2F	Written	Extn	G–C	60	25%
	Higher	3H	Written	Sc 3	D–A*	90	50%
	Higher	4H	Written	Extn	D–A*	60	25%
	Both	7	Coursework	Sc 3	G–A*	–	
MEG							
	Foundation	1	Written	Sc 3	G–C	90	50%
	Higher	2	Written	Sc 3	D–A*	105	50%
	Foundation	3	Written	Extn	G–C	45	25%
	Higher	4	Written	Extn	D–A*	60	25%
	Both	5	Coursework	Sc 1	G–A*	–	25%
NEAB							
	Foundation	F	Written	Sc 3	G–C	120	75%
	Higher	H	Written	Extn	D–A*	135	75%
	Both		Coursework	Sc 1	G–A*	–	
NICCEA							
	Foundation	1	Written	Sc 3	G–C	60	30%
	Higher	1	Written	Extn	D–A*	90	32%
	Foundation	2	Written	Sc 3	G–C	90	45%
	Higher	2	Written	Extn	D–A*	120	43%
	Both		Coursework	Sc 1	G–A*	–	25%
SEG							
	Both	1	Coursework	Sc 1	G–A*	–	25%
	Foundation	2	Written	Sc 3	G–C	90	50%
	Foundation	3	Written	Extn	G–C	60	25%
	Higher	4	Written	Sc 3	D–A*	90	50%
	Higher	5	Written	Extn	D–A*	60	
WJEC							
	Both	1	Coursework	Sc 1	G–A*	–	25%
	Foundation	2	Written	Section A	G–C	120	37.5%
			Written	Section B			37.5%
	Higher	3	Written	Section A	D–A*	150	37.5%
			Written	Section B	D–A*		37.5%

N.B. For WJEC Section B of the Foundation is the same as Section A of the Higher.

equation and use understanding of bonding to explain the simple properties of the material.

- Use detailed scientific knowledge and understanding to identify patterns and draw conclusions by combining data from more than one kind or from more than one source.
- Draw together and communicate knowledge from more than one area; you will routinely use scientific or mathematics conventions in support of arguments; you will use a wide range of scientific and technical vocabulary throughout your work.

Grade C

You will be able to:

- Use scientific knowledge and understanding to identify key factors to vary and control and where appropriate to make predictions; present data systematically, in graphs where appropriate, and use lines of best fit; draw conclusions consistent with the evidence and explain these using scientific knowledge and understanding;
- Use a range of apparatus to make careful and precise measurements and systematic observations and recognize when it is necessary to repeat measurements and observations.
- Recall a range of scientific information from all areas of the syllabus: for example, you will be able to recall simple chemical symbols and formulae and the correct units for quantities.
- Use and apply scientific knowledge and understanding in some general contexts: for example, you will be able to write simple balanced equations and use quantitative relationships between physical quantities to perform calculations.
- Use scientific knowledge and understanding to make inferences and to identify and explain patterns within data; you will be able to make predictions from data.
- Describe links between related phenomena in different contexts; you will be able to use diagrams, charts and graphs to support arguments; you will use the appropriate scientific and technical vocabulary in a range of topics.

Grade F

You will be able to:

- Devise fair tests in contexts which involve only a few factors; record observations and measurements in tables and graphs and offer simple explanations consistent with the evidence obtained.
- Use simple apparatus to make measurements appropriate to the task.
- Recall a limited range of information: for example, state some uses of materials obtained from oil.
- Use and apply knowledge and understanding in some specific everyday context: for example, suggest a way of speeding up a particular chemical reaction or explain that fuels are energy resources and that energy is sometimes 'wasted'.
- Obtain information from simple tables, charts and graphs and identify simple patterns in information and observations.
- Describe links cause and effect in simple contexts; make use of scientific and technical vocabulary and make simple generalizations from information.

Finally, make sure you have sufficient knowledge and understanding to reach at least a grade C. This book will help you, but you will have to make the effort.

Chapter 3

Social, economic and environmental aspects of the chemical industry

GETTING STARTED

As a reader of a GCSE guide, you will not be completely new to the study of chemistry. You will already have become aware of many of the achievements of professional chemists. One of the most important jobs of chemists in industry is to convert naturally occurring substances (raw materials) into more useful materials.

From these raw materials **industrial chemists** can separate elements, compounds or mixtures to make them into such everyday products as plastics, fertilizers, medicines, detergents, insecticides, dyes and paints.

Chemists not only *make* useful substances, they also use their knowledge and technical expertise to *analyse* substances to discover what is present in them. **Analytical chemists** play an important role in the fields of forensic science (crime detection), medical diagnosis, food inspection and quality control.

However, a very large section of the chemical industry relies upon *just five basic raw materials* for its huge range of products:

- crude oil/natural gas;
- ores and minerals (salt, limestone, metallic ores, sulphur);
- water;
- air;
- fuels.

These sources of chemicals will be considered in detail in the following chapters. They are our chemical **resources.**

Unfortunately, the process of making useful chemicals almost always results in some undesired by-products. If these are not carefully handled they easily become pollutants. The chemical industry is not alone in this. Consider the unwanted by-products of everyday human activities—human and animal excrement, rotten and waste vegetable matter, waste paper, plastic packing, glass, etc. All are potential pollutants if not properly disposed of or recycled. We realize the problem of waste more now than ever. There is a growing industry researching and developing methods of using water or by-product materials.

TOPIC CHART

LONDON	MEG	NEAB	NICCEA	SEG	WJEC	TOPIC	STUDY	REVISION 1	REVISION 2
✓	✓	✓	✓	✓	✓	The economics of the chemical industry			
✓	✓	✓	✓	✓	✓	The work of the chemist			
✓	✓	✓	✓	✓	✓	Technology, society and the environment			
✓	✓	✓	✓	✓	✓	Pollution			

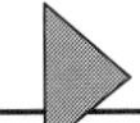

WHAT YOU NEED TO KNOW

The economics of the chemical industry

The siting of a chemical plant

If you were to plot on a map the positions of the main chemical plants in the country, you would soon realize that the **sites** had been very carefully chosen. A chemical company must compete against other companies to sell its products. It must make its chemicals as cheaply as, or more cheaply than, its competitors, or it will not be profitable and will fail. An important factor in the profitability of a chemical plant is the site chosen. The main factors to consider are:

- easy access to cheap raw materials—ores, water, fuel and power;
- good transport—ships or rail for large tonnages, roads for smaller quantities;
- a good supply of skilled labour nearby.

A little thought given to these points will show how obvious they are. The siting of several important plants in the chemical industry will be considered in the following chapters. It should be realized, however, that the factors which influence the choice of site change continuously. In the days of poor transport, it was important for a chemical plant to be close to supplies of its raw materials. Houses, even small towns, would then often be built nearby for the labour force. Today, with more effective transport systems, it might be cheaper to site a factory close to the labour force and transport raw materials to the site. If the raw materials come from overseas, then the site may be close to a port where there is also a suitable labour force.

Raw materials

For a chemical product to sell well it must be as cheap as its competitor's product—or cheaper. It is a big advantage to be able to buy the **raw materials** as cheaply as possible by building the plant *close to their source*. An iron works should be close to sources of coal, iron ore and limestone. A nitric acid plant must be built close to an ammonia plant. Compound fertilizers must be made where the components of the mixture are manufactured. Aluminium smelters would only be sited where electricity was cheap and bauxite could be cheaply shipped in from overseas, and so on.

Fuel

The choice of **fuel** will depend upon its **cost** and also the ease of maintenance of heating equipment. Gas, oil and electricity are easy to 'transport', but coal requires a nearby mine or a good transport system. Here, again, correct siting can help. A plant producing heat as a by-product of its chemical processes may be in a position to provide heat energy to another plant nearby. This is just *one* reason why parts of the chemical industry tend to congregate in one area, such as Teesside.

The search for increased efficiency

Finally, success can often depend upon a very small increase in **efficiency of operation** of the plant. **Catalysts** play an important role here. They can be expensive, but their role is to speed up chemical reactions and help to reduce costs. They are required in relatively small quantities and, with more research, even the small quantities now used will be reduced further. In theory, extremely minute amounts of catalysts could provide effective action if they could be spread *a mere one atom thick* on large surface areas of support material.

Since chemical reactions are mainly **exothermic**, there will frequently be a great deal of 'waste heat'. The sale or re-use of this 'waste heat' can sometimes be responsible for high profitability or low cost of the product (see Chapter 9). A plant requiring energy can be built close to one producing excess energy. Both plants can benefit from the sale of energy from one to the other.

The work of the chemist

Chemists make use of a variety of reaction processes and separation techniques to convert natural resources into useful products.

The **processes** used include:

- dissolving
- precipitation
- crystallization
- thermal decomposition
- oxidation—often combustion
- reduction
- electrolysis
- hydrolysis
- dehydration
- neutralization

'Find examples of each of these processes in other chapters of this Guide and write them in your notebook for future reference.'

The **techniques** used include:

- filtration or centrifugation
- distillation and fractional distillation
- solvent extraction
- chromatography
- sublimation

'Try to draw diagrams of the apparatus used in each of these techniques from memory. After you have drawn them, look up the correct diagrams to check your work.'

The techniques of the chemist are one of the subjects of Chapter 4. The chemical processes used by chemists will be discussed as they arise in the other chapters of this book.

Technology, society and the environment

Britain's chemical industry **earns money for the country** by selling its product abroad. Its research effort is constantly improving the efficiency of the manufacturing processes and devising new ones. Chemists do not work in ivory towers, however. What they do can benefit, as well as damage, the real world in which they work and live. They fully realize this!

Every chemical process which produces a **useful product** is likely also to produce a **waste product**. The simple process of burning fuel for the energy to heat our homes or cook our food gives waste products. The process of digestion of our food creates waste products which, incidentally, require huge expenditure to prevent them from polluting our environment.

We hope you will become aware, whilst studying the chapters of this guide, that most chemists work hard not only at making useful substances but also at protecting the environment in which we live. They help to feed and clothe us; help to house us and to cure our ills; and help to make life more pleasant and safer to live. Above all they produce, with a few exceptions, only what we *ask* them to make.

Major aspects of the work of chemists will be discussed *as they arise* in this study. The social and environmental impact of chemistry is now such an important part of its study, however, that some aspects of this are best discussed here.

The future of our chemical resources

Most people are aware that our coal and oil resources will not last for very long if we continue to use them at the current rate. What is not so well known is that this concern extends to our mineral resources as well. Marvellous though the work of chemists often is, there is not much they can make from air and water only!

Ever since we have been able to use energy sources on a large scale—e.g. coal and oil—we have been extracting increasing quantities of chemical substances from the earth. We now realize that the earth cannot continue forever to provide the minerals we need.

You may share the concern for conservation. But why do we need to conserve our resources? **Total conservation** of chemical resources means that we do not use them at all. Will we benefit from ceasing to use them at all? Does it help to use them at a slower rate? The answer to these questions is that it also depends on what else we are doing.

Conserving energy and material resources

We could conserve energy by rationing it, by allowing a limited amount to be used daily. Our fuel resources would last longer but our standard of living would decrease and in the end we should still run short—it would simply take longer. It makes more sense

'It is important to recognize the difference between renewable and non-renewable (fossil) sources of energy.'

(i) to use **renewable sources** of energy, such as water, wind, solar power and vegetation;
(ii) to **recycle** the materials already in existence at a lower 'energy cost', thus conserving both the energy resource and the mineral resource and, at the same time, gaining the benefit of the re-use of the old material;
(iii) to devise more **energy-efficient** and **resource-efficient** ways of carrying out chemical processes;
(iv) to make better use of **'waste'** products.

The chemical industry is involved in all of these activities.

(i) In Brazil, which has no oil resources and cannot afford to import all the oil it needs, sugar cane is grown as a source of ethanol for running motor vehicles. Sugar is extracted from the cane, **fermented** to **ethanol** solution and then **distilled** to produce nearly pure ethanol. The energy needed to carry out the distillation process comes from burning the cane waste, left after the sugar has been removed. Sugar cane will grow again and the process can be repeated. In sugar cane the Brazilians have a **renewable energy resource.**

(ii) In Western Europe, nearly a half of all aluminium used is eventually recycled. To make 'new' aluminium from scrap requires *only about 5%* of the energy spent in making the original aluminium from its ore. The saving of energy and mineral resources is obvious.

(iii) The history of the production of aluminium illustrates point (ii) equally well. The metal is extracted by **electrolysis** of aluminium oxide. Energy consumption is large. However, the most recently built aluminium smelters use only 30% of the energy used by the very first smelters which were built a hundred years ago.

(iv) The use of 'waste products' can be beneficial in several ways. Firstly, it saves the expense of disposal and so makes the main product cheaper. Secondly, it makes more efficient use of natural resources. Thirdly, it can reduce environmental pollution.

For example, many metal extraction processes produce large amounts of sulphur dioxide waste. If dispersed in the atmosphere, this oxide is a pollutant, producing 'acid rain' and an unhealthy atmosphere. The metal extraction industry uses the gas as a source of sulphur to make sulphuric acid. Pollution is reduced, a useful product is made, and the mineral ore has been more fully used.

Pollution

Pollution — its causes

In the last section we touched on pollution from industrial activities. The problem has been with us ever since large-scale chemical manufacturing started. However, we must take care to be fair in our judgement of where the blame lies. It is a useful exercise to try to answer the question 'What would your daily life be like without the objects made with the products of the chemical industry?' If we cannot honestly answer 'wonderful' then we ourselves must accept *some* of the responsibility for keeping the industry going. If we did not want its products, the chemical industry would not make a profit and would cease to exist.

All this *does not excuse* pollution by chemical processes, of course. There are strict rules for regulating the amounts of waste chemicals that can be dumped into our rivers and atmosphere or onto our land. However, because we demand more and more chemicals, even very small amounts of pollution for *individual* factories become large amounts *globally*.

What is being done to reduce or prevent pollution?

Pollution — the remedies

Although we do not have remedies for every situation, much has been done during the past century. Some processes which were serious pollutants of our environment a hundred years ago are no longer so. The chemical process used at that time for producing the alkali used in soap and glassmaking, from salt, also produced hydrogen chloride as a waste product. The serious pollution caused by this acid gas led to the first law to control air pollution. This was the Alkali Act of 1863.

Even the 'smogs' of forty years ago are no longer seen in Britain. The Clean Air Act of 1956 became law soon after the serious health risk from smog was recognized and smokeless zones were established in which the burning of coal was not allowed. This led to a big reduction in the concentration of smoke particles and sulphur dioxide in the air of our towns and cities.

Twenty years ago some of our rivers were polluted with detergent and almost permanently 'froth-covered'. Detergent manufacturers voluntarily took steps to change the chemical composition of their detergent so that it was 'biodegradable'. We no longer see frothy rivers, and bacteria have a new dish on their menu!

These improvements have been achieved by a combination of public concern and commercial responsibility. Those who run our industries also have to live with pollution if they cannot reduce it!

One of the most important pollution issues at present is the atmospheric pollution from oxides of sulphur and nitrogen. These come mainly from coal-fired power stations and motor vehicles. Both sources can be made pollution-free—but at a cost.

Planned removal of oxides of sulphur from power station flue gases is making very slow progress. To date (1996) no commercial station operates a flue-gas desulphurization plant. However, power producers are building more stations using natural gas which has almost no sulphur content and so will not require the costly flue-gas cleaning process.

Power station pollution

The acidic oxides emitted by power stations can be **neutralized** and converted into salts by the use of **alkaline reagents.**

Lime scrubbing

$$Ca(OH)_2(s) + SO_2(g) \rightarrow CaSO_3(s) + H_2O(l)$$

Lime + sulphur dioxide → calcium sulphite + water

$$CaSO_3(s) + \tfrac{1}{2}O_2(g) \rightarrow CaSO_4(s)$$

calcium sulphite + oxygen → calcium sulphate

The process can be expensive but it works well. The salt formed, usually calcium sulphate, $CaSO_4$, may have to be dumped, however. This could create another source of pollution, though a less unpleasant one. Calcium sulphate has a commercial use in the manufacture of wall plaster. If the product formed from the removal of sulphur dioxide could be made to the standard required for it to be made into plaster, the waste would be re-usable!

It is interesting to note that many solid wastes can be dumped on land and eventually landscaped. When covered with a layer of topsoil, trees and shrubs and even crops can be grown. An ICI farm on Teesside grows crops on top of thirty feet of gypsum waste from the fertilizer industry!

Ammonia scrubbing

An alternative process would be to convert oxides of sulphur and oxides of nitrogen into ammonium salts. The oxides react with water and air to form sulphuric and nitric acids. These acids are then neutralized by ammonia gas to form ammonium salts. Ammonium salts are used as fertilizers. This process uses waste to make a useful product.

$$2NH_3(g) + H_2SO_4(aq) \rightarrow (NH_4)_2SO_4(aq)$$

ammonia + sulphuric acid → ammonium sulphate

$$NH_3(g) + HNO_3(aq) \rightarrow NH_4NO_3(aq)$$

ammonia + nitric acid → ammonium nitrate

Nitrogen oxides can also be reduced by more efficient burning of the coal, for example by fluidized bed combustion. Sulphur oxides can be reduced by using coal with a lower sulphur content.

Motor vehicle pollution

Any high-temperature burning process using **air** will produce nitrogen oxides as pollutants—equation (1). If the fuel is a carbon compound, such as coal, oil or natural gas, then carbon monoxide may be produced also—by incomplete oxidation of the carbon in the fuel—equation (2).

$$N_2(g) + O_2(g) \rightarrow 2NO(g) \quad (1)$$

nitrogen + oxygen → nitrogen(II) oxide

$$CH_4(g) + 1\tfrac{1}{2}O_2(g) \rightarrow CO(g) + 2H_2O(g) \quad (2)$$

methane + oxygen → carbon monoxide + water vapour

Atmospheric pollution from motor vehicles is often more noticeable than that from power stations because it is near ground level—power stations spread their pollution over a wide area by having very tall chimneys—as the inhabitants of Scandinavia will confirm!

A great deal of work has been done on the perfection of catalytic converters for motor vehicles using petrol or diesel fuels, to remove atmospheric pollutants from their exhaust gases. Countries such as the USA, Japan and Europe now insist on the fitting of exhaust emission control systems to all cars. The British company Johnson Matthey Chemicals Limited produces a converter called an **autocatalyst** which uses a platinum/rhodium catalyst to speed up the reaction of pollutant components of the exhaust gases with each other to produce harmless substances.

The commonest pollutants from motor vehicles are carbon monoxide (CO) and nitrogen oxide (NO), both toxic gases, and unburned hydrocarbons (HC) from the fuel. These are removed in the autocatalyst by conversion to harmless carbon dioxide, water and nitrogen.

Typical reactions occurring in autocatalysts are:

'Reactions in autocatalysts.'

$$2CO(g) + 2NO(g) \rightarrow 2CO_2(g) + N_2(g)$$

carbon monoxide + nitrogen(II) oxide → carbon dioxide + nitrogen

$$2CO(g) + O_2(g) \rightarrow 2CO_2(g)$$

carbon monoxide + oxygen → carbon dioxide

$$HC(g) + NO(g) \rightarrow CO_2(g) + H_2O(g) + N_2(g)$$

hydrocarbon + nitrogen(II) oxide → carbon dioxide + water vapour + nitrogen

(The last 'equation' is not a balanced equation; it is simplified to show the possible products. A typical hydrocarbon in petrol would be octane, C_8H_{18}. Try working out the balanced equation for the reaction to form the products shown.)

At present, autocatalysts require the use of **unleaded** petrol. This is because lead compounds in leaded petrol 'poison' the active surface of the catalyst, destroying its converting power. The polluting power of petrol engined cars registered after January 1993 has been much reduced by the compulsory fitting of catalytic converters. The progressive introduction of unleaded petrol will produce the *bonus* of less lead pollution of the atmosphere as well.

Pollution of water sources

So far, discussion of pollution has centred around the atmosphere. Equally important, however, is pollution of the rivers and seas. River pollution is usually from two main sources—industry and sewage. Industrial pollutants are often complex chemical compounds and mixtures which are difficult to 'degrade' to harmless substances. Even so, there are ways of rendering most chemical wastes harmless.

A dozen or so water boards are responsible for the standard of drinking water in England and Wales. European standards have forced them to consider measures to reduce nitrate levels in areas where run-off from agricultural land causes these to be excessive, e.g. in East Anglia. Phosphate, largely from detergent mixtures, is also removed chemically in some areas, though on a small scale at the moment. The method is to precipitate phosphate as calcium phosphate. This can be recycled either as a constituent of washing powder or as a fertilizer.

Removal of factory wastes

Chemical methods

Industrial waste containing toxic matter can be incinerated at very high temperatures in specially designed furnaces. Such techniques, used by Rechem Limited of Southampton, can render many wastes harmless. The waste gases from these processes are carefully monitored during the combustion to ensure the formation of harmless gaseous products, which are then vented to the atmosphere. Thermal combustion processes can achieve a measure of saving by making use of the heat produced by the combustion processes—see also Chapter 7 (disposal of plastic waste).

Catalytic oxidation or **reduction** of solid and liquid chemical wastes offer ways of decomposing the **chlorinated hydrocarbons** which are so persistent in the soil and are responsible for the near extinction of many species of birds of prey.

Biochemical methods

Today, water containing toxic chemicals is often treated by sewage works and, because it is toxic, causes difficulties to the bacteria which 'work' there. Heavy metal compounds such as those of chromium and mercury, and toxic organic compounds such as phenol, are particularly difficult to treat. The wastes from many industrial processes such as papermaking, sugar and mineral ore processing, textile treatment and agricultural processes cannot be accepted by many sewage works and are sometimes discharged into rivers either untreated or partly treated.

Even relatively simple compounds such as nitrates and phosphates are among the chemicals which are not completely removed by normal sewage treatment methods. In a later chapter we shall discuss the effects of allowing nitrates and phosphates into our rivers—causing **eutrophication** and damage to the ecology of the river.

Any method which allows treatment of such wastes at their place of origin, using inexpensive materials, has much to recommend it.

One such method in current use is the **root zone** method. This process uses the natural ability of certain water plants—reeds—in association with bacteria, to detoxify water percolated through their root systems. These plants can be grown on specially prepared beds close to the source of industrial pollution, and the effluent from that source becomes purified *before* entering a water course. This type of system, already in use for treatment of sewage and industrial waste, offers a more economical and socially acceptable waste treatment method than land fill and river disposal. The 'root zone' method will detoxify almost any waste, especially that from common polluting processes of the sugar, textile and mineral processing industries.

A novel treatment method which could become important in the future is the use of 'man-made' microorganisms to degrade hazardous and toxic substances. Many microorganisms are known which will digest substances that are toxic to humans. By the technique known as **genetic engineering**, it may be possible to *change* a microorganism's digestive capabilities to enable it to digest almost any chemical substance we would like to be removed from waste. This exciting possibility is one for the future, perhaps the near future!

We hope to have shown that the work of chemists is important to modern society. Their manufactures are useful and often vital to our daily lives. Their processes can pollute our environment, yet they work hard to reduce and even prevent that pollution. Their future efforts will extend the useful life of our material resources and generate products not yet imagined—who knows!

EXAMINATION QUESTIONS

Question 1

This question is about pollution. Carefully study the map (Fig. 3.1) and answer the questions below.

Answer the first part of each question, using the letters A to Q, writing your answer in the space provided. Each letter may be used once, more than once or not at all. In each case give a reason for your choice of site.

Write the letter representing a place on the map **most likely** to be

(i) a **source** of radioactive waste;
Place ______________________
Reason ______________________ *[1]*

(ii) a **source** of pollution caused by nitrogenous chemicals;
Place ______________________
Reason ______________________ *[1]*

Fig. 3.1

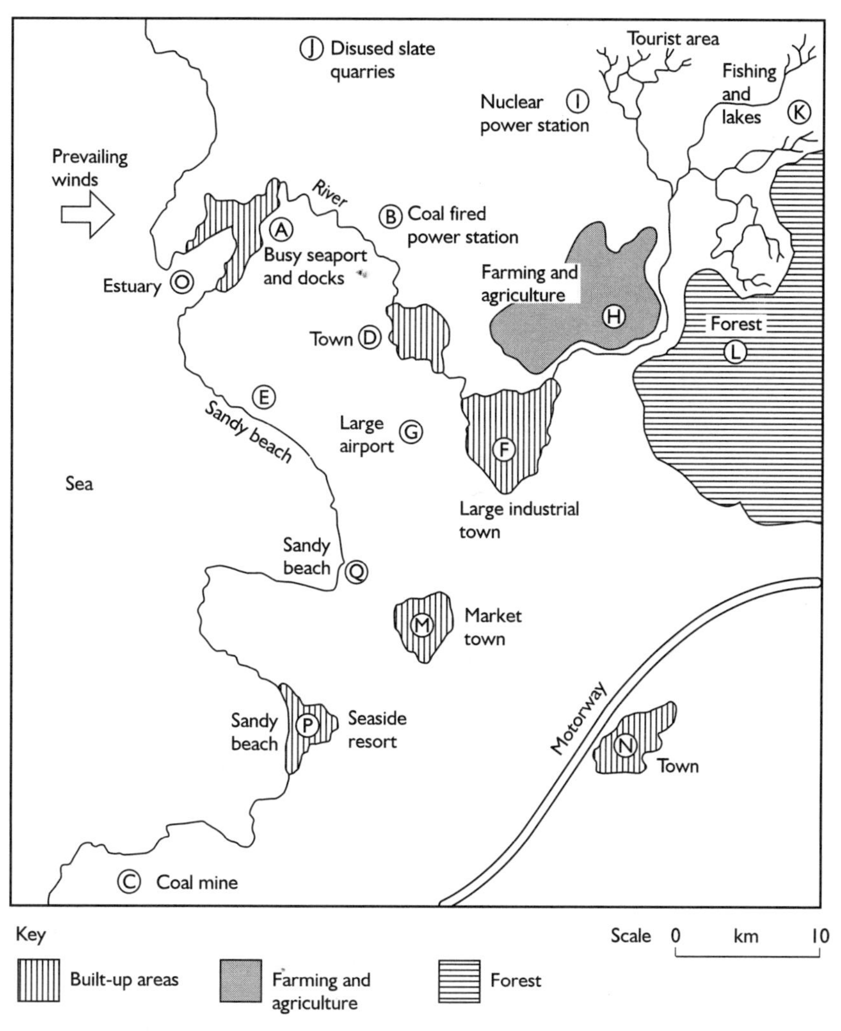

(iii) a **source** of factory effluent;
Place ______
Reason ______ *[1]*

(iv) a **source** of pollution which causes 'acid rain';
Place ______
Reason ______ *[1]*

(v) **affected** by 'acid rain';
Place ______
Reason ______ *[1]*

(vi) **affected** by unsightly spoil heaps;
Place ______
Reason ______ *[1]*

(vii) **permanently affected** by oil spillages;
Place ______
Reason ______ *[1]*

(viii) **affected by** atmospheric lead pollution;
Place ______
Reason ______ *[1]*

(ix) **affected** by noise pollution;
Place ______
Reason ______ *[1]*

Fig. 3.2

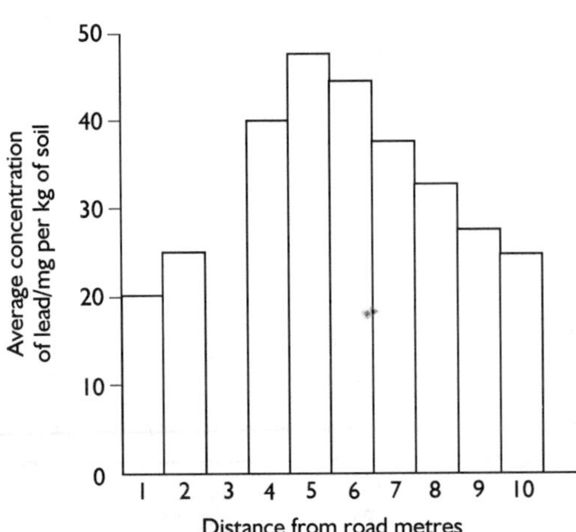

Question 2

Some petrol today contains small quantities of lead compounds. This means that more petrol can be made from the same amount of petroleum. When petrol burns in car engines, lead compounds escape into the atmosphere.

The bar chart (Fig. 3.2) shows the average concentrations of lead in soil samples at different distances from the edge of a road.

(a) What is the average concentration of lead in the soil 7 metres from the edge of the road? *[2]*

(b) At a distance of 3 metres from the road the average concentration of lead is 33 mg/kg of soil.
Complete the bar chart by putting in this result. *[1]*

(c) At what distance from the road is the average concentration of lead in soil greatest? [1 line] *[1]*

(d) Why is it wise to collect several samples at each distance to test for lead? [3 lines] *[2]*

(e) Organolead plc, a company making lead compounds for adding to petrol, tried to get lead from soil by the side of a busy road.
Why is this not likely to be economically worthwhile? [2 lines] *[1]*

(f) Why may it be unwise to eat vegetables grown in an allotment by the side of a busy road? [2 lines] *[2]*

(g) Give one advantage and one disadvantage of using 'lead free' petrol in place of 'leaded' petrol.
Advantage [2 lines]
Disadvantage [2 lines] *[2]*

[Total 11 marks]

Fig. 3.3

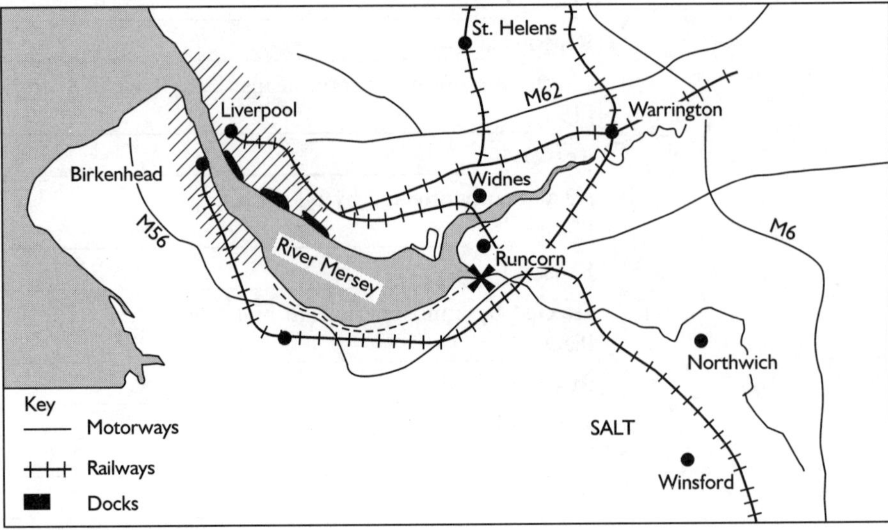

Question 3 Margarine is produced when imported oils are 'hardened' by reaction with hydrogen.

The diagram (Fig. 3.3) shows a map of the area around salt deposits in Cheshire. Suggest two reasons why the place marked **X** would be suitable for building a factory to produce margarine.

1. ______________________________ *[2]*
2. ______________________________

OUTLINE ANSWERS

Question 1

(i) **Place.** I.
Reason. Nuclear power stations renew their fuel rods every few years. (The 'spent' nuclear fuel is radioactive and is sent for reprocessing to remove the waste products of the 'fission' process.)

(ii) **Place.** H.
Reason. Farming and agriculture would use fertilizer, some of which is washed into nearby streams and rivers during rainy periods.

(iii) **Place.** F.
Reason. Factories in a large industrial town will produce waste such as chemical wastes. These may be discharged into the river which flows through town F.

(iv) **Place.** B or F.
Reason. Any coal-fired furnace such as is used in power stations and factories needing heat supply will produce sulphur dioxide and some nitrogen oxides. Both of these gases are atmospheric pollutants which are acidic in water (non-metal oxides).

(v) **Place.** K or L.
Reason. The prevailing (commonest) wind direction is from the left. *Winds* will carry *power station emissions* towards the areas on the right of the map. Acid rain will affect forest, L, and lakes, K.

(vi) **Place.** J or C.
Reason. Slate quarries, as do most quarries and coal mines, produce waste rock. Such waste is usually piled in heaps until of large enough size to landscape.

(vii) **Place.** O or A.
Reason. A busy port means many ships. Fuel oil leakage is impossible to avoid. Prevailing wind drives it into the estuary.

(viii) **Place.** N.
Reason. Lead compounds are present in motor car exhausts. The motorway, carrying a large volume of motor traffic, is only 2 or 3 km downwind.

(iv) **Place.** N or F.
Reason. N is the town which is near a motorway. The edge is only 2 km from the noise of traffic. F is a town which will have aircraft flying overhead to *land into the prevailing wind* at airport G.

Question 2 This is a comprehension question. Candidates are not expected to know all the details of the use of lead in petrol. *Some* chemical knowledge and an ability to *use information* which is given in the text of the question are required to succeed on this type of question.

The bar chart shows average lead concentrations in the soil as it changes with distance from the road where lead is emitted by motor vehicles.

(a) The average lead concentration in the soil at 7 metres from the road is 37 milligrams per kilogram of soil. A figure one mg/kg either way would be acceptable because the graph axis is marked every ten units and so an **estimate** has to be made of the required figure. **Units** are important as well as the *figure*. There is one mark for each.

(b) The top of the bar should come one-third of the distance between 30 and 40 on the vertical scale. It is a good practice to mark the side scale at 33 and *then* draw in the bar. In this way the examiner can see that you have attempted the estimate and not guessed it. You will also have made a more accurate estimate on the scale itself.

(c) Reading a **maximum** is usually easy if you know what the phrase **greatest average concentration** means. The answer is 5 metres. Can you see why?

(d) Collecting *several samples* is like doing an experiment *more than once*—we do it to make sure that we have not made an **error** in any *one* measurement. The first result *may be correct* but until the others *confirm it* we cannot be sure. Note also that even several measurements are likely to vary a little between themselves and so an *average* is taken because we cannot be sure *which one is most correct.*

(e) The concentration of lead in the soil in question is not very large—milligrams in every thousand grams of soil. 20 000 tonnes of soil would have to be treated to get one tonne of lead!

(f) The tests were done on roadside soil. The lead has probably come from motor vehicles. Fumes will deposit lead compounds *on* the leaves of vegetables and lead from the soil may get *into* the plants through their roots. The toxic effect of lead compounds makes it unwise to eat these vegetables regularly.

(g) Advantage: No more lead compounds in exhaust fumes.
Disadvantage: Many cars cannot use lead-free petrol because their engines are not designed for it—they are fitted with autocatalysts.

Question 3

This *part-question* illustrates a type of question to be expected in GCSE papers. It tests understanding of the reasons for choosing a particular site for a chemical factory and the recognition that factories cannot simply be built where they are 'out of the way' of towns and people.

Factories are usually built close to supplies of raw materials, labour and transport routes.

Margarine manufacture, you are told, needs **hydrogen** and **imported natural oils**. Electrolysis of salt solution will produce hydrogen gas as a by-product of the production of chlorine, see Table 10.2.

1. Place X is close to a port for imports of the oils needed.
2. It is close to salt supplies and so electrolysis of salt will probably be carried out in the area. Hydrogen will therefore be available.

Other reasons are: nearby supply of labour—several towns and a large city; plenty of good transport facilities for taking product to markets in other parts of Britain or even abroad.

STUDENT ANSWER WITH EXAMINER'S COMMENTS

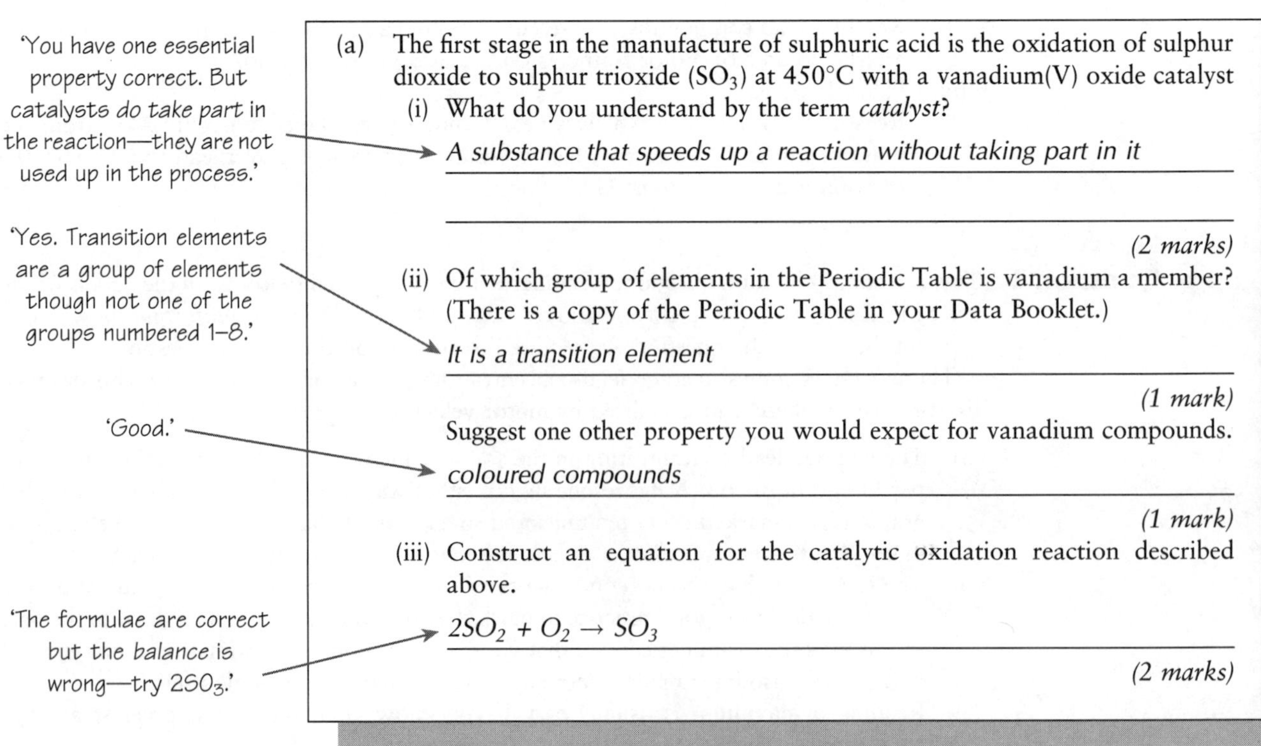

(a) The first stage in the manufacture of sulphuric acid is the oxidation of sulphur dioxide to sulphur trioxide (SO_3) at 450°C with a vanadium(V) oxide catalyst

(i) What do you understand by the term *catalyst*?

A substance that speeds up a reaction without taking part in it

'You have one essential property correct. But catalysts *do take part* in the reaction—they are not used up in the process.'

(2 marks)

(ii) Of which group of elements in the Periodic Table is vanadium a member? (There is a copy of the Periodic Table in your Data Booklet.)

It is a transition element

'Yes. Transition elements are a group of elements though not one of the groups numbered 1–8.'

(1 mark)

Suggest one other property you would expect for vanadium compounds.

coloured compounds

'Good.'

(1 mark)

(iii) Construct an equation for the catalytic oxidation reaction described above.

$2SO_2 + O_2 \rightarrow SO_3$

'The formulae are correct but the *balance* is wrong—try $2SO_3$.'

(2 marks)

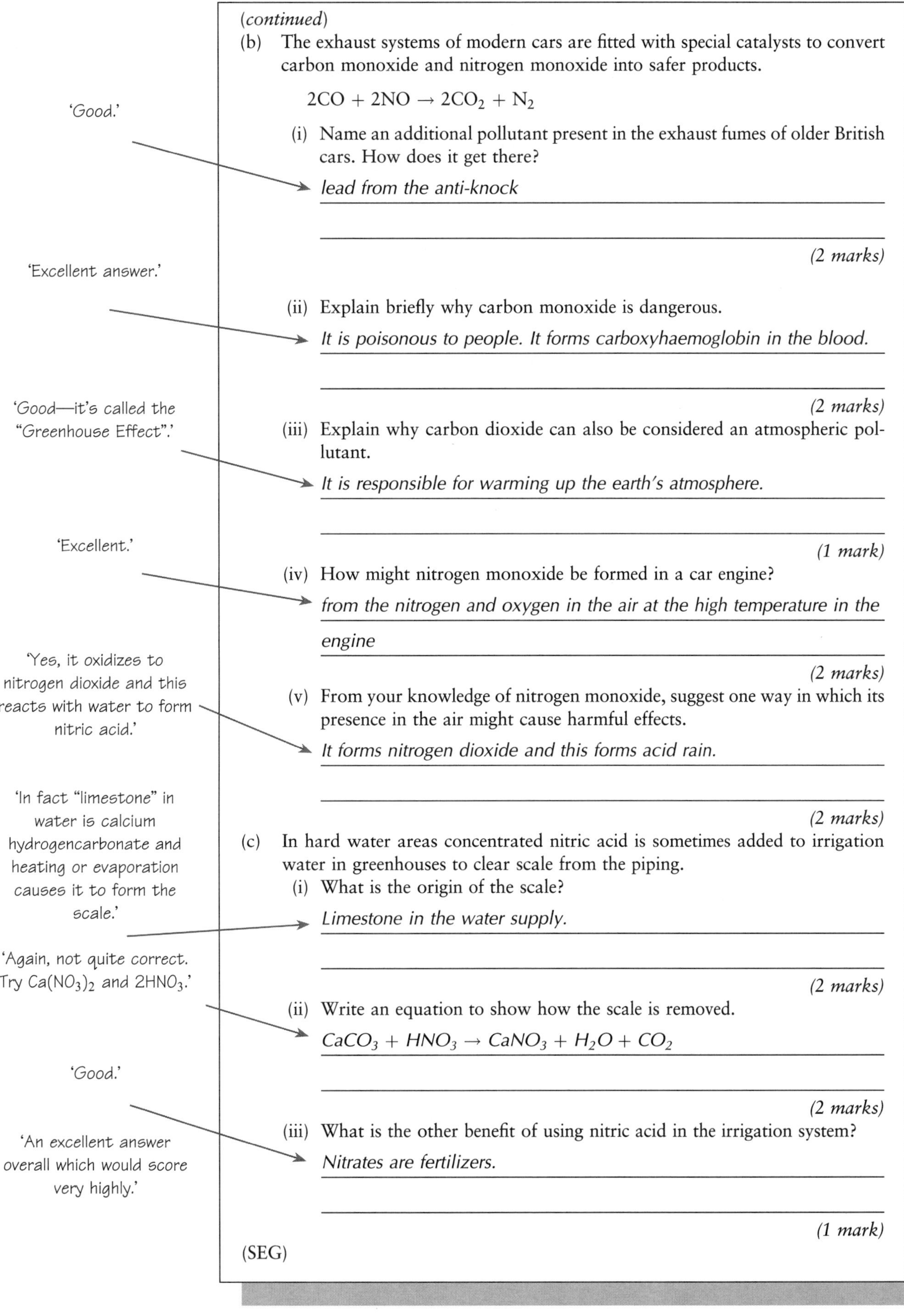
'Good.'
'Excellent answer.'
'Good—it's called the "Greenhouse Effect".'
'Excellent.'
'Yes, it oxidizes to nitrogen dioxide and this reacts with water to form nitric acid.'
'In fact "limestone" in water is calcium hydrogencarbonate and heating or evaporation causes it to form the scale.'
'Again, not quite correct. Try $Ca(NO_3)_2$ and $2HNO_3$.'
'Good.'
'An excellent answer overall which would score very highly.'

(*continued*)

(b) The exhaust systems of modern cars are fitted with special catalysts to convert carbon monoxide and nitrogen monoxide into safer products.

$$2CO + 2NO \rightarrow 2CO_2 + N_2$$

(i) Name an additional pollutant present in the exhaust fumes of older British cars. How does it get there?

lead from the anti-knock

(2 marks)

(ii) Explain briefly why carbon monoxide is dangerous.

It is poisonous to people. It forms carboxyhaemoglobin in the blood.

(2 marks)

(iii) Explain why carbon dioxide can also be considered an atmospheric pollutant.

It is responsible for warming up the earth's atmosphere.

(1 mark)

(iv) How might nitrogen monoxide be formed in a car engine?

from the nitrogen and oxygen in the air at the high temperature in the engine

(2 marks)

(v) From your knowledge of nitrogen monoxide, suggest one way in which its presence in the air might cause harmful effects.

It forms nitrogen dioxide and this forms acid rain.

(2 marks)

(c) In hard water areas concentrated nitric acid is sometimes added to irrigation water in greenhouses to clear scale from the piping.

(i) What is the origin of the scale?

Limestone in the water supply.

(2 marks)

(ii) Write an equation to show how the scale is removed.

$CaCO_3 + HNO_3 \rightarrow CaNO_3 + H_2O + CO_2$

(2 marks)

(iii) What is the other benefit of using nitric acid in the irrigation system?

Nitrates are fertilizers.

(1 mark)

(SEG)

SUMMARY

Use this list to help you with your revision. Tick off the points as you revise them in the text.

- ▷ The chemical industry **earns money** for the country.
- ▷ The products of chemical industry. are important to our **well-being** and **convenience** in everyday life.
- ▷ Chemical manufacturers only produce what the **public demands**.
- ▷ Most chemical companies are as **concerned not to pollute** the environment as you or I.
- ▷ Pollution from modern cars is greatly reduced by the use of catalytic converters (**autocatalysts**).
- ▷ Autocatalysts remove pollutants by reacting them together on a catalyst to produce harmless gases, e.g.

  $2CO + 2NO \rightarrow N_2 + 2CO_2$
- ▷ Water pollution can produce **eutrophication.**
- ▷ A lot of ingenuity goes into finding methods of **reducing pollution** and **recycling waste** products.

Chapter

4 Elements, compounds and mixtures

GETTING STARTED

We can imagine that human beings have been using substances they found in the ground or obtained from the seas of our planet for as long as they have been on earth. Our ancestors will have used some of the **elements** that are to be found 'native', i.e. in a pure state naturally, such as gold for ornaments, sulphur for burning and perhaps medicinal purposes, and copper for tools. They will have found many uses for **mixtures** such as crude oil and sea water which are to be found widely throughout the globe. They will even have managed to produce some reasonably pure **compounds** for their use, such as common salt for preserving and flavouring food. However, the number of useful substances available to our ancestors was minute compared to those now used in our everyday lives.

- An **element** is a substance that cannot be separated into anything simpler. It is composed of atoms all of which have the same number of protons and electrons, but may have different numbers of neutrons.
- A **compound** is a substance formed by chemical reaction between two or more elements.
- A **mixture** consists of two or more components (elements, compounds or both) not chemically combined together. The properties of each component are not altered by the process of mixing.

TOPIC CHART

LONDON	MEG	NEAB	NICCEA	SEG	WJEC	TOPIC	STUDY	REVISION 1	REVISION 2
✓	✓	✓	✓	✓	✓	Elements			
✓	✓	✓	✓	✓	✓	Compounds and mixtures			
	✓	✓	✓	✓		Separating mixtures			
✓	✓	✓	✓	✓	✓	Purity of a substance			
✓	✓	✓	✓	✓	✓	Laboratory apparatus and techniques			

WHAT YOU NEED TO KNOW

Elements

'Draw a portion of the periodic table to contain the first twenty elements. Put the symbols of the elements onto your table and learn them.'

Elements are the building blocks of all matter. There are 89 naturally occurring elements of which 21 are non-metals and 68 metals. Each element is a collection of atoms with identical numbers of protons in the nucleus. A knowledge of the symbols of the first twenty elements is required for GCSE courses.

The naturally occurring elements represent a global store of atoms which cannot be destroyed but which can become part of any of a larger number of different compounds. So the carbon atoms in the hydrocarbon molecules present in the petrol we buy at a garage were once possibly a part of the molecules in the body of a living creature and will, when used to power a motor car, become part of the gaseous carbon monoxide and carbon dioxide that comes out of the exhaust system. From there, these carbon atoms will eventually become part of yet other molecules—even possibly part of a human body. Atoms of elements are therefore re-usable 'building blocks' of matter.

Compounds and mixtures

If elements are the 'building blocks' of matter then compounds are the 'buildings'. Compounds are formed when elements combine together to form new substances. They must be clearly distinguished from mixtures of elements. Two examples will make the difference clearer.

Compounds

If we mixed the two elements hydrogen and oxygen, for instance in equal volumes, in a flask we could make them react or combine together by *heating*. There would be an explosion, heat would be produced, a liquid would appear on the sides of the flask as it cooled and we would find that there was *some oxygen left* which had *not* reacted. After heating, a product would be present which would not look like either oxygen or hydrogen. It would be a compound of the two elements oxygen and hydrogen called hydrogen oxide. Hydrogen oxide, commonly known as water, is a colourless, tasteless, non-toxic, non-flammable liquid quite different from the gases from which it was made.

What about the oxygen gas which had not reacted? Water is formed by the reaction of *exactly* twice as much hydrogen (by volume) as oxygen gas. Any extra hydrogen or extra oxygen is not used (we call it an *excess*) and is left over at the end of the reaction. *There is only one 'recipe' (formula) for the compound, water*, whereas there are *many possible 'recipes' for mixtures of oxygen and hydrogen gases*.

'Draw diagrams of oxygen molecules, hydrogen molecules and water molecules.'

Again, if we could *see* the particles of matter present in the reaction vessel after the explosion we should see *two* different types. *Water* molecules have three atoms, two of them hydrogen and one oxygen. In addition, there would be some *oxygen* molecules, unreacted because they were in excess, which have two identical atoms in the molecule. We would have a **mixture** of one **element** with one **compound**.

Separation of the elements of a compound

Unlike the separation of hydrogen and oxygen from a mixture of the two (see below), no **physical process** will separate the two elements from water. A chemical reaction is needed to obtain oxygen or hydrogen from water, e.g. reaction of sodium with water to get hydrogen or electrolysis to get both oxygen *and* hydrogen.

Mixtures

Hydrogen and oxygen are two elements. They are colourless gases and further they are both non-metals. If we put equal volumes of hydrogen and oxygen into the same flask and cork it, we will have a *mixture of two gaseous non-metallic elements*. If we could see the particles in this mixture, we should see *two different types of molecules* consisting of pairs of atoms. Because the particles present are *not all identical*, we obviously have a **mixture**.

No noticeable change will occur in the flask no matter how long we leave the mixture there. The mixture formed here would, if used to inflate a toy balloon, cause the balloon to float in the air because the mixture of hydrogen and oxygen will be lighter than air. Also, we could mix oxygen and hydrogen in *other proportions* and still make a mixture of the two.

Every mixture would look the same but those with the most hydrogen in would make the balloon rise faster than those with less hydrogen in. Animals could live in the mixtures which contained 20% or more of oxygen. Each element in the mixture behaves exactly as it does without the others being there! There can be *many* mixtures of these two gases, each one different from the others.

Separation of hydrogen and oxygen from a mixture
If we wished to separate the hydrogen from the oxygen in these mixtures it could be done by processes such as liquefying the oxygen, or allowing the hydrogen to diffuse through a palladium thimble which would not allow passage of the oxygen. Most mixtures can be separated by **physical processes** which are simpler than those mentioned for hydrogen and oxygen.

Solutions
Aqueous solutions are particular examples of mixtures. They are common because water is such a good solvent that many compounds dissolve in it. It is important to be able to determine the solubility of any compound in water. See Chapter 16.

Separating mixtures

Mixtures can be of several types:

(i) two or more elements, e.g. alloys or air;
(ii) two or more compounds, e.g. sea water or crude oil;
(iii) a mixture of elements and compounds, e.g. native gold or crude sulphur.

We usually want to obtain only *one* of the components of a mixture. The methods given below, however, will sometimes give more than one component in a pure state.

Separating a solid from a liquid in which it does not dissolve

Filtration
This will separate a solid from a liquid (usually a solution) in which the solid is insoluble, e.g. sand from salt solution, a solid from its saturated solution or mud from water to be used for drinking. The solid remaining on the filter paper is called the **residue** (Fig. 4.1) and the solution running through the filter paper is the **filtrate.**

Decantation
This does the same as filtration but the liquid is carefully *poured* away from the solid, which (Fig. 4.2) is usually heavy and at the bottom of the vessel, e.g. a saturated solution can be poured away from crystals, or wine from its sediment.

Centrifugation
This method also does what (i) and (ii) do. If the solid mixed with the liquid is very fine and slows down filtration by blocking the pores of the filter paper, then using a centrifuge will

Fig. 4.1 Filtration

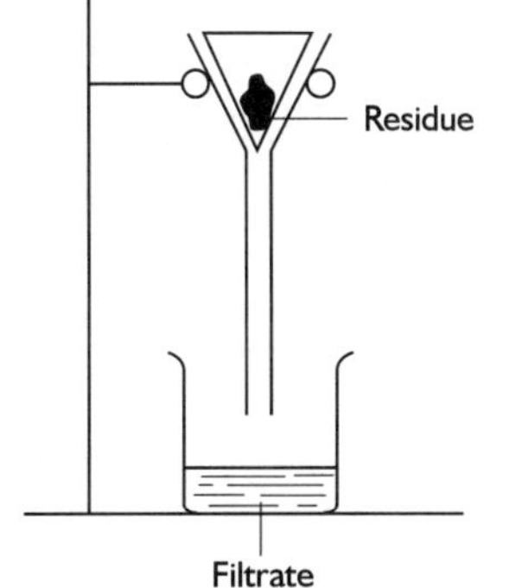

Fig. 4.2 Decantation

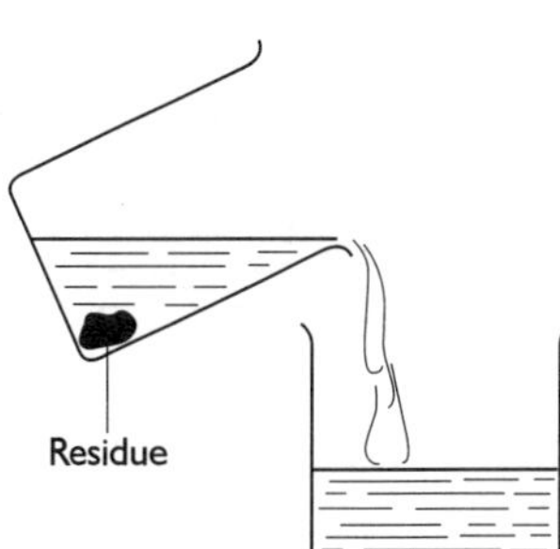

Fig. 4.3 Evaporation

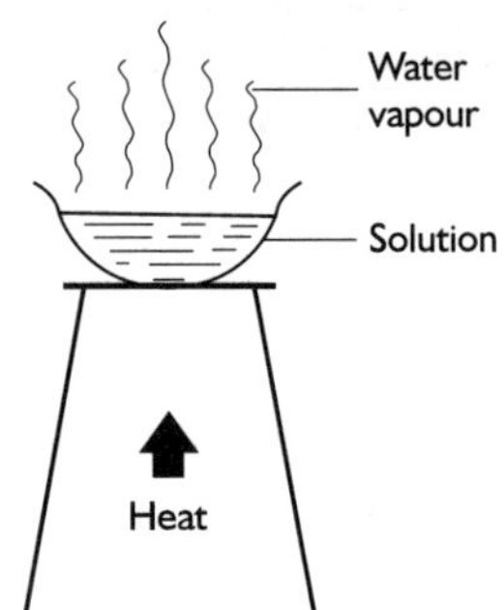

cause the solid to settle quickly. The solid and liquid are then separated by decanting the liquid into another vessel.

Separating a solid from its solution in a solvent

Evaporation

This is used when a solid is to be **extracted** from its solution, e.g. salt from sea water or brine. Evaporation will allow the liquid part of the mixture to be lost into the air, leaving the solid (Fig. 4.3). If the liquid part of the mixture is needed then its vapour must be condensed and one of the distillation processes described below must be used.

Crystallization

This is the process where *complete evaporation* of water from a solution would not produce the desired **crystalline** product. Many crystals **decompose** when heated to dry them. They may give off water to become powders.

Crystallization is the process of evaporation which is *stopped* at the stage where a saturated solution has formed. The resulting solution is then cooled to room temperature and produces **crystals**. See also Chapter 15 (p. 229). The apparatus used is as for evaporation above.

Separating a liquid from a solution

Distillation

There are two types of distillation:

(i) **Simple distillation.** This is used to separate a single liquid from one or more solids in a solution, e.g. to obtain pure water from sea water or tap water (Fig. 4.4).

(ii) **Fractional distillation.** This is used to separate several liquids from a mixture or a liquid from a solution of one liquid in another, e.g. getting 'fractions' from crude oil or ethanol from wine (Fig. 4.5).

Crude oil consists of more than 200 different hydrocarbons. The industrial separation of crude oil into its component fractions involves separating these into a dozen or so major 'fractions'. The fractions are not single compounds, but mixtures having a narrow boiling point range. See Chapter 7, p. 77.

Fractional distillation of crude oil in the laboratory For the purpose of the following description of fractional distillation, each fraction can be thought of as a component having a single boiling point. When the crude oil is boiled, the components vaporize. The vapours move up the fractionating column. The component with the *lowest* boiling point rises to the top of the column and passes into the condenser. On condensing, the liquid component collects as the distillate. The thermometer registers the boiling point of the component passing over. The temperature remains constant until all of the component has distilled over. When this has

Fig. 4.4 Simple distillation

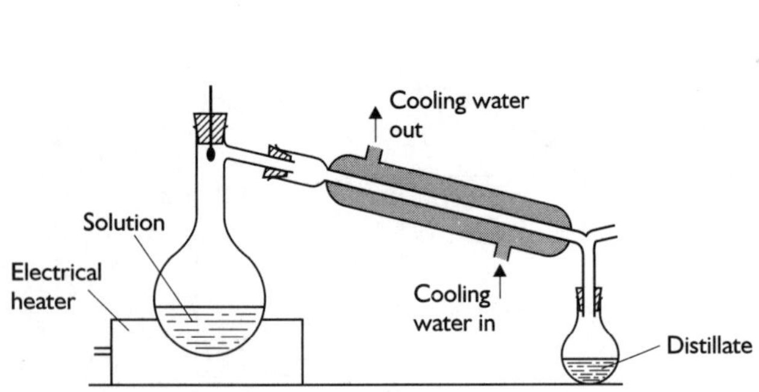

Fig. 4.5 Fractional distillation

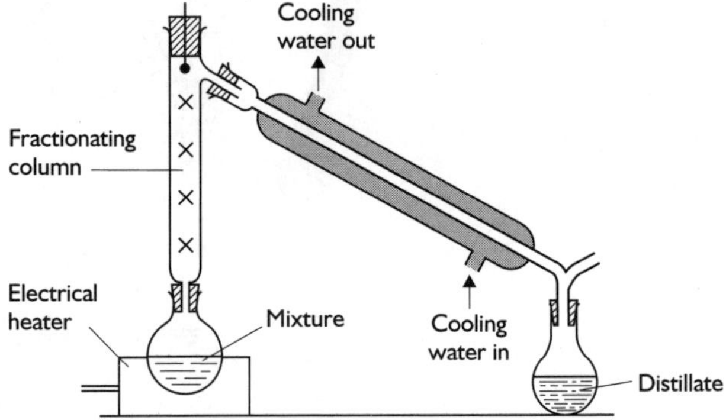

Fig. 4.6

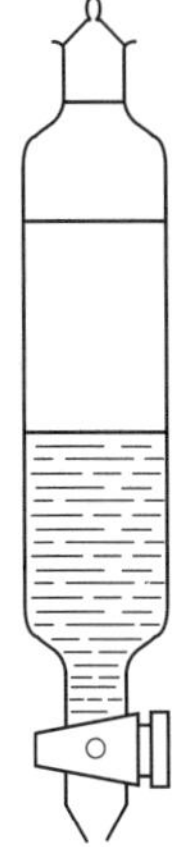

happened, the next component will pass over, register its boiling point on the thermometer and condense into the receiver. The receiver must be changed everytime a new component distils. The last component to distil over is the one with the *highest* boiling point.

Separating liquids which do not mix

Liquids which do not mix, of course, do not really form mixtures. However, the method of separating them is useful to know. Liquids which do not mix are said to be **immiscible**, like mercury and water or oil and water. The 'mixture' is poured into a separating funnel or tap funnel (Fig. 4.6). The liquids are allowed to stand until they separate and a clear boundary can be seen. The lower (more dense or heavier) layer is then run out through the tap. If the top (less dense or lighter) layer that is left is wanted, it can be poured out through the top of the separating funnel.

Separating several solids from a mixture in solution

Chromatography

It is sometimes necessary to separate several substances from a mixture in solution, e.g. mixed dyes in water (ink), or several sugars in water. Paper chromatography will do this quickly and efficiently (Figs 4.7 and 4.11).

Fig. 4.7 Chromatography

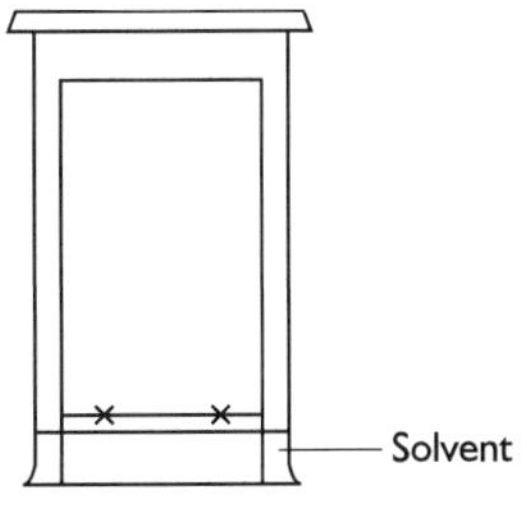

Fig. 4.8 Sublimation

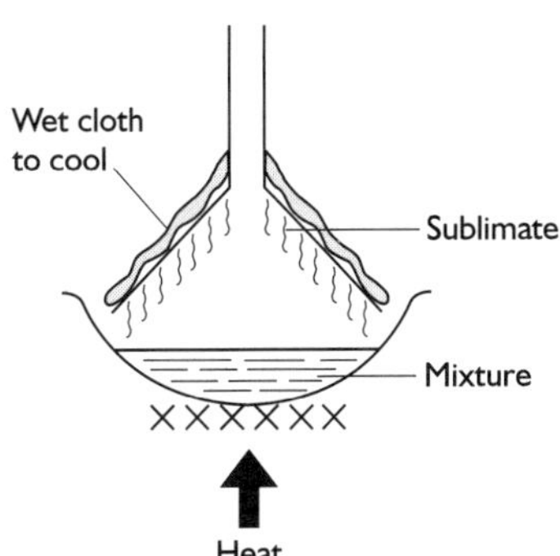

Separating one solid from a mixture of solids

Sublimation

This method has limited uses because very few solids will **sublime.** A solid that does sublime iodine. This iodine can be separated from *other* solids by this process, which is similar to the process of distillation, but for purifying solids:

sublimation solid $\xrightarrow{\text{heat}}$ vapour $\xrightarrow{\text{cool}}$ solid

compare

distillation liquid $\xrightarrow{\text{heat}}$ vapour $\xrightarrow{\text{cool}}$ liquid

Sublimation is an unusual process. In it, the heated solid becomes a vapour without first melting, i.e. the solid boils before it melts! On cooling, the vapour condenses to a solid rather than a liquid. The *two processes together* are called sublimation (Fig. 4.8).

Purity of a substance

A pure substance has a *sharp* melting point and a *fixed* boiling point. For example, pure water freezes at 0 °C and boils at 100 °C at normal atmospheric pressure. The presence of impurity lowers the freezing point (melting point) and increases the boiling point of a substance. The more impurity present, the greater its effect. For example, water containing about 4% common salt boils at 7 °C above its normal boiling point.

Adding about 20% of common salt to ice lowers the freezing temperature by some 20 °C. However, at all temperatures below 0 °C more and more ice will form as the temperature drops but the mixture will not freeze *completely* until the temperature reaches about −20 °C. So the freezing point is no longer sharp but occurs over a range of temperatures.

The melting point of lead (mp 327 °C) is lower by 2.3 °C for every 1% of tin added up to a maximum lowering at 62% of tin. As a quick test of your mathematical ability, what would be the melting temperature of the 62% tin: 38% lead mixture?

Measuring melting point and boiling point

Measuring boiling and melting points (Figs 4.9 and 4.10) is a suitable way of finding out whether a substance contains small amounts of impurity. However, it will not tell us *how many* different substances are present in the mixture.

Fig. 4.9

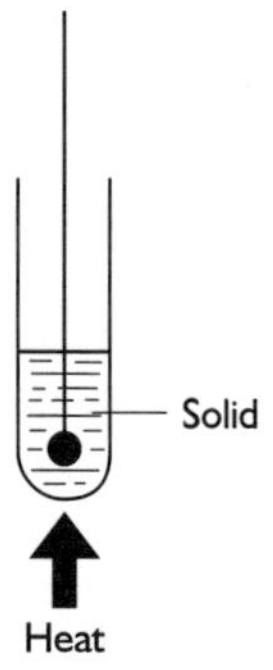

Solid

Heat

Fig. 4.10

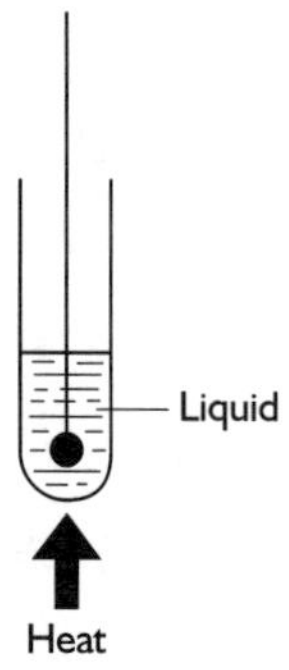

Liquid

Heat

Fig. 4.11 Chromatogram

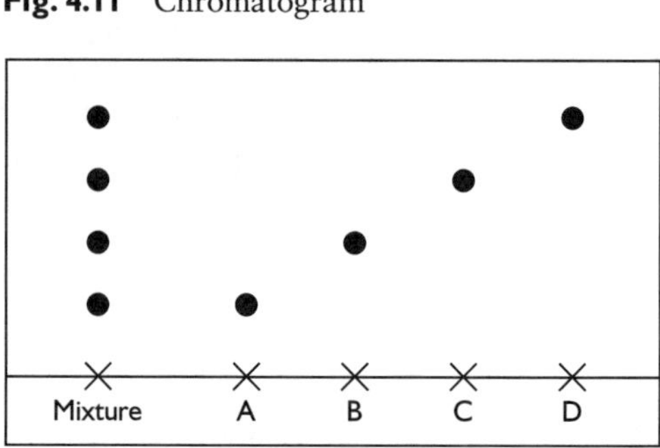

Chromatography

An easy way of determining the number of substances present in a solution (liquid mixture) is by chromatography (Fig. 4.11). We can find out the number of different coloured dyes in an ink, for example. Chromatography can even be used where the substances are colourless. In this case colourless spots are present on the chromatogram and need a special chemical to show them up.

Use of separation processes in industry

Industrial chemistry deals with:

(i) natural mixtures from which pure compounds are to be extracted; or
(ii) compounds from which elements are to be extracted; or
(iii) elements and compounds from which other substances are to be synthesized.

In almost every case, the raw materials have first to be purified by methods involving the processes described earlier in this chapter. A thorough understanding of these processes is therefore invaluable for further study.

Once pure chemicals are available, the chemist can use them to produce a wide variety of different substances. To do this a knowledge and experience of additional techniques will be required.

Laboratory apparatus and techniques

The chemical reactions carried out in school and college laboratories do not require a wide variety of apparatus. Figure 4.12 shows pieces that would be used in most student practical work. It may be necessary to draw some of these pieces of apparatus in your examination.

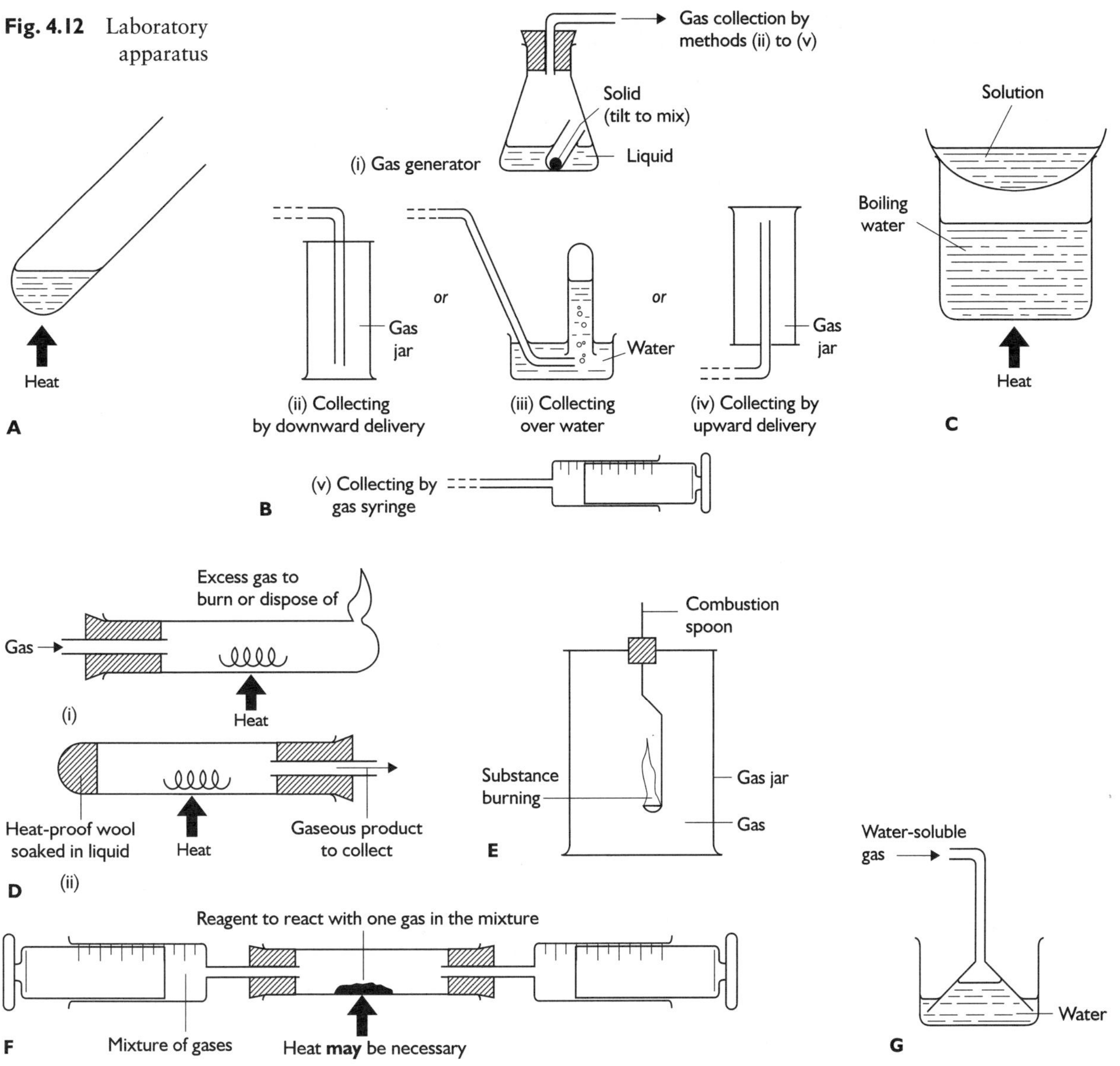

Table 4.1

Apparatus	What it is designed to do	Typical experiment in which it could be used
A	Heating solids or liquids	Decomposing a solid/testing for a gas produced
B	(i) react solid with solution	(ii) collect gases denser than air, e.g. HCl, Cl_2, CO_2 (iii) collect insoluble gases over water, e.g. H_2, O_2 (iv) collect gases less dense than air, e.g. H_2, NH_3 (v) collect any gas
C	Crystallization	Getting pure salts from their saturated solutions
D	(i) Passing a gas over a heated solid (ii) Passing a vapour over a heated solid	Reduction of metal oxides with H_2 Reacting steam with a heated metal
E	Burning solid or liquid in a gas	Burning metals in oxygen or chlorine
F	Removing one gas from a mixture, with measurement	Finding percentage of O_2 in air or CO_2 in a mixture
G	Will dissolve a water—soluble gas without suck-back	Dissolving hydrogen chloride to make hydrochloric acid or ammonia to make ammonia solution

EXAMINATION QUESTIONS

Questions 1–3 (F)

The type of questions represented by Questions 1–3 ask for the identification of a process.

Name the separation process shown in each of the following diagrams.

1. diagram (a) ______
2. diagram (b) ______
3. diagram (c) ______

(SEG)

Fig. 4.13

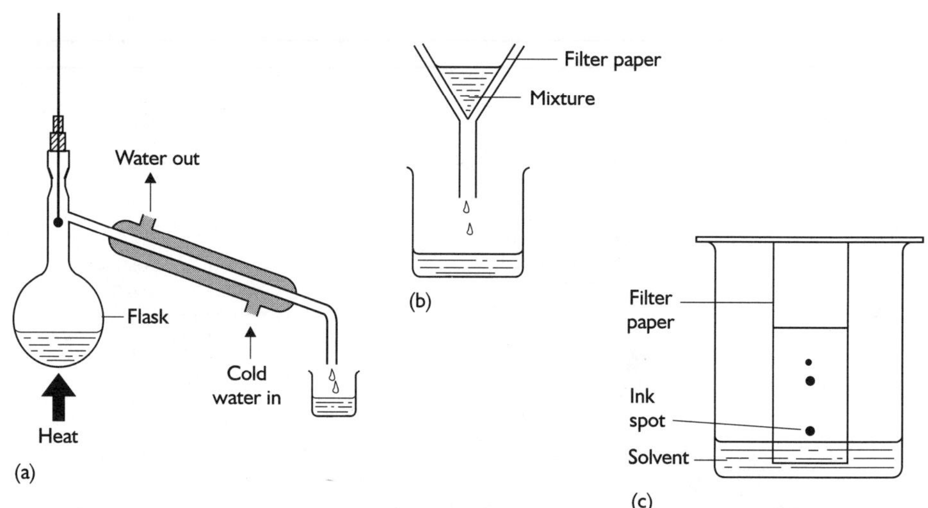

Question 4 (F)

(a) (i) How is filtration of reservoir water carried out? [2 lines] *[1]*
(ii) What is the purpose of this filtration? [2 lines] *[1]*

(b) (i) How may a sample of pure water be obtained from sea water? *[1]*
(ii) Explain the process of evaporation in terms of movement of molecules. [3 lines] *[3]*
(iii) Why does the salt in sea water not circulate through the atmosphere in the way the water does? [2 lines] *[2]*

(SEG)

Question 5 (F)

To show that a shampoo contains a mixture of colours, chromatography can be used. Two brands, X and Y, of yellow-coloured shampoo were compared and the chromatogram below was obtained.

(a) What is meant by the solvent front? [1 line] *[1]*

Fig. 4.14

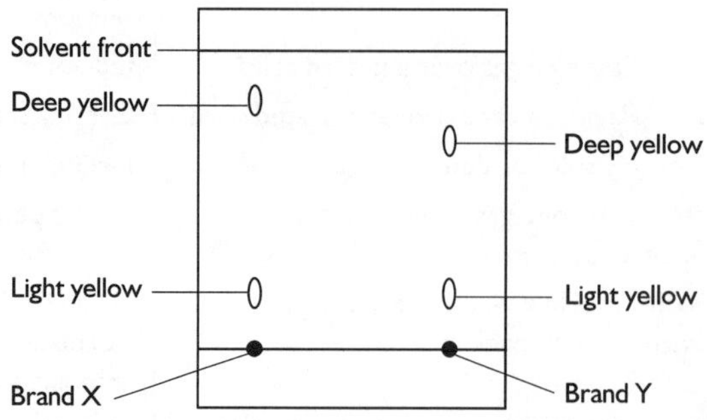

(b) Name a suitable solvent to use in the experiment. [1 line] *[1]*
(c) Explain whether you think brands X and Y contain the same coloured chemicals. [3 lines] *[3]*

(WJEC)

Question 6 (F) In each of the diagrams below, different atoms are shown by ○ and ●:

Fig. 4.15

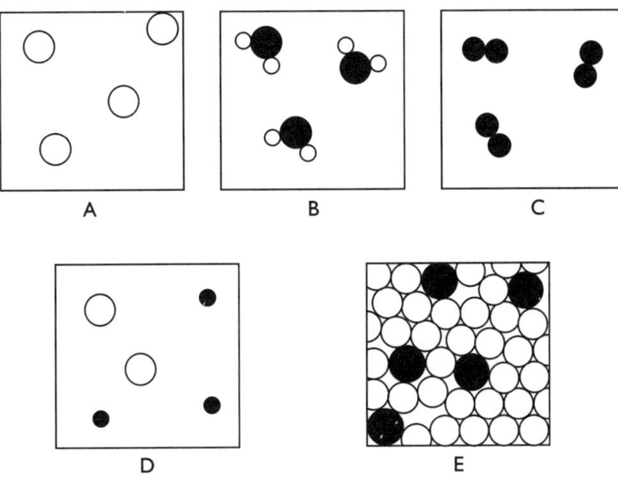

Which of the diagrams could represent

(a) oxygen gas (O_2)? *[1]*
(b) an alloy? *[1]*
(c) steam? *[1]*
(d) a gas such as argon (Ar)? *[1]*
(e) a gaseous mixture of helium (He) and neon (Ne)? *[1]*

Question 7 (F) Cars use both air and petrol in their engines.

Fig. 4.16

(a) State whether each of the gases in the air is an element or a compound. *[2]*
(b) Petrol is a mixture of hydrocarbons.
  (i) What is the meaning of the word *mixture*? *[1]*
  (ii) Explain the meaning of the word *hydrocarbon*. *[2]*
(c) (i) Which gas in the air reacts with petrol in the engine? *[1]*
  (ii) Name *two* substances formed when petrol burns in air. *[2]*

[Total 8 marks]

Question 8 (H) Rock salt contains insoluble solids and the soluble salt, sodium chloride. The following processes are needed to separate sodium chloride from rock salt.

evaporation   crystallization   addition of water   filtration   stirring

Put each process in the correct order for separating sodium chloride from rock salt.

Explain the purpose of each process.

First process ______________________________

Purpose ______________________________ *[1]*

Second process ______________________________

Purpose ______________________________ *[1]*

Third process ______________________________

Purpose ______________________________ *[1]*

Fourth process ______________________________

Purpose ______________________________ *[1]*

Fifth process ______________________________

Purpose ______________________________ *[1]*

[Total 5 marks]

OUTLINE ANSWERS

Question 1 This is a diagram of a **simple distillation** apparatus.

Question 2 The process here is **filtration.**

Question 3 This is **chromatography.**

Question 4 (a) (i) Reservoir water is filtered through sand and gravel filter beds.
Filter paper would not be appropriate for the large-scale process—it would be expensive on paper and replacement of the filter would be time consuming.

(ii) The purpose is to remove any fine solid particles. (These will be trapped by the sand and gravel. Eventually the sand layer becomes clogged and must be washed clean to be reused. The washing process is carried out by 'back-flushing'—a process of pumping water *up* through the beds of sand and gravel and carrying the residue from the sand bed out of the filter vessel. When clean, the sand and gravel are allowed to settle again and are ready to be re-used.)

(b) (i) The process is distillation.
(Sea water contains salts. Water is easily vaporized but salts have high boiling points. Boiling the sea water will vaporize the water but not the salt. Passing the steam through a condenser will condense it to liquid water. The water will have been separated from the salt.)

(ii) Molecules of a liquid are always in motion. When heated, the molecules gain more energy. Those with the most energy are able to escape from the liquid and so form a vapour.
(All substances contain moving particles if they are not at absolute zero of temperature (−273 °C). Liquids, like water, contain particles which move about freely, at random, in all directions. Some of these molecules have enough energy to escape from the liquid into the space above the liquid. They are said to have vaporized. The higher the temperature, the more molecules are able to vaporize. In the vapour state molecules are much further apart than in the liquid state. They occupy at least one thousand times as much volume as the same number of molecules in the liquid.)

(iii) As explained above salts are not easily vaporized; they have high boiling points. Sea salts will not evaporate into the atmosphere.

Question 5 (a) The solvent front is, as it suggests, the front edge of the solvent as it travels up the paper. On the finished chromatogram the solvent front shows the distance the solvent has travelled up the paper—for comparison with the distances travelled by the spots.

(b) The shampoos are soluble in water. Water could, therefore, be used as a solvent. *Any solvent* you might have used in chromatography would be accepted.

(c) The coloured spots from the two brands of shampoo show that both contain *the same* light yellow dye (spots at the same level) but each brand contains a *different* deep yellow dye (spots at different levels).

Question 6 (a) C (b) E (c) B (d) A (e) D

Question 7 (a) Nitrogen, oxygen and argon are elements *[1]*; carbon dioxide and water vapour are compounds *[1]*.

(b) (i) A mixture contains two or more components not combined together, e.g. two or more compounds or two or more elements or two or more elements and compounds *[1]*.

(ii) Hydrocarbons are compounds of hydrogen and carbon *[1]* only *[1]*.

(c) (i) Oxygen *[1]*.

(ii) Any *two* of carbon monoxide, carbon dioxide, nitrogen dioxide, water vapour *[2]*.

Question 8

1. Addition of water—to dissolve the soluble sodium chloride *[1]*.
2. Stirring—to speed up the dissolving process *[1]*.
3. Filtration—to separate the insoluble solids from the salt solution *[1]*.
4. Evaporation—to remove sufficient of the water to form a saturated solution *[1]*.
5. Crystallization—allows crystals to form on cooling *[1]*.

STUDENT ANSWER WITH EXAMINER'S COMMENTS

Student task

You have been asked to discover by experiment which of TWO different indigestion tablets will give the fastest relief from acid indigestion. Give details of what you would do and how you would do it. Say how you would interpret the results of your experiments.

(An acid is provided which is similar to stomach acid.)

Student answer

I would first take one of each of the two different tablets and put them in separate beakers. I would then add some of the acid, an equal volume, to each tablet. I would find the time taken to dissolve each tablet. The fastest tablet to dissolve would be the one which gives fastest relief from stomach ache.

'Your plan is a good one. It states clearly what you would do. It falls down on the detail of how you would do it. Remember that there are many ways of adding a liquid to a solid and you have not given precise details of your method. Would you add the acid slowly through a burette or quickly using a measuring cylinder? You do not state a volume of acid to be used. Would you use enough to dissolve the whole tablet? How would you find out how much this was? I presume you would use a stop-watch to time the reaction though you do not say so.'

'A point about setting out your plans. Divide your answer up into paragraphs. One paragraph for the method to be used, another for the results you would expect to obtain and a third for the way in which you would interpret the results to find the answer to the problem. So many students, when they get a set of results, forget the aim of the experiment. Fortunately you did not. Could you take the problem one step further? How could the slower of the two tablets be made to give faster relief from acid indigestion?'

SUMMARY

Use this list to help with your revision. Tick off the points as you learn them.

▷ **Elements** contain only atoms with the same atomic (proton) number.

▷ **Compounds** are formed from two or more elements combined together.

▷ Compounds have **compositions fixed** by their formula: mixtures are of **variable composition**.

▷ The **formula** of a compound tells us:

(i) what **elements** it contains;
(ii) the relative **numbers** of atoms of each element.

For example, **MgO** contains magnesium and oxygen in the ratio of **one atom** of magnesium for every **one atom** of oxygen.

▷ To separate elements from compounds, **chemical reactions** are needed.

▷ To separate components of mixtures **physical processes** are used.

▷ Mixtures contain **two or more** substances **not combined**—easily separated by a variety of methods which have to be learned.

▷ The processes used to separate a solid from its solution are different from those used to separate a liquid from a mixture.

▷ **Chromatography** can be used to separate the solid components of a solution, especially if they are coloured.

▷ Solids can be purified by **crystallization** from solution.

▷ **Filtration** separates a solid from a solution in which it has not dissolved.

▷ Different pieces of **laboratory apparatus** have different purposes; you may be required to draw one or more of those illustrated.

▷ **Gases** are collected in different ways depending on their **Density** or **Water-solubility**.

Chapter 5

Particles and their behaviour

GETTING STARTED

The kinetic theory of matter is the hypothesis that best explains the behaviour of solids, liquids and gases. The theory states that:

(i) matter is composed of tiny particles which may be atoms, molecules or ions;
(ii) these particles are in unceasing motion at temperatures above absolute zero (0 K or −273 °C);
(iii) at close quarters these particles attract each other, at larger distances the attractive force disappears;
(iv) the motion of the particles causes them always to be colliding with each other;
(v) the higher the temperature of the matter, the greater the motion of its particles;
(vi) pressure in a gas is the result of bombardment of the sides of the containing vessel by the moving particles. The higher the rate of bombardment, the higher the pressure.

TOPIC CHART

LONDON	MEG	NEAB	NICCEA	SEG	WJEC	TOPIC	STUDY	REVISION 1	REVISION 2
✓	✓	✓	✓	✓	✓	States of matter			
✓	✓	✓	✓	✓		Changes of state			
✓	✓		✓	✓		Expansion and contraction			
✓		✓	✓	✓		Diffusion			
✓	✓	✓	✓	✓		Pressure in gases			
			✓			The gas law			

WHAT YOU NEED TO KNOW

States of matter

All substances can be put into one of the three categories we call **states of matter**.

We can study this topic by looking at

(i) the properties of each of these states, and
(ii) the explanation of these state properties.

Properties

Solids

- retain their shape and volume indefinitely—their shape does not change unless they are converted into the liquid state or rolled into sheets or extruded into wire by pressure;
- are the densest of the three possible states;
- do not flow and are incompressible (cannot be shrunk by applying pressure).

Liquids

- take the shape of their container;
- have a fixed volume (like solids);
- are not compressible (like solids);
- flow when poured or under pressure.

Gases

- take up the shape and volume of a container but escape if the container is open;
- can be compressed into a smaller volume;
- flow when poured and under pressure (like liquids).

Modelling the three states of matter

The diagrams in Fig. 5.1 show how we visualize the three states of matter. The atoms, molecules or ions that make up any of the three states are in unceasing motion and so the diagrams represent a greatly magnified 'snapshot' of the substance.

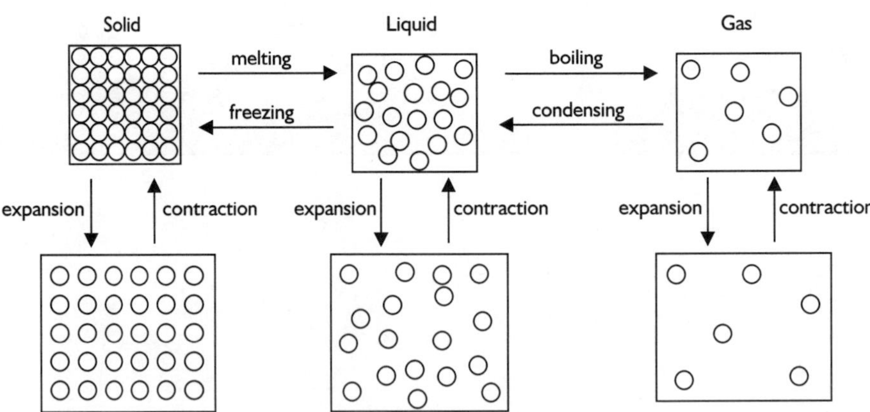

Fig. 5.1 Changes of state, expansion and contraction

Explanation

- **Solids** have their particles arranged in an orderly manner within a crystal structure. The particles are touching and have strong forces of attraction. They are not able to move about within the structure (but they do vibrate), so solids retain their shape and volume.
- **Liquids** have particles that are slightly farther apart than in solids. The forces of attraction are therefore slightly less than in solids. This gives particles the ability and space to move about and around each other within the liquid, giving it the property of a fixed volume but allowing it to take up the shape of its vessel.
- **Gases** have particles that are very much farther apart than in liquids. The attractive forces are virtually non-existent. The particles have completely free movement in all

directions and are no longer held together, so a gas will take up the volume and shape of its container.

Changes of state

Melting

- Particles in a solid are vibrating but cannot move very far. They are trapped in a 'box' or 'lattice' composed of their nearest neighbours: there are no gaps between particles large enough for them to pass through.
- As heat energy is added to this crystalline structure, the vibrating particles push their neighbours further away—*temperature* stays the same **during the melting process** but particles *attract each other less* at greater distances. See Fig. 5.2.
- Eventually the energy of this motion produces gaps in the lattice large enough for the particles to move about freely. This is characteristic of the **liquid state.**
- Melting absorbs energy—it is an **endothermic** process.

Fig. 5.2 Changes of state on heating: solid–liquid; liquid-gas

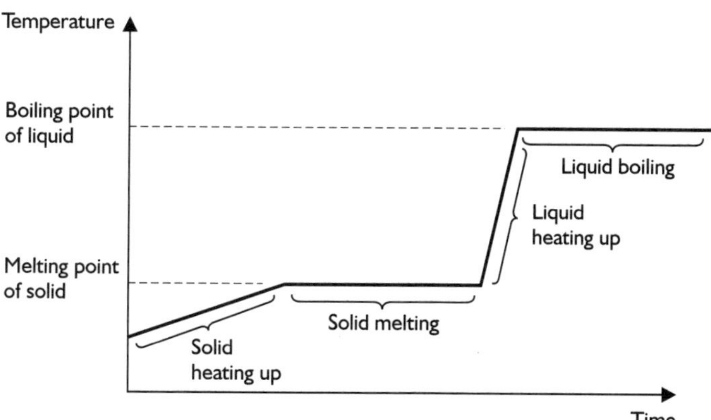

Freezing is just the opposite.

- Energy is removed and particles in the liquid become less energetic and closer together—**cooling.**
- The box or lattice re-forms and particles become trapped again, simply vibrating each inside its 'box'—**freezing.**
- Freezing gives out energy—it is an **exothermic** process.

Heating and boiling

- Particles in hot liquids are moving around freely because of their **high energy** and fairly **wide spacing.**
- As the temperature increases, so does the energy and spacing of the particles—**expansion.**
- The most energetic particles have enough energy to escape from the surface of the liquid—**evaporation.**
- At the boiling point the number of particles with high energies has increased to a maximum and evaporation is most rapid—**boiling.**
- Any increase in energy at the boiling point only serves to make more particles evaporate—the average energy of those left in the liquid state does not change: **a liquid cannot be heated to a temperature above its boiling point** (but see the effect of pressure).

Condensation is just the opposite

- Particles above a liquid at its boiling point bounce off each other on collision because of their high energy—**vapour state.**
- Lowering the temperature reduces the energy of the particles, which no longer bounce apart but stick to each other on collision—**condensation.**

Solid, liquid and gas are called the three states of matter. Figure 5.3 shows the words used to describe the changes from one state to another.

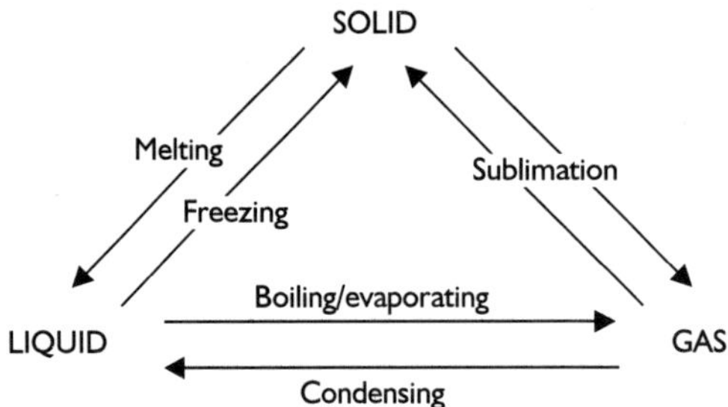

Fig. 5.3 Changes of state summarized

Expansion and contraction

Expansion occurs on heating matter in any state. It occurs because as heat is added:

- it causes the particles of matter to vibrate (solids) or move around (liquids and gases) with increased speed—**increased temperature**;
- greater numbers of collisions result and the particles move farther apart—**expansion** results from an increase in *empty space* between the particles and *not* from an increase in the size of the particles (see Fig. 5.1, p. 46);
- cooling reduces the space between particles—**contraction** occurs.

Note The expansion of water as it freezes and the contraction of ice on warming do not appear to support this explanation. However, it is *not part of GCSE studies* to consider this anomaly. Water is odd in its behaviour between 0 °C and 4 °C. There are *hydrogen bonds* in ice which cause water molecules to be held much further apart than would be expected of particles in a solid lattice. When ice melts the added energy breaks these bonds, allowing the molecules to become closer and contraction occurs. The reverse—expansion as molecules take up the more open ice structure—occurs on cooling.

Diffusion

Diffusion is a **mixing process** caused solely by the natural random motion of particles of matter. Diffusion usually involves two substances—they diffuse into each other.

- The fact of diffusion is **evidence** for the assumptions of the kinetic theory of matter.
- In gases, diffusion involves the molecules of two or more gases—**intermixing.**
- Gaseous diffusion is rapid because of the **large spaces** between molecules.
- The **speed** of diffusion increases with
  smaller molecules;
  higher temperatures;
  lower pressures.
- Diffusion is fastest in gases, slower in liquids, and slowest in solids—at the *same temperature.*

All of these effects on the rate of diffusion can be understood by considering how these factors affect the *speed of molecules* and/or the *likelihood of collision*; for example, the spacing of the particles is decreased by higher pressure leading to slower diffusion.

The different rates of diffusion in gases and liquids can be seen by carrying out the experiments shown in Figs 5.4 and 5.5.

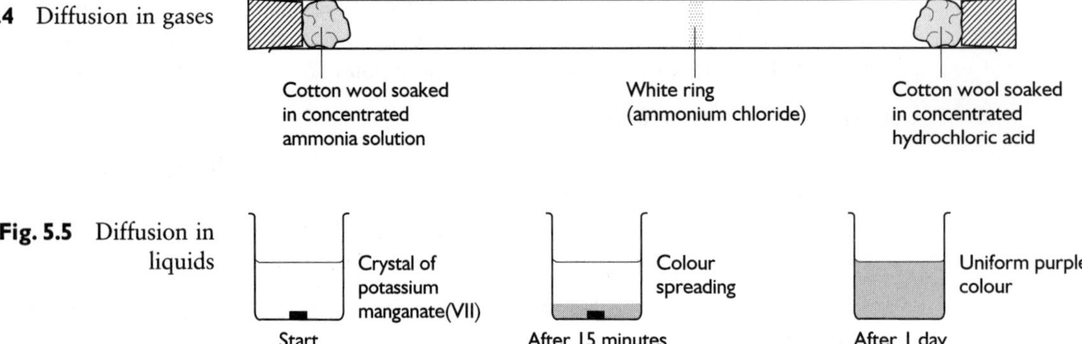

Fig. 5.4 Diffusion in gases

Fig. 5.5 Diffusion in liquids

- Diffusion in solids cannot be seen without breaking the solid apart but is extremely slow.

Diffusion and pollution

Diffusion has a major part to play in the removal of atmospheric pollutants. **Pollutants** are usually formed in confined areas, e.g. from car exhaust pipes and factory chimneys. The pollutant from petrol engines is a mixture of carbon monoxide, unburnt petrol and oxides of nitrogen. This quickly spreads into the surrounding air and eventually into the world's atmosphere. The burning of fossil fuels in power stations causes a large amount of sulphur dioxide in the atmosphere and this reacts with water in the atmosphere to form '**acid rain**'. Power stations are built with tall chimneys to make sure that pollutants diffuse high into the atmosphere, thus keeping the concentration at ground level lower. This only removes the pollution problem from local areas to more distant parts. The tall chimneys release sulphur dioxide into the atmosphere and this is swept miles away, sometimes into other countries.

Brownian motion

Named after the botanist Robert Brown who noticed when viewing with a microscope that pollen grains in water moved in an erratic way. This is explained as the effect of large numbers of invisible water molecules randomly bombarding the much larger pollen grains. It is regarded as *evidence for the kinetic theory* idea that molecules move about randomly and at high speeds. Brownian motion can also be observed in smoke and in milk.

Pressure in gases

The pressure of a gas is an effect caused by bombardment of a surface by the rapid random movement of gaseous particles (molecules).

- **Pressure** is associated with the number of gas molecule collisions per second (collision rate) per unit area of surface.
- If now the volume containing the same number of gas molecules is doubled, the *same* number of particles will bombard unit area of surface at only *half the number of collisions per second*—the pressure will be halved.

Effects of heat and pressure on gases

The effects described below are for a *fixed mass of gas*.

- Heating causes gases to expand—see expansion and contraction.
- Doubling the temperature (measured in degrees kelvin) doubles the *volume* if expansion is possible, e.g. in a gas syringe.
- Doubling the temperature doubles the *pressure* in a closed vessel of fixed volume.
- Increasing the pressure reduces the volume.
- *Doubling* the pressure of a gas *halves* the volume.

We see that the volume of a fixed mass of gas

- is proportional to its absolute temperature;
- is inversely proportional to its pressure.

Gas law

The relationships described above are combined in an expression called the **gas law**. In mathematical terms:

$V \propto T$ and $V \propto \frac{1}{P}$ which leads to $\frac{PV}{T} = \text{constant}$

So

$$\frac{P_1V_1}{T_1} = \frac{P_2V_2}{T_2}$$

Application of the gas law equation (NICCEA only)

Problem

Suppose the pressure, volume and temperature of a given mass of gas are as follows:

$P_1 = 1$ atmosphere
$V_1 = 1$ litre
$T_1 = 300\,\mathrm{K}$

What would be its new pressure, P_2, if its temperature, T_2, were changed to 600 K but its volume was kept the same, $V_2 = V_1 = 1$ litre?

Answer

Step 1 Write down all the values in the form

$P_1 = 1$ atmosphere $\quad P_2 = ?$ (to be calculated)
$V_1 = 1$ litre $\quad V_2 = 1$ litre (volume remains the same)
$T_1 = 300\,\mathrm{K}$ $\quad T_2 = 600\,\mathrm{K}$

Using the equation and substituting the given values:

$$\frac{P_1V_1}{T_1} = \frac{P_2V_2}{T_2} \quad \text{so} \quad \frac{1 \times 1}{300} = \frac{P_2 \times 1}{600}$$

Step 2 Rearrange the figures to solve for P_2:

$$P_2 = \frac{1 \times 1 \times 600}{1 \times 300} = 2 \text{ atmospheres}$$

In fact, a calculation of this sort is not always necessary to obtain the answer. Since only the temperature is changed, and that is *doubled*, the pressure will also double—from 1 to 2 atmospheres. If examination problems are set with simple multiple or sub-multiple temperature or pressure changes, mental arithmetic may be all that the candidate requires to get to the answer using a knowledge of the gas law.

EXAMINATION QUESTIONS

Question 1 (F) (a) The diagram (Fig. 5.6) shows a burning candle.

Fig. 5.6

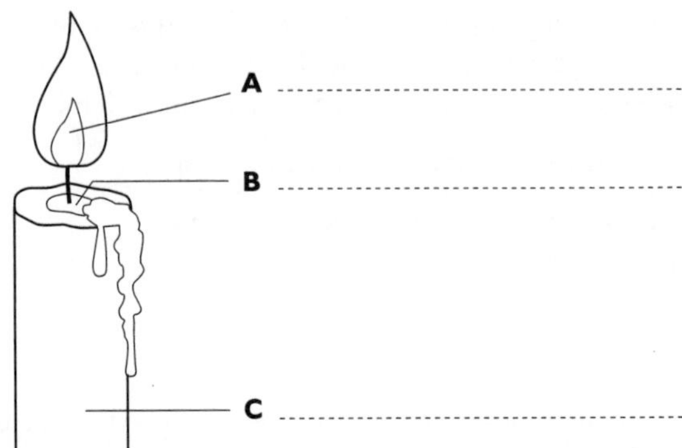

Write beside each letter A, B and C to show if the candle wax there is *solid*, *liquid* or *gas*. *[3]*

(b) (i) The first box (Fig. 5.7) shows the particles in solid argon. Complete the other boxes to show the particles when argon is a liquid and when it is a gas. *[2]*

Fig. 5.7

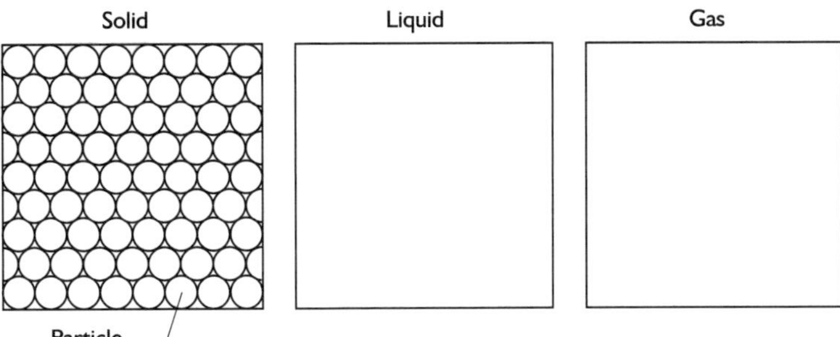

(ii) When the solid argon is heated, it expands. Explain what happens to the particles as the solid argon expands. *[3]*

Question 2 (F)

Diagram B shows the arrangement of the particles in a liquid (Fig. 5.8).

Fig. 5.8

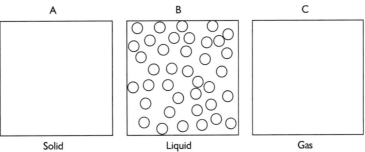

(a) Complete the diagrams A and C to show the arrangement of the particles in a solid and gas. *[2]*

(b) How would you change liquid B into a gas? [2 lines] *[1]*

Question 3 (F)

A mixture of heptane (b.p. 100 °C) and 2,2-dimethylpentane (b.p. 80 °C) was separated by distillation. The graph below shows the temperature of the vapour entering the condenser over a period of time (Fig. 5.9).

Fig. 5.9

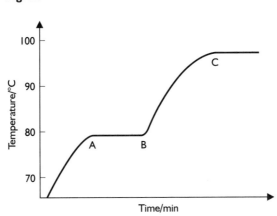

(i) Why is the graph flat between A and B? [1 line] *[1]*

(ii) Comment on the composition of the vapour entering the condenser between times B and C. [2 lines] *[1]*

Question 4 (F) (a) The diagrams below show two experiments to demonstrate diffusion. Describe what you would observe in each experiment (Figs 5.10 and 5.11).

(i) ______________________________

(ii) ______________________________

____

[3]

Fig. 5.10

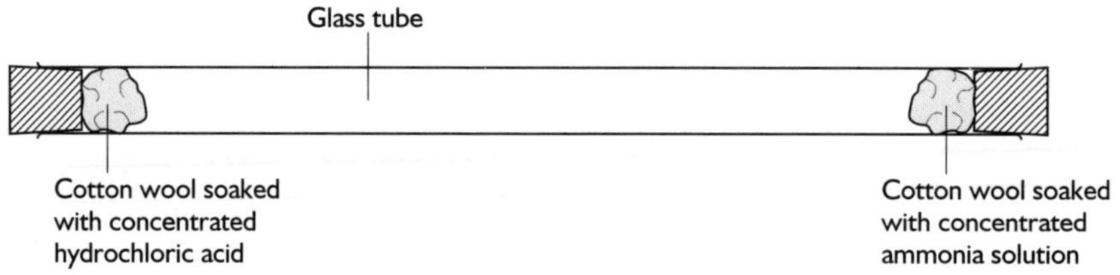

Glass tube
Cotton wool soaked with concentrated hydrochloric acid
Cotton wool soaked with concentrated ammonia solution

Fig. 5.11

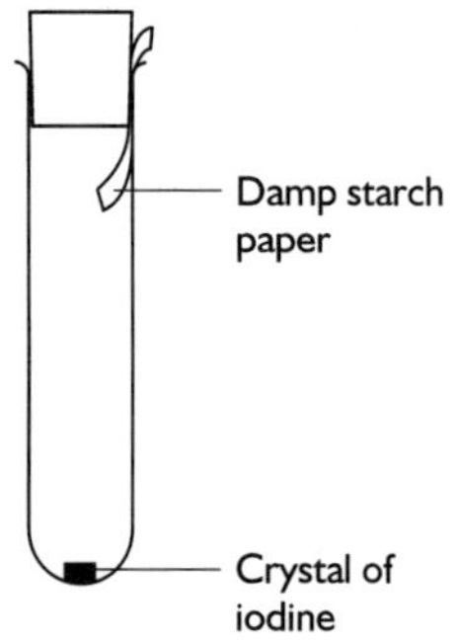

Damp starch paper
Crystal of iodine

(b) The experiment shown in the diagram below was set up (Fig. 5.12).
How would you show that potassium hydroxide had diffused through the liquid? [2 lines] *[2]*

(c) In the manufacture of ammonia by the Haber process, nitrogen and hydrogen are mixed and then passed along a pipe to the reacting vessel. If this pipe became porous would the gas mixture

(i) become richer in nitrogen?
(ii) become richer in hydrogen?
(iii) be unchanged?

Fig. 5.12

Water
Pellet of potassium hydroxide

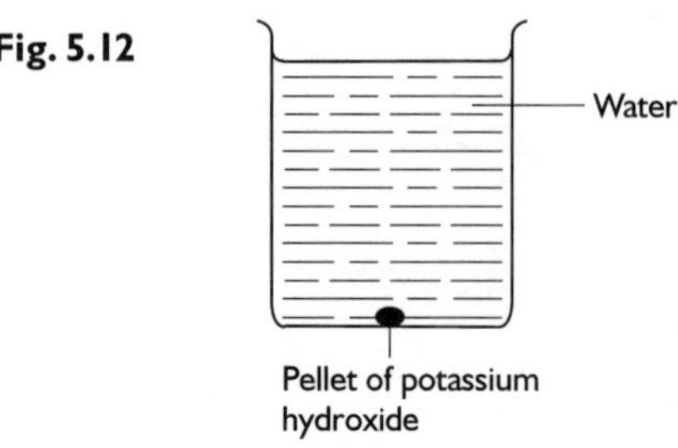

Given an explanation.
Answer ______________________________

____

____

[3]

OUTLINE ANSWERS

Question 1

(a) A = gas *[1]*—it is paraffin wax vapour.
B = liquid *[1]* it is liquid wax.
C = solid *[1]* wax.

(b) (i) The 'liquid box' should contain almost as many particles as the 'solid' box, but in disorderly or random array *[1]*. The 'gas' box should contain only a few—say 6 or 7 particles randomly spread out *[1]*.
(ii) The particles gain energy from heat *[1]*, vibrate more rapidly *[1]* and are pushed farther apart *[1]*.

Question 2

(a) (See Fig. 5.13.)

Fig. 5.13

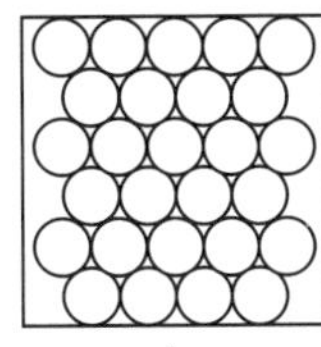

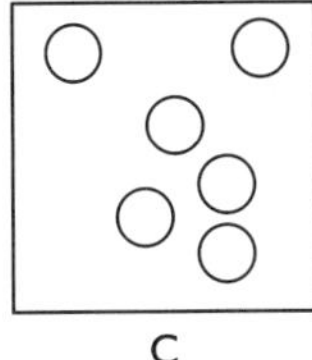

[1] each

Note in diagram A particles in a solid are orderly and vibrate in fixed positions. In diagram C, particles in a gas are far apart and move randomly.

(b) Liquid B would have to be heated to convert it into a gas *[1]*.

Question 3

(i) One of the vapours, 2,2-dimethylpentane, is condensing *[1]*.
(ii) The vapour contains a little 2,2-dimethylpentane mixed with greater proportions of heptane until at 100 °C the vapour is pure heptane *[1]*.

Question 4

(a) (i) A white solid is formed nearer the hydrochloric acid end *[1]*.
(ii) A faint purple colour is seen in the tube (iodine vapour), and the starch paper turns blue. (Starch paper is used as a test for iodine.) *[1]*

(b) Place a piece of red litmus paper in the top of the solution *[1]*; eventually the paper will turn blue *[1]*. (N.B. potassium hydroxide is a white solid and a solution of potassium hydroxide is colourless and alkaline.)

(c) The mixture becomes richer in nitrogen *[1]*.
Nitrogen is 14 times denser than hydrogen , therefore hydrogen *[1]* will diffuse more quickly *[1]* out of the porous pipe, leaving the mixture richer in nitrogen.

STUDENT ANSWER WITH EXAMINER'S COMMENTS

A plug of cotton wool was soaked in concentrated hydrochloric acid and placed in one end of a long dry glass tube and, at the same time, a similar plug soaked in concentrated ammonia solution was placed in the other end. After several minutes a white deposit of ammonium chloride formed in the tube.

'Yes,—you could have said that HCl molecules are heavier than NH_3 molecules.'

(a) Explain why ammonium chloride was formed nearer the end of the tube soaked in concentrated hydrochloric acid.

Because the molecules of ammonia move faster than the particles of hydrogen chloride therefore meeting at a point nearer the hydrogen chloride.

(2 marks)

(b) Explain why the tube must be

(i) level

The tube must be level to make sure gravity has no effect on the movement of the molecules.

'Draughts would also affect the result.'

(ii) corked

It has to be corked so that the molecules cannot go out into the air but are forced to join together and be concentrated

'No! Both the gases are soluble in water.'

(iii) dry.

It has to be dry so that there is no water vapour affecting the movement of the molecules.

(4 marks)

'Good.'

(c) What name is used to describe the movement of molecules?

Diffusion

(1 mark)

(d) Molecules of ammonia and hydrogen chloride move at very high speeds. Explain why it took several minutes before ammonium chloride was formed.

The molecules collide with molecules in the air which prevents them moving very quickly.

(2 marks)

'More is needed here, as there are three marks for this section. It dissociates to give the invisible gases NH_3 and HCl which combine again on cooling.'

(e) Explain why, when ammonium chloride is heated in a test tube, the white solid disappears and then re-appears on the cold part of the test tube.

It sublimes

(3 marks)

'Yes, nearly all ammonium compounds are white.'

'Careless—should be ammonium.'

(f) If a similar experiment were repeated using concentrated hydrobromic acid (HBr) instead of hydrochloric acid, describe all you would see and name the product formed.

A white deposit would be formed near the hydrobromic end. The product formed is ammonia bromide.

(3 marks)

'Some good answers overall, but you have not used your Chemistry knowledge in (b) (iii). Also you have missed a few points. Still there is enough here for a mark of 9/15.'

SUMMARY

Use this list to help you with your revision. Tick off the points as you revise them in the text.

- ▷ There are three states of matter—**solid, liquid and gas**.
- ▷ **Solids** retain their shape and volume and cannot be compressed.
- ▷ **Liquids** take the shape of their container and cannot be compressed.
- ▷ **Gases** take the shape of their container and **can be compressed**.
- ▷ Solids are usually **denser** than their liquid state but water is an exception at 0 °C.
- ▷ As a solid **melts** it absorbs heat and expands. Its particles become free to move about randomly.
- ▷ As a liquid **heats** from melting point to boiling point it expands as its randomly moving particles get further apart.
- ▷ **Boiling** absorbs energy and the particles escape from the strong attractive forces in the liquid to move around at **random**.
- ▷ **Forces of attraction** between particles in solids and liquids are many times greater than those in gases.
- ▷ When a solid vaporizes and the vapour solidifies again, without any liquid forming in either change, **sublimation** has occurred.
- ▷ When expansion occurs in solids, liquids and gases the particles themselves do not get bigger but the **distances** between them **increase**.
- ▷ The spaces between particles in gases are so large that putting pressure on the gas can compress the particles **closer together**. This cannot happen in liquids and solids where the spaces are very small.
- ▷ **Diffusion** is the process of mixing two gases or liquids by the random motion of their particles.
- ▷ Diffusion occurs in gases and liquids at a noticeable rate. Gases diffuse faster than liquids.
- ▷ The speed of diffusion is highest with **small particles** at **high temperatures**. Light particles move faster than heavier ones.
- ▷ Pressure in a gas is the result of its particles **bombarding** the sides of its container. The more particles in the container the greater the pressure.
- ▷ **Doubling the pressure** on a gas halves its volume if the temperature remains constant.
- ▷ Doubling the **absolute temperature** of a gas doubles its volume if the pressure is constant.
- ▷ Absolute temperatures are measured in **kelvin** and are equal to the temperature in degrees Celsius plus 273.

Chapter

6 Atomic structure and bonding

GETTING STARTED

All elements are made up of atoms. The properties of those atoms are characteristic of the elements. Atoms rarely exist singly (noble gas atoms being the exception) but normally join together with other atoms to form **molecular** or **ionic** structures.

An atom is the smallest particle of an element which can still have the chemical properties of that element.

In this chapter we consider what happens to **atoms** when they encounter those of a different element. We see that atoms of noble gas elements have no tendency to react and have **full outer shells** (or **energy levels**). We apply this idea (concept) to the **transfer** or **sharing** of electrons which occurs when atoms combine.

TOPIC CHART

LONDON	MEG	NEAB	NICCEA	SEG	WJEC	TOPIC	STUDY	REVISION I	REVISION 2
✓	✓	✓	✓	✓	✓	Inside the atom			
✓	✓	✓	✓	✓	✓	The nucleus of an atom			
✓	✓	✓	✓	✓	✓	Isotopes of elements			
✓	✓	✓	✓	✓	✓	Relative atomic mass and isotope abundance			
✓	✓	✓	✓	✓	✓	The electrons			
✓	✓	✓	✓	✓	✓	Periods and groups			
✓	✓	✓	✓	✓	✓	Noble gas structures and bond formation			
✓	✓	✓	✓	✓	✓	Properties of molecular and ionic substances			
✓	✓	✓	✓	✓	✓	Molecular liquids as solvents			
✓	✓	✓	✓	✓	✓	Macromolecules			
✓	✓	✓	✓	✓	✓	Metallic structures			

WHAT YOU NEED TO KNOW

Inside the atom

Atoms are made up of particles which are even smaller than the atoms themselves. We call these particles **sub-atomic** particles. They are protons and neutrons (together called nucleons) and electrons. The relative masses and relative charges of these sub-atomic particles are shown in Table 6.1.

Table 6.1 Relative masses and charges of nucleons and electrons

Sub-atomic particle	Relative mass	Relative charge
Proton	1	1+
Neutron	1	0
Electron	Negligible—about 0.0005	1−

The nucleus of an atom

The nucleus of an atom contains protons and neutrons (except the nucleus of a hydrogen atom). Compared with the size of the atom as a whole, the nucleus is minute, occupying only one thousand, million, million, millionth of the volume of the atom.

Atomic number (proton number)

The number of protons in a nucleus is the **atomic number** of the atom.

Mass number (nucleon number)

The sum of the numbers of protons and neutrons (nucleons) in an atom is its **mass number**.

The positions of the mass number and atomic number of an atom are usually shown as below. From these values the number of neutrons in this atom can be calculated to be 14.

Mass number 27   27 (neutrons + protons)

$$^{27}_{13}\mathrm{Al}$$

Atomic number 13   13 protons (13 electrons)

'The hydrogen atom is unusual.'

The hydrogen atom is the only atom which does not have neutrons (see Table 6.2). It consists of a proton and an electron only.

Hydrogen ions are also unique among ions because they have *no electrons or neutrons.* Hydrogen ions are just **protons**.

Table 6.2 gives data for some common elements.

Table 6.2 Data for some common elements

Element	Atomic number	Number of protons	Number of neutrons	Mass number	Symbol
Hydrogen	1	1	NONE	1	$^{1}_{1}\mathrm{H}$
Helium	2	2	2	4	$^{4}_{2}\mathrm{He}$
Carbon	6	6	6	12	$^{12}_{6}\mathrm{C}$
Nitrogen	7	7	7	14	$^{14}_{7}\mathrm{N}$
Oxygen	8	8	8	16	$^{16}_{8}\mathrm{O}$
Fluorine	9	9	10	19	$^{19}_{9}\mathrm{F}$
Neon	10	10	10	20	$^{20}_{10}\mathrm{Ne}$
Sodium	11	11	12	23	$^{23}_{11}\mathrm{Na}$
Magnesium	12	12	12	24	$^{24}_{12}\mathrm{Mg}$
Aluminium	13	13	14	27	$^{27}_{13}\mathrm{Al}$
Sulphur	16	16	16	32	$^{32}_{16}\mathrm{S}$
Chlorine	17	17	18	35	$^{35}_{17}\mathrm{Cl}$
Argon	18	18	22	40	$^{40}_{18}\mathrm{Ar}$
Potassium	19	19	20	39	$^{39}_{19}\mathrm{K}$
Calcium	20	20	20	40	$^{40}_{20}\mathrm{Ca}$

Table 6.2 (*cont*)

Element	Atomic number	Number of protons	Number of neutrons	Mass number	Symbol
Iron	26	26	30	56	$^{56}_{26}Fe$
Copper	29	29	35	64	$^{64}_{29}Cu$
Zinc	30	30	35	65	$^{65}_{30}Zn$
Bromine	35	35	45	80	$^{80}_{35}Br$
Iodine	53	53	74	127	$^{127}_{53}I$

Isotopes of elements

'Fixed number of protons'

A fixed characteristic of all the atoms of a given element is the **atomic number, or number of protons in the nucleus of each atom of that element.**

However, a sample of almost any pure element will show the presence of several kinds of atoms *differing only in mass number*. These are called **isotopes.**

For example, there are three different kinds of hydrogen atom in any pure sample of hydrogen gas. The atomic number of each of the different hydrogen atoms is 1, which means they are all *identical* in **chemical properties**. They *differ* in the number of neutrons in each nucleus. **In chemical reactions there is no difference in the reactions of different isotopes of the same element.**

^{1}H hydrogen 1 proton : 0 neutrons, atomic number 1, mass number 1,
^{2}H deuterium 1 proton : 1 neutron, atomic number 1, mass number 2,
^{3}H tritium 1 proton : 2 neutrons, atomic number 1, mass number 3.

The element chlorine, atomic number 17, similarly has different kinds of atom:

^{35}Cl chlorine-35 17 protons : 18 neutrons mass number 35,
^{37}Cl chlorine-37 17 protons : 20 neutrons mass number 37.

Relative atomic mass and isotopic abundance

The **relative atomic mass** of an element is measured on a natural sample of the element. It is based on the **average mass of all the atoms in the sample.** You can see from the information above, about isotopes, that the presence of several kinds of atom of the same element with different masses will give the average mass of an atom a value which **will not be a whole number.**

The relative atomic mass of chlorine is 35.5 because there are 25 atoms of mass 37 and 75 atoms of mass 35 in every 100 chlorine atoms: the isotopic abundances are Cl-35, Cl-37, 75%, 25%. So, for 100 chlorine atoms chosen at random, the total **mass** is

$$(25 \times 37) + (75 \times 35) = 3550 \text{ units}$$

Therefore, the average relative atomic mass of a chlorine atom is

$$3550/100 = 35.5 \text{ units.}$$

The electrons

The electron structures of atoms

The negatively charged **electrons** of an atom surround the positively charged nucleus as a 'cloud' of negative charge. This 'cloud' of electrons is normally considered to exist as spherical layers—like the skins of an onion—called **shells of electrons** or electron **energy levels.** The number of electrons is the same as the number of protons in the nucleus of the atom. For each shell there is a limit to the number of electrons it can hold. This 'shell limit' is the same for all atoms. The concepts of shells and energy levels are equivalent. Some exam boards use one, some the other.

The FIRST shell maximum is 2 electrons
The SECOND shell maximum is 8 electrons
The THIRD shell maximum is 18 electrons

In Table 6.3 the symbol in brackets is the corresponding noble gas atom.

Table 6.3 The electron structures of the first twenty elements and their ions

Element	Electron structure of the element				Electron structure of the ion formed	Formula of ion
H	1				0	H^+
He	2				NO IONS	NO IONS
Li	2	1			2 (He)	Li^+
Be	2	2			NO IONS	NO IONS
B	2	3			NO IONS	NO IONS
C	2	4			NO IONS	NO IONS
N	2	5			2 8 (Ne)	N^{3-}
O	2	6			2 8 (Ne)	O^{2-}
F	2	7			2 8 (Ne)	F^-
Ne	2	8			NO IONS	NO IONS
Na	2	8	1		2 8 (Ne)	Na^+
Mg	2	8	2		2 8 (Ne)	Mg^{2+}
Al	2	8	3		2 8 (Ne)	Al^{3+}
Si	2	8	4		NO IONS	NO IONS
P	2	8	5		NO IONS	NO IONS
S	2	8	6		2 8 8 (Ar)	S^{2-}
Cl	2	8	7		2 8 8 (Ar)	Cl^-
Ar	2	8	8		NO IONS	NO IONS
K	2	8	8	1	2 8 8 (Ar)	K^+
Ca	2	8	8	2	2 8 8 (Ar)	Ca^{2+}

Periods and groups

Examination of the contents of Table 6.3 will show that there are patterns in the arrangement of electrons in the atoms of the elements shown. Two patterns are seen: atoms may differ in

(i) the number of **shells** of electrons they contain;

and/or

(ii) the number of electrons they have in their **outer shell.**

'Periods'

The number of shells (not necessarily complete shells) an atom has tells us which **period** of the table the element is placed in, e.g. hydrogen is in period one; sodium is in period three (see Table 6.3). **Periods** are **horizontal rows** of elements.

The number of electrons in the outer shell of an atom (called **valency electrons**) tells us which **group** the element is in, e.g. lithium is in group 1; chlorine in group 7 (Table 6.4).

Groups are **vertical** columns of elements having similar properties. It should be clear from Table 6.2 and Table 6.3 that the number of electrons in atoms increases by one as the atomic number increases by one. An increase of one electron in the atom of each successive element in a period will cause the outer electron shell to become full *as the eighth group is reached* (called Group 0). Since the eighth group contains noble gas elements, an outer shell of eight electrons evidently makes atoms very unreactive (stable).

The start of a new period occurs with the start of a new shell of electrons.

Table 6.4 The electron structures of elements of groups 1, 2, 7 and 0

'Groups'

Period	Group 1	Group 2	Group 7	Group 0
2	Li 2 1	Be 2 2	F 2 7	Ne 2 8
3	Na 2 8 1	Mg 2 8 2	Cl 2 8 7	Ar 2 8 8
4	K 2 8 8 1	Ca 2 8 8 2	Br 2 8 18 7	Kr 2 8 18 8

Noble gas structures and bond formation

The discovery of a group of elements which were *totally unreactive* to other elements was of great importance to chemists. What was the cause of this **inertness**? The electron structures of these gases gave the answer. The electrons of each element *filled the shells available to them.*

When chemists looked at what happened to the electrons in atoms of other elements when these elements reacted, they found that elements always reacted in such a way that their atoms gained the electron structure of the nearest noble (inert) gas atom.

There are many ways of drawing the electron structures of molecules. In this book we shall show you *two* ways. Both are perfectly acceptable and you may be familiar with one or with the other. Figure 6.1 shows one way; the other way is illustrated in Fig. 17.9 in Chapter 17, pp. 264 and 266.

Noble gas structures by gain or loss of electrons

If the process of achieving a noble gas structure occurs by *gain* of one or more electrons, then a negatively charged atom (called an **anion**) is formed. If the process occurs by *loss* of one or more electrons, then a positively charged atom (called a **cation**) is formed.

Compounds formed by transfer of electrons from one atom to another are **ionic compounds.** Ionic compounds are held together by **strong forces of attraction between oppositely charged ions.**

'Ions with noble gas structures'

Where gain or loss of electrons happens, these electrons have to be given to, or taken from, the other reacting element. So if the atoms of one element *gain* electrons, the atoms of the other reacting element must *lose* electrons. At the end of the reactions the atoms of *both* elements will have full electron shells.

In the following examples of reactions in which ionic bonds are formed, remember that reaction occurs *between free atoms.*

Sodium atoms reacting with chlorine atoms

$$Na(g) + Cl(g) \rightarrow Na^+(s) + Cl^-(s)$$

The electron structures are:

Atoms	*Electron structure*	*Ions*	*Electron structure*	
Na(g)	2 8 1	Na^+	2 8	(1 electron lost)
Cl(g)	2 8 7	Cl^-	2 8 8	(1 electron gained)

To represent these electron structures *fully* we should use a diagram such as Fig. 6.1.

However, since only the **outer electrons** are involved in the reaction, we can represent the combination as shown in Fig. 6.2. Here only the outer two shells of each atom are shown.

Figure 6.1

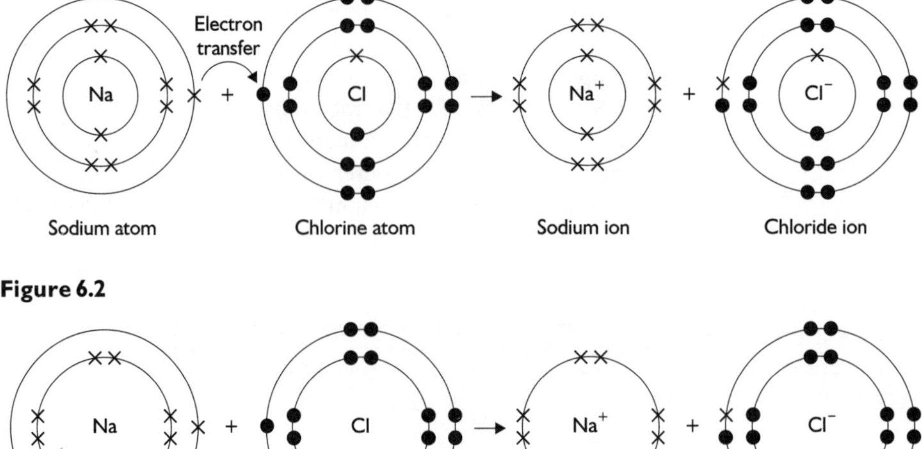

Figure 6.2

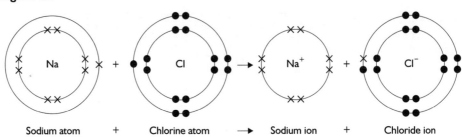

In this case the single electron in the outer shell of the sodium atom is lost to the chlorine atom and the next shell inside becomes the full outer shell. Similar changes occur in the formation of ions from other elements.

Magnesium atoms reacting with oxygen atoms

$Mg(g) + O(g) \rightarrow Mg^{2+}(s) + O^{2-}(s)$

From Table 6.3 the electron structures of magnesium and oxygen atoms and the ions formed are:

Atoms	*Electron structure*	*Ions*	*Electron structure*	
Mg(g)	2 8 2	Mg^{2+}	2 8	(2 electrons lost)
O(g)	2 6	O^{2-}	2 8	(2 electrons gained)

This change is represented as shown in Fig. 6.3.

Figure 6.3

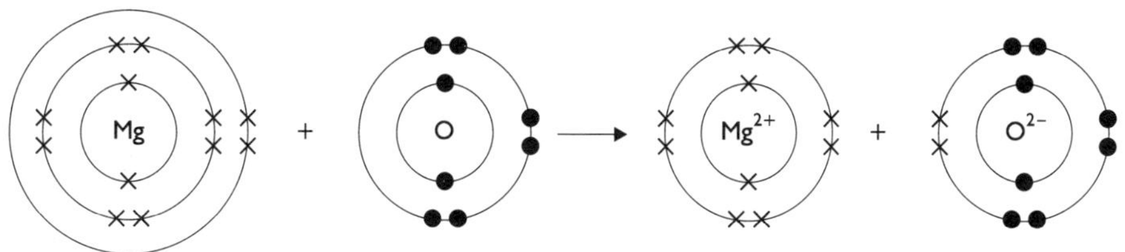

Calcium atoms reacting with chlorine atoms—an example to try yourself

$Ca(g) + 2Cl(g) \rightarrow CaCl_2(s)$

Fill in the required data from Table 6.3 and represent the change in the way shown above, Fig. 6.4.

Atoms	*Ions*
Ca(g)	Ca^{2+}
Cl(g)	Cl^-

Figure 6.4

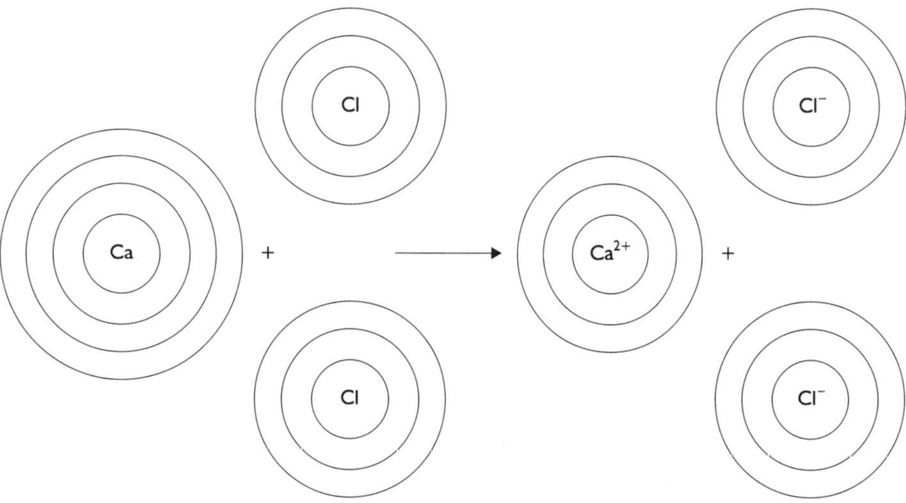

The shells (energy levels) are drawn for you. Insert the electrons as dots and/or crosses

Note: Some examination questions ask for **'dot and cross' diagrams**. In such questions it is best to use dots for one type of atom and crosses for the other. In this way the examiner can see more clearly how the **electron transfer** has occurred.

Some of the commonest atoms and their ions are shown in Table 6.5.

Table 6.5 Some atoms and their ions

Metal atoms	Group	Electrons lost	Ion formed
Lithium	1	1	Li^+
Sodium	1	1	Na^+
Potassium	1	1	K^+
Magnesium	2	2	Mg^{2+}
Calcium	2	2	Ca^{2+}
Aluminium	3	3	Al^{3+}
Non-metal atoms	**Group**	**Electrons gained**	**Ion formed**
Oxygen	6	2	O^{2-}
Sulphur	6	2	S^{2-}
Chlorine	7	1	Cl^-
Bromine	7	1	Br^-
Iodine	7	1	I^-

The above table summarizes the formation of various ions.

Electron sharing

Table 6.3, p. 59, contains details of elements which *do not usually form ions*. The atoms of these elements achieve noble gas electron structures by electron **sharing**. For example,

Figure 6.5 A hydrogen molecule

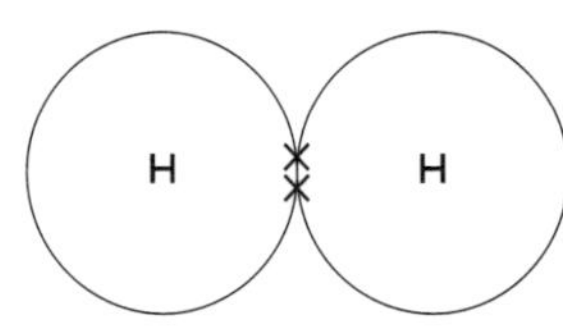

In elements

Each *hydrogen atom* (Fig. 6.5), by contributing its single electron to the bond, gains the noble gas electron structure of *helium*. The sharing of two electrons in this way creates a **single bond**.

'Single bond'

Each *chlorine atom* (Fig. 6.6) contributes *one* electron to the bond. The total number of electrons in the outer shell of each chlorine atom will then be *eight*.

Because *oxygen* atoms (Fig. 6.7) have *two* electrons fewer than eight, two oxygen atoms must *each* contribute two electrons to the bond. A four-electron bond is called a **double bond**. Each oxygen atom will then have the electron structure of the noble gas neon. The nitrogen molecule, N_2 is formed in a similar way with a **triple** bond by the sharing of six electrons (Fig. 6.8).

'Double bond'

Figure 6.6 A chlorine molecule

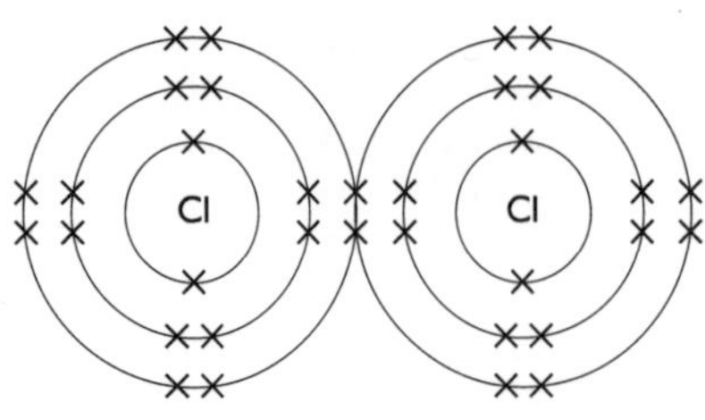

Figure 6.7 An oxygen molecule

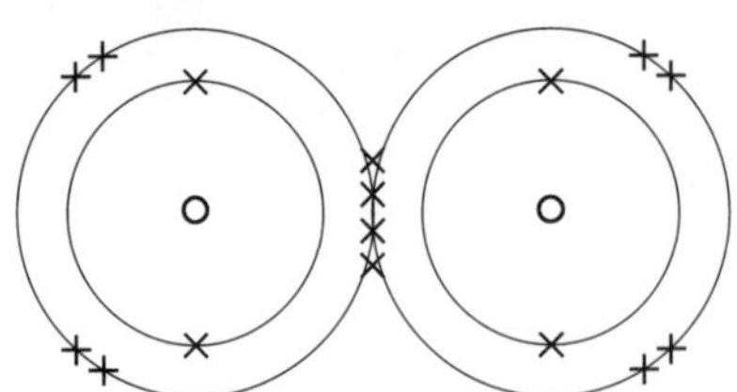

Figure 6.8 A nitrogen molecule

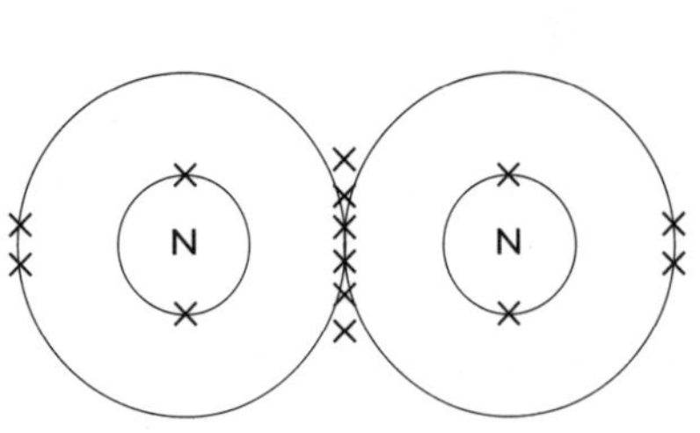

In compounds

The electron structure of hydrogen and chlorine atoms are:

hydrogen 1
chlorine 2 8 7

Hydrogen cannot achieve the electron structure of its nearest noble gas unless it gains one electron. However, that electron could only come from a chlorine atom. The chlorine atom can only achieve the electron structure of *its* nearest noble gas by gaining an electron. Since *both* atoms cannot *gain* one electron, they *share* two electrons—one from each atom. This gives *each* atom a noble gas electron structure. In Fig. 6.9, the outer shells only are shown. All inner shells are full.

Figure 6.9 A hydrogen chloride molecule

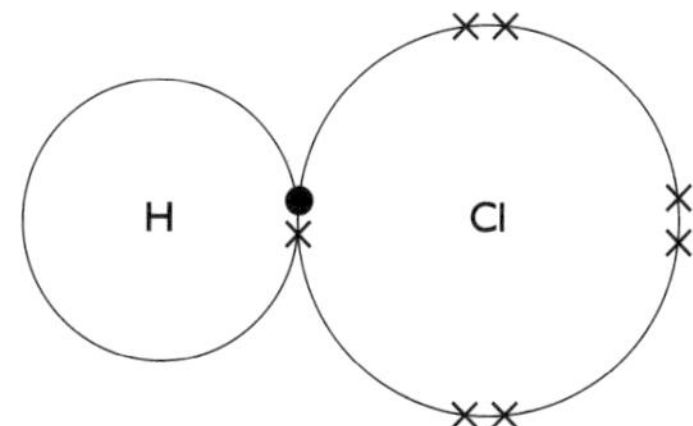

Formulae of molecular compounds

'The structures shown in this section are not all required for every syllabus. Consult the syllabus you are studying to see which structures you are expected to know.'

The relative numbers of atoms combining to form molecules determines the formula of the compound (Fig. 6.10).

Methane

Carbon is in group 4 and so has four electrons in its outer shell. Hydrogen has a single outer electron. For both atoms to gain the electron structure of their nearest noble gas, four hydrogen atoms must share their outer electron with a single carbon atom. Each carbon—hydrogen bond is a single, two-electron bond.

Figure 6.10 Some common molecules

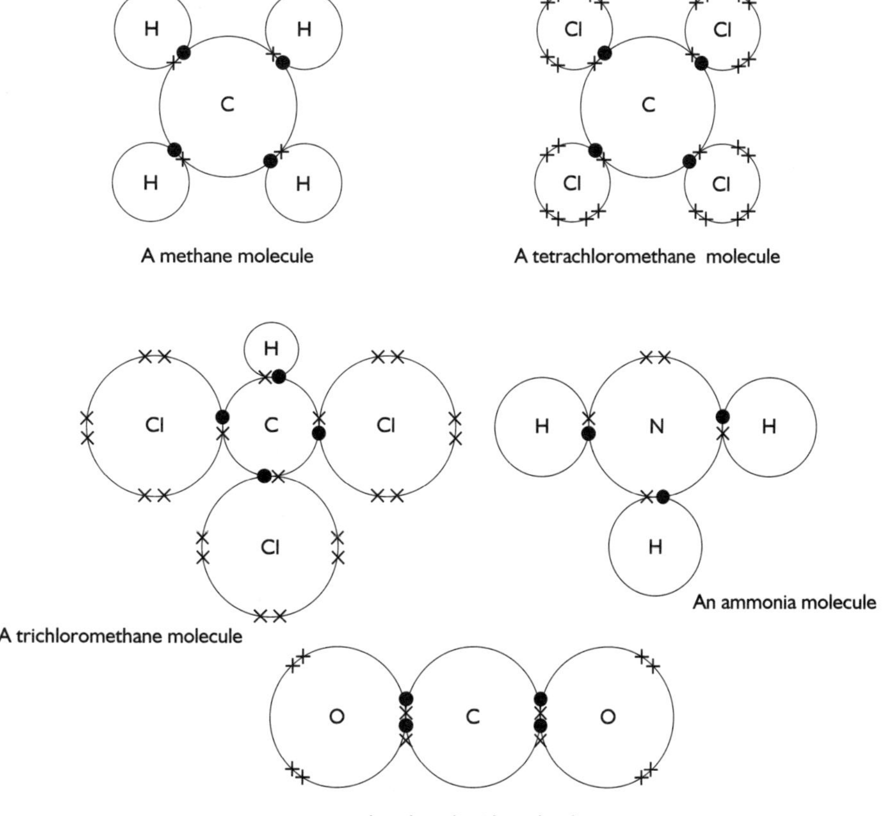

Tetrachloromethane

Here the four electrons in the outer shell of the carbon atom need an additional four electrons from chlorine atoms for a complete octet of electrons. Chlorine atoms, however, need only a single extra electron each to achieve the octet. Both atoms gain the noble gas electron structure if four chlorine atoms share an electron each with the four outer electrons on a single carbon atom. Each of the four carbon—chlorine bonds is a single, two-electron bond, hence the formula is CCl_4.

Trichloromethane

This is similar to both methane and tetrachloromethane. The four single bonds form by sharing a pair of electrons contributed to equally by each of the atoms forming the bond. The carbon—chlorine bond forms as in Tetrachloromethane above. The carbon—hydrogen bond forms as in Methane above.

Ammonia

Here, the nitrogen atom has five outer electrons. It needs three more for an octet. It gains these by sharing the outer electrons from three hydrogen atoms. At the same time the hydrogen atoms achieve the duet of electrons which is characteristic of helium. This gives a formula of NH_3.

Carbon dioxide

As before, carbon requires a further four electrons from the atoms it combines with to make up the outer octet. Oxygen atoms require two electrons to give them an outer octet. Both atoms achieve the octet by contributing two electrons each to a carbon—oxygen bond. Two such bonds form, each with four electrons. There are two double carbon—oxygen bonds in the carbon dioxide molecule—hence the formula, CO_2.

Properties of molecular and ionic substances

Molecules do not have a charge. Because of this, and unlike ions, molecules attract each other *only very weakly*. The forces of attraction holding molecules together in a solid molecular crystal can easily be overcome by adding quite small amounts of energy. Gently heating will thus cause the **molecules** of a molecular crystal to **break free from each other**, making the solid **melt** at a low temperature. Note that when the molecules break free from each other's attraction they **do not break into atoms**. Melting is not the same as decomposing!

Even when molecules are in the liquid state and moving around freely among themselves, the forces of attraction between them are small. Therefore, it does not require very much added energy to cause the molecules to break **completely free from each other** and leave the liquid state altogether. This process is known as vaporization—the substance boils or vaporizes at a low temperature.

'The important point here is that in *melting* and *boiling*, the bonds (or attractive forces) ***between*** molecules are broken. In *decomposing*, the bonds ***within*** molecules break.'

From what has been said earlier, the melting and boiling of **molecular compounds** require very little energy. The melting and boiling points are low and the amount of energy needed to melt or vaporize one mole of a molecular substance is much less than that for **ionic** compounds or **giant molecular** substances.

Because molecules are not charged, they cannot be conductors—they do not conduct electricity in solid or in molten form.

The formation of ions by the reaction of the atoms of a **metallic element and a non-metallic element** produces particles which attract each other strongly. The ions, therefore, form an arrangement called a giant ionic lattice or structure. Such structures are always solids at room temperature (see Fig. 6.11).

Ions which collect together in a giant structure are held together by strong forces called ionic bonds. These bonds are forces of attraction of oppositely charged particles. They are the cause of high melting and boiling points.

At room temperature, the ions in the structure are vibrating. As the temperature is raised, the ions vibrate more strongly. Eventually, a temperature is reached when the ions break free from the close-packed structure of the solid. As the ions begin to move around freely, the solid melts. Further heating will give the mobile ions more energy until they vaporize at the boiling point of the compound.

Figure 6.11 Arrangement of ions in sodium chloride structure

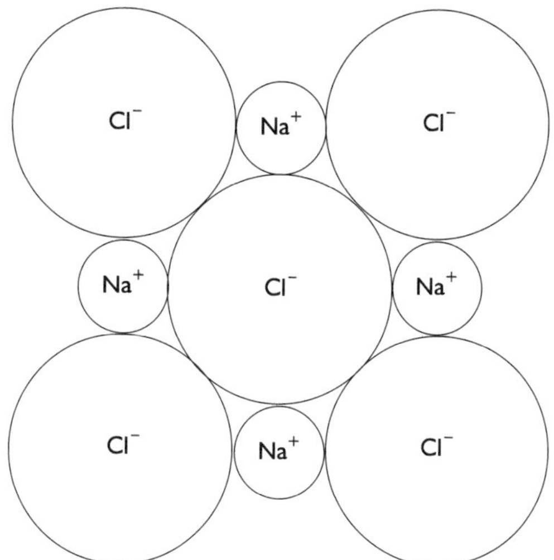

When molten, the ions of an ionic compound are mobile and can move towards the electrodes in an electrolysis cell. When ionic compounds dissolve in water, their ions also become mobile and can conduct electricity as they do in the molten state.

'Magnesium oxide'

The structure of magnesium oxide, MgO, is very similar to the structure of sodium chloride (Fig. 6.11). In the magnesium oxide structure, however, the ions have double charges, Mg^{2+} and O^{2-}, and are therefore much more strongly attracted to each other. This results in a very high melting point (2852 °C) and insolubility in water. Magnesium oxide is used as a lining for furnaces. You can deduce for yourself which property is crucial to this use.

Table 6.6 summarizes the properties of compounds in which **ions** are present and those in which **covalently bonded molecules** are present. Note that the temperatures given are intended to be a rule-of-thumb guide to deciding whether a substance is molecular or ionic by considering its melting or boiling point.

Table 6.6 Properties of ionic and molecular substances in terms of their structures

Property	Giant structures		Simple molecular structures
	Ionic	Molecular	
Melting point	High (> 250 °C)	High (> 1000 °C)	Low (< 250 °C)
Boiling point	High (> 500 °C)	High (> 2000 °C)	Low (< 500 °C)
Electrical conductivity	**Solid**: all types non-conductors		
	Molten: conductor	**Molten**: non-conductor	Non-conductors
Solubility in water	Usually soluble	Not soluble	Not soluble
Solubility in organic solvents	Not soluble	Not soluble	Usually soluble

Molecular liquids as solvents

Any substance that will **dissolve** another substance is a **solvent** for the substance it dissolves. Water is a solvent for many ionic compounds. Organic compounds such as ethanol, propanone and xylene are solvents for many molecular compounds.

Water as a special solvent

Water is a molecular compound with a difference! The structure of the water molecule is shown in Fig. 6.12.

The bonds between the atoms of hydrogen and oxygen are covalent. However, the **electron pairs** forming these bonds are more strongly attracted to the oxygen atoms than to the hydrogen atoms. The result is a pair of *polar* bonds. The molecule has a slight positive charge ($\delta+$) on each hydrogen atom and a slight negative charge ($\delta-$) on the oxygen atom. The effect of these slight charges is to give the water molecule the power to attract

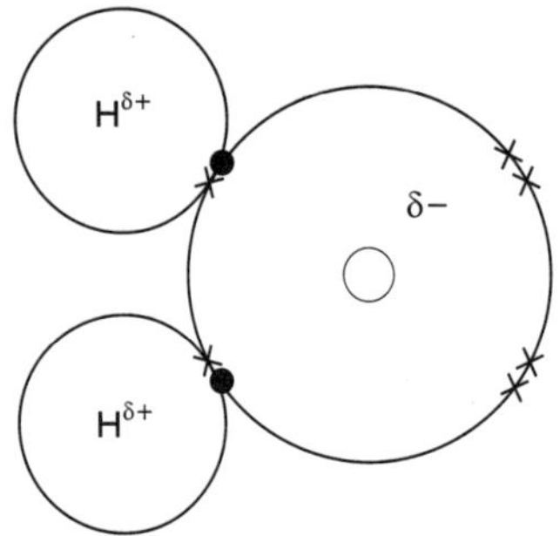

Figure 6.12 The polar water molecule

particles which are charged, i.e. ions. Water molecules can, therefore, 'drag' ions out of ionic lattices: the ionic compound **dissolves** (Fig. 6.13).

Water can also dissolve molecular compounds which are **similar to water**—polar compounds such as sugar, ethanol and propanone. Water will not dissolve molecular substances which are not polar, such as hydrocarbons (in petrol), or sulphur.

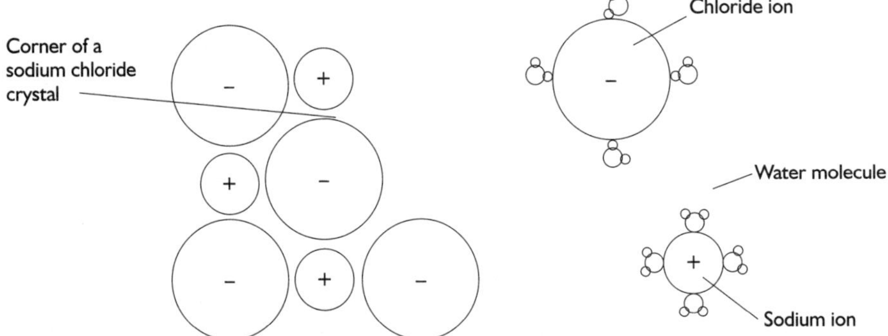

Figure 6.13 How water molecules dissolve sodium chloride

Other molecular solvents (non-aqueous liquids)

Many of the liquids we use as solvents do not have polar molecules like water. They dissolve substances because of the attraction of their molecules for the molecules of the substance they are dissolving (*solute*). Thus, propanone will dissolve nail varnish, xylene will dissolve sulphur, ethanol will dissolve ball-pen ink dyes. They dissolve by the process of **attraction** of neutral molecules for each other. Molecules which can attract each other are able to mix freely and so form solutions.

- One important use of non-aqueous liquids, as liquids **other than water** are called, is in 'dry' cleaning. The solvent here is called 'dry' because it is not water. The best dry-cleaning solvents are chlorinated hydrocarbons, such as perchloroethene, which dissolve grease and oil well but have low toxicity and are easily purified after use by distillation (low boiling points). These properties are characteristic of molecular compounds.
- Another use of non-aqueous liquids is as general solvents for such everyday materials as paints, adhesives, inks and perfumes. Even Tipp-Ex, which is the standby of almost every student, contains a solvent for the white plastic coating. A glance at the small print on some bottles will show it to be 1,1,1-trichloroethane. This solvent is harmful, and the bottle should carry a hazard label to that effect.

Macromolecules

Some substances have structures which do not fit the description given of ionic and molecular structures. These substances consist of extremely large molecules or even giant molecules. Such structures are sometimes called **macromolecules**. Figures 6.14 and 6.15 show the relationship between examples of giant and large molecules.

Giant molecules—carbon

Such substances as the allotropes of carbon—diamond and graphite—are made up of atoms bonded together by strong covalent bonds in a lattice which extends to the edges of the crystal. For diamond, any crystal is one giant molecule! For graphite, which is composed of

Figure 6.14 Giant molecule

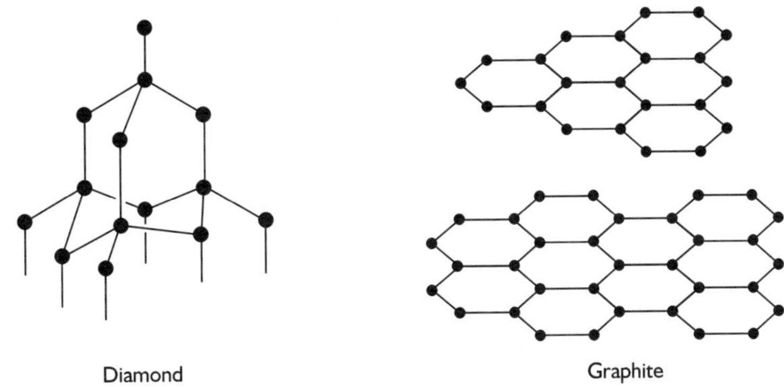

layers of closely bonded atoms, each **layer** is itself a giant molecule. The hardness of diamond results from

- the great strength of the bonds between carbon atoms and
- the way in which every carbon atom is bonded to its four nearest neighbours to make a single giant molecule the size of a diamond.

Graphite is different. A lump of graphite is composed of millions of layers—each layer being a giant molecule. What gives graphite its softness is the weak bonds **between** these layers which allow them to slide over each other and even completely separate from each other easily. The strength of the bonding **within** a graphite layer is in fact greater than that between atoms in diamond!

Giant molecules—silicon and its oxide

The element silicon, well known now for its use in microchips in computers, has a giant structure similar to that of diamond. The difference in hardness between the two structures arises because the bonds between carbon atoms are stronger than those between silicon atoms. By looking at the diamond structure in Fig. 6.14 above, and visualizing silicon atoms in place of carbon atoms, the structure of the element silicon can be pictured.

Silicon dioxide is a giant structure of silicon and oxygen atoms bonded by the covalent bond formed between silicon and oxygen atoms.

Properties of giant molecules

- The structures discussed above have no free electrons and so do not conduct electricity when solid.
- They also have no ions and so cannot conduct when molten either.
- The size of their molecules prevents them from dissolving in water.
- The strong bonds between the atoms make these structures the hardest known.
- The strong bonds also give the structures high melting and boiling points.

Graphite is something of an exception here:

- 'Free' electrons between the layers of carbon atoms allow the structure to conduct electricity like a metal (see also Fig. 6.16).
- The layers are also able to slide over one another when pressure is placed on them, and this makes graphite smooth and slippery—quite unlike diamond and silicon.
- Because the layers are themselves giant structures, however, the element has a high melting point.

Large molecules—plastics

This is another type of macromolecule. Large molecules are distinguished from giant molecules by the numbers of atoms in their molecules. Large molecules have thousands rather than billions of atoms per molecule. All polymers—starch, proteins and plastics—are large molecules.

Properties of large molecules

- They have lower melting points than giant molecular structures but higher melting points than simple molecular compounds.
- The size of their molecules lies between the sizes of simple molecules (often called **small molecules**) and giant molecules
- They do not conduct electricity for they have no ions or free electrons
- They are not very soluble in water.

An example of a large molecular structure is that of poly(ethene), Fig. 6.15.

Figure 6.15 A large molecule

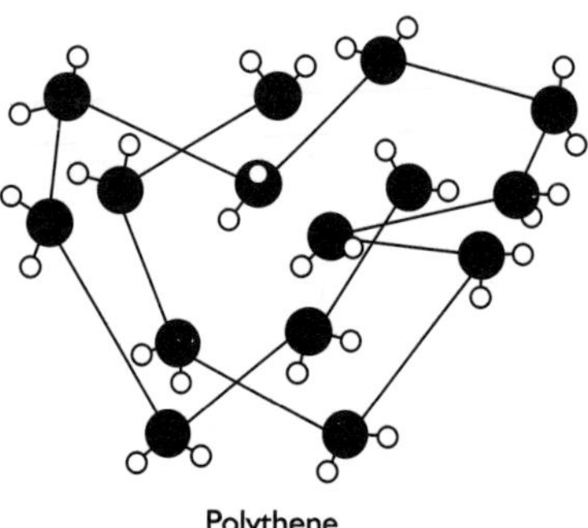

The structures of diamond, graphite and poly(ethene) are shown in Fig. 6.15. Chapter 7 deals with the structures and properties of plastics (p. 87).

Metallic structures

Metals form giant structures—but with a difference. There is ample evidence to suggest that **metallic structures** are composed of positively charged ions embedded in a 'sea of electrons'.

- The positively charged ions are held together by the electrons, giving the metal strength, hardness and high melting and boiling points.
- The electrons can be made to flow on application of a potential difference across the ends; in other words, the metal will **conduct electricity** in the solid state (see Fig. 6.16).

Figure 6.16 The structure of a metal

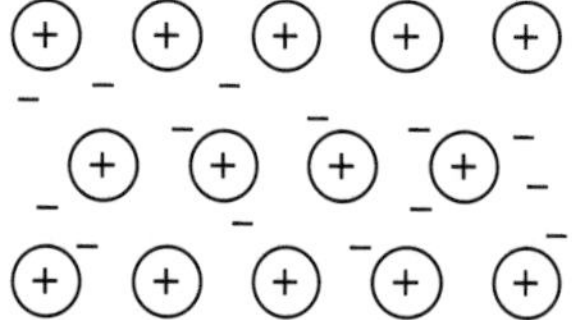

Shaping metals

A striking property of pure metals is the ease with which they can be shaped—they are malleable and ductile. Gold can be hand-beaten into sheets so thin that they become transparent!

This property is related to the structure. **Metals do not have 'localized' bonds that exist in covalently bonded solids.**

The property can be explained in the following way. Any atom (actually an ion) in the metal is surrounded by the 'sea of electrons' mentioned earlier. This sea acts as a 'glue' holding the ion in the metallic structure. Usually, solids break on being stressed because covalent or ionic bonds are broken and do not reform when the stress is removed. In metals, rolling or hammering causes layers of atoms to slide over one another. At each stage of this sliding process, the ions move from one place to another in which the bonding is constant—'the sea of electrons'. Like a shoal of fishes moving through water, no matter where an atom stops it is in exactly the same environment as where it started. Only when a metal is stretched to the point where its atoms are pulled apart, does its structure fail.

The connection between the way in which the atoms, molecules or ions of a substance are arranged, and its properties, is an important part of the study of chemistry. A knowledge of the relationship between structure and properties helps to free us from the need to remember the individual properties of every substance we might use. An understanding of the principles discussed in this chapter will be crucial to success in any chemistry course.

EXAMINATION QUESTIONS

Question 1 (F)

Use the information in Table 6.7 below to answer the following questions.

Table 6.7

Substance	Conducts electricity when solid	Melting point/°C	Dissolves in water
Sodium chloride	No	808	Yes
Sand	No	1 610	No
Titanium	Yes	1 660	No
Wax	No	35–50	No
Lead	Yes	328	No

(a) Name *one* substance in the table which is a metal. *[1]*

(b) How can you tell from the information above that wax is a mixture and not a pure compound? [2 lines] *[2]*

(c) Suggest how you could obtain solid sodium chloride from a mixture of sand and sodium chloride. [3 lines] *[3]*

(d) Describe how the arrangement of particles in lead changes as the temperature rises from 327 °C to 329 °C. [2 lines] *[2]*

[Total 8 marks]

Question 2 (H)

The element sodium (atomic number 11) reacts with chlorine (atomic number 17) to form the compound sodium chloride, NaCl.

(a) Give the meaning of each of the following words.

Element ________________________________

____

Compound ________________________________

____

[2]

(b) Complete the diagrams to show the arrangements of electrons in a sodium atom and in a chlorine atom. *[2]*

Figure 6.17

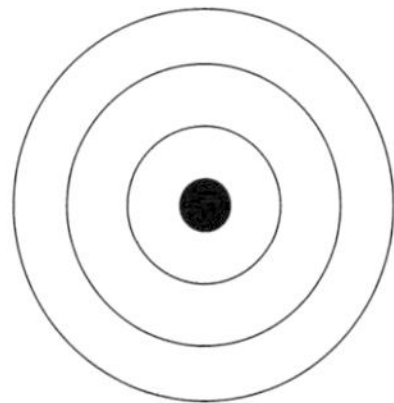

Sodium atom (Na)

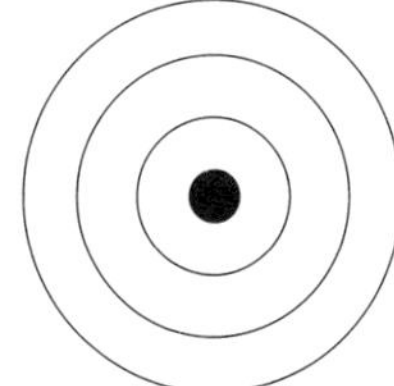

Chlorine atom (Cl)

(c) What happens to these electron arrangements when sodium reacts with chlorine to form sodium chloride, NaCl? [8 lines] *[4]*

(d) The compound sodium chloride has *ionic bonding*. Explain what this means. [3 lines] *[2]*

[Total 10 marks]

Question 3 (H)

(a) Magnesium has an atomic number of 12 and a mass number of 24. This is often represented by the symbol

$^{24}_{12}Mg$

(i) State the number of neutrons, protons and electrons which make up a neutral atom of this element.

Table 6.8

Neutrons	
Protons	
Electrons	

(ii) Sometimes atoms of the same element occur with a different number of neutrons in the nucleus. What do we call such atoms?

(iii) Using the symbolism seen at the start of the question, how would you represent an atom of magnesium that had 14 neutrons?

$^{...}_{...}Mg$

(iv) Atoms of magnesium form ions by the loss of two electrons. Write the formula of a magnesium ion. *[7]*

(b) (i) Give the electronic structure of a single, uncombined atom of oxygen.

(ii) Draw, showing only the outer electrons of each atom, the structure of an oxygen molecule, O_2. *[2]*

(c) Show what happens to the electronic structure of an atom of oxygen when it forms an oxide ion and say whether the atom has been oxidized, reduced or neither of these. *[2]*

(d) Magnesium oxide has a similar crystal structure to sodium chloride. Both contain ionic bonding. The melting points of magnesium oxide and sodium chloride are 2800 °C and 800 °C respectively.

Suggest why the melting point of magnesium oxide is much higher than that of sodium chloride. (Sodium chloride contains Na^+ and Cl^- ions.) *[3]*

[Total 14 marks]

Question 4 (H)

(a) Name two types of particle contained in an atom in addition to the electron. *[2]*

(i) ____________ (ii) ____________

(b) In what part of the atom are they found? [1 line] *[1]*
(c) Show by means of a diagram how the electrons are arranged in an atom of aluminium (atomic number of aluminium is 13). *[2]*
(d) State how many of each of the three particles are contained in an atom of fluorine (atomic number of fluorine is 9, mass number is 19). *[3]*

Name of particle	*Number*
__________	__________
__________	__________
__________	__________

(e) State how a fluoride ion differs from a fluorine atom [1 line]. *[1]*
(f) Draw a diagram to show how the electrons are arranged in the covalent compound NH_3. *[2]*
(g) Show by means of a diagram how the electrons are arranged in the ionic compound potassium chloride (KCl). *[2]*
(h) Describe two ways in which covalent compounds usually differ from ionic compounds in their physical or chemical properties [3 lines]. *[2]*

[Total 15 marks]

(NICCEA)

Question 5 (H)

(a) State three differences in the properties of sodium chloride and tetrachloromethane (carbon tetrachloride) [3 lines]. *[3]*
(b) Explain in terms of the electronic structures of the compounds why they have these differences in properties [6 lines]. *[6]*
(c) Use your knowledge of chemistry to explain the following facts as fully as you can. *[2]*
  (i) Aluminium wire carries electricity in power lines [3 lines].
  (ii) Graphite is used as a lubricant [3 lines]. *[2]*

[Total 13]

(NEAB)

OUTLINE ANSWERS

Question 1

(a) Titanium or lead *[1]*.
(b) The melting point *[1]* of a pure compound is a *single* temperature and not a *range* *[1]* as given.
(c) Add water, stir or warm to dissolve *[1]* the salt. Filter *[1]* and evaporate off the water *from the filtrate* to leave solid salt *[1]*.
(d) At 327 °C the particles in solid lead are closely packed and orderly *[1]*—the crystal lattice. At 329 °C the particles are randomly free-moving *[1]*, still close but farther apart than in the solid.

Question 2

(a) An element is a substance containing atoms with the same atomic (proton) number *[1]* or a substance that cannot be broken down into anything simpler *[1]*.
A compound contains more than one type of atom bonded or combined together *[1]*.
(b) The sodium atom has the electron arrangement 2 electrons in the innermost shell, 8 electrons in the next shell out and 1 electron in the outer shell *[1]*. For the chlorine atom the numbers are 2 (innermost), 8 (next) and 7 (outer shell) *[1]*.
(c) Sodium atom loses one electron *[1]* to become the ion Na^+ with structure 2,8 *[1]*. Chlorine atom gains one electron *[1]* to become the ion Cl^- with structure 2,8,8 *[1]*.
(d) Ionic bonding is the attractive force *[1]* operating between oppositely charged ions: Na^+ and Cl^- *[1]*.

Question 3

(a) (i) The magnesium atom has 12 protons *[1]*, 12 neutrons *[1]* and 12 electrons *[1]*.
  (ii) Atoms of the same element with different numbers of neutrons are **isotopes** *[1]*.

(iii) 14 neutrons plus the 12 protons of magnesium makes a mass number of 26. The top figure is 26 *[1]*; the **lower figure is still 12** *[1]*.
(iv) Mg^{2+} *[1]* is the **formula** of the ion.

(b) (i) Oxygen is 2,6. *[1]*.
(ii) The two oxygen atoms must be joined by **two pairs of electrons** but in total each atom has 8 electrons around it *[1]*.

(c) The atom **gains 2** electrons *[1]* and so is reduced *[1]*.

(d) The attractive forces *[1]* between two **doubly charged** ions (Mg^{2+} and O^{2-}) are much greater than those between the **singly charged** sodium and chloride ions *[1]* and so more energy is needed *[1]* to overcome them to melt the compound.

Question 4

This is a fairly wide-ranging question. It is largely based on recall but the answers can be worked out from a knowledge of the principles discussed in Chapter 6.

(a) and (b) require knowledge of the composition of the nucleus (see the section on the nucleus at the beginning of this chapter).

(c) Here the atomic number is given to enable you to deduce the number of electrons. The aluminium atom will have 3 shells. The arrangement is 2, 8, 3 (Table 6.3).

(d) This requires a calculation of the numbers of the three types of sub-atomic particle in the atom of fluorine. 9 protons, 9 electrons and 10 neutrons.

(e) Fluorine is a non-metal. Will it gain or lose electrons to become an ion? In fact the ion has one more electron than the atom (Table 6.3).

(f) Ammonia contains an atom (nitrogen) which has five electrons in its outer shell. How will it share electrons with hydrogen to achieve an octet whilst hydrogen atoms achieve the duet of helium? (See Fig. 6.10.)

(g) Potassium chloride is similar to sodium chloride—sodium and potassium are in the same group. The structures of the two chlorides are similar, but not identical. Potassium has one more shell than sodium (see Table 6.3).

(h) Remember that ions attract each other strongly but molecules are weakly attracted to each other (Table 6.6). Physical properties are those in which the substance is not changed into a different substance—like melting and boiling points.

Question 5

(a) (i) Sodium chloride would have much higher melting and boiling points than tetrachloromethane. This is usually judged to be ONE difference despite the mention of two physical properties.
(ii) Sodium chloride would conduct electricity when molten or in solution: tetrachloromethane would not.
(iii) Sodium chloride would give a positive test for chloride ions with silver nitrate solution; tetrachloromethane would give no reaction in this test.

(b) Sodium chloride is an ionic compound; tetrachloromethane is covalently bonded—a molecular compound. The explanation of the three differences stated in (a) are:
(i) The presence of charged particles, ions, in a structure creates strong bonds which require high temperatures to break, so the melting and boiling points will be high. Molecules do not attract each other strongly and so **molecular** compounds are easily melted and boiled.
(ii) The **ions** in sodium chloride allow it to conduct electricity when they become mobile—in a molten state or in solution. Tetrachloromethane **molecules** cannot carry an electric current.
(iii) Chloride ions will react with silver ions to form a white precipitate of silver chloride. Tetrachloromethane does not contain ions and this reaction cannot occur:

$$Cl^-(aq) + Ag^+(aq) \rightarrow AgCl(s).$$

(c) (i) Aluminium wires carry electricity because the structure of the aluminium is that of aluminium ions in a 'sea of electrons'. A diagram might attract credit here but in any case would help to reinforce the explanation. An electric current is a stream of electrons. Electrons entering the metal wire can push the electrons in the 'sea' along the wire to the other end, where they enter the electrical circuits of a building.

(ii) Graphite is a giant structure with a difference! It is made of giant structured *layers* which are weakly bonded *to* each other. *Putting a sideways force onto graphite causes these layers to slide over each other very readily.* The whole structure 'spreads' like a pack of playing cards pushed sideways whilst being held between the palms of two hands. The sliding layers of carbon atoms allows movement of metal surfaces over each other if graphite is present between them.

STUDENT ANSWER WITH EXAMINER'S COMMENTS

'You have not read this carefully. Your answer refers to the same *group*. Perhaps you thought (ii) was the same question as (i), but for a different group! You have seven elements to chose from in the period Li → F.'

(a) Name an element in

(i) the same group of the Periodic Table as chlorine; *bromine* *(1 mark)*

(ii) the same period of the Periodic Table as carbon. *silicon* *(1 mark)*

(b) Write down or draw a diagram of the electronic structure of

(i) an atom of carbon (atomic number = 6);

(ii) an atom of chlorine (atomic number = 17).

carbon
C = 2.4

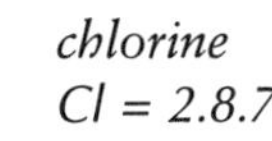

'Excellent diagrams. Full marks for accuracy and careful drawing.'

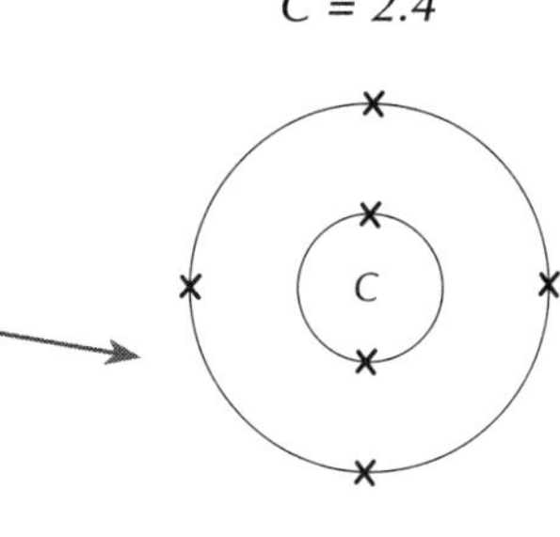

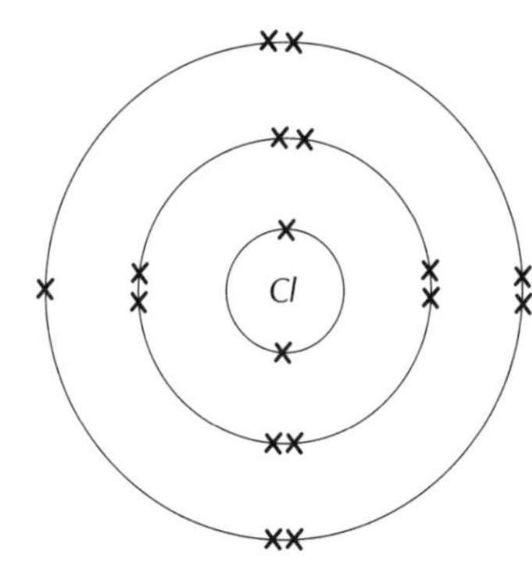

(2 marks)

'Again—excellent. You noticed that the question allowed you to simplify the diagram by drawing outer electrons only.'

(c) Draw a diagram to show the electron arrangement in a molecule of tetrachloromethane (CCl_4). Only the outer electron shells need to be shown in your diagram.

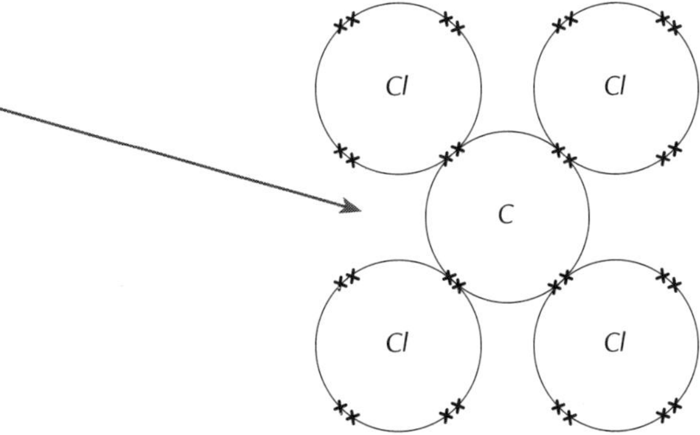

'This answer shows a good understanding of the nature of covalent bonding and electron structure.'

'Examiner's mark 5/6.'

(NEAB) *(2 marks)*

SUMMARY

Use this list to help with your revision. Tick off the points as you learn about them.

▷ Atoms contain **protons, neutrons** and **electrons**: different elements have atoms with different numbers of these particles.

▷ Protons, neutrons and electrons have different **masses**.

▷ The **sum** of the masses of all the particles in an atom (**averaged** over many atoms) gives the **relative atomic mass**.

▷ **Isotopes** have the same proton (atomic) number but different atomic masses because of having **different numbers of neutrons**.

▷ The arrangement of **electrons in atoms** of elements controls the **chemical reactions** of their atoms.

▷ Two types of bonds are formed when elements react and achieve noble gas electron structures:
1. **covalent**, by electron sharing;
2. **ionic**, by electron transfer.

▷ Substances with covalent bonds are of two types:
1. **simple** molecules;
2. **giant** molecules (macromolecules).

▷ A single bond involves a **pair** of shared electrons; a double bond involves **two shared pairs**.

▷ The physical properties of simple ionic and molecular compounds depend on the **force of attraction** between their particles.

▷ The differences in properties is best illustrated in tabular form: to include **melting** and **boiling** point, electrical **conductivity** and **solubility**.

▷ Water is a special solvent because it is a polar molecule attracted to ions and molecules alike.

▷ Giant molecules such as **diamond**, **graphite** and **silica** are composed of very large single molecules with **strong internal bonding** which determines their properties.

▷ Metals have different structures, being composed of **ions in a sea of electrons**. When placed between battery terminals, **electrons** from the negative terminal enter the 'sea' and **move through** to the positive terminal: this is **electrical conduction**.

Chapter

7 Organic chemistry

GETTING STARTED

Organic chemistry is the study of carbon compounds other than carbon dioxide, carbonate and hydrogencarbonates. Originally organic chemistry was confined to those chemicals found in living things such as animals and plants. However, in 1882, a chemist called Wohler managed to make urea from inorganic substances. Organic compounds contain a few elements such as hydrogen and the halogens combined with carbon. The biggest source of organic compounds is plants and animals (past or present). Coal and oil are non-renewable sources of energy made from living things many years ago. Wood is a renewable source of energy. It is very important that newer forms of energy are developed to ensure that our non-renewable fossil fuels are not used up.

Large molecules, such as polymers, are very important. Unfortunately, a large number are made from oil and thus use up valuable resources. Hopefully, as time goes on, we will be able to economically use naturally occurring large molecules such as protein and starch to make polymers.

TOPIC CHART

LONDON	MEG	NEAB	NICCEA	SEG	WJEC	TOPIC	STUDY	REVISION 1	REVISION 2
✓	✓	✓	✓	✓	✓	Fossil fuels			
	✓	✓	✓	✓		Homologous series			
✓	✓	✓	✓	✓	✓	Alkanes			
	✓	✓			✓	Isomers			
✓	✓	✓	✓	✓	✓	Alkenes			
✓	✓	✓	✓	✓	✓	Polymerization of alkenes			
✓	✓	✓	✓	✓	✓	Cracking			
✓	✓	✓	✓	✓	✓	Alcohols			
	✓	✓	✓	✓		Carboxylic acids			
✓		✓	✓	✓	✓	Fuels			
✓	✓	✓	✓	✓	✓	Properties and uses of polymers			
		✓		✓		Vegetable oils			

WHAT YOU NEED TO KNOW

Fossil fuels

Coal, petroleum and natural gas are all formed from plant and animal remains deposited hundreds of millions of years ago.

Coal

Two hundred million years ago, the remains of trees and plants became covered with water in the swamps where they had grown in abundance. This slowed down the normal rapid bacterial decay and so preserved the plant material. **Coal** results from the long-term effect of pressure and heat on this slowly decomposing mass of vegetation.

Peat is the first stage towards the formation of coal. Large deposits of peat are found in Ireland. Peat is dark brown in colour and has a high carbon content. Dried peat is used as a fuel but it is not as efficient as coal because it has a high water content and leaves considerably more ash.

Peat retains moisture and is used by gardeners to improve the soil. Conservationists are trying to encourage the use of other substances to improve the soil, such as bark and coir (made from the husks of coconuts). It is feared that digging up the peat will deprive many animals and plants from their natural habitat.

Lignite is a variety of coal. It is also known as brown coal. Lignite is another stage in the formation of coal. Its properties are between those of peat and coal. It is not as good a fuel as coal because it has a high water content (about 44%) and a low carbon content. Lignite contains many **volatile** substances and rapidly deteriorates when it is left exposed to the air.

Crude oil (petroleum—'rock-oil')

Petroleum is believed to have formed from the remains of animals and plants which lived in the sea in a similar way to the formation of coal from plant remains. These remains accumulated in fine-grained sediments on the sea bed. Heat, pressure and time have combined to force out the oily products. This oil moved upwards through permeable rock until it met rock that stopped its flow. Here it accumulated—to be found by oil prospectors for the first time about a century ago.

Natural gas

Petroleum almost always contains a certain amount of natural gas. It is brought to the surface with oil when a well is drilled. Some wells produce only natural gas.

Before natural gas (**methane**) can be used as fuel, butane, propane and octane have to be removed. Methane also occurs in nature.

Oil and natural gas are less dense than water and so they rise to the top. Frequently, the oil and gas get trapped below a layer of non-porous rock. The oil and gas can be obtained by drilling (see Fig. 7.1).

Fig. 7.1

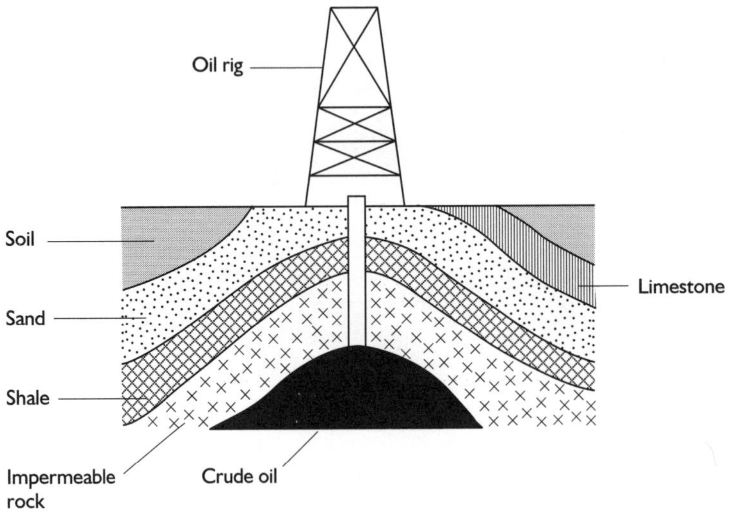

The hydrocarbon molecules in crude oil vary in size. As the number of carbon atoms increases, so does the size of the molecule. The larger the molecule, the higher the boiling temperature, the less volatile the fraction, i.e. the less easily vaporized it becomes (see Table 7.1). Since it is the vapour that burns, the higher the boiling temperature of a fraction the more difficult it is to ignite. Hence, higher-boiling fractions are not useful as fuels (see **cracking**).

As the molecules get larger, the hydrocarbons get less **viscous**, i.e. they flow less readily. The opposite to viscous is **mobile** (flows easily). The smaller hydrocarbons such as octane (C_8H_{18}) are mobile. You might remember this by thinking of one of the petrol giants—MOBIL. Other petrol companies get their name from the source of oil—SHELL—or the country it comes from Q8 (Kuwait).

Table 7.1

Boiling range (°C)	Fraction	Use
< 30	Liquefied gases	Calor gas, butane, bottled gas
20–200	Petrol	Petrol for cars, solvents
175–250	Paraffin (kerosene)	Oil stoves, aircraft fuel
200–350	Diesel oil	Diesel engine fuel in trains, lorries, tractors, etc.
300–400	Lubricating oil	Lubricant
350–450	Fuel oil	Fuel for power stations and ships
350–500	Wax, grease	Candles, wax paper, lubricant
$>$500 (solid)	Bitumen	Road making, roofing material

Homologous series

Over 2 million carbon compounds are known. This is more than all the compounds of the other 88 elements added together. How is carbon able to form so many compounds? Carbon atoms are the only atoms able to bond together extensively in chains and rings. Hydrocarbons are known containing from one to several hundred carbon atoms joined in chains. As the chain length increases, the possibility of **isomerism** multiplies the number of different compounds possible. Substitution of other atoms in place of the hydrogens multiplies the possibilities further. The existence of rings of carbon atoms and their variants adds more permutations until the huge number of compounds known begins to look small by comparison with those that can be imagined!

Organic compounds are divided into groups of compounds with similar chemical properties. Each group is known as an **homologous series**. Organic compounds that are in the same homologous series have the following properties in common:

- they can be represented by a **general formula**;
- they have **similar chemical properties** (because they contain the same functional group);
- they can be **made by similar reactions**;
- there is a **regular change in their physical properties**, e.g. the boiling points increase as the relative molecular masses increase.

Naming compounds

The *first part* of the name indicates the number of carbon atoms in the compound (Table 7.2).

Table 7.2

Number of carbon atoms	Start of name
1	meth-
2	eth-
3	prop-
4	but-
5	pent-
6	hex-

The order can be remembered by the initial letters of the sentence Many Elephants Pass By Public Houses.

Functional groups

The *name ending* shows the homologous series of the compound. Compounds in the same homologous series contain the same **functional group** (Table 7.3).

Table 7.3

Functional group	Name ending	Homologous series
C—C	-ane	alkane
C=C	-ene	alkene
C—O—H	-ol	alcohol
CO_2H	acid	acids

Thus:

'Make sure your writing is clear. "Ethaene" would be marked wrong'

Methane is an alkane with one carbon atom.
Ethene is an alkene with two carbon atoms.
Propanol is an alcohol with three carbon atoms.
Butanoic acid is an acid with four carbon atoms.

N.B. Methene does not exist.

Physical properties

Physical properties include boiling point, melting point, density and viscosity.

These vary with the relative molecular mass of the members of the series, increasing as the molecular mass rises. The change of melting point and boiling point with molecular mass for alkanes is shown in Table 7.4. (Note that the melting point of propane does not fit the pattern. Remember that for a substance to be a gas its melting point and boiling point have to be below room temperature (25 °C); and to be a liquid its melting point must be below room temperature and its boiling point above room temperature.)

The vapours of the volatile liquids are denser than air and remain near the surface of the ground. This is why people must not smoke in petrol stations.

Table 7.4

Hydrocarbon	Methane	Ethane	Propane	Butane	Pentane	Hexane
Melting point °C	−183	−172	−188	−135	−130	−95
Boiling point °C	−162	−89	−42	−0.5	36	69
Density/g cm^{-3}	gas	gas	gas	gas	0.62	0.66

Finding the formula of hydrocarbons by complete combustion of the hydrocarbon

25 cm^3 of a hydrocarbon burns to give 100 cm^3 of carbon dioxide and 125 cm^3 of water vapour (measured under the same conditions and pressure). What is the formula of the hydrocarbon?

By Avogadro's law, equal volumes of gases contain the same number of molecules. Since the volumes are in the ratio of 1 volume of hydrocarbon (25/25) to 4 volumes of carbon dioxide (100/25) to 5 volumes of water (125/25) we can say that: 1 volume of hydrocarbon gives 4 volumes of carbon dioxide and 5 volumes of water. Since the hydrocarbon gives 4 moles of CO_2, it must contain 4 carbon atoms and since it gives 5 moles of H_2O, it must contain 10 hydrogen atoms (5×2).

The formula of the hydrocarbon is C_4H_{10}.

Alkanes

Alkanes are hydrocarbons. Alkanes have the general formula C_nH_{2n+2}.

Structure of methane (electronic)

Fig. 7.2

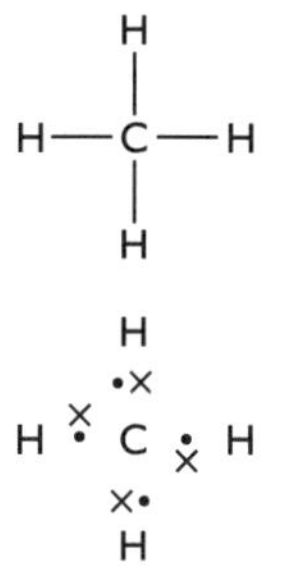

The first member of the homologous series of alkanes is methane. The formula of methane is CH_4. There is a pair of electrons between each hydrogen atom and the carbon atom (Fig. 7.2).

Structure of ethane

The next member of the series is ethane, C_2H_6. This contains a pair of electrons between the carbon atoms. The molecule contains a carbon—carbon single bond (Fig. 7.3).

Alkanes are said to be **saturated** hydrocarbons. They contain no double bonds. Other members of the alkane series are propane, C_3H_8, butane, C_4H_{10}, pentane C_5H_{12} and hexane C_6H_{14}.

Fig. 7.3

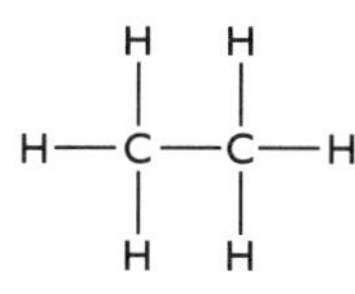

Properties of methane

Methane is a colourless, odourless gas. It is less dense than air. It is insoluble in water and neutral. It burns in an excess of air to give carbon dioxide and water.

methane + oxygen → carbon dioxide + water

$$CH_4(g) + 2O_2(g) \rightarrow CO_2(g) + 2H_2O(l)$$

ethane + oxygen → carbon dioxide + water

$$2C_2H_6(g) + 7O_2(g) \rightarrow 4CO_2(g) + 6H_2O(l)$$

The combustion of hydrocarbons is an exothermic reaction.

In a limited supply of oxygen, carbon monoxide and/or carbon together with water are formed. Carbon monoxide is very poisonous; therefore, if you are burning natural gas in your home, your rooms must be well ventilated (see below).

A burning splint does not continue to burn in methane.

Alkanes react with chlorine and with bromine in the presence of sunlight:

methane + chlorine → chloromethane + hydrogen chloride

$$CH_4(g) + Cl_2(g) \rightarrow CH_3Cl(g) + HCl(g)$$

'Learn this definition'

This is called a substitution reaction. **A substitution reaction is a reaction in which a hydrogen atom is replaced by another atom or groups of atoms.**

Uses of alkanes

Alkanes are mainly used as **fuels**. Methane is the main part of natural gas. Butane is used in camping gas and in lighter fuel, and octane is used in petrol. Alkanes are used to make alkenes by a process known as cracking (see below).

Poisonous nature of carbon monoxide

Carbon monoxide is a very poisonous gas. It combines with haemoglobin in the blood to form **carboxyhaemoglobin.** This compound is about two hundred times more stable than the compound formed with oxygen, **oxyhaemoglobin**. Carboxyhaemoglobin cannot carry oxygen around the body, and the victim dies from lack of oxygen.

Carbon monoxide is an **atmospheric pollutant.** It is formed in the manufacture of iron and steel, in the paper industry and in petroleum refineries. It is formed during the incomplete combustion of carbon-containing compounds such as petrol, diesel, coal and cigarettes. Large quantities of carbon monoxide are formed when there are forest fires. Fortunately, there are many soil microorganisms using their enzyme catalysts to convert carbon monoxide into carbon dioxide, keeping the percentage of carbon monoxide in the atmosphere low.

Isomers

Isomers are compounds with the same molecular formula but different structural formula.

Isomers have different physical properties. As the carbon chain gets longer, the strength of the intermolecular forces increases. However, the intermolecular forces decrease as the amount of branching increases. Thus branched-chain alkanes have lower boiling points than their straight-chain isomers. As branching increases, the boiling point decreases.

Butane has two isomers (Fig. 7.4)

Fig. 7.4 Two isomers of butane

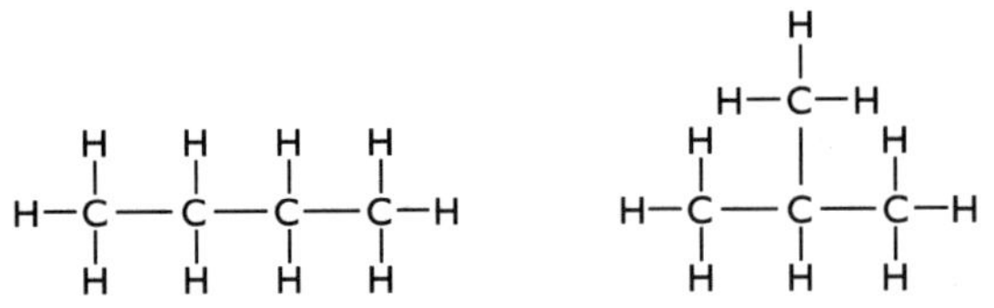

and pentane three isomers (Fig. 7.5).

Fig. 7.5 Three isomers of pentane

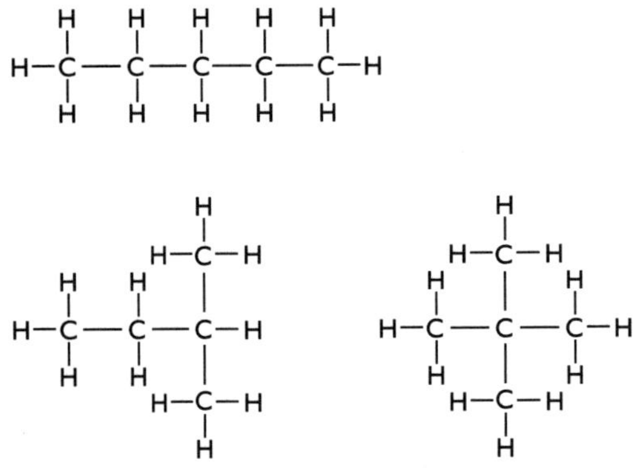

You should be able to predict the isomers of hexane (C_6H_{14}), and to know that the isomer of pentane with the most branching will have the lowest boiling point.

Alkenes

Alkenes have the general formula C_nH_{2n}.

The first member of the homologous series of alkenes is ethene.

Structure of ethene (electronic)

The formula of ethene is C_2H_4.

There are two pairs of shared electrons between the carbon atoms. The molecule contains a carbon—carbon double bond (see Fig. 7.6).

Fig. 7.6 Ethene

Other alkenes

Alkenes are said to be **unsaturated** hydrocarbons. Other members of the alkene series are propene, C_3H_6, and butene, C_4H_8. The structure of propene is shown in Fig. 7.7

Fig. 7.7 Propene

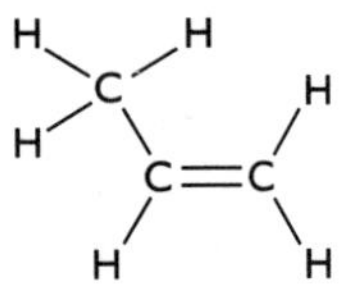

Note that methene CH_2 cannot exist, because it leaves carbon with two unshared electrons and only six electrons in the outermost energy level. You will remember that carbon needs eight electrons in the outermost energy level (outer shell) to be stable.

'Note that ethene is made by dehydrating ethanol. Ethanol can be made by hydrating ethene'

Preparation of ethene

Alkenes can be made by dehydrating the corresponding alcohol. Ethene is made by heating ethanol with an excess of concentrated sulphuric acid:

$$\text{ethanol} \rightarrow \text{ethene} + \text{water}$$

$$C_2H_5OH(l) \rightarrow C_2H_4(g) + H_2O(l)$$

Ethene can also be dehydrated by passing ethanol vapour over a catalyst of hot aluminium oxide.

Propene can be made by dehydrating propanol, and butene by dehydrating butanol. Alkenes can also be made by cracking saturated hydrocarbons from crude oil distillation (see later).

Properties of ethene

Ethene is a colourless gas. It has a slight sweet smell. It is slightly less dense than air. It is insoluble in water and therefore it is neutral.

In a plentiful supply of air, ethene, like all hydrocarbons, burns to form carbon dioxide and water:

$$\text{ethene} + \text{oxygen} \rightarrow \text{carbon dioxide} + \text{water}$$

$$C_2H_4(g) + 3O_2(g) \rightarrow 2CO_2(g) + 2H_2O(g)$$

In a limited supply of air, carbon monoxide and/or carbon and water are the products.

A burning splint does not continue to burn in ethene.

'Addition reactions'

Alkenes are very reactive because they are unsaturated. They undergo **addition reactions. An addition reaction is a reaction in which two or more molecules react together to form one molecule only:**

$$\text{compound AB} + \text{compound CD} \rightarrow \text{compound CABD}$$

$$AB + CD \rightarrow CABD$$

Bromine dissolves in water to form a brown solution called bromine water. **If bromine water is shaken with an alkene a colourless product is formed.** This reaction is used as a test for alkenes.

$$\text{ethene} + \text{bromine} \rightarrow \text{1,2-dibromoethane}$$

$$\underset{}{C_2H_4(g)} + \underset{\text{(brown)}}{Br_2(aq)} \rightarrow \underset{\text{(colourless)}}{C_2H_4Br_2(aq)}$$

You will note that ethene is unsaturated but 1,2-dibromoethane is saturated. This can be shown by writing the equation using structural formulae (see Fig. 7.8).

Fig. 7.8

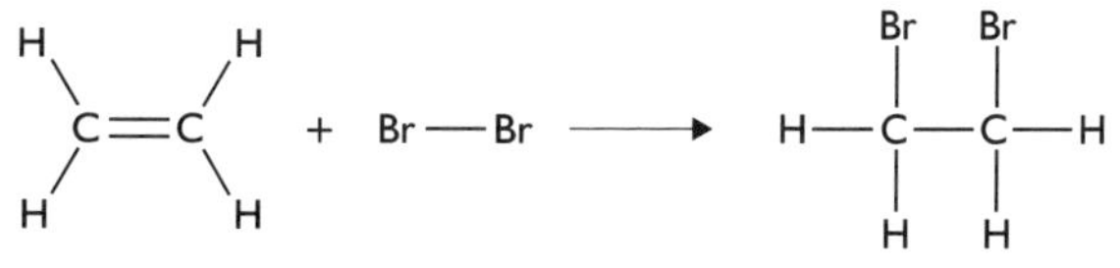

```
H       H                          Br  Br
 \     /                           |   |
  C═══C    +  Br──Br  ──────▶  H──C───C──H
 /     \                           |   |
H       H                          H   H
```

The easiest way to distinguish between an alkane and an alkene is to shake each with bromine water. Alkanes do not decolorize bromine water but alkenes do decolorize bromine water.

Comparing alkanes with alkenes

Table 7.5

Test reagent	Alkanes	Alkenes
React with bromine water	No reaction	Bromine water is decolorized rapidly
React with acidified potassium manganate(VII) solution	No reaction	The reagent changes from purple to colourless
Combustion	Burns with clean yellow flame	Burns with a sooty yellow flame

Ethene reacts with steam in the presence of a catalyst of phosphoric(V) acid to form ethanol:

ethene + water → ethanol

$C_2H_4(g) + H_2O(g) \rightarrow C_2H_5OH(g)$

'Examples of addition reactions'

Ethene reacts with hydrogen in the presence of a hot catalyst of nickel to form ethane:

ethene + hydrogen → ethane

$C_2H_4(g) + H_2(g) \rightarrow C_2H_6(g)$

The addition of hydrogen to a carbon—carbon double bond is an important reaction in the conversion of vegetable oils into margarine (see later).

Polymerization of alkenes

Because ethene is unsaturated it will also undergo **addition polymerization.**

Ethene polymerizes to form the polymer **poly(ethene)**, commonly known as polythene. The conditions required are a high pressure and a catalyst. **Propene** polymerizes to form **poly(propene).**

A polymer is a long-chain molecule formed by the joining together of many small molecules called monomers.

The conversion of ethene to poly(ethene) (commonly called polythene) can be represented by the equation

ethene → poly(ethene)

$n(H_2C{=}CH_2)(g) \rightarrow {(}CH_2{-}CH_2{)}_n(s)$

Other examples of polymerization are

styrene → poly(styrene)

$n(C_6H_5{=}CH_2)(l) \rightarrow {(}C_6H_5{-}CH_2{)}_n(s)$

and

vinyl chloride → poly(vinyl chloride) (PVC)

$n(CH_2{=}CHCl(g) \rightarrow {(}CH_2{-}CHCl{)}_n(s)$

Cracking

Large hydrocarbon molecules can be broken down (**cracked**) to produce smaller, more useful products. Some of these products can be used as **fuels** and others can be used to make **plastics** (**polymers**) such as poly(ethene) and poly(vinyl chloride) (PVC).

Cracking always produces a mixture of alkanes and alkenes and usually hydrogen. Cracking takes place at a high temperature in the presence of a catalyst. The high temperature causes the bonds in the alkane to break producing smaller molecules. The smaller molecules are more useful; for example, ethene is manufactured by cracking.

decane → ethene + octane

$C_{10}H_{22}(l) \rightarrow C_2H_4(g) + C_8H_{18}(l)$

Cracking is the process of breaking a long-chained hydrocarbon molecule into smaller hydrocarbon molecules.

Alkenes are produced in large quantities because they are important raw materials in the petrochemical industry.

Uses of ethene

Ethene is used for the manufacture of ethane-1,2-diol (also known as ethylene glycol), which is used as an antifreeze, and ethanol, which is used as a solvent. Ethene is also used to make the well-known polymers poly(ethene), poly(styrene) and poly(vinyl chloride) (PVC).

Alcohols

Alcohols have the general formula $C_nH_{2n+1}OH$. They have the functional group —OH. The first member of the homologous series of alcohols is methanol. The formula of methanol is CH_3OH. The structures of the first five straight-chain members of the alcohols homologous series are shown in Fig. 7.9.

Fig. 7.9

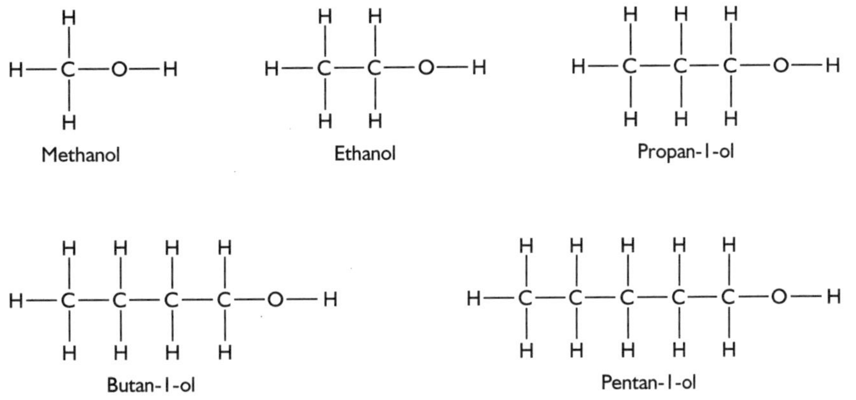

```
     H                  H   H                 H   H   H
     |                  |   |                 |   |   |
  H—C—O—H            H—C—C—O—H            H—C—C—C—O—H
     |                  |   |                 |   |   |
     H                  H   H                 H   H   H
  Methanol             Ethanol              Propan-1-ol

     H   H   H   H                  H   H   H   H   H
     |   |   |   |                  |   |   |   |   |
  H—C—C—C—C—O—H                H—C—C—C—C—C—O—H
     |   |   |   |                  |   |   |   |   |
     H   H   H   H                  H   H   H   H   H
      Butan-1-ol                      Pentan-1-ol
```

Properties of ethanol

Ethanol is a colourless liquid. It has no smell. It is completely miscible (mixable) with water and it is a neutral liquid.

In a plentiful supply of air, ethanol burns to form carbon dioxide and water:

ethanol + oxygen → carbon dioxide + water

$$C_2H_5OH(l) + 3O_2(g) \rightarrow 2CO_2(g) + 3H_2O(l)$$

In a limited supply of air, carbon monoxide and/or carbon and water are the products.

Ethanol is slowly oxidized by the air and bacteria to ethanoic acid:

ethanol + oxygen (from the air) → ethanoic acid + water

$$C_2H_5OH(l) + 2[O](g) \rightarrow CH_3CO_2H(l) + H_2O(l)$$

This is why wine and beer turn sour after a period of time if they are not kept in sealed containers.

The oxidation process can be speeded up by using an oxidizing agent such as acidified potassium dichromate(VI) or acidified potassium manganate(VII). The solution changes from purple to colourless.

The functional group —OH gives alcohols their characteristic properties.

Alcohols react with acids to give esters and water. The reaction is **reversible.**

methanol + ethanoic acid ⇌ methyl ethanoate + water

$$CH_3OH(l) + CH_3CO_2H(l) \rightleftharpoons CH_3CO_2CH_3(l) + H_2O(l)$$

ethanol + ethanoic acid ⇌ ethyl ethanoate + water

$$C_2H_5OH(l) + CH_3CO_2H(l) \rightleftharpoons CH_3CO_2C_2H_5(l) + H_2O(l)$$

Alcohols react with sodium to form hydrogen:

methanol + sodium → sodium methoxide + hydrogen

$2CH_3OH(l) + 2Na(s) \rightarrow 2CH_3ONa(alc) + H_2(g)$

ethanol + sodium → sodium ethoxide + hydrogen

$2C_2H_5OH(l) + 2Na(s) \rightarrow 2C_2H_5ONa(alc) + H_2(g)$

N.B. (alc) indicates that the substance is dissolved in alcohol.

Manufacture of ethanol

Ethanol can be manufactured by reacting ethene with steam in the presence of a catalyst of phosphoric(V) acid. The reaction needs a temperature of about 3000 °C and 65 atmospheres pressure. This is a **continuous process**. Reactants are fed in at one end and products are removed from the other. This is much more convenient and faster than having to fill reaction vessels at the beginning and empty them at the end, as happens in a batch process.

ethene + steam → ethanol

$C_2H_4(g) + H_2O(l) \rightarrow C_2H_5OH(l)$

'Remember that enzymes are destroyed at about 45 °C'

Ethanol can also be manufactured by **fermentation**. Yeast is added to a solution of sugar (e.g. glucose) and the mixture is kept at room temperature until all the carbon dioxide has been given off. It is important to prevent air from entering the reaction vessel, otherwise ethanoic acid will be formed. Yeast contains biological catalysts known as **enzymes**. This is a batch process and so production is slow.

glucose → ethanol + carbon dioxide

$C_6H_{12}O_6(aq) \rightarrow 2C_2H_5OH(aq) + 2CO_2(g)$

Ethanol can be obtained from this mixture by **fractional distillation**.

Fermentation is a renewable source of ethanol, ethene from crude oil is not (see Table 7.6). However, it would be difficult in many countries to produce enough fermentable plant material to create the quantity of ethanol required by industry or as a fuel for cars. For this reason only a small fraction of the ethanol used in Europe is made by fermentation.

Table 7.6 Comparing two ways of manufacturing alcohol

	Fermentation	Steam + ethene
Rate of reaction	Slow	Fast
Quality of product	Needs to be fractionally distilled	Pure
Use of finite resources	Renewable source, e.g. sugar cane, sugar beet	Fossil fuel—non-renewable source
Type of process	Batch	Continuous

Fermentation takes place when bread is made. Yeast is added to the mixture of flour, water and sodium chloride. Carbon dioxide is given off and this causes the bread to rise. Ethanol escapes as a vapour during baking.

Uses of ethanol

Ethanol is used as a solvent. '**Tincture of iodine**', which is used as an antiseptic, is iodine dissolved in ethanol. **Shellac** dissolved in ethanol is used as a liquid polish. Perfumes are solutions of fragrances in ethanol or in an ethanol–water mixture.

Ethanol is used as a fuel and is the main constituent of methylated spirits, which is used in burners for cooking. Methylated spirits has chemicals added to it to make it unsuitable for drinking. This process is called **denaturing**.

Ethanol is present in spirits, beers and wines. Unfortunately some people become addicted to alcohol and this can lead to mental and physical problems which, in the most serious cases, cause death.

Carboxylic acids

Carboxylic acids have the general formula $C_nH_{2n+1}CO_2H$. They have the functional group $—CO_2H$. The first member of the homologous series of acids is methanoic acid. The formula of methanoic acid is HCO_2H and its structure is shown in Fig. 7.10.

Fig. 7.10

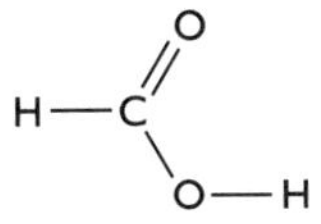

The old name for methanoic acid was formic acid, because it is found in ants. (The Latin word 'formica' means 'ant'.)

Other members of the acid series are ethanoic acid (acetic acid, CH_3CO_2H), propanoic acid ($C_2H_5CO_2H$), and butanoic acid ($C_3H_7CO_2H$). Organic acids are sometimes known as 'fatty acids' because they are found in natural fats.

Formation of carboxylic acids

Carboxylic acids are formed when alcohols are oxidized by the action of atmospheric oxygen in the presence of certain bacteria:

ethanol + atmospheric oxygen → ethanoic acid + water

$$C_2H_5OH(l) + 2(O)(g) \rightarrow CH_3CO_2H(l) + H_2O(l)$$

This is the reason why beers and wines turn sour if they are left open to the atmosphere. The sour taste is because ethanoic acid has been formed.

Ethanol can also be oxidized to ethanoic acid by using oxidizing agents such as acidified potassium dichromate(VI) and acidified potassium manganate(VII).

The first five members of the carboxylic acids are shown in Fig. 7.11.

Fig. 7.11

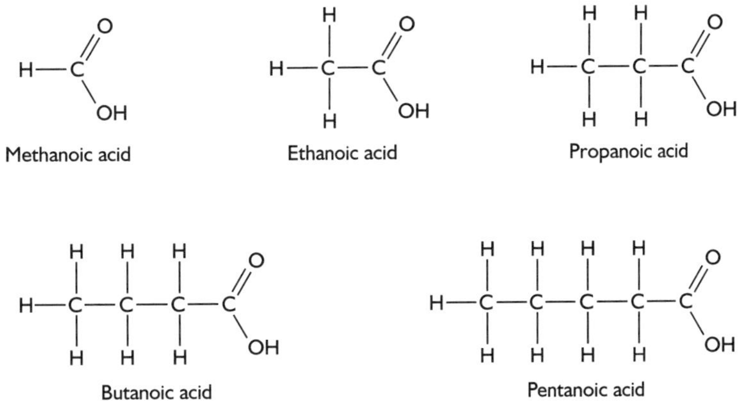

Methanoic acid

Ethanoic acid

Propanoic acid

Butanoic acid

Pentanoic acid

Properties of carboxylic acids

Carboxylic acids are weak acids with pH between 3.5 and 6. A weak acid produces fewer $H^+(aq)$ ions in solution than strong acids such as hydrochloric acid.

Carboxylic acids are typical acids.

- They have a pH less than 7.
- They react with metals to form hydrogen:

magnesium + ethanoic acid → magnesium ethanoate + hydrogen

$$Mg(s) + 2CH_3CO_2H(aq) \rightarrow (CH_3CO_2)_2Mg(aq) + H_2(g)$$

- They are neutralized by alkalis to give a salt and water:

sodium hydroxide + ethanoic acid → sodium ethanoate + water

$$NaOH(aq) + CH_3CO_2H(aq) \rightarrow CH_3CO_2Na(aq) + H_2O(l)$$

- They react with carbonates to form a salt, carbon dioxide and water:

calcium carbonate + ethanoic acid → calcium ethanoate + carbon dioxide + water

$$CaCO_3(s) + 2CH_3CO_2H(aq) \rightarrow (CH_3CO_2)_2Ca(aq) + CO_2(g) + H_2O(l)$$

- They react with alcohols, in the presence of concentrated sulphuric acid, to form esters:

ethanol + ethanoic acid ⇌ ethyl ethanoate + water

$$C_2H_5OH(l) + CH_3CO_2H(aq) \rightleftharpoons CH_3CO_2C_2H_5(l) + H_2O(l)$$

Note. Acids are named by the number of carbon atoms they contain; remember that there is always a carbon atom in the carboxylic acid group $—CO_2H$. Thus CH_3CO_2H is called ethanoic acid because it contains *two* carbon atoms.

Uses of ethanoic acid

Pure ethanoic acid is used as a solvent. Dilute ethanoic acid is used as an acid for purposes for which mineral acids would be too corrosive, e.g. removing fur from inside kettles.

Ethanoic acid is a component of vinegar. (Vinegar is used as a good preservative, e.g. in pickles.) Ethanoic acid is also the starting material for important plastics such as cellulose acetate.

Fuels

Domestic fuels

A fuel is any combustible matter that burns in air to give out heat. Domestic fuels must have additional properties. Some of these are considered below.

Table 7.7

Fuel	Requirement for storage	Source: renewable/fossil	Polluting rate	Cost
Coal	Yes	Fossil	High SO_2	Low
Oil	Yes	Fossil	Medium	High
Natural gas	Yes	Fossil	Low	Medium
Wood	Yes	Renewable	High	Low
Bottled gas and paraffin	Yes	Fossil	Low	High

Industrial fuels

Fuels used by industry include fuels which could not be used in homes. For example, sulphur may be burned as a cheap source of energy. The highly polluting sulphur dioxide that is formed in nearly 100% yields is converted to sulphuric acid—a valuable by-product with a ready market! The initial cost of the acid plant must be met, but the use can be economically advantageous if much energy is used.

Ethanol is not exploited as a fuel in many countries. It could be used instead of fuel oil but it cannot be supplied in such large quantities to compete.

Motor vehicle fuels of the future?

Here we have little choice as yet. Although there are about a million vehicles worldwide running on methane, and many more using mixtures of petrol and ethanol, the chief fuel is petrol or diesel. These are liquids with high energy-densities.

The energy per gram for petrol is higher than any fuel except liquid methane. To replace petrol would require the development of high energy-density fuels with the same ease of use as petrol. Among the suggested alternatives are liquid methane (bp −160 °C) and hydrogen (bp −253 °C). Both are gases at normal temperatures but would have to be much compressed or liquefied for storage in fuel tanks on vehicles. Methane is stored as a refrigerated liquid and some success has been achieved in its use. Hydrogen can only be stored in a combined form as a hydride of, for example, magnesium or nickel. Unfortunately, the storage tanks must be strong and are therefore very heavy to avoid exploding. The situation may improve with development of electric vehicles, but electricity is not itself a fuel and is mostly produced by burning fossil fuels.

All organic fuels can be explosive when mixed with air. If fuel tanks leak, methane and hydrogen will rapidly diffuse into the air whereas petrol vapour is denser than air and hangs around the vehicle. Thus, the gases may be safer although more explosive!

Pollution from fuel burning

All fossil fuels produce carbon dioxide, a 'greenhouse gas'. They will also produce some carbon monoxide and carbon if burned inefficiently. Within a very short time, carbon monoxide is converted to carbon dioxide in the atmosphere and in the soil. Coal, in addition, contains sulphur compounds and these give sulphur dioxide, which causes acid-rain. Petrol, diesel, natural gas and bottled gas are all relatively free from sulphur compounds. All high-temperature combustion using air for combustion produces nitrogen oxides. This is because nitrogen and oxygen will combine together at high temperature in the combustion chambers of cars or the furnaces of industry.

Reducing pollution from fuel burning

The catalytic converter effectively reduces emissions of oxides of nitrogen and carbon monoxide. Sulphur dioxide from power stations can be reduced by fitting desulphurizing plant which removes the pollutant in an alkaline scrubbing process. Benzene pollution from unleaded petrol is likely to be reduced by finding a substitute additive.

The properties and uses of polymers

Because polymers are very large molecules, their structures can be complicated. They are made up of many (sometimes thousands of) small molecules joined together in a 'chain'. The small molecules making up the chain are called **monomers**. The chain is called the **polymer**. The chemical reaction in which monomers combine to form a polymer is called **polymerization**.

Some natural polymers decompose on heating, others soften and become pliable. Polymers which soften on heating are said to be **thermosoftening** or **thermoplastic**. Tortoise shell is one such natural polymeric material that was once used to make shaped objects, such as ladies' hair-brushes.

Thermosoftening plastics—thermoplastics

Thermoplasticity is a property of most synthetic plastics. Those in common use are nylon, polythene, PVC, polystyrene, Terylene and Perspex. These plastics can be heated to soften them and then shaped into everyday articles. Table 7.8 gives some examples.

Table 7.8

Thermoplastic	Finished article
PVC	Bottles and other containers
Polythene	Sheet, film and tubing/piping
Perspex	Baths and record player covers

A glance at Table 7.8 will show how the uses of many plastics are related to their ability to be easily shaped by heat.

Thermosetting plastics—thermosets

Thermosets cannot be melted once they have been formed. This makes them resistant to softening when heated. Examples include Bakelite, melamine and Araldite resin.

They find uses in making heat-proof containers and surfaces (melamine), electrical fittings and pan handles (Bakelite). Araldite resin is a strong, heat-resistant adhesive.

Fig. 7.12 Monomers, polymers and their uses

Monomer	Polymer	Properties	Uses
H H C=C H H Ethene	[H H —C—C— H H]$_n$ Poly(ethene)	'Polythene'. Cheap, strong, resists food, acids, and solvents. Waterproof. No need for plasticizer	Film and bags. Containers, water pipes, kitchenware. Food wrapping.
H H C=C H Cl Chloroethene	[H H —C—C— H Cl]$_n$ Poly(chloroethene)	'PVC'. Tough, strong, rubbery and very flexible when plasticized. Flame resistant. Electrical insulator. Resists solvents.	Raincoats, wellingtons, artificial leather, electrical wire insulation.
H H C=C H C_6H_5 Phenylethene	[H H —C—C— H C_6H_5]$_n$ Poly(phenylethene)	'Polystyrene'. Strong, flexible, but brittle. Retains strength when cold. Easily worked with hand tools.	Food containers, toys and 'fridge parts. Foam is used for heat insulation and packing.
H H C=C H CH_3 Propene	[H H —C—C— H CH_3]$_n$ Poly(propene)	Harder, more rigid than polythene. Higher softening temperature (>100°C).	Moulded furniture, carpet fibre, ropes.
F F C=C F F Tetrafluoro-ethene	[F F —C—C— F F]$_n$ Poly(tetra-fluoroethene)	'PTFE'. Unaffected by everyday chemicals. Non-stick, low friction. Heat-and solvent-resistant.	Non-stick pans. Acid-resistant containers in chemical plant.

Fig. 7.13

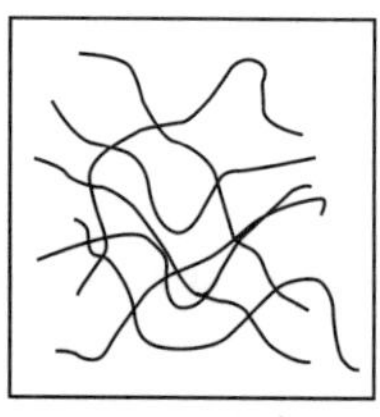

Fig. 7.14

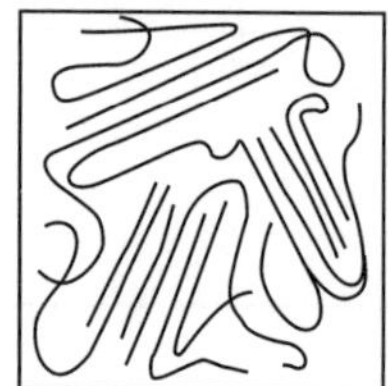

Fig. 7.15

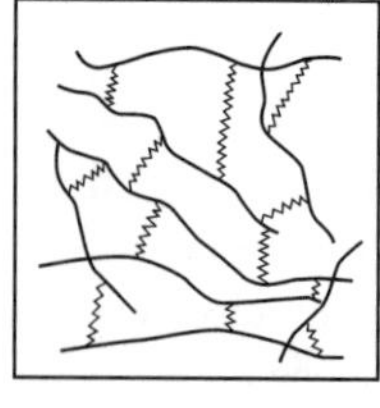

The different properties of the two types of plastic discussed above are related to their structures. Thermoplastics, such as polythene, are composed of long polymer molecules in a state of constant motion. These molecules vibrate, rotate and generally become entangled with each other. The entangled molecules are attracted to each other by weak forces which increase as the molecules come closer together (Fig. 7.13).

Warming increases the motion of the polymers, increasing the distance between them and reducing the forces of attraction. The mass then changes shape more easily when force is applied. Cooling reverses this series of changes.

Polythene behaves in this way. There are, however, two types of polythene, high- and low-density. They differ, as would be expected from their names, on the closeness of packing of their molecules.

In high-density polythene (HDP) the molecules are much closer together, lying parallel to each other for much of their length, and so attractive forces between them are greater. HDP is more rigid, stronger and has a higher softening temperature than low-density polythene (LDP) (Fig. 7.14).

HD polythene is used instead of LD polythene where increased wear and tear is expected, e.g. polythene buckets, or where extra rigidity is required as in large containers, or where a higher softening temperature is vital as in sterilizable vessels.

Thermosets are quite different. In effect a single molecule is built up from polymer molecules by a 'cross-linking' process which chemically links them together. The polymer is rigid and, since warming cannot cause increased motion of the interconnected chains, will not soften at higher temperatures (Fig. 7.15).

Table 7.9 Plastics consumption

Packaging	36%
Building	20%
Electrical	10%
Transport	5%
Furniture	5%
Toys/leisure	5%
Others	19%

Thermosets such as Bakelite have been used for decades to meet electrical fittings which might become hot in use. (See Table 7.9.)

Advantages of plastics

The greatest advantage of plastics is their wide range of desirable properties. They can be literally 'tailor-made' to suit the product. Many of these properties are shown in Fig. 7.12. Such properties allow a wide range of applications.

A summary of the most important properties of plastics:

- cheap and easy to make into intricate shapes
- lightweight
- uncorrodable
- easily self-coloured
- resistant to decay and chemical attack
- tough and waterproof

Write down a few everyday uses of plastics for each of the properties listed. Can you think of other properties not listed?

Disadvantages of plastics

Fire risk

Plastics are polymers of substances obtained from crude oil. It is not surprising, then, that many plastics are flammable. The ease with which a plastic will burn is a constant hazard to be guarded against wherever plastics are in use.

Plastics used in the manufacture of furniture are responsible for many of the deaths in housefires each year. Toxic gases are produced when plastics burn in inadequate supplies of air, such as you would expect in closed rooms, and death from poisoning often occurs before the fire reaches the inhabitants.

Plastics used in furniture also emit smoke. A sensible precaution against poisoning by combustion gases would be the installation of smoke alarms in every household. These would give a warning before flames had taken a hold.

Pollution problems

The most useful properties of polymers are their strength, resistance to corrosion, water resistance and resistance to bacterial decay. These properties, however, are not enough to ensure that plastic objects will remain *usable for ever*. Synthetic fabrics wear, nylon gears break, polythene basins become scratched and may split. When the time comes to dispose of our polymer waste these *same properties become disadvantages*.

One 'problem' of disposing of plastic waste is that it will not rot away if dumped on refuse tips or buried. This problem is not limited to plastics, since concrete, brick and many metals are also resistant to decay, but we do not grumble as much about these materials. So why is there a problem with plastics?

Chiefly, it is that plastic waste is often light and easily blown about, spreading around the environment—like paper, but much more permanent. Carelessly disposed plastic waste quickly becomes a **permanent eyesore** in the environment.

The *proposed* solution to this problem is to develop plastics which can be decomposed by bacteria in the same way that paper and vegetable matter are. This solution, namely **biodegradable** plastics, as they are called, is becoming more widely available.

The development of biodegradable plastics would be a big step in reducing the effect of careless disposal of unsightly plastic waste in rural areas. *Collected waste* would be *more usefully* recycled or used as an energy source.

Vegetable oils

Vegetable oils are complex esters formed from long-chained, unsaturated carboxylic acids. If these fatty acid monomers contain more than one carbon—carbon double bond they are polyunsaturates. They can each contain up to three such double bonds. The presence of unsaturated fatty acid parts in the oil lowers the melting point and ensures that oils are liquids at room temperature. Complete saturation of these oils using hydrogen gas to saturate the carbon—carbon double bonds results in a fat which is solid at room temperature. Partial hydrogenation gives soft fat/oil mixtures which are known as margarines or soft fat spreads.

Soaps

Soaps are sodium or potassium salts of long-chain fatty acids such as stearic acid ($C_{17}H_{35}CO_2H$) and/or octadecanoic acid.

Preparation of a simple soap

Saponification is easily carried out as follows. Mix 2 cm^3 of a vegetable oil such as castor oil with about 10 cm^3 of 5 mol dm^{-3} sodium hydroxide solution in an evaporating basin. Warm the mixture, with constant stirring, for 15 minutes. During this time the oil will have been hydrolysed to its component fatty acids and glycerine. At this stage the soap is still mainly dissolved in the solution and must be precipitated. The addition of 10 cm^3 of saturated sodium chloride solution, with stirring, will cause the solid soap to separate out as a crust on the mixture. The product is filtered off and washed free from alkali with distilled water.

The active particle in soaps is the **ion** (see Fig. 7.16).

Fig. 7.16

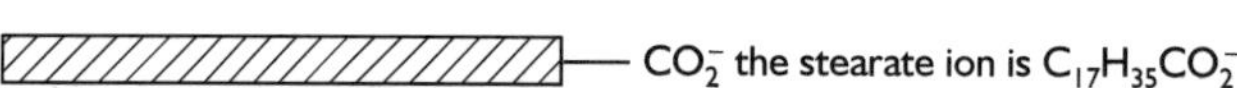

Sodium ions are ‘spectator ions’ in the activity of soaps. The complicated stearate ion (octadecanoate ion) is often more simply represented as in Fig. 7.17. It has a water-loving ‘head’, a carboxylate group CO_2^-. The ‘tail’ is a hydrocarbon chain $C_{17}H_{35}^+$ which is grease/oil-loving.

Fig. 7.17

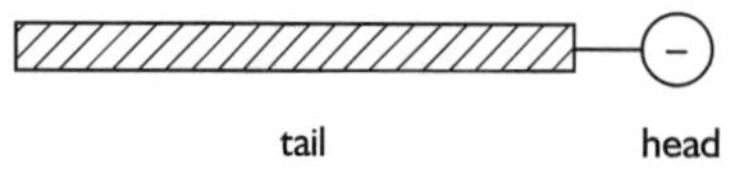

Soaps and detergents have the ability to reduce the surface tension of water and so to ‘wet’ surfaces and fabrics, that normally shed water.

EXAMINATION QUESTIONS

Question 1 (F)

The gas which is used for gas fires and bunsen burners consists mainly of methane. When it is burned in a bunsen burner which gives a good supply of air, carbon dioxide and steam are formed.

(a) Complete the equation for this reaction:

methane + oxygen → *[2]*

(b) Give the name and formula of another compound which might be formed if methane is burnt in a limited supply of air.

Name: ______________________

Formula: ______________________ [2]

The apparatus shown below was used to identify the substances formed when methane burns.

Fig. 7.18

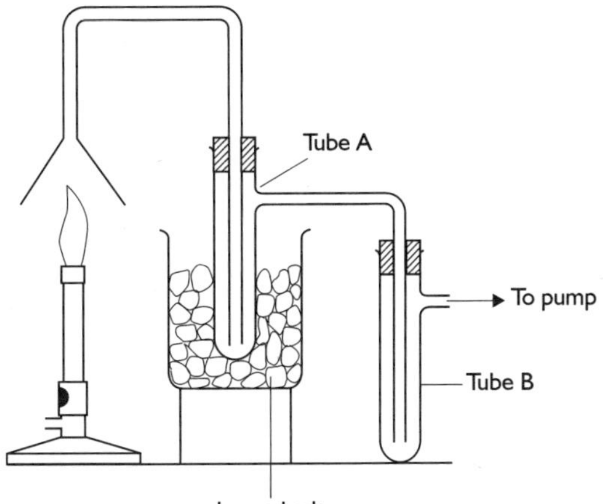

(c) A colourless liquid collected in tube A. How could you test it to show it contains water?

Test: ______________________

Result: ______________________ [2]

(d) What liquid could be placed in tube B to detect carbon dioxide?

Liquid: ______________________

Result if CO_2 present: ______________________ [2]

Question 2 (F)

(a) Explain how crude oil was formed. [3]
(b) How is crude oil extracted from the ground? [1]
(c) Explain how fractional distillation can be used to separate compounds in crude oil. [2]
(d) Explain what is meant by *cracking*. [1]
(e) Ethene can be made into poly(ethene).
  (i) Name the process by which poly(ethene) is made. [1]
  (ii) What is the main difference between a molecule of ethene and a molecule of poly(ethene)? [1]
  (iii) Explain why poly(ethene) is a good material to make into carrier bags. [1]
(f) Over twenty years ago, carrier bags were made out of paper. Today they are made out of plastics. Why do carrier bags cause a problem today, but did not cause a problem twenty years ago? [2]

Question 3 (F)

(a) (i) What type of hydrocarbons have the general formula C_nH_{2n}? [1]
  (ii) Name a hydrocarbon that has the formula C_nH_{2n}. [1]
  (iii) What is a hydrocarbon? [1]
(b) (i) Name the compounds formed when hydrocarbons burn in an excess of air. [2]
  (ii) Name the poisonous compound formed when hydrocarbons burn in a limited supply of oxygen. [1]

Question 4 (F) Sugar can be fermented to make ethanol under *anaerobic* conditions.

(a) What is meant by the word '*anaerobic*'? *[2]*
(b) Name the gas given off during fermentation, and how would you test for the presence of this gas? *[2]*
(c) (i) Name the catalyst used in fermentation. *[1]*
(ii) What is the best temperature for fermentation to take place? *[1]*
(d) How can you tell when fermentation has finished? *[1]*
(e) Give one use for ethanol (other than its use in alcoholic drinks). *[1]*
(f) Some beer will taste very sour because the ethanol has reacted with the air to form an acid.
(i) What gas in the air has reacted with the ethanol? *[1]*
(ii) How would you show that the beer contained an acid? *[1]*

Question 5 (F) Crude oil can be separated using the apparatus shown in the diagram (Fig. 7.19). The fractions are collected over various temperature ranges.

Fig. 7.19

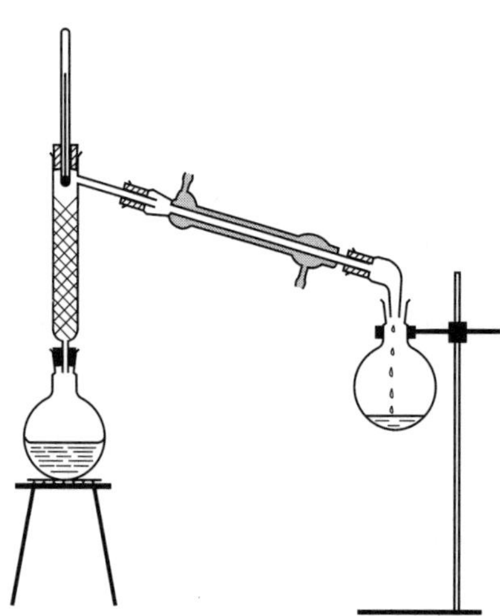

(a) What is the name of this method of separating crude oil? *[1]*
(b) Why is the thermometer bulb level with the column outlet and not in the crude oil? *[1]*

Table 7.10 shows some of the properties of the various fractions.

Table 7.10

Fraction	Temperature range	Mobile or viscous	Type of flame
A	up to 65 °C	Very mobile	Clear flame—no smoke
B	65–175 °C	Mobile	Slightly smoky
C	175–275 °C	Viscous	Smoky

(c) How would you prove that fraction C was a mixture and not a compound? *[2]*
(d) Suggest a use for fraction A. *[1]*

Fraction D was collected between 275 °C and 400 °C.

(e) Describe fraction D using the headings in the table. *[3]*
(f) Name the process by which the compounds in fraction C could be broken down into smaller molecules. *[1]*

Question 6 (H)

Look at the list below (Fig. 7.20), which shows the structural formula of six different organic compounds.

Fig. 7.20

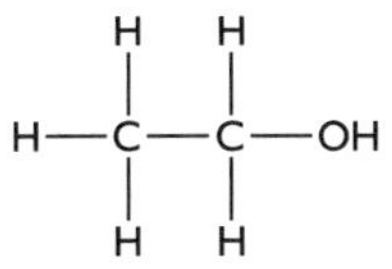

A

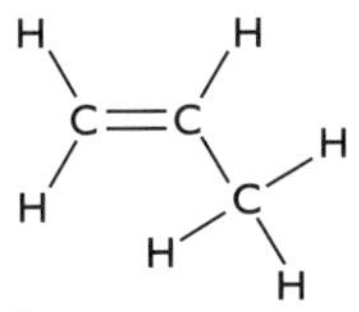

B

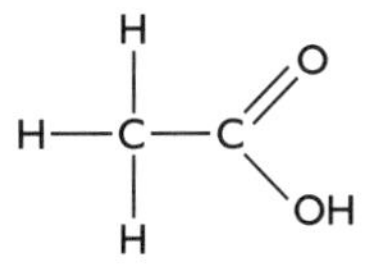

C

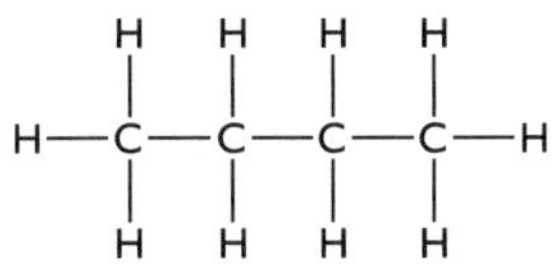

D

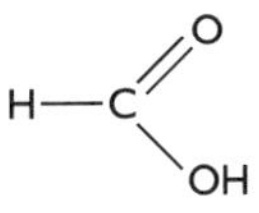

E

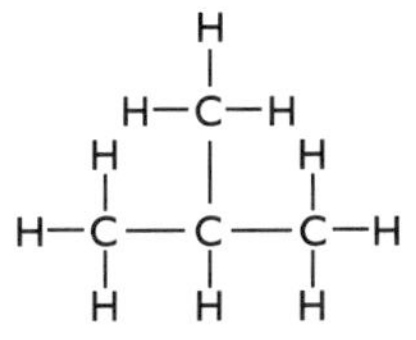

F

Choose the substance, A, B, C, D, E or F from the list to answer the following questions.

(a) Give one example of a compound that is an alkane. *[1]*
(b) Which substance is ethanoic acid? *[1]*
(c) Which two substance are in the same homologous series? *[1]*
(d) Which two substances are isomers? *[1]*
(e) Which two substances react together to give an ester? *[1]*
(f) Which substance will polymerize? Name the polymer. *[2]*
(g) What substance is formed when compound A is dehydrated? *[1]*

Question 7 (H)

Table 7.11 shows the names and formulae of various monomers, and the names, formulae and uses of the corresponding polymers.

(a) Complete the table by identifying A, B, C and D. *[4]*
(b) In which group of the periodic table are fluorine and chlorine? *[1]*
(c) Name one polymer from the table below that is a hydrocarbon. *[1]*

Table 7.11

Monomer	Structural formula	Polymer	Structural formula	Use of polymer
Ethene	A	Poly(ethene)	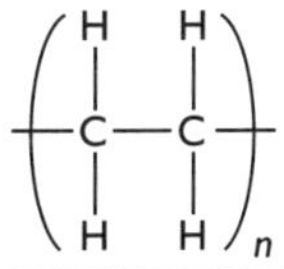 $\left(-\underset{H}{\overset{H}{C}}-\underset{H}{\overset{H}{C}}- \right)_n$	Plastic bags
Propene	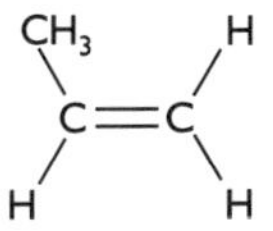 CH_3, H, H, H around C=C	B	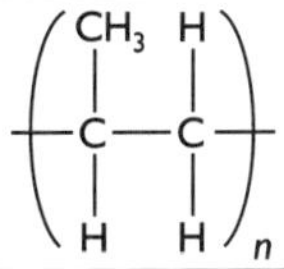 $\left(-\underset{H}{\overset{CH_3}{C}}-\underset{H}{\overset{H}{C}}- \right)_n$	Plastic bowls
Chloroethene	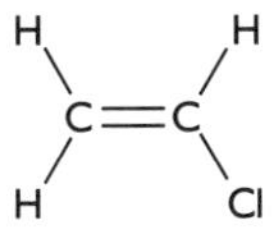 H, H, H, Cl around C=C	Poly(chloroethene)	C	PVC raincoats
Tetrafluoroethene	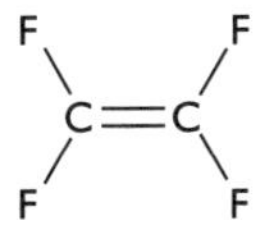 F, F, F, F around C=C	Poly(tetrafluoroethene)	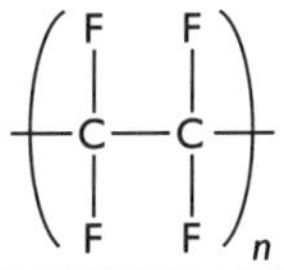 $\left(-\underset{F}{\overset{F}{C}}-\underset{F}{\overset{F}{C}}- \right)_n$	D

(d) What do all the monomers have in common that enables them to polymerize? [1]

(e) Write down

(i) the molecular formula of propene; [1]

(ii) the empirical formula of propene. [1]

Question 8 (H)

Table 7.12

Compound	Formula	Boiling point
A	CH_4	−162 °C
B	C_2H_6	−89 °C
C	C_3H_6	−48 °C
D	C_3H_8	−42 °C
E	C_4H_{10}	
F	C_5H_{12}	+25 °C

(a) Five of the six hydrocarbons listed above belong to the homologous series called alkanes.

(i) Which hydrocarbon listed does *not* belong to the alkanes? [1]

(ii) Is compound F a solid, a liquid or a gas at 35 °C? [1]

(iii) By studying the table, predict the boiling point of compound E. [1]

(iv) Which *one* of the hydrocarbons is the main compound in natural gas? [1]

(b) Hydrocarbon B is said to be saturated and has the structural formula

Fig. 7.21

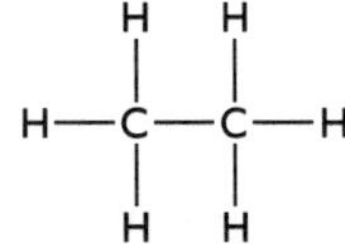

State what would happen if this compound was bubbled into bromine. [1]

Question 9 (H)

It was found that a hydrocarbon contained 80 per cent of carbon by mass.

(a) (i) Calculate the percentage of hydrogen in the hydrocarbon. [1]

(ii) Calculate the number of moles of carbon atoms and hydrogen atoms in 100 grams of the hydrocarbon. [2]

(iii) Find the empirical formula of the hydrocarbon. [2]

(iv) The mass of one mole of the hydrocarbon is 30 grams. What is the molecular formula of the hydrocarbon? [2]

(b) (i) Is the hydrocarbon an alkane or an alkene? Explain how you decided on your answer. [1]

(ii) Describe a chemical test that you would carry out, and the expected result of the test to confirm your answer to (b)(i). [2]

Question 10 (H)

The general formula for the alkene series of hydrocarbons is C_nH_{2n}. Ethene, C_2H_4, is the first member.

(a) (i) Work out the molecular formula of the fifth member, hexene. [1]

(ii) Ethene may be prepared by passing ethanol vapour over a heated aluminium oxide catalyst. Sketch an apparatus which you might use to carry out this reaction, showing how you would collect the ethene. [4]

(iii) What would you do when using the apparatus shown in your answer to part (ii) to make sure that the ethene collected was reasonably free of air? [1]

(iv) Write an equation for the reaction in (ii). [1]

(b) An organic compound X undergoes the following reactions.
   (i) It burns completely in oxygen forming carbon dioxide and water only.
   (ii) It rapidly decolorizes bromine water.
   (iii) It reacts with sodium carbonate solution to give carbon dioxide.

State as fully as possible what you can deduce about the structure of compound X from each reaction. [6]

OUTLINE ANSWERS

Question 1

(a) Carbon dioxide and water.
(b) Carbon monoxide, CO.
(c) Add anhydrous copper(II) sulphate; colour changes from white to blue.
(d) Lime-water; gives a white precipitate.

Question 2

(a) From remains of plants and animals that lived under the sea many millions of years ago, under high pressures and temperature.
(b) By drilling.
(c) Crude oil is heated; different compounds boil at different temperatures.
(d) The breaking down of larger molecules into smaller molecules.
(e) (i) Polymerization.
   (ii) Ethene is unsaturated but poly(ethene) is saturated.
   (iii) Strong/does not tear.
(f) Poly(ethene) is very stable and does not react with air or water (it is *not* biodegradable); paper rapidly decomposes in the atmosphere.

Question 3

(a) (i) Alkenes.
   (ii) Ethene, a compound containing hydrogen and carbon *only*.
(b) (i) Carbon dioxide and water.
   (ii) Carbon monoxide.

Question 4

(a) In the absence of air.
(b) Carbon dioxide; gives a white precipitate with lime-water.
(c) (i) Yeast.
   (ii) Any figure between 35 °C and 45 °C.
(d) No more carbon dioxide is given off.
(e) Solvent for perfumes.
(f) (i) Oxygen.
   (ii) Add pH paper; pH less than 7.

Question 5

(a) Fractional distillation.
(b) It will measure the temperature of the boiling point of the fraction being collected (not the boiling point of the mixture in the flask).
(c) Fractionally distil again, it can be separated into further fractions.
(d) Fuel.
(e) Temperature range 275–350 °C or above; very viscous; will burn with a very smoky flame.
(f) Cracking.

Question 6

(a) D or F; (b) C; (c) C and E; (d) D and F; (e) A and C or E; (f) B, propene, poly(propene); (g) ethene.

Question 7 (a) A, $H_2C{=}CH_2$; B, poly(propene); C, $\text{+}CH_2{-}CHCl\text{+}_n$; D, non-stick pans.

(b) Group 7 or the halogens.
(c) Poly(ethene) or poly(propene).
(d) They are unsaturated.
(e) (i) C_3H_6; (ii) CH_2.

Question 8 (a) (i) C.
(ii) Liquid; boiling point below 25 °C.
(iii) between +10 °C and −10 °C (it is in fact −0.5 °C).
(iv) A (methane).
(b) No change (only unsaturated hydrocarbons decolorize bromine water).

Question 9 (a) (i) 20 per cent.
(ii) Moles of carbon atoms = 80/12 = 6.67 and moles of hydrogen = 20/1 = 20.
(iii) Ratio of above is 1 : 3, empirical formula is CH_3.
(iv) $n(CH_3) = 30$; $15n = 30$; hence n is 2 and the formula is C_2H_6.
(b) (i) It is an alkane; it fits the formula C_nH_{2n+2}.
(ii) Shake the gas with bromine water; if it is decolorized it is an alkene; if it is not decolorized it is an alkane.

Question 10 (a) (i) C_6H_{12} (note the first member is C_2H_4 because CH_2 does not exist).

Fig. 7.22

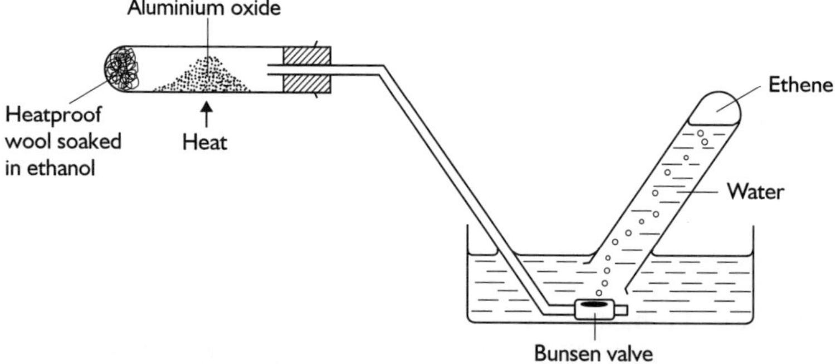

(ii) See Fig. 7.22.
(iii) Discard the first few test tubes of gas until all the air has been removed from the apparatus.
(iv) $C_2H_5OH(l) \rightarrow C_2H_4(g) + H_2O(g)$.
(b) It contains carbon, and hydrogen and possibly oxygen; it is unsaturated; it is acidic. Hence X must be an unsaturated organic acid.

STUDENT ANSWER WITH EXAMINER'S COMMENTS

This question is about the formation of alcohol (ethanol) from sugars and its possible use as an alternative to petrol as a fuel for car engines.

One source of sugars is sugar cane, which is crushed and the juices mixed with yeast. The mixture is allowed to stand for two to three days at around 30 °C.

The liquid product is then fractionally distilled, most of the ethanol being in the middle of the three fractions.

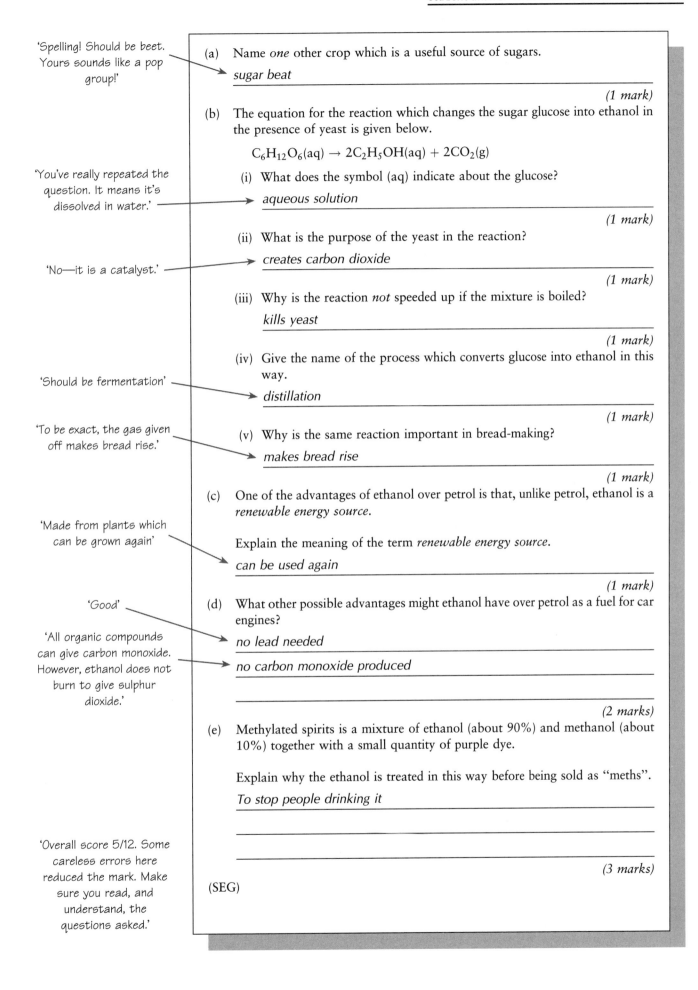

'Spelling! Should be beet. Yours sounds like a pop group!'

(a) Name *one* other crop which is a useful source of sugars.

sugar beat

(1 mark)

(b) The equation for the reaction which changes the sugar glucose into ethanol in the presence of yeast is given below.

$$C_6H_{12}O_6(aq) \rightarrow 2C_2H_5OH(aq) + 2CO_2(g)$$

'You've really repeated the question. It means it's dissolved in water.'

(i) What does the symbol (aq) indicate about the glucose?

aqueous solution

(1 mark)

'No—it is a catalyst.'

(ii) What is the purpose of the yeast in the reaction?

creates carbon dioxide

(1 mark)

(iii) Why is the reaction *not* speeded up if the mixture is boiled?

kills yeast

(1 mark)

'Should be fermentation'

(iv) Give the name of the process which converts glucose into ethanol in this way.

distillation

(1 mark)

'To be exact, the gas given off makes bread rise.'

(v) Why is the same reaction important in bread-making?

makes bread rise

(1 mark)

(c) One of the advantages of ethanol over petrol is that, unlike petrol, ethanol is a *renewable energy source.*

'Made from plants which can be grown again'

Explain the meaning of the term *renewable energy source.*

can be used again

(1 mark)

(d) What other possible advantages might ethanol have over petrol as a fuel for car engines?

'Good'

no lead needed

'All organic compounds can give carbon monoxide. However, ethanol does not burn to give sulphur dioxide.'

no carbon monoxide produced

(2 marks)

(e) Methylated spirits is a mixture of ethanol (about 90%) and methanol (about 10%) together with a small quantity of purple dye.

Explain why the ethanol is treated in this way before being sold as "meths".

To stop people drinking it

(3 marks)

(SEG)

'Overall score 5/12. Some careless errors here reduced the mark. Make sure you read, and understand, the questions asked.'

SUMMARY

Use this list to help with your revision. Tick off points as you learn them.

- ▷ Fossil fuels include coal, peat, lignite, petroleum and natural gas.
- ▷ Coal, peat and lignite originated from the remains of trees and plants.
- ▷ Petroleum and natural gas are believed to have originated from the remains of animals and plants that lived in the sea.
- ▷ Hydrocarbons are compounds of carbon and hydrogen only.
- ▷ Natural gas is methane.
- ▷ Crude oil can be separated into various fractions by fractional distillation.
- ▷ A fraction is a mixture of hydrocarbons with similar boiling points.
- ▷ An homologous series consists of a series of compounds that
    - ▷ can be represented by a general formula;
    - ▷ have similar chemical properties;
    - ▷ are made by similar reactions;
    - ▷ show regular change in their physical properties.
- ▷ Alkanes have the general formula C_nH_{2n+2}. The first six members of the series are methane, ethane, propane, butane, pentane and hexane.
- ▷ Hydrocarbons are saturated and therefore unreactive; they are mainly used as fuels.
- ▷ Saturated hydrocarbons contain no double bonds.
- ▷ In a limited supply of air, hydrocarbons burn to form the poisonous gas carbon monoxide.
- ▷ Alkenes have the general formula C_nH_{2n}. The first five members are ethene, propene, butene, pentene and hexene.
- ▷ Alkenes are unsaturated and therefore very reactive.
- ▷ Unsaturated compounds contain double bonds between carbon atoms.
- ▷ Bromine water can be used to distinguish between an alkane and an alkene—an alkene decolorizes bromine water.
- ▷ Isomers are compounds with the same molecular formula but different structural formula.
- ▷ An addition reaction is a reaction in which two or more molecules react together to form one molecule only.
- ▷ A polymer is a long-chain molecule formed by the joining together of many very small molecules called monomers.
- ▷ Poly(ethene), poly(propene), poly(styrene) and poly(vinyl chloride) are examples of polymers.
- ▷ Cracking is the process of breaking large molecules of hydrocarbons into smaller hydrocarbon molecules.
- ▷ Alcohols have the general formula $C_nH_{2n+1}OH$. The functional group is $-OH$.
- ▷ Ethanol can be made by either a batch method (from sugars) or a continuous method from ethene.
- ▷ Carboxylic acids have the general formula $C_nH_{2n+1}CO_2H$. The functional group is $-CO_2H$.
- ▷ Carboxylic acids are typical weak acids.
- ▷ A fuel is any combustible material that burns; the properties, uses and costs of fuels depend on their origins.
- ▷ Thermosoftening plastics can be heated to soften them and then shaped.
- ▷ Thermosetting plastics cannot be melted once they have been shaped.
- ▷ Vegetable oils can be used to make margarine and soaps.

Chapter

8 Industrial chemistry—metals and other strong materials

GETTING STARTED

Metals and composite materials are extracted from **mineral resources** known as ores. An **ore** is a concentrated mineral from which a useful product can be extracted economically. Ore bodies are **rare** and difficult to find. It is not known whether new sources of scarce minerals will be discovered before **known reserves** run out. It has become necessary to use the resources we have more responsibly by **recycling** and **reusing** as many metals as possible.

The most commonly used metals are

- iron;
- aluminium; and
- copper.

Aluminium is the most abundant **metal** in the Earth's crust. However **iron**—and its alloys, the **steels**—are in commoner use because of the ease and cheapness of extraction of iron. **Copper** is expensive to produce but there are no cheap, effective substitutes for it in the electrical and plumbing industries. You will see, in this chapter, how the **properties** of metals and composites fit the tasks for which they are chosen.

TOPIC CHART

LONDON	MEG	NEAB	NICCEA	SEG	WJEC	TOPIC	STUDY	REVISION 1	REVISION 2
✓	✓	✓	✓	✓	✓	Sources of metals			
✓	✓	✓	✓	✓	✓	Uses of metals			
✓	✓	✓	✓	✓	✓	Structure and properties of metals			
✓	✓	✓	✓	✓	✓	Alloys			
	✓	✓	✓	✓		Other strong materials			
✓	✓	✓	✓	✓	✓	The extraction of metals			
✓	✓	✓	✓	✓	✓	The abundance of metal resources			
✓	✓	✓	✓	✓	✓	Aluminium extraction			
✓	✓	✓	✓	✓	✓	Iron extraction and steelmaking			
✓	✓	✓	✓	✓	✓	Copper purification			

WHAT YOU NEED TO KNOW

Sources of metals

There are two sources of metals in everyday use:

- **mineral ores**—concentrated minerals that are economic to extract and process, e.g. iron ore;
- **used metals** that can be melted down and reused, e.g. aluminium drink-cans and lead plates for car batteries.

Metal ores most commonly found are **oxides** and **sulphides.**

- Sulphides were formed in those past ages of the Earth's evolution when sulphur was abundant from volcanic activity.
- Oxides formed later when oxygen began to be produced by the first photosynthesizing organisms.

Sulphides are easily converted to oxides by roasting the ore in a good supply of air. The oxide formed is more convenient to reduce with carbon.

- The sulphur from these ores forms highly polluting **sulphur dioxide** in the roasting process. This gas is always converted to sulphuric acid **on site.**
- Sulphuric acid is a valuable and industrially useful **by-product** of sulphide ore treatment.

Ores must be dug out of the ground by either opencast or deep mine methods.

- Opencast mining is cheapest but leaves a large scar on the landscape. Operations to excavate coal and limestone leave huge holes or chop away parts of mountains.
- Deep mining is expensive but has less obvious environmental impact—subsidence sometimes occurs beneath deep mines and accidents are more common.
- Both methods involve massive transport facilities to transfer the ore to processing plants. This may have an additional environmental and social impact.

Recycling of metals is now common for iron and steel, aluminium, lead, copper and, of course, precious metals. Recycling saves much of the **energy** that has to be used to extract the ore and then to reduce the ore to a metal.

Recycling saves both energy and mineral resources

Some metals are so unreactive that they have never formed compounds with other elements in the Earth's crust even over the few billion years of their existence. Such metals are gold and platinum. Others, like silver and copper are found in compounds and also as free metal (called *native* metal). Metals more reactive than lead are never found in an unreacted state and must be extracted from their ores by **reduction.**

Uses of metals

Table 8.1 shows those common **characteristics** of metals that are used in the manufacture of everyday items of equipment and machinery.

Individual metals have characteristics of their own which make them more useful than other metals for a particular purpose. **Iron**, for instance, has the special property of being **easily magnetized; gold** has the rare property of **never corroding.** It would be pointless to try to make a magnet out of gold so that it would last forever, because gold will not magnetize! It would be equally pointless to make a wedding ring out of iron rather than gold just because iron is cheaper.

Structure and properties of metals

Metals (including alloys) are giant structures of atoms. Metallic structure has been described in Chapter 6.

The properties of metals that make them useful are described below. Although it is not always possible to select out those properties we do not want, we can enhance some and reduce others by **alloying.**

Table 8.1 Common characteristics of metals

Property	Use	Metal
Toughness	Equipment and machinery that will be knocked about with use—steel	Iron
Metallic sheen	Mirrors, reflectors	Aluminium, silver
Reflecting heat and light	Coating of firemen's protective clothing; Space Shuttle heat shield of gold foil	Aluminium, gold
Malleability	Easy shaping of metal structures by presses; also 'hand beating' of metals into shape—brass	Zinc, copper
Ductility	Wide variety of wires—electrical and ornamental	Copper, aluminium, gold
High melting point	Wires for electric fires; metals for boilers, cookers, pans; electric light filaments	Iron, aluminium, tungsten (m.p. about 3500 °C)
Good heat conductivity	Radiators in central heating systems; copper for cooking pans	Aluminium, iron, copper
Good electrical conductivity	Electrical wiring	Copper, aluminium
Corrosion resistance	Roofing, flashings; foil and food containers—soft drink and beer cans; zinc coating—'galvanized' steel	Lead, aluminium, iron, zinc
Low density	Aircraft construction; lightweight vehicles and wheels	Aluminium, magnesium

The component elements of the alloy must have similar structures. In alloys the alloying atoms

- take up spaces in the 'parent' metal structure, or
- replace atoms in the structure of the 'parent' metal.

The properties that arise from alloying are described later.

- **Tensile strength** is a measure of the pull required to stretch and break the material. It measures strength under tension—a stretching or pulling force—as on the wires supporting a lift. This term is often shortened simply to strength.
- **Compressive strength** is a measure of the strength under a compressing force, as when a concrete foundation supports the weight of a building.
- **Hardness** is a measure of the material's resistance to being deformed. It is usually measured by scratching or denting the material.
- **Tough materials** resist cracking and breaking on being struck. It is important not to confuse hardness with toughness. A diamond is hard but hit it with a hammer and it will shatter. Diamond is brittle, not tough. On the other hand mild steel is tough—it bends but does not crack or break when treated in this way.
- **Brittle** materials crack and break easily, e.g. glass. **Tough** materials do not snap or crack easily.
- **Ductile** materials are easily drawn into wire.
- **Malleable** materials are easily shaped by rolling or beating.
- **Hard** materials do not dent or scratch easily.

Alloys

Alloys are solid mixtures of metals with other elements—usually but not always other metals. A wider range of properties can be developed by alloying than would be found in pure metals. Table 8.2 lists the uses of alloys.

The hardening of gold by alloying it with copper illustrates a major change that occurs to metals when they are mixed with other metals. Copper is hardened by alloying with zinc (to make brass) or nickel (to make 'nickel silver' for silver coins). Alloying can also make metals easier to shape, mould or cast.

Alloying combines the **strength** required of nearly all metals used in construction with the **particular properties** of the main metal in the alloy, the so-called 'parent' metal.

Table 8.2 Uses of alloys

'Alloying can also be used to produce *coloured* metal as with *green* gold alloys and the gold coloured cupro-nickel alloy used to make one-pound coins.'

Alloy	Composition	Property	Uses
Brasses	Copper 66–70%, zinc 30–34%	Harder and cheaper than copper, resists corrosion	Ornaments, screws, rivets, cartridges, watertaps
Bronze	Copper 90%, tin 10%	Hard, strong, can be cast into intricate shapes, corrosion-resistant	Castings
Coinage bronze	Copper 95%, tin 3.5%, zinc 1.5%	Hard, strong and corrosion-resistant	Coinage, penny and twopenny pieces
Cupro-nickel	Copper 75%, nickel 25%	Strong, corrosion-resistant, easy to shape cold without annealing	'Silver' coins
Duralumin	Aluminium 95%, copper 4%, magnesium 1%	Higher strength/weight ratio than steel or aluminium, low density	Aircraft framework
Solder	Lead 67%, tin 33%	Low melting point, stronger than tin or lead	Joints in electrical work plumbing and tin-can making
Steel	Iron 99%, carbon 0–1%	Strong, cheap, easily shaped and welded	Bridges, ships, vehicles, rails, gears
Stainless steel	Iron 73%, chromium 18%, nickel 8%, carbon 1%	Very resistant to rusting, strong and hard wearing	Cutlery, kitchen utensils, chemical plant
Type metal	Lead 74%, antimony 16%, tin 10%	Easily cast but hardened by the antimony to keep its shape in use	Printer's type
Titanium alloys	e.g. titanium 90%, aluminium 6%, vanadium 4%	Light, hard, corrosion-resistance to seawater and oxygen	Aircraft, marine components, chemical plant

Newer alloys

The metals and alloys described above have been in use for a long time—some of them for thousands of years. Since metallurgists began to understand why alloying changed the properties of metals, they have sought to 'tailor' alloys for particular purposes. The number of alloys in use increases yearly.

The use of the very strong, light and corrosion-resistant metal **titanium** in alloys for making gas turbine engines for aircraft and hip replacement parts is an example of the discovery of newer useful alloys.

Steels

Carbon steels are the commonest alloys in use. There are several types in common use (see Table 8.3).

Heat treatment of metals—especially steels

The rate of cooling of metals from the molten state controls the grain size and hence the properties of the solid metal. The smaller the grain size the harder the metal.

Different crystalline forms of metals have different properties. If a 'high-temperature' form has desirable properties the hot metal must be cooled very quickly to room temperature to retain the structure and properties. This is done by **quenching in cold water or oil. Quenching** and also **cold-working** of metals makes them stronger *and* harder. Cold-worked metals are said to be **work-hardened.** Hard metals can, however, be too brittle for use and must be softened. There are two softening processes:

Table 8.3 Common steels and their properties

Type	Composition	Properties	
Mild steel	0.1%–0.25%	Becomes less ductile. Hardness increases. More brittle & difficult to shape ↓	Tensile strength increases ↓
Medium carbon	0.25%–0.5%		
High carbon	0.5%–1.5%		↑ Tensile strength decreases
Cast iron	> 2.5%	Very brittle, moderate strength and hardness	
Manganese steel	e.g. 86% iron, 13% manganese, 1% carbon	Intensely hard	Railway crossings and rock-breaking machinery

(i) **Annealing.** This involves heating the metal to a temperature below the melting point after working. It relieves stresses in the metal, making it less brittle (softer) but also reducing its strength. **Hot-working** allows stresses to be relieved at the same time so does not make the metal too hard as it gets stronger.

(ii) **Tempering.** This is carried out by heating the metal to a lower temperature than any previous heat treatment. Then the metal is allowed to cool **naturally**. It is intended to make steel tough and springy from being hard and brittle.

Other strong materials

The variety of engineering and building materials is greater than it has ever been. Materials which were non-existent only a short time ago are now in common use. The average car now has up to 40% plastic in its construction where forty years ago there was virtually none. Fishing rods and tennis racquets were once only made of wood and now use the most advanced composites. We shall find a continuing substitution of specially designed materials with 'tailor-made' structures and properties in place of the more traditional metals and wood. Some of these are discussed in this section.

Ceramics

The term means 'of pottery'. Pottery and glass are common ceramics. Ceramics are materials other than metals formed by heating at high temperatures during their fabrication. They are heat and chemical resistant.

Composites

Normally of strong but brittle material in a crack-stopping matrix. The choice of fibre affects the strength and stiffness of the composite; the matrix largely governs its chemical resistance and temperature stability. The matrix prevents brittle fracture of the fibres, so exploiting the best possible combination of properties of the composite structure. Ancient composites include 'wattle and daub' for house walls.

Examples of composites

- **Bone** is a composite of collagen fibres in a matrix which is mainly calcium phosphate. Calcium phosphate on its own is brittle. The collagen prevents brittle fracture. Bone will withstand pressures up to 2 tonnes per square inch. Spaces in bone ensure lightness; long bones are hollow for part of their length.
- **Carbon fibre** composites. Carbon fibres are even stronger than glass fibres. The composite contains carbon fibres in woven mat form in a resin matrix. Carbon is less dense than glass and so carbon fibre composites have greater strength *and* lower densities than glass-reinforced plastic (GRP).
- **Concrete** consists of various sizes of rock particles (called aggregate) set in a matrix of sand and cement. It is very strong in compression but weak in tension. If steel reinforcing rods are laid in concrete in the same way that glass and carbon fibre mats are used as described above, tensile strength is much increased. This gives **reinforced concrete** and **prestressed concrete.** In the latter, the steel wires are tensioned before being set in con-

crete. The tensioned steel holds the concrete in compression—where it has the greatest strength.

- **Glass fibre** composites are usually mats of woven glass laid parallel to each other in a resin matrix. Glass is strong but brittle. The matrix prevents surface cracks from reducing the fibre strength.
- **Wood** is a naturally occurring composite cellulosic fibre (on average about 70%) bonded together by lignin. Wood is attractive to look at and generally light, tough and flexible. It has good chemical resistance. Unfortunately, wood must be seasoned or it shrinks and distorts in use. As a natural material, its characteristics can vary from sample to sample. Table 8.4 summarizes the main properties of the materials discussed here.

Table 8.4 Properties of composite materials

Material	Structure	Properties	Examples and uses
Ceramics	Giant ionic structures	Strong, brittle, hard, temperature resistant chemically inert	Alumina (Al_2O_3) for bearings and abrasives. Aero engine parts, oven pottery, glass test tubes
Metals and alloys	Metallic structure Alloys are solid solutions	Malleable and ductile Tough and strong Some alloys very hard	Structural steels. Cutting and drilling metals. Sheet steel for car bodies. Wire and cable
Plastic-reinforced glass	Plastic sheet sandwiched between glass plates	Shatterproof	Car windscreens
Glass-reinforced plastic	Glass fibre in an acrylic or epoxy resins matrix	Stronger than steel but not as stiff. Resistant to water and chemicals	Canoes, boats, fishing rods, kitchen sinks, rooflights, shower cubicles
Carbon fibre	Carbon fibre in an epoxy resin matrix	Very strong and stiff. Chemical and water resistant. Expensive	Fishing rods, aeroplane and racing car bodies and seating
Reinforced concrete	Small stone pebbles in mortar matrix. Steel reinforcing wires	Strong in compression. Weak in tension unless reinforced. Cheap, high density	Foundations for buildings. If reinforced, bridge structures
Natural composites:			
Bone	Collagen fibres in an inorganic matrix of calcium phosphate	Twice the strength of mild steel—weight for weight	Animals—bony limbs. Prehistoric people used bone as cutting and piercing tools
Wood	Cellulose fibre in a lignin matrix	High strength to weight ratio. Flexible. Cheap	Building and carpentry. In the past boats and ships
Plastics	Long molecules tangled or cross-linked	Strength to weight ratio comparable with metals. Mouldable. Cheap	Common as cheap containers, plastic film, bags. Paints and glues

Property	Metals	Ceramics	Composites	Polymers
Density (water = 1)/g cm^{-3}	1–22	2–16	2–3	1–2
Melting point/°C	100–3500	2000–4000	100–200	70–200
Tensile strength*	100–2500	10–400	50–1400	30–300
Stiffness*	40–400	150–450	10–200	0.5–3.5
Heat conductivity	High	Medium	Low	Low
Electrical conductivity	High	Low	Low	Low

*Units omitted for simplicity. Strength and stiffness are compared by comparing the values.

The extraction of metals

Very few metals can be obtained from the ground as pure metals—called 'native' metal. Only the least reactive metals have been able to stand up to millions of years of exposure to oxygen, water, heat and pressure and remain uncombined.

Most metals over this period have combined to form oxides, carbonates, sulphides and chlorides. **The metals are present in these compounds as ions.**

When these compounds occur in the ground—usually mixed with more or less rocky substance—they are called 'ores'. Only a small number of metals can be extracted from their ores by heat alone—see p. 106.

To convert these compounds (the metal ions really) into metallic elements (metal atoms) requires a more reactive element to **reduce** them (see Chapter 17). It is **possible** to make any element from its ore by reduction with a more reactive element. In practice this will only be done if it is economic.

Metal extraction is a redox process

The metal ions present in minerals can be converted to metals by reduction. In the process the agent of this reduction is itself oxidized—the total process involves both reduction and oxidation (redox). For example:

- Iron oxide is reduced to iron metal by the action of carbon monoxide at high temperatures in a blast furnace. The reaction is

  $$Fe_2O_3(s) + 3CO(g) \rightarrow 2Fe(l) + 3CO_2(g)$$

- Iron ions in the oxide have been reduced to iron atoms in the metal. This could be written

  $$Fe^{3+}(s) + 3e^- \rightarrow Fe(l)$$

These two equations show that **removal of oxygen** and **addition of electrons** are two aspects of the same process—called reduction.

Metal ores are reduced to metals in all metal extraction processes

The choice of reduction method for metal extraction

The reactivity series, which is studied in Chapter 17, helps us to choose a reducing agent for any particular metal ore, see Table 8.5. The **electron** has been placed at the top of the table

Table 8.5 Reactivity series showing choice of reducing agents

Element	Reducing capability	Reducing agent used
ELECTRONS	Highest	
Potassium Lithium Sodium Calcium Magnesium Aluminium	↓	Only **electrolysis** is used to reduce ores of these elements to the free metal. **Carbon** has not sufficient reducing power to do this.
CARBON	↓	
Zinc Iron Tin Lead	↓	**Carbon** is used to reduce ores of all these elements to the free metal.
HYDROGEN	↓	
Copper Silver	↓	**Hydrogen** or **carbon** will reduce ores of these elements.
Gold Platinum	Lowest	Gold and platinum are found native—need no reduction.

because, in electrolysis, the electron is the reducing agent. The table is used in the following way:

- An element (or electrons = electricity) will reduce compounds of elements lower down than it in the table
- After choosing an element from the table to extract (from its ore), we select an **element above it** to be the reducing agent

Alternatively:

- Any chosen element (or electricity) will reduce compounds of elements below it.

We shall see these ideas in operation in what follows.

'Extractions and purification in all syllabuses'

All syllabuses require knowledge of the chemistry of the

- extraction of aluminium (electrolysis);
- extraction of iron (carbon reduction);
- purification of copper (electrolysis).

Carbon reduction

The reactivity series, as displayed in Table 8.5, shows that a non-metal, carbon, is a suitable reducing agent for obtaining many metals from their oxides. Carbon, in the form of coke, is cheap and abundant and very suitable for large-scale metal extraction, such as for iron, lead and zinc.

Electrolytic reduction

But what of those metals which are **more reactive** than carbon? Carbon will not reduce their oxides to metal.

For these metals **electrolysis** is the general method chosen. The process of **reduction occurs at the cathode** in electrolysis. In theory any metal can be made from its molten compounds by electrolysis. The cathode, as it were, is at the top of the reactivity series and its electrons will displace any metal from any metal compound that can be electrolysed!

Metals obtained in this way are the alkali metals, magnesium and aluminium—metals of groups 1, 2 and 3.

The electrolysis reactions occurring are given in detail in Chapter 10.

Methods which do not require an added reducing agent

The **least reactive** metals can be extracted without the use of any of the methods discussed above.

Mercury, found as the sulphide, is first roasted in air to convert it to its oxide. The oxide decomposes at 500 °C to the metal and oxygen:

$$2HgO(s) \rightarrow 2Hg(g) + O_2(g)$$

mercury oxide → mercury + oxygen

A similar reaction would convert silver oxide Ag_2O into silver. Try writing a balanced equation for this reaction.

Gold and platinum are not found as compounds but as pure metals—called **native metal.** They are mostly found as such fine particles that they have to be separated by dissolving and then extracted by electrolysis—in this case a **convenient** method for obtaining metals from solutions.

Taking it further

Metallurgical chemists can go even further in their use of the principles of the reactivity series to extract metals. They make use of other metals and, in one case, hydrogen to reduce metal compounds:

'This section is for background reading only'

Reduction using another metal

Titanium is produced by the reduction of its chloride using either sodium or magnesium (depending on the company of manufacture). This is called the Kroll process:

$$TiCl_4(l) + 4Na(l) \rightarrow Ti(s) + 4NaCl(s)$$

titanium chloride + sodium → titanium + sodium chloride,

or

$$TiCl_4(l) + 2Mg(l) \rightarrow Ti(s) + 2MgCl_2(l)$$

titanium chloride + magnesium → titanium + magnesium chloride.

Such a process must make the titanium more expensive than either sodium or magnesium. Look up the uses of titanium and it may be clear why such expense is justified.

Reduction using hydrogen

Hydrogen is used to reduce only one metal compound on a large scale—tungsten oxide:

$$WO_3(s) + 3H_2(g) \rightarrow W(s) + 3H_2O(g)$$

tungsten oxide + hydrogen → tungsten + water

The abundance of metal resources

Metals in history

We get clues about the reactivity of metals by a study of their use in the past. The earliest metals to be used were those which could be found pure in the ground—gold, silver and, in some parts of the world, copper.

The discovery and use of fire would eventually have resulted in the heating of rock mixtures on wood (charcoal) fires. Metals which can be extracted by low-temperature reduction with carbon include copper and tin. Since many ores occur **mixed**, these would produce mixed metals—the early alloys such as bronze.

Higher temperatures from the use of coal would allow the production of iron and zinc, but metals more reactive than these could not be produced by reduction with carbon and had to wait for the discovery of electricity.

Volta's discovery of the electric current in the early years of the nineteenth century led to the discovery of the more reactive metals. Group 1 and 2 metals could then be obtained by electrolysis of their **easily melted** compounds.

The extraction of aluminium proved difficult on a large scale until the discovery of a method of melting aluminium oxide by dissolving it in molten cryolite. The first large-scale production of aluminium was not until 1868! Since then, of course, metals which are even harder to extract from their ores have been obtained and are 'in service', e.g. titanium.

The reactivity series not only helps to explain why we find our metals combined in nature, but also helps us understand the difficulties in their extraction.

The **cost** of production of a metal depends on many factors, see Chapter 3. Some of these are:

- the abundance of its ore in the Earth's crust;
- the richness of the ore;
- the amount of energy used in its extraction;
- the amount of metal that can be recycled;
- labour costs.

The most commonly used metals are those with useful physical and chemical properties. They are either

- abundant, such as iron or aluminium;
- less abundant but cheap to produce, such as copper, zinc and lead;
- less abundant and expensive to produce, but have very important uses like manganese which is used in many steels.

The abundance of the most common metals in the Earth's crust is shown in Fig. 8.1. The figures are rounded up to the nearest whole number.

Fig. 8.1 Abundance of common elements in the Earth's crust

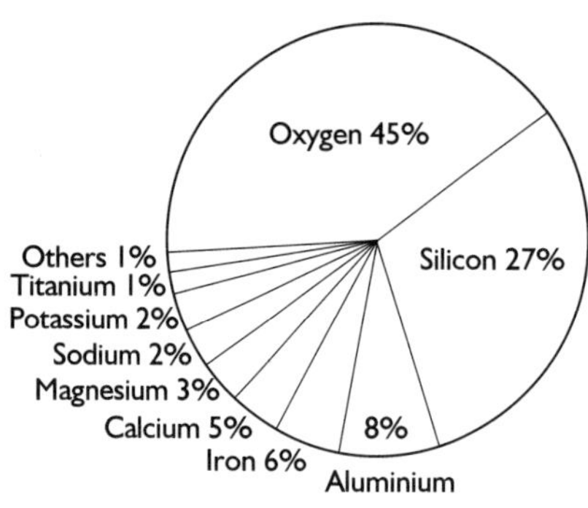

How long will our metal resources last?

Since cheap sources of energy, in the form of coal, became available to industry during the Industrial Revolution, ever-increasing quantities of metals have been extracted from their ores. The increasing pace of the use of the world's resources has resulted in a concern for the future of the supply of these minerals.

Some metals are so abundant that it is difficult to believe that they could ever 'run out'. Aluminium and iron are examples. Yet even these two metals can only be extracted from concentrated ores and the supply of these is not large. Without recycling or the discovery of alternative materials, the extraction of these two metals could become difficult within 500 years.

The situation is more serious for other metals. Known sources suggest the following 'lifetimes':

'These figures are a rough guide to the lifetime of metal ores. New sources are being found continually and any set of figures becomes quickly out of date'

copper	50 years
lead	20 years
zinc	20 years
tin	20 years
gold	20 years

One way of extending the use of scarce metals is by recycling. For example, a large proportion of lead in use is recycled, extending the lifetime of the resource considerably.

Recycling metals

'Over sixty per cent of steel, tin and lead, and over forty per cent of copper and aluminium, is recycled in the UK annually'

Recycling makes metals cheaper as well as making our resources last longer. The energy needed to extract a metal from its ores has already been paid for in its first use. Re-melting and refining scrap needs only a small fraction of the energy needed to extract the metal from its ore. Scrap metal recycling is widely used for iron, aluminium, lead, zinc and precious metals. Lead–acid batteries are a source of lead scrap, drink cans of aluminium, building scrap of lead and copper, old cars of scrap iron, and so on.

There are, of course, other costs of recycling. The collection, transport, separation and cleaning of the scrap all add to the cost of the re-processed product.

Siting a metal extraction plant

The choice of site depends upon similar factors to those discussed in Chapter 3.

For metals, the ores generally come from abroad.

- The siting of extraction plant close to deep-water ports reduces transport costs.
- If electricity is required, as in aluminium extraction, there must be a large power station nearby, supplying *cheap* electricity.
- If there are pollutant emissions, rarer now than in the past, the site must not be too close to a town or city and preferably downwind of it.
- A labour supply is required close by.
- The plant must not be built on valuable agricultural land. It is preferable to use reclaimed land.
- Transport of the product to places within and outside the area of the plant must be convenient.

Energy costs of metal production

Carbon offers the cheapest source of energy because of its abundance. **Electrolysis** is expensive and usually used only if no alternative method is available. The amount of electricity used depends upon

- the charge on the metal ion
- the temperature required for the electrolysis.

For example, to produce sodium (ions, Na^+) should require only one-third of the electricity required to produce an equal amount (in moles) of aluminium (ions Al^{3+}).

Aluminium extraction

Aluminium is the third most abundant element and **the** most abundant metal in the Earth's crust. Only one important ore is known—**bauxite**—which contains hydrated aluminium oxides, $Al_2O_3.H_2O$, with iron oxide as the main impurity.

Before use, bauxite is treated to remove iron oxide and water, both of which would interfere with the extraction process. Can you suggest how they would interfere? The purified product is dry alumina, Al_2O_3.

Like all the metals which are more reactive than zinc, aluminium is produced by electrolysis. However, the electrolyte in this case is the oxide of the metal **dissolved** in a molten salt.

The melting point of aluminium oxide is 2072 °C which is too high for practical use in electrolysis. The discovery that aluminium oxide could be electrolysed if **dissolved** in molten cryolite (sodium aluminium fluoride) at 970 °C made the electrolysis process possible.

The electrolysis cell consists of a steel container lined with carbon. The carbon lining acts as the cathode. The anodes are carbon rods which are suspended in the electrolyte. The anodes are consumed in the process. See also Tables 10.2 and 10.3.

The electrolyte is aluminium oxide (alumina) dissolved in molten cryolite. About 5% alumina in cryolite is used. The reactions occurring are

'Note the need to make the number of electrons involved in each electrode reaction equal.'

At the anode(+) $6O^{2-}(l) - 12e^- \rightarrow 3O_2(g)$

At the cathode(−) $4Al^{3+}(l) + 12e^- \rightarrow 4Al(l)$

The overall reaction is

$$2Al_2O_3(l) \rightarrow 4Al(l) + 3O_2(g).$$

- Molten aluminium forms at the bottom of the cell
- Oxygen is taken from the top of the cell.
- The carbon anodes are oxidized away slowly in the process:

$$2C(s) + O_2(g) \rightarrow 2CO(g)$$

carbon + oxygen → carbon monoxide

Aluminium of 99.9% purity is siphoned off daily. More alumina is added as it is decomposed (Fig. 8.2).

Cost of aluminium extraction

Aluminium is relatively expensive to extract from its ores because it requires the use of large amounts of electricity. Electricity is produced largely by combustion of coal (but at an

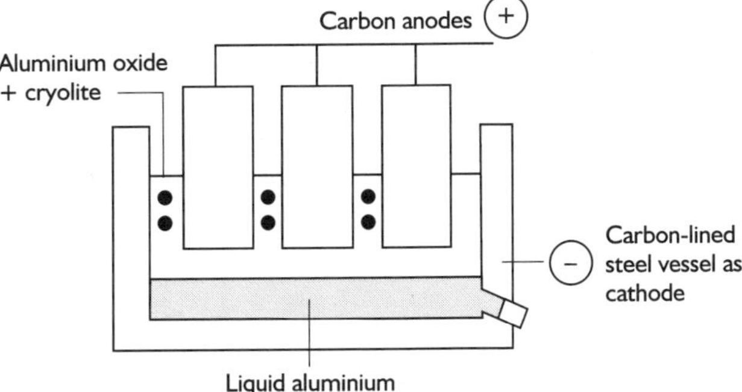

Fig. 8.2 Electrolysis of molten alumina; aluminium production

efficiency of conversion level of only about 30%). So metals like iron which can use coke in their extraction have a fuel or energy 'advantage', this makes them potentially cheaper.

Use of recycled aluminium

Recycling aluminium is now common. Drink cans are collected and melted down; impurities are removed. The production consumes only 5% of the energy needed to extract the metals from its ore by electrolysis.

Aluminium is a useful metal because of its **low density** and its **resistance to corrosion.** But why is it resistant to corrosion when it is placed so high in the reactivity series? The position of aluminium in the reactivity series would suggest that it would react with steam and oxygen readily—as magnesium (above) and zinc (below) do. Yet aluminium is unaffected by either.

The chemical resistance of aluminium

It is the reactivity of aluminium to oxygen that protects it against attack by some chemicals. When a clean aluminium surface is exposed to air an invisibly thin oxide film forms immediately. The film covers the metal surface and protects it from attack by any chemical that cannot **dissolve** the film. This protective film prevents corrosion by water and air, though common salt can attack it. Unprotected aluminium surfaces remain clean and shiny except in salty atmospheres, e.g. near or on the sea.

Breakdown of the protective film

Any chemical that can dissolve aluminium oxide will destroy the oxide film and the aluminium surface will be exposed and may react.

Aluminium oxide is an **amphoteric oxide.** It acts as *either* an acidic oxide *or* a basic oxide. It will, therefore, dissolve in acids *and* alkalis to form a salt and water. Dilute acids and alkalis will remove the protective film and expose the aluminium to reaction.

Since aluminium will also react with both acids and alkalis to form soluble salts and hydrogen gas, then as soon as the oxide film is dissolved by an acid or an alkali, the exposed metal will also react and dissolve, with the formation of an aluminium salt and hydrogen gas:

aluminium oxide + acid/alkali → aluminium salt + water,

followed by

aluminium + acid/alkali → aluminium salt + hydrogen.

This breakdown of the oxide film in acids and alkalis shows us a limitation in the corrosion resistance of aluminium.

Aluminium is commonly used in the kitchen in **foil, pans** and **cooker parts.** None of these should be brought into prolonged contact with acids (vinegar, fruit juices, kettle-fur remover), or even brief contact with alkalis such as the caustic soda used to clean ovens, or aluminium will be dissolved. High concentrations of aluminium in food are dangerous.

Anodizing

The thin oxide layer can be thickened by the process known as **anodizing,** see Chapter 17, p. 262. This is done where extra corrosion resistance is required and also where aluminium is to be coloured by dyeing.

Iron extraction and steelmaking

Iron is the second most abundant metal and the fourth most abundant element in the Earth's crust. It is found mainly as oxide (Fe_2O_3), sulphide (FeS_2) or carbonate ($FeCO_3$). Haematite contains mainly Fe_2O_3, magnetite is mainly Fe_3O_4 and pyrite is mainly FeS_2. The world is still strongly dependent on the use of iron as a constructional material in spite of the ease with which it corrodes. This is mainly because it is

- cheap;
- strong;
- easily worked into shape;
- easily and cheaply alloyed for increased strength or hardness.

The cheapness of iron arises from

- the widespread occurrence of its ores;
- high concentration of iron in the ores;
- cheapness of the reducing agent (carbon) and the flux (limestone);
- large amounts of available scrap for recycling.

Iron is smelted in a blast furnace (Fig. 8.3). Here, iron oxide is reduced to molten iron by carbon (actually carbon monoxide is the reducing agent). Iron ore contains much impurity—mainly silica—which would 'clog' the furnace if not removed. By adding limestone, silica can be converted to calcium silicate—a glassy substance which melts at the furnace temperature and flows from the furnace with the molten iron. In this way *all* the products are removed from the furnace as liquids. With constant addition of raw materials, the process can work continuously. **The extraction of iron from its oxide ores is equivalent to a reversal of the process of rusting.**

Fig. 8.3 The blast furnace: iron production

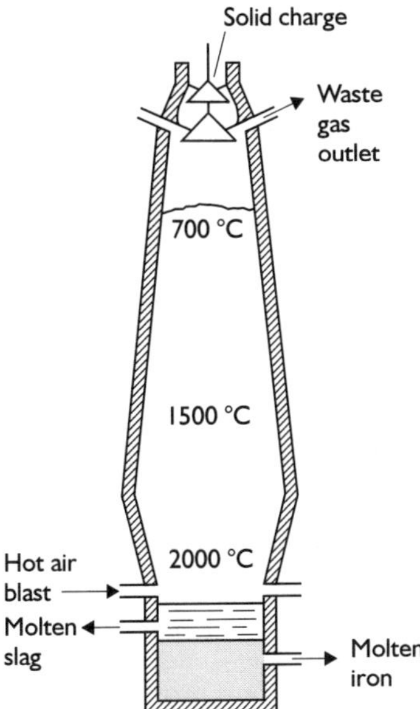

The processes in the blast furnace

(i) Coke (carbon), iron oxide ore and limestone are added at the top.
(ii) A **blast** of hot air enters near the bottom.
(iii) Reduction occurs and iron is formed.
(iv) Molten iron falls to the bottom of the furnace and is tapped off when necessary.
(v) Slag (molten impurities) forms and runs to the bottom of the furnace. It floats on the iron, protecting the iron from oxidation by the air blast. Slag is tapped off when necessary.
(vi) Hot, waste gases containing carbon monoxide, carbon dioxide and nitrogen exit from the top of the furnace.

The reactions

(i) Coke is first oxidized by air to carbon monoxide:

$$2C(s) + O_2(g) \rightarrow 2CO(g)$$

carbon + oxygen → carbon monoxide

This occurs mainly round the air blast inlet at 2000 °C.

(ii) Carbon monoxide **reduces** iron oxide to iron:

$$3CO(g) + Fe_2O_3(s) \rightarrow 2Fe(l) + 3CO_2(g)$$

carbon monoxide + iron oxide → iron + carbon dioxide

Molten iron flows to the bottom of the furnace.

(iii) Limestone is decomposed by heat to calcium oxide at 1000 °C:

$$CaCO_3(s) \rightarrow CaO(s) + CO_2(g)$$

calcium carbonate → calcium oxide + carbon dioxide

(iv) Calcium oxide (basic oxide) reacts with silica (acidic oxide) to form molten calcium silicate (slag) which flows to the bottom of the furnace and floats on the molten iron.

$$CaO(s) + SiO_2(s) \rightarrow CaSiO_3(l)$$

calcium oxide + silicon dioxide → calcium silicate

The molten iron tapped from the furnace contains about 5% of carbon, which has dissolved in the iron on its way down the furnace.

Waste gases

The gases formed in these reactions are carbon monoxide and carbon dioxide. Nitrogen from the air blast passes through unchanged. The hot waste gases pass out through the top of the furnace. Their heat energy is used to **preheat** the incoming air blast. In this way economies in energy use are achieved. Over the years, the process has been made more economical. The weight of coke now needed to produce a tonne of iron is about one-third what it used to be.

Pig-iron/cast iron

The molten iron from a blast furnace is tapped off into large preheated containers. It is taken to the nearby steelworks where it is converted into a large number of different steels, many of them tailor-made to the customer's specification.

Some of the molten iron is cast into moulds called 'pigs'. This is **cast** or **pig-iron,** it has 5% carbon and is very brittle. It is used where cheapness and little strength combined with a greater corrosion resistance than ordinary steel is required—which is not often.

Wrought iron

If **all the carbon** is removed from pig iron, **pure iron** or **wrought iron** is formed. This is very easily bent to shape and is mainly used for ornamental ironwork such as gates and scrolls.

Steel

Steel is an alloy of iron and other elements. The commonest and cheapest steels contain carbon as the alloying element. See Table 8.3.

mild steel contains	0.1–0.25% carbon (easily pressed into complex shapes)
medium carbon steel contains	0.25–0.5% carbon
high carbon steel contains	0.5%–1.5% carbon (strong but brittle)
cast iron contains	2.5–5% carbon (weak and brittle)

Alloying elements other than carbon—alloy steels

- Manganese is added for increased strength and hardness.
- Chromium and nickel are added for increased corrosion resistance.
- Tungsten and vanadium are added for increased hardness, especially at high temperatures.

Making steels

The basic oxygen process

The first requirement of steelmaking is to remove the carbon from the pig-iron which comes, molten, from the blast furnace. This is done by oxidizing the carbon and other non-metal impurities to oxides by blowing in **pure oxygen** through a water-cooled lance under pressure.

Carbon oxides are gases and leave the reaction vessel—called a 'converter'—through the mouth of the vessel, usually burning as they do so.

Phosphorus oxides are not gases, but like all non-metal oxides they are acidic. They combine with the special 'basic' lining of the converter (magnesium oxide) to form solid phosphates and are thereby removed.

Lime may also be added and this too reacts with non-metal oxides to form a slag which can be poured away. Up to 20% scrap steel can be used in this process. The resulting iron is mixed with the calculated amounts of alloying elements and steel results.

These processes, used in steelmaking, are all **exothermic** and this helps to keep the metal molten whilst the reactions are being carried out.

Copper purification

Copper is extracted by heating its sulphide ores. This directly produces an impure form of copper called 'blister copper'. Further refinement is carried out by electrolysis **using the impure copper as the anode.**

Fig. 8.4 Electrolytic purification of copper

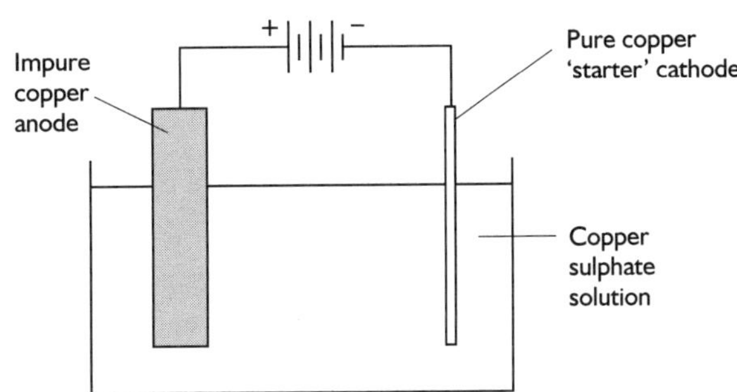

The anode is a cast block of impure copper. The cathode is a thin sheet of pure copper. In the process, the anode is 'eaten away' and the cathode becomes thicker. When the process is finished, the cathodes are melted down and cast into bars for sale to manufacturers of wire and sheet.

In this process:

- copper **dissolves at the anode** (+) by **oxidation** (electron loss):

$$Cu(s) - 2e^- \rightarrow Cu^{2+}(aq)$$

- the impure copper **anode becomes smaller** as pure copper **dissolves.**
- Copper **deposits on the cathode** (−) by **reduction** (electron gain):

$$Cu^{2+}(aq) + 2e^- \rightarrow Cu(s)$$

It is evident that the cathode process is a **reversal** of the anode process. This means that the concentration of the copper sulphate solution, which is the electrolyte, does not change. What happens to the impurities?

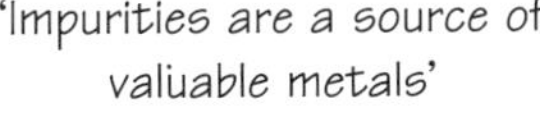

- Soluble impurities remain in the electrolyte and are later extracted.
- Insoluble impurities from the anode fall to the bottom of the cell as a sludge and are later refined to extract precious metals, e.g. platinum.

EXAMINATION QUESTIONS

Question 1 (F)

Iron ore is found in the Earth. It is mined, crushed and heated in a blast furnace to change it into iron metal.

(a) Suggest one method which could be used to mine iron ore. [1 line] *[1]*

(b) (i) Name *one* solid heated in the blast furnace with the iron oxide. [1 line] *[1]*

(ii) What element is removed from the iron oxide in this process? [1 line] *[1]*

(c) Iron has to be protected from air and water, for example by painting, or it rusts. Aluminium is above iron in the reactivity series, is used in similar conditions to iron, but does not need protection. Why is aluminium so unreactive? [2 lines] *[3]*

(d) Aluminium is used in aircraft construction.
 (i) What property of aluminium makes it specially suited to this use? [1 line] *[1]*
 (ii) What property of pure aluminium makes it unsuitable for use in aircraft construction and how is this problem overcome? [2 lines] *[2]*

[Total 9 marks]

Question 2(F)

(a) Iron is extracted from its ores in a blast furnace. In the empty boxes (Fig. 8.5) write the names of *two* other materials that are fed into the furnace. *[2]*

Fig. 8.5

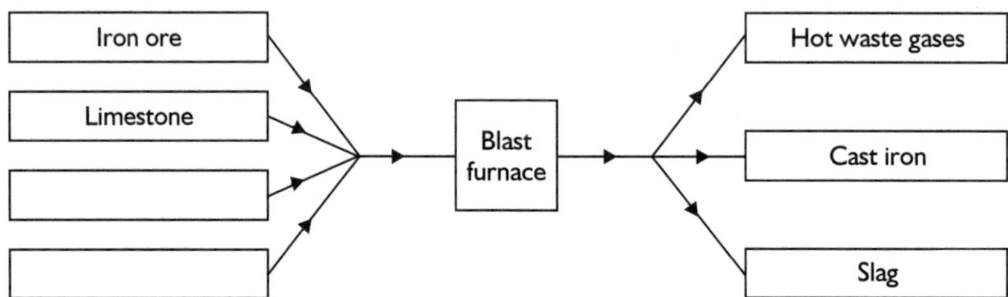

(b) (i) Name an ore of iron. [1 line] *[1]*
 (ii) Use your named ore to describe the extraction of iron in the blast furnace. Explain the chemical reactions used in the extraction process. You do *not* need to write about the formation of slag. [8 lines] *[4]*
 (iii) Give *one* use for cast iron. [1 line] *[1]*
 (iv) Give *one* use for the hot waste gases. [1 line] *[1]*

(c) The corrosion of iron is called rusting. Explain the meaning of the word *corrosion.* [4 lines] *[2]*

(d) The metal sodium is extracted by electrolysis. What does this suggest about sodium compared with iron? [1 line] *[1]*

(e) On what property of iron does each of the uses in Table 8.6 depend? Complete the Table by writing each property in the space provided. *[3]*

Table 8.6

Use of iron	Property of iron
Building car bodies Compass needles (for finding North) Weights for weight-lifters	

[Total 15 marks]

Question 3(F)

Aluminium oxide is an ionic compound, melting point 970 °C. It is found in the Earth's crust in the ore bauxite. Aluminium oxide is used to make aluminium.

(a) (i) What holds the aluminium ions and oxide ions together in aluminium oxide? [2 lines] *[1]*
 (ii) Why has aluminium oxide a very high melting point? [2 lines] *[1]*
 (iii) What is the chemical formula of aluminium oxide? [1 line] *[1]*

(b) To make aluminium, the aluminium oxide is first melted and then electricity is passed through it.
 (i) Why must aluminium oxide be melted before electricity will pass through it? [3 lines] *[2]*
 (ii) The diagram (Fig. 8.6) shows an aluminium cell.
 At which electrode is aluminium formed? *[1]*
 (iii) Why do the positive electrodes in this cell need to be replaced at regular intervals? [4 lines] *[2]*

Fig. 8.6

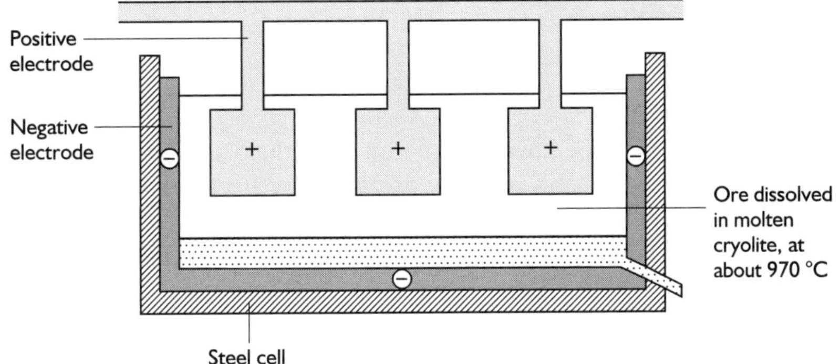

(c) Complete the following equation to show how aluminium is formed in the cell.

Al^{3+} .... e^- → Al *[1]*

[Total 9 marks]

Question 4(H)

(a) During the extraction of iron from iron(III) oxide, Fe_2O_3, in the blast furnace, air is passed in at the bottom and reacts with coke to give carbon dioxide.
  (i) Write a balanced equation for this reaction. [1 line]
  (ii) What type of energy change occurs during the reaction? [1 line]
  (iii) What is the importance of the energy change to the extraction process? [1 line] *[3]*

(b) The carbon dioxide then reacts with more coke to form carbon monoxide.
  (i) Write a balanced equation for this reaction. [1 line]
  (ii) What is the importance of carbon monoxide in the extraction process? [1 line]
  (iii) Write a balanced equation to show the reaction of carbon monoxide in the extraction process. [1 line] *[4]*

(c) Explain the purpose of limestone in the extraction of iron. [6 lines] *[4]*

[Total 11 marks]

Question 5(H)

(a) Malachite is one of the minerals in copper ores. The diagram (Fig. 8.7) shows some of the substances that can be made from malachite.

Fig. 8.7

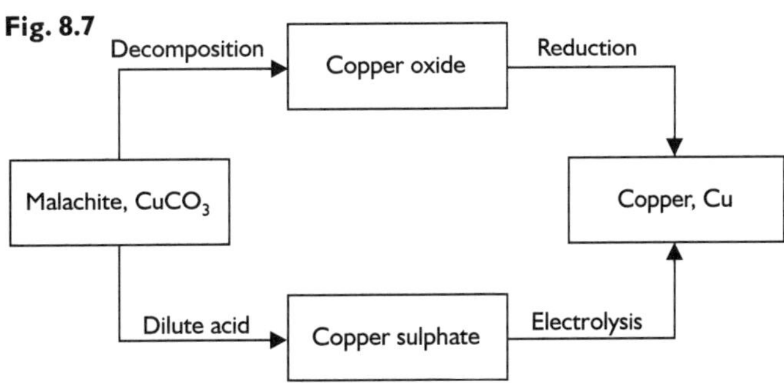

Choose *one* of the two possible routes from malachite to copper.

For **each** chemical change on your chosen route:

  (i) state how the chemical change is carried out;
  (ii) give *one* observation that would be made during the chemical change;
  (iii) write a balanced chemical equation for the chemical change. [8 lines] *[8]*

(b) Why is pure copper metal always produced by electrolysis? [2 lines] *[1]*

(c) How do metals, such as copper, conduct electricity? [4 lines] *[2]*
(d) Scrap copper is recycled. Give three reasons why. [8 lines] *[3]*

[Total 14 marks]

Question 6(F)

(a) Describe how impure iron from the blast furnace is made into mild steel. Explain how the process removes one impurity from the iron and state one effect this has on the properties of the iron. [10 lines] *[7]*
(b) What is meant by the term *alloy steel*? Give one example of an alloy steel with one of its uses. [4 lines] *[3]*

[Total 10 marks]

Question 7(H)

Aluminium is manufactured by passing electricity through a molten mixture of aluminium oxide and cryolite (a mineral containing sodium, aluminium and fluorine). The cryolite is not used up in the process. The melting point of this mixture is much lower than that of pure aluminium oxide. The cell which holds the molten mixture is lined with carbon. Molten aluminium collects at the bottom of the cell. The current is supplied through carbon rods. Oxygen formed from the aluminium oxide burns these rods away as carbon monoxide.

(a) Answer the following questions about this process:
  (i) Explain why it is necessary to melt the aluminium oxide. [2 lines]
  (ii) What are two advantages of the low melting point for the mixture in the cell? [2 lines]
  (iii) From the information given above, what factors are most likely to affect the cost of making aluminium? [3 lines] *[6]*
(b) The map (Fig. 8.8) shows the British Isles. The grey dotted areas are called **development** areas, where the government will help to pay some of the costs of starting a new industry. The black circles show deepwater ports. The arrow shows the direction of the prevailing winds. The ore of aluminium is imported by sea. Aluminium refineries may produce airborne fluoride fumes and should be placed where there are no large towns **downwind** of the factory.

Fig. 8.8

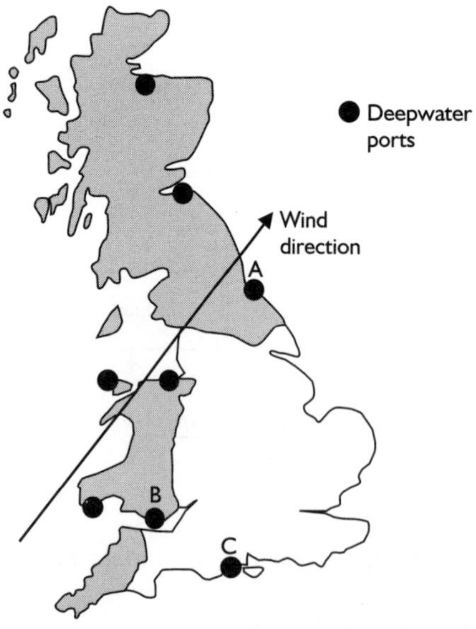

Three possible sites for aluminium refineries are shown (A, B and C). For **each** of these sites list the **advantages** and **disadvantages** of siting a refinery at that place. [8 lines] *[6]*
(c) Many drink cans are now made of aluminium and that used cans are collected so that the metal can be recycled. Explain what factors must be considered when deciding whether the material from disposable items such as cans ought to be recycled. [4 lines] *[5]*

OUTLINE ANSWERS

Question 1

(a) Opencast mining or deep mining *[1]*.
(b) (i) Coke *or* limestone *[1]*.
(ii) Oxygen is removed *[1]*.
(c) A surface *[1]* oxide layer *[1]* protects the metal beneath *[1]*.
(d) (i) Low density *[1]*.
(ii) Pure aluminium is not very strong *[1]* but is strengthened by alloying *[1]*.

Question 2

(a) Coke *[1]* and air *[1]*.
(b) (i) Haematite *[1]*.
(ii) Coke reacts with oxygen to form carbon dioxide *[1]*:

$$C(s) + O_2(g) \rightarrow CO_2(g)$$

Coke reacts with carbon dioxide to form carbon monoxide *[1]*:

$$C(s) + CO_2(g) \rightarrow 2CO(g)$$

Carbon monoxide reduces iron oxide (haematite) to iron *[1]*:

$$Fe_2O_3(s) + 3CO(g) \rightarrow 2Fe(l) + 3CO_2(g)$$

[1 mark for one of the equations]

(iii) Underground pipes or manhole covers or cricket-pitch rollers *[1]*.
(iv) Used to preheat the air blast *[1]*.
(c) (i) Reaction of metal *[1]* with air or water *[1]* *or* oxidation of a metal *[2]*.
(d) It must be more reactive/higher in the reactivity series *[1]*.
(e) Car bodies require **malleable** metal *[1]*.
Compass needles must be **magnetized** *[1]*.
Weights must be heavy but small—**high density** *[1]*.

Question 3

(a) (i) Force of attraction between oppositely charged ions *[1]*.
(ii) The strong ionic attraction *[1]*.
(iii) Al_2O_3 *[1]*.
(b) (i) Electrolysis requires ions *[1]* that are free to move *[1]*.
(ii) Negative electrode, cathode *[1]*.
(iii) They are made of carbon *[1]*, which react with oxygen given off *[1]* or burn away *[1]*.
(c) $Al^{3+}(l) + 3e^- \rightarrow Al(l)$ *[1 mark for $+3e^-$]*.

Question 4

(a) (i) $C(s) + O_2(g) \rightarrow CO_2(g)$ *[1]*.
(ii) Exothermic *[1]*.
(iii) It raises the temperature for faster reaction *[1]*.
(b) (i) $C(s) + CO_2(g) \rightarrow 2CO(g)$ *[1]*.
(ii) It is the (main) reducing agent *[1]*.
(iii) $Fe_2O_3(s) + 3CO(g) \rightarrow 2Fe(l) + 3CO_2(g)$ *[1 for formulae correct] [1 for balance]*.
(c) Limestone is decomposed to calcium oxide *[1]*, which reacts with acidic impurities *[1]* to form slag *[1]*, which is calcium silicate *[1]* which does not mix with the molten iron *[1]*. $CaO(s) + SiO_2(s) \rightarrow CaSiO_3(l)$ *[1]*. *[Any 4 maximum.]*

Question 5

(a) There are four points to make for each of the two steps of the reaction route you choose.
Route 1 is malachite → copper oxide → copper
Malachite is *heated* to decompose it to copper oxide *[1]*.
The malachite is green and **changes to black** in this process *[1]*.

$$CuCO_3(s) \rightarrow CuO(s) + CO_2(g) \quad [2]$$

Black copper oxide is reduced by heating with **hydrogen, carbon** or **zinc** *[1]*, when its colour changes from black to **pink/brown** *[1]*.

$CuO(s) + H_2(g) \rightarrow Cu(s) + H_2O(g)$ *[2]*

Route 2 malachite → copper sulphate → copper

Malachite is reacted with **dilute sulphuric acid** *[1]* which **fizzes** and **dissolves** the malachite *[1]* to give copper sulphate solution.

$CuCO_3(s) + H_2SO_4(aq) \rightarrow CuSO_4(aq) + H_2O(l) + CO_2(g)$ *[2]*.

Electrolysis of this solution gives **pink** *[1]* copper at the **cathode** *[1]*.

$Cu^{2+}(aq) + 2e^- \rightarrow Cu(s)$ *[2]*

(b) Only **crude** copper can be produced by chemical methods of reduction. Electrolysis deposits only a single metal on the cathode *[1]*.

(c) Metals are ions in a **sea of electrons** *[1]*. **Movement** of these electrons is the cause of conduction *[1]*.

(d) 1. **Conserves** mineral resources *[1]*.
2. **Saves** the energy needed to extract copper *[1]*.
3. **Reduces** pollution/environment damage *[1]* created during extraction.

Question 6

(a) Essays are marked on the basis of major points.

Points which score: impure iron must be purified by a described method. Oxygen *[1]* is blown *[1]* into molten *[1]* pig (impure) iron. Carbon *[1]* (impurity) is oxidized to carbon oxides *[1]* which escapes into the air.

$C(s) + O_2(g) \rightarrow CO_2(g)$ or $2C(s) + O_2(g) \rightarrow 2CO(g)$ *[1]*

The removal of carbon makes the iron softer and more malleable *[1]*.

(b) Alloys are mixtures of metals—the 'parent' metal, in this case iron, plus added metals(s) *[1]*, e.g. manganese *[1]* for railway crossings *[1]* or vanadium *[1]* for screwdrivers *[1]*. *[3 marks maximum.]*

Question 7

Question 7 is a comprehension question. This type of question is not found on every chemistry paper. However, many questions have **new material** in them which may not be in the syllabus but which is presented with **enough information** for the candidate to produce an answer using known principles and techniques.

The question is about the process of aluminium extraction, how it is done, economic factors, pollution possibilities and recycling. It is therefore within the area of each syllabus which deals with the social, economic, environmental and industrial aspects of chemistry.

Look up the following section as you plan your answer.

(a) (i) See Aluminium Extraction, p. 109.
(ii) Common sense will help here.
(iii) Re-read the passage looking for the expenses of the process.

(b) A little common sense comes in handy here. The factors to consider in each case are
(i) wind-borne pollution;
(ii) development area payments;
(iii) deep water facilities.

One has all three, another only two and the third only one of these advantages. A total six points for a mark each.

(c) There are many factors here. Look for some **cost reduction factors** and some **expenses** of the operation of scrap collection.

STUDENT ANSWER WITH EXAMINER'S COMMENTS

Titanium is the ninth most abundant element in the Earth's crust. One form in which it occurs is rutile, TiO_2. In extracting titanium from its ore, rutile is first converted to titanium(IV) chloride, $TiCl_4$. This is then reduced to the metal by heating it with sodium or magnesium in an atmosphere of argon.

Magnesium and its alloys are used in aircraft construction. In spacecraft titanium is used rather than magnesium. In space the temperature is very low; on re-entering the atmosphere the surface temperature of the craft becomes very high.

Table 8.7

	Melting point °C	Boiling point °C	Density in/g m^3	Relative atomic mass
Magnesium	650	1 117	1.7	24
Titanium	1 677	3 277	4.5	48

(a) Titanium(IV) chloride is a simple molecular covalent substance. It is a liquid at room temperature. Given that the titanium atom has four outer electrons used for bonding, draw a diagram to show the bonding in titanium(IV) chloride (only the outer electrons of the chlorine atoms should be shown).

'An excellent start—but why did you miss out the electrons around three of the chlorine atoms? You must give a *complete* set'

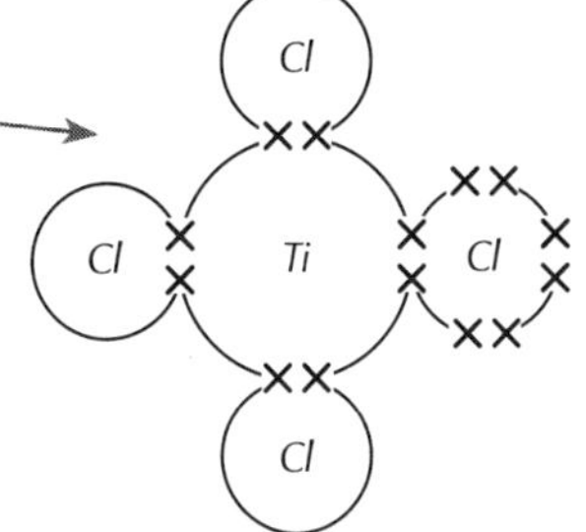

(2 marks)

(b) Write a balanced equation for the reaction of titanium(IV) chloride with sodium.

'Correct'

$TiCl_4 + 4Na \rightarrow Ti + 4NaCl$

(1 mark)

(c) Suggest a reason why it is necessary to carry out the reaction of titanium(IV) chloride with sodium in an atmosphere of argon.

'Almost right. If air was present sodium would oxidize'

Sodium would react with most other gases—argon is inert.

(1 mark)

(d) (i) Explain why the physical state of titanium(IV) chloride differs from that of sodium chloride at room temperature.

titanium chloride is a simple molecular compound but sodium chloride is ionic.

'Worth a mark out of two. You give, correctly, the structures of the compounds but do not explain *why* they are liquid or solid. Molecules have weak forces of attraction between them. Sodium chloride is an ionic giant structure with strong forces of attraction leading to the solid state'

(ii) Do you consider that electrolysis of the liquid titanium(IV) chloride would be a suitable method for obtaining titanium? Give a reason.

No, because titanium chloride is molecular and would not conduct electricity.

'Good. Spot on!'

(3 marks)

(continued)

'A good answer.'

'Difficult to find a second property? Spacecraft carry oxygen as a fuel and also for the space crew. In a fire, magnesium + oxygen would be a very dangerous combination!'

'Yes'

'Overall a good answer which might score 8/12'

(continued)

(e) Titanium is expensive in spite of the fact that it is relatively abundant in the Earth's crust. Suggest a reason for this.

It must cost a lot to extract. If sodium or magnesium is needed they would both be expensive.

(1 mark)

(f) Use your knowledge of magnesium and the information in the question to explain

(i) how TWO properties of magnesium makes it less suitable than titanium for spacecraft construction

Its melting point is quite low so it would melt on re-entering the atmosphere.

(ii) how ONE property of magnesium makes it suitable for aircraft construction

low density.

(4 marks)

(Total 12 marks)

SUMMARY

Use this list to help you with your revision. Tick off the points as you revise them in the text.

- Most metals have to be extracted from ores.
- Ores are concentrations of metal-bearing mineral, economic to exploit.
- Extracting a metal from its ore is always **reduction**.
- Reduction involves either removal of oxygen *or* gain of electrons.
- The **method chosen** to reduce a metal ore depends on the **reactivity** of the metal in the ore—expect to be asked to explain it.
- The chemistry of the methods of extraction of
  - aluminium by **electrolysis** of molten alumina, and
  - iron by **carbon-reduction** of iron(III) oxide

  are to be studied **in detail** (no detail of plant is required).
- The **purification** of copper by electrolysis uses impure copper as the starting material (anode).
- The electrolytic methods are also explained in Chapter 10.
- **Alloys** are solid mixtures of metals (but steels may contain non-metals—carbon or silicon).
- Alloys can be formulated to have a **wider range of properties/uses** than pure metals.
- Properties of the common alloys—brass, solder, mild steel and stainless steel—may be required by some syllabuses.
- To make any of the numerous steels:
  - iron first has its carbon impurity removed by passing oxygen through the molten metal. Carbon becomes carbon dioxide and escapes.
  - Next the required mixture of alloying elements is added and the steel is cast into ingots.
- The modern car contains dozens of different steels in its construction.
- Alloys can be hard or soft, hard-wearing or easily shaped, depending upon the alloying elements added to the 'parent' metal.

(continued)

(continued)

- Composite materials are combinations of non-metallic substances with properties comparable to those of alloys but usually lighter.
- Recycling of metals is now common and saves energy resources, reducing pollution and greenhouse-gas emissions.
- Metal resources may not last for ever—100% recycling may become normal.
- **Energy costs** for metal extraction are high for aluminium because
  - fuel is consumed to keep the electrolyte **molten** (1000 °C);
  - electricity is consumed in **reducing Al^{3+} ions** to aluminium.
- Aluminium resists corrosion because of an invisible, protective **oxide film** which breaks down in contact with acids or alkalis.
- **Iron/steel rusts** by forming iron oxide but the **oxide flakes off** and does not protect the underlying metal.
- Pure copper of at least 99.99% purity can only be produced by electrolysis. It is used for electrical wiring and copper water pipes and boilers.

Chapter

9 Industrial chemistry—non-metallic compounds

GETTING STARTED

The elements nitrogen and sulphur form compounds which have proved to be among the most useful products of the chemical industry. These compounds are:

- ammonia, NH_3;
- sulphuric acid, H_2SO_4;
- nitric acid, HNO_3;
- fertilizers, NH_4NO_3 and others.

The chief source of **nitrogen** is the atmosphere. The **nitrogen cycle** ensures that eventually most of the nitrogen compounds we use—**ammonia, ammonium nitrate** and **nitric acid**—will find their way back into the atmosphere as nitrogen gas.

Sulphur is found as the native element, but most European supplies come from the removal of sulphur from crude oil and hydrogen sulphide from 'sour' natural gas. These processes

- remove the potentially corrosive and polluting compounds from many crude oil products (including petrol)—sulphur compounds burn to sulphur dioxide;
- remove the smell (bad eggs) and potential corrosive properties of hydrogen sulphide from some natural gas supplies;
- provide a useful source of sulphur for **sulphuric acid** manufacture.

TOPIC CHART

LONDON	MEG	NEAB	NICCEA	SEG	WJEC	TOPIC	STUDY	REVISION 1	REVISION 2
✓	✓	✓	✓	✓	✓	Nitrogen fixation			
✓	✓	✓	✓	✓	✓	Ammonia manufacture			
✓	✓	✓	✓	✓	✓	Fertilizer manufacture			
		✓	✓	✓		Nitric acid manufacture			
✓	✓	✓	✓	✓	✓	Sulphuric acid manufacture			

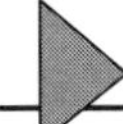

WHAT YOU NEED TO KNOW

Nitrogen fixation

The conversion of the **element** nitrogen into **compounds of nitrogen** is called **fixation.** It is both a natural and a synthetic process.

Natural fixation occurs through lightning and bacterial action called **nitrification.**

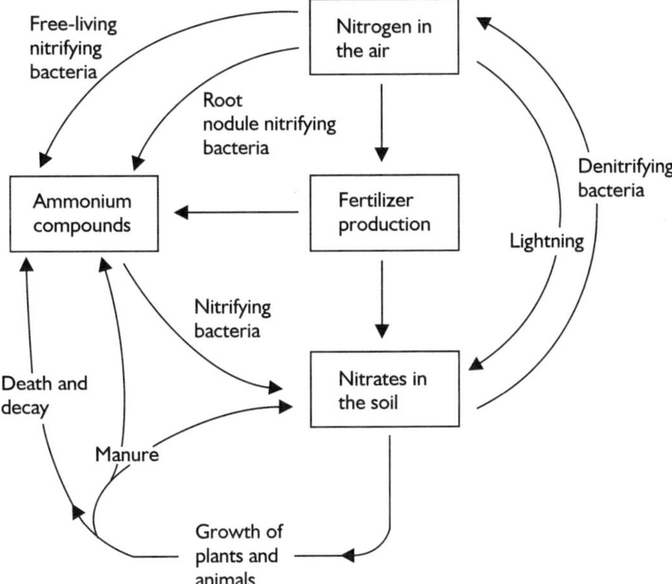

Fig. 9.1 The nitrogen cycle

The reverse process also occurs through bacteria (denitrification) and through decay of animal and plant remains.

Total nitrogen fixation is made up roughly of

- Haber process, NH_3—30%;
- motor vehicle pollution, NO_x—10%;
- natural fixation—60% (STILL THE LARGEST PROPORTION!).

Ammonia manufacture

The credit for our ability to manufacture large quantities of ammonia to make nitrates and ammonium compounds cheaply belongs to Fritz Haber and Herman Bosch, two German chemists who invented the method and engineered the machinery to produce ammonia from its elements—nitrogen and hydrogen gases.

The Haber process—synthetic nitrogen fixation

The elements are produced from the cheapest sources available. For nitrogen this is always the air, free and abundant! Hydrogen was once produced from **water** by electrolysis and later from **coal**, but is now made from either **naphtha** or **natural gas**, whichever happens to be more economical at the time and place of manufacture:

Naphtha process: $C_6H_{14}(g) + 12H_2O(g) \rightarrow 6CO_2(g) + 19H_2(g)$;

Natural gas process: $CH_4(g) + 2H_2O(g) \rightarrow CO_2(g) + 4H_2(g)$.

In both cases the **hydrocarbon** chosen is heated with steam and carbon dioxide and hydrogen are produced.

Carbon dioxide is removed by

(i) dissolving in water or in an alkali; or
(ii) liquefaction by pressure and cooling.

The hydrogen gas flows on to the next stage of the process.

A mixture of three parts of hydrogen to one part of nitrogen (synthesis gas) is

- compressed to a pressure of 200 atmospheres,

- heated to about 400 °C, and
- passed over an iron catalyst:

$$3H_2(g) + N_2(g) \rightleftharpoons 2NH_3(g).$$

The reaction is exothermic and reversible. The high pressure and relatively low temperatures are the conditions used to push the position of the equilibrium as far to the right as is practicable (see equilibria in Chapter 18).

The gas leaving the reaction vessel contains about 15% ammonia. Ammonia can be liquefied by cooling at this pressure. The unreacted gases are **recycled** after mixing with more synthesis gas.

The economics of the process

It is valuable to look briefly at the **savings** gained by the change from using coal to make the hydrogen to using **hydrocarbons** for that purpose (Table 9.1).

The change of feedstock produced considerable savings in most areas and an increase in ammonia yield by nearly four times.

Table 9.1 Difference between coal-based and hydrocarbon-based ammonia plants

Process	Annual ammonia production/thousand tonnes	Land use/ hectares	Labour (hundreds)	Capital/ £ million	Energy use/ gigajoules
Coal-based	225	20	23	75	75
Hydrocarbon-based	800	7	24	80	40

The siting of an ammonia plant

The place chosen to make an important industrial chemical is vital to the economic success of the process (see Chapter 3). The following flowchart shows the processes involved in ammonia manufacture and sale:

RAW MATERIALS →	FACTORY →	PRODUCT →	MARKET
natural gas or oil, air and water	labour and other costs	transport provision—roads, rail, port for exports; costs of transport	advertising costs

Ammonia 'plants' as factories are called, must be sited near to the supplies of raw materials and must be able to transport the product to the customer. The site will be close to oil or to natural gas supplies (this is transported by a national pipeline). Air of course is everywhere and free! Water will have to come from a river since the quantities needed cannot be supplied through the piped water system.

Two major sites are at Billingham on Tees and Severnside near Bristol (Fig. 9.2). Both are close to a deep water port, a river, gas pipeline or oilfields and good road and rail transport systems.

Fertilizer manufacture

The main uses of ammonia

- Manufacture of fertilizer, e.g. ammonium nitrate—agricultural fertilizer
- Oxidation to nitric acid
- Manufacture of nylon
- Other uses including urea/formaldehyde plastics

(See Fig. 9.3.)

Ammonia can also be added directly to the soil as a fertilizer but

- conditions must be damp or the gas escapes;
- the alkalinity of pure ammonia can also be a problem.

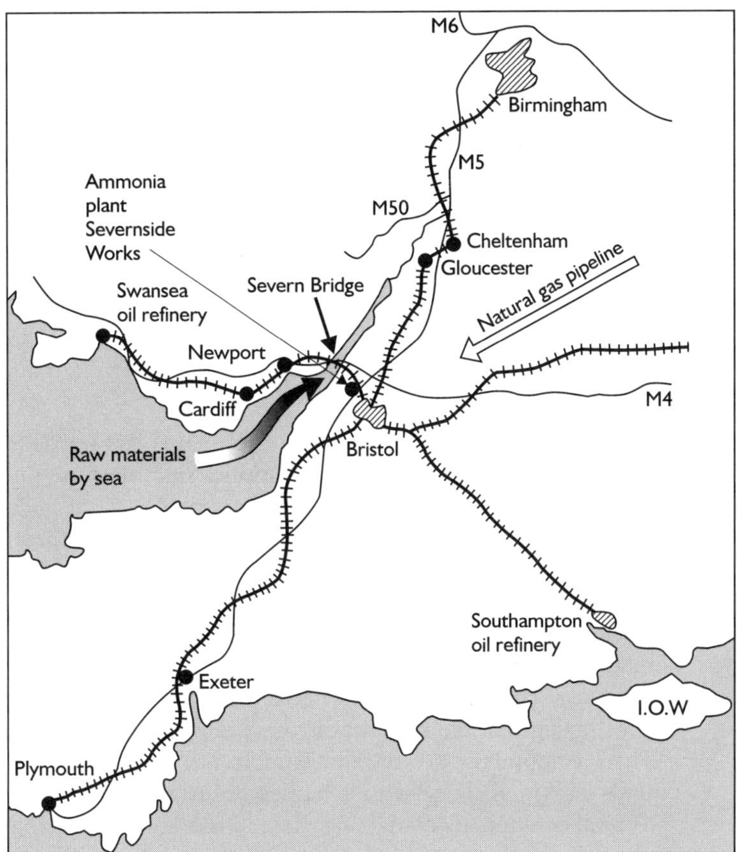

Fig. 9.2 Map of the Severnside Industrial Complex

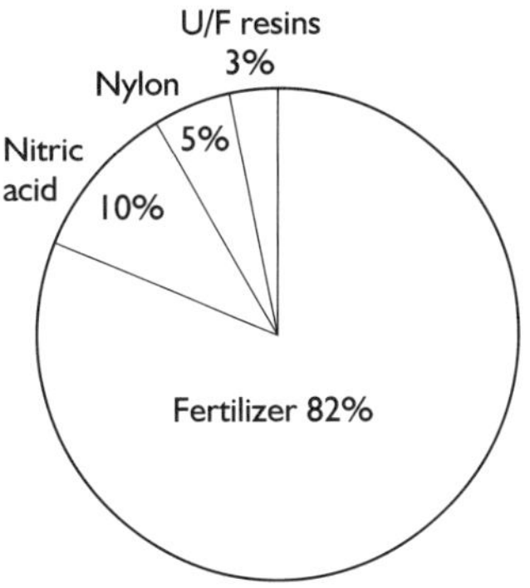

Fig. 9.3 Uses of ammonia

It is for these reasons that ammonia is neutralized with acid before application to the soil. Table 9.2 shows the proportion of nitrogen in the common fertilizers made from ammonia. It will be seen that pure ammonia and urea both have percentages of nitrogen greater than that of ammonium nitrate. Urea is more expensive than ammonium nitrate but is sold to horticultural merchants coated with sulphur as a **slow-release fertilizer**—one that allows small amounts of nutrient to dissolve over a few months. The common use of ammonium nitrate is a compromise between cheapness and nitrogen concentration.

The reactions by which two ammonium compounds are made can be carried out in the laboratory as they are on a larger scale in industry. They are:

Table 9.2 Percentages of nitrogen in common fertilizers

Fertilizer	Formula	Percentage nitrogen by mass
Ammonia(g)	NH_3	$14/17 \times 100 = 82$
Urea(s)	CON_2H_4	$2 \times 14/60 \times 100 = 47$
Ammonium nitrate(s)	NH_4NO_3	$2 \times 14/80 \times 100 = 35$
Ammonium sulphate(s)	$(NH_4)_2SO_4$	$2 \times 14/132 \times 100 = 21$

$NH_3(aq) + HNO_3(aq) \rightarrow NH_4NO_3(aq)$

ammonia + nitric acid → ammonium nitrate

$2NH_3(aq) + H_2SO_4(aq) \rightarrow (NH_4)_2SO_4(aq)$

ammonia + sulphuric acid → ammonium sulphate

If an excess of dilute ammonia is added to either of the dilute acids, the excess ammonia will evaporate away on heating (remember ammonia is a gas). The ammonium compound can be crystallized from the solution, filtered off and dried. This is an example of salt formation by acid–alkali neutralization (Chapter 15).

NPK

Nitrogen is the most important of the three main plant nutrients. The others, phosphorus and potassium, are required in smaller quantities since they are not removed from cultivated soil in such large amounts when crops are harvested.

It is important to recognize that the need of plants for these three elements does not mean that these elements can be applied to the soil **as elements.** Nitrogen gas cannot normally be absorbed by any part of a plant and the same is true of the elements phosphorus and potassium. If you remember what happens to yellow phosphorus when it comes into contact with air or what happens to potassium in contact with water you will understand the point being made. The phrase 'a plant needs nitrogen, phosphorus and potassium' is a convenient way of saying that the plant needs these elements **in the form of compounds.**

These compounds are nitrates (supply N), phosphates (supply P) and potassium compounds (supply K) in which the named elements are present as ions.

Typical compounds containing these ions are listed in Table 9.3. All these ions, if present in the soil or the compost the plant is growing in, will be acceptable as nutrients. Small amounts of sulphur are required by plants but are normally already present in the soil in large quantities. A good biology book should be consulted for the principles of plant nutrition.

Table 9.3 Agricultural fertilizers

Compound	Nutrient ion	Nutrient element
NH_4NO_3	NO_3^-	Nitrogen
	NH_4^+	Nitrogen
$(NH_4)_2SO_4$	NH_4^+	Nitrogen
$(NH_4)_3PO_4$	NH_4^+	Nitrogen
	PO_4^{3-}	Phosphorus
$Ca_3(PO_4)_2$	PO_4^{3-}	Phosphorus
K_2SO_4	K^+	Potassium
KCl	K^+	Potassium

Although plants need adequate supplies of the three main nutritional elements for balanced growth, only *one* of them is normally in short supply in the soil—nitrogen. For this reason the greatest need in agriculture for fertilizer is for the **nitrogenous type**—nitrates and ammonium compounds. Plants use the **nitrogen in these compounds** in the production of **proteins.**

Because of our need for proteins, we grow and harvest plants which contain plenty of this nutrient, and so in eating the plant as food we remove nitrogen previously in the soil. The more such plants we grow, such as wheat, barley, rye and maize, the more nitrogenous fertilizer we need to add to the soil to replace what we have removed. Failure to do this results in reduced yields of these vital foods.

The nitrogen cycle

Figure 9.1 shows how the element nitrogen is used and re-used, much as water and carbon are in their 'cycles'.

Much of the nitrogen in food for animals (including human animals) is passed through the body unused and becomes a waste product. Such wastes can be recycled as manure. In effect the nitrogen which animals have been unable to use goes back into the soil to be fertilizer for the next crop. The same could be said of the dead remains of plants and small animals.

Food supply

It is obvious that, as the population of the world increases, so the volume of food production must increase if many people are not to die of hunger. The changes in population and fertilizer production this century are shown in Fig. 9.4.

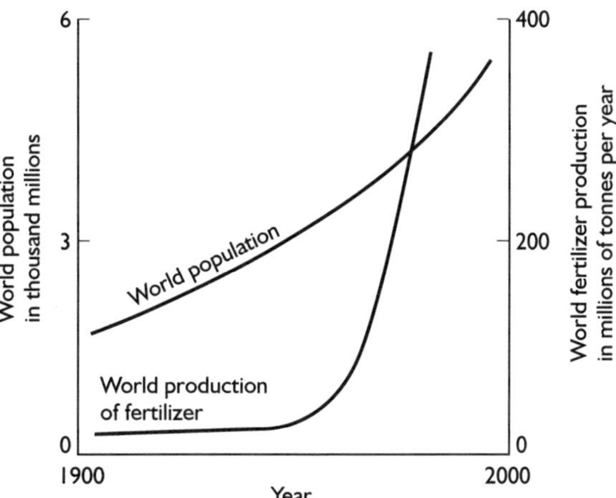

Fig. 9.4 World population and fertilizer production

The need for more and more food has forced us to increase the amount of food we grow. This has been done in many ways, such as:

- Growing varieties of plants which give bigger yields of wheat, barley, maize, etc. This has been described as 'making two ears of corn grow where one grew before'. **More fertilizer is needed** but the saving is on the area of land required.
- Reducing the amount of food wasted by pest damage and rot. For this, pesticides and fungicides are in widespread use. The use of such chemicals has to be carefully controlled to avoid their toxic effects on animals and humans.

The most significant increase arises from the increased use of chemical fertilizer throughout the world.

Disadvantages of synthetic fertilizer use

- Used without an understanding of their properties, fertilizers have been responsible for the pollution of some of our rivers and lakes. If fertilizer gets into water in which plants are growing, the fertilizing effect causes increased growth of water plant life. Unlike land plants, these are not harvested and, like all plants, eventually die. Bacterial decay of the dead plant materials uses up oxygen from the water and results in foul-smelling waterways in which nothing will grow. This process is called **eutrophication.**

Nitric acid manufacture

The conversion of ammonia into nitric acid is a three-stage process:

(i) Ammonia can be oxidized to nitrogen monoxide and water:

$$4NH_3(g) + 5O_2(g) \rightarrow 4NO(g) + 6H_2O(l)$$

ammonia + oxygen → nitrogen monoxide + water

A mixture of air and ammonia (10% ammonia) is burnt over a platinum catalyst at 850 °C. The heat produced by this exothermic reaction is **recovered** by a heat exchanger.

(ii) Nitrogen monoxide is readily oxidized further to nitrogen dioxide:

$$4NO(g) + 2O_2(g) \rightarrow 4NO_2(g)$$

nitrogen monoxide + oxygen → nitrogen dioxide

(iii) The nitrogen dioxide is reacted with water and more oxygen:

$$4NO_2(g) + 2H_2O(l) + O_2(g) \rightarrow 4HNO_3(aq)$$

nitrogen dioxide + water + oxygen → nitric acid

Uses of nitric acid

The main use is in the production of ammonium nitrate (see Fig. 9.5).

Fig. 9.5 Uses of nitric acid

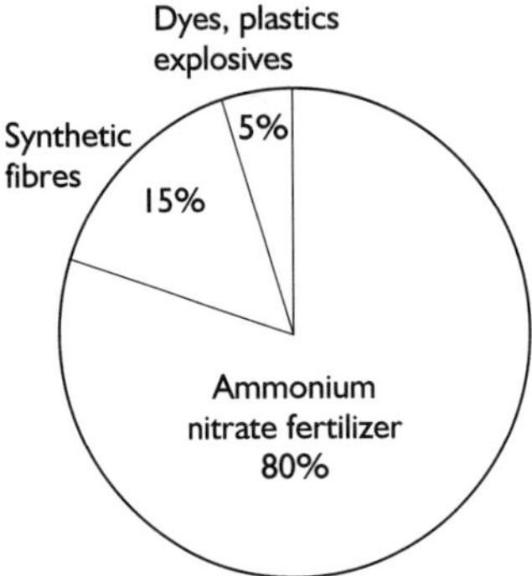

The main use of explosives such as dynamite is in the construction of roads, mining and quarrying operations.

Factory siting

As would be expected, nitric acid is made close to the plant producing the ammonia from which it is made. This means that wherever nitric acid is made there will be an ammonia plant nearby and usually on an adjacent site.

Sulphuric acid manufacture

Making sulphur dioxide

The raw materials for sulphuric acid manufacture are sulphur dioxide gas and air.

There are two main sources of sulphur dioxide gas:

(i) **Sulphur.** Sulphur is available from purification of 'sour' natural gas and from the removal of sulphur from crude oil.
Burning sulphur produces sulphur dioxide:

$$S(s) + O_2(g) \rightarrow SO_2(g) \quad \textbf{(exothermic)}$$

sulphur + oxygen → sulphur dioxide

(ii) **Sulphide ores.** The first stage of the extraction of lead or zinc from their sulphide ores produces large quantities of sulphur dioxide as a by-product:

$$2PbS(s) + 3O_2(g) \rightarrow 2PbO(s) + 2SO_2(g)$$

lead sulphide + oxygen → lead(II) oxide + sulphur dioxide

To prevent atmospheric pollution this sulphur dioxide has to be absorbed. The most favoured process is to turn it into sulphuric acid.

This method of production accounts for about 10% of UK production and about 40% of world production of sulphuric acid.

Oxidation of sulphur dioxide to sulphur trioxide

In this process, sulphur dioxide is mixed with oxygen (air) and passed through a converter containing several beds of catalyst.

'This process is called the Contact process'

The catalyst is **vanadium(V) oxide**, supported on porous silica and promoted with potassium sulphate. The catalyst is only active at temperatures above **400 °C**. The reaction is

sulphur dioxide + oxygen ⇌ sulphur trioxide

$$2SO_2(g) \quad + \quad O_2(g) \rightleftharpoons \quad 2SO_3(g) \qquad \textbf{(exothermic)}$$

The reaction is reversible and exothermic. This means that the product is a mixture of sulphur dioxide, oxygen and sulphur trioxide. The essential conditions are therefore **450 °C, normal pressure,** with a vanadium(V) oxide **catalyst.**

The effect of temperature on the equilibrium

If a reversible reaction is exothermic (gives out heat) then, in theory, **the higher the temperature the less product is obtained.** Applying this principle to the above reaction shows that **more** product, which is what is desired, is obtained at lower temperatures. Because the catalyst requires a temperature of at least 400 °C the temperature chosen must be at least that value.

The effect of temperature on the speed of reaction

Reactions go faster at higher temperatures. **If possible** then, the highest possible temperature would be chosen.

There are now *three* requirements for the process to work **economically:**

(i) a temperature of at least 400 °C for the catalyst to work;
(ii) as low a temperature as possible to push the equilibrium as far to the side of products as possible;
(iii) as high a temperature as possible for a fast reaction.

Requirements (ii) and (iii) conflict. A temperature is chosen which is as far above 400 °C as possible while still producing a good yield of the desired sulphur trioxide. The process is run at 450 °C with a yield of 99.5%.

Conversion of sulphur trioxide to sulphuric acid

Sulphur trioxide reacts strongly with water to form sulphuric acid:

$$SO_3(g) + H_2O(l) \rightarrow H_2SO_4(aq) \ \textbf{(highly exothermic)}$$

If this is carried out as shown a dangerous acid mist is produced which cannot be easily condensed to the acid. This apparently simple process is, therefore, carried out in two stages:

(i) Sulphur trioxide, $SO_3(g)$ is dissolved in 98% sulphuric acid, $H_2SO_4(l)$, without mist formation. This produces 98.5% sulphuric acid $H_2S_2O_7$ (known as oleum).
(ii) The acid concentration is then reduced to 98% by adding oleum to water.

Pollution control in the Contact process

Sulphur oxides are atmospheric pollutants. If the conversion of sulphur dioxide to sulphur trioxide is not nearly 100% then waste gases containing these oxides will be passed into the atmosphere. Because there are now strict pollution controls applied to this process, these 'emissions', as waste gases passed to the atmosphere are called, are not allowed.

This requires sulphuric acid manufacturers to make their processes extremely efficient to reduce pollution. The level of efficiency required is achieved by having a sulphur trioxide absorption section *after* the mixture has passed through three catalyst beds. Removal of the product of a reversible reaction assists formation of more products. The final stage will then remove most of the remaining unreacted sulphur dioxide. Emissions from such a process can be as low as 300 ppm of sulphur dioxide. (ppm is parts per million, a common unit of measurement for pollution. One cubic centimetre of pollutant gas in one thousand litres is 1 ppm.)

Economics of the process

The economics of a chemical process demand that the product be made as quickly as possible

- 'Time is money' when labour is paid for by the hour and bank interest has to be paid on money borrowed to build the factory and its chemical plant. It is for these reasons that catalysts and high temperatures are used where possible.
- The oxidation of sulphur to sulphur trioxide, followed by reaction with water, produces a lot of heat. This heat is removed by 'heat exchangers' and is sold as steam to nearby users.
- The running costs of a sulphuric acid plant include the cost of sulphur, maintenance materials and wages of workers at the plant. However, the income from the sale of steam normally covers all running costs except the cost of the sulphur.

'Several existing sulphuric acid plants were originally sited close to a source of sulphur—calcium sulphate. It is now more economical, however, to import sulphur from overseas, than to use the naturally occurring sulphur compounds nearby'

Siting of a sulphuric acid plant

The acid is expensive to transport. It requires stainless-steel-lined tankers. There are dangers from tanker accidents. The plant is normally built close to places of use. If imported liquid sulphur is used to make the sulphur dioxide, then the plant must be close to a port or have good rail access.

Uses of sulphuric acid (Fig. 9.6)

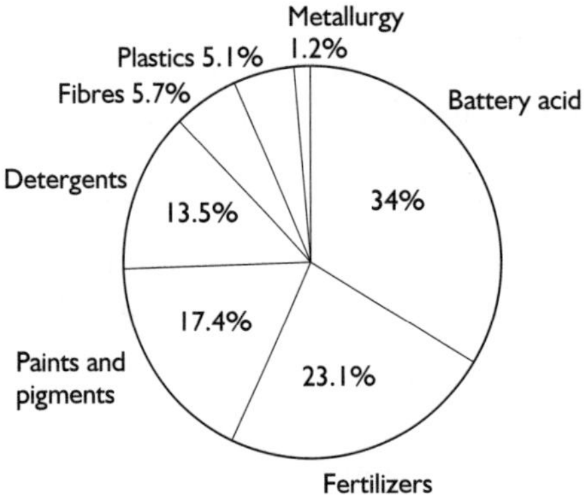

Fig. 9.6 Uses of sulphuric acid

Superphosphate manufacture

Rock phosphate, an ore containing calcium phosphate, is being mined in many parts of the world as a phosphatic fertilizer. The phosphate in it is not, however, very soluble in water and so is not rapidly available to plants. Plants use phosphates for root development and a good supply is vital for strong growth. Rock phosphate can be **made more soluble** by treatment with concentrated sulphuric acid. In the process **calcium 'superphosphate'** is formed which is quite soluble in water.

Rock phosphate can also be converted into phosphoric acid by reaction with sulphuric acid. The phosphoric acid is then neutralized with ammonia to form ammonium phosphate, which is both a nitrogenous and a phosphatic fertilizer.

Prosperity and acid production

Sulphuric acid is used in the production of many of the country's most important products (see Fig. 9.6). The production of sulphuric acid used to be an indicator of industrial prosperity. The more sulphuric acid used, the more a country's industry was producing. This is no longer so. Industrial production has remained fairly level in Britain since 1980 but manufacture of sulphuric acid has dropped because many of the products manufactured using sulphuric acid are now imported from abroad.

EXAMINATION QUESTIONS

Question 1 (F)

Sulphuric acid is essential to any country with a chemical industry.

(a) The charts below show the uses of sulphuric acid in an industrialized country and a developing country in 1990 (Fig. 9.7). By 1994, the chart for the industrialized country had hardly changed, but the chart for the developing country had changed significantly.

Fig. 9.7

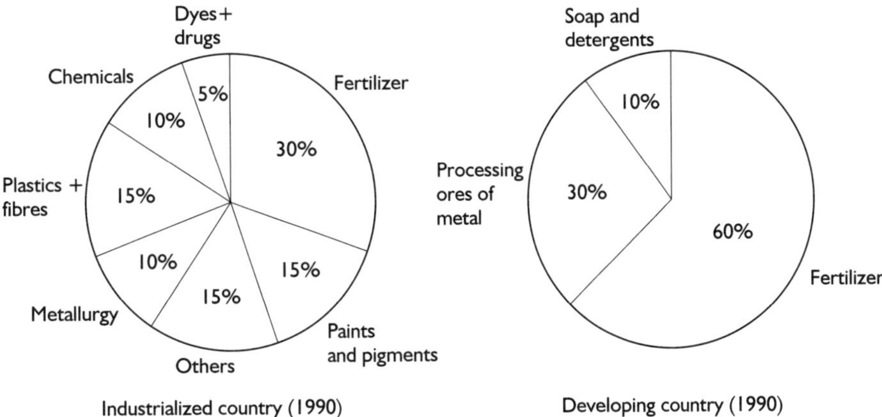

(i) What were the two major industries in the developing country in 1990? [1 line] *[2]*

(ii) Draw a chart for the developing country in 1994, showing the likely changes as the country becomes more industrialized (Fig. 9.8). *[2]*

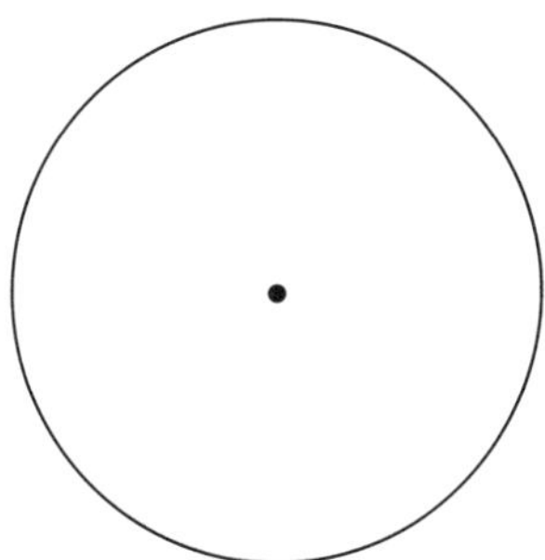

Fig. 9.8 Suggested chart for developing country in 1994

(b) Sulphuric acid is manufactured by the Contact process. The reactions involved are as follows:

sulphur + oxygen ⟶ gas A

gas A + oxygen $\xrightarrow{\text{catalyst B}}$ sulphur trioxide

sulphur trioxide + liquid C ⟶ oleum

oleum + liquid D ⟶ sulphuric acid

Give the name of:

gas A ______________________ *[1]*

catalyst B ______________________ *[1]*

liquid C ______________________ *[1]*

liquid D ______________________ *[1]*

[Total 8 marks]

(IGCSE)

Question 2(H)

Sulphuric acid is an important industrial acid; about 130 million tonnes were made in 1982. The following flow diagram (Fig. 9.9) shows the main steps in its manufacture by the Contact process.

Fig. 9.9 The main stages are:
1. obtaining sulphur dioxide;
2. oxidizing sulphur dioxide to sulphur trioxide;
3. converting the sulphur trioxide to sulphuric acid

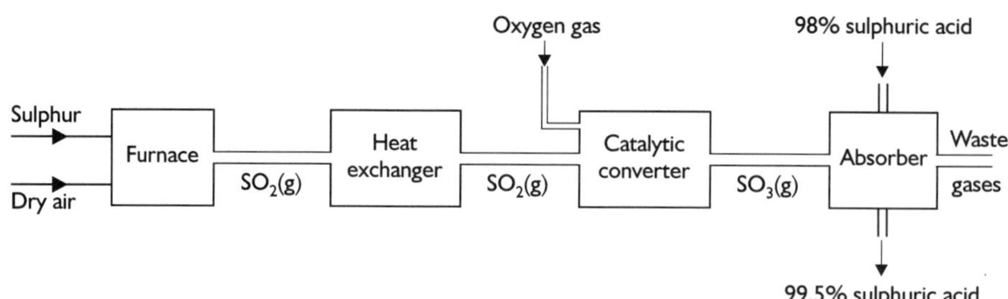

(a) Write an equation for the burning of sulphur. [1 line] *[1]*
(b) Name another substance that would react with dry air on heating to form sulphur dioxide. [1 line] *[1]*
(c) What is the use of the heat exchanger? [1 line] *[1]*
(d) Write the equation for the reaction taking place in the catalytic converter and name the catalyst used. [1 line] *[2]*
(e) The sulphur trioxide is absorbed in 98% sulphuric acid and not in water, give a reason for this and write the equation for the absorption. [2 lines] *[2]*
(f) Explain why manufacturers build sulphuric acid plants near other chemical works. [2 lines] *[2]*
(g) Sulphur dioxide is one pollutant that forms 'acid rain'. Give one important source of this sulphur dioxide. [1 line] *[1]*
(h) Give one reason why 'acid rain' is a problem. *[1]*

(WJEC)

Question 3(H)

Ammonia is manufactured by the Haber process in which nitrogen and hydrogen are combined over an iron catalyst at, for example, 200 atmospheres pressure and 400 °C.

$$N_2(g) + 3H_2(g) \rightleftharpoons 2NH_3(g)$$

(a) What mass of ammonia could be manufactured from 1 tonne of nitrogen (assuming 100% yield was obtained). (Relative atomic masses: H = 1, N = 14) [5 lines] *[4]*
(b) Explain why a high pressure is used in this process. [5 lines] *[3]*
(c) Ammonia is used to manufacture nitrogenous fertilizers.
   (i) Why do nitrogenous fertilizers need to be soluble in water?
   (ii) How can excessive use of such fertilizers cause environmental problems? *[3]*

[Total 10 marks]

Question 4(H)

In the manufacture of sulphuric acid sulphur dioxide is oxidized to sulphur trioxide.

$$\text{sulphur dioxide} + \text{oxygen} \xrightarrow{\text{catalyst}} \text{sulphur trioxide}$$

(a) (i) Name the catalyst used in the industrial process. [1 line] *[1]*
   (ii) Why is a catalyst used in this reaction? Give two reasons. [1 line] *[2]*
   (iii) Write the balanced equation for this reaction. [1 line] *[2]*
(b) State one use of concentrated sulphuric acid. [1 line] *[1]*
(c) Dilute sulphuric acid is made by mixing concentrated sulphuric acid with water.
   (i) Why is it important that the acid is added to the water and not the other way round? [2 lines] *[2]*
   (ii) Explain why the acidic properties of sulphuric acid only appear when water is present? [2 lines] *[2]*

[Total 10 marks]

Question 5(H) Carefully read the following passage and then answer the questions which follow it. The map (Fig. 9.10) shows the location of a fertilizer factory and two power stations in the Belfast area.

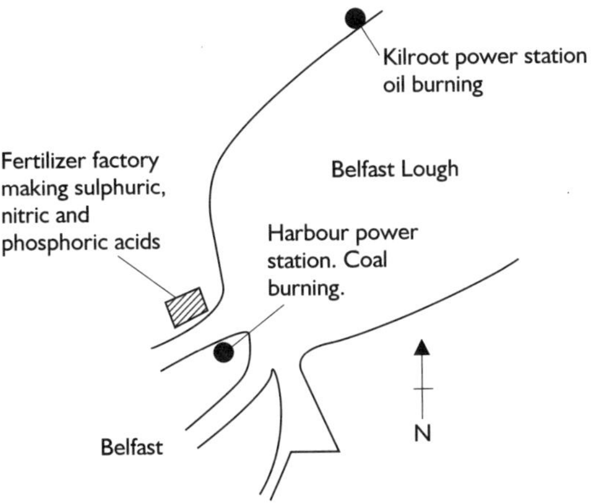

Fig. 9.10 (This illustration is by courtesy of the British Plastics Federation.)

All the raw materials needed at the power stations and fertilizer factory must be imported, although it is hoped to generate power from locally mined lignite at some time in the future.

The location of the power stations means that the giant cooling towers seen at power stations in England are not needed.

Both sulphuric and nitric acids are manufactured in the fertilizer factory. The sulphuric acid produced at the fertilizer factory is used to make phosphoric acid from phosphate rock. The fertilizer factory markets fertilizers which are mixtures of the ammonium salts of the acids made at the factory. A plume of brown smoke is often seen rising from the nitric acid plant, and this, and other gases from the factory and power stations, contributes to the atmospheric pollution in the area.

(a) List *four* raw materials which must be imported for use either in the power stations, or the fertilizer factory. [2 lines] *[4]*

(b) (i) Name the main chemical found in phosphate rock. *[1]*

(ii) Write a word equation for the reaction between sulphuric acid and phosphate rock. *[1]*

(iii) Write a word equation for the reaction between ammonia and phosphoric acid. *[1]*

(c) Write a symbol equation for the reaction between ammonia and sulphuric acid. *[2]*

(d) Name another chemical made at the factory which is an ingredient of the mixed fertilizers. *[1]*

(e) (i) Name the brown gas in the smoke given off at the fertilizer factory. *[1]*

(ii) Name *two* other gases which pollute the atmosphere over these industries and state which process gives off the gas. *[4]*

(f) Winds in the Belfast area blow mostly from the south-west. Does this have any effect on atmospheric pollution over Belfast caused by these industries? *[1]*

(g) (i) Why are large cooling towers not needed at the power stations? [1 line] *[1]*

(ii) How does this affect the environment? [1 line] *[1]*

(h) Would burning lignite make much change to atmospheric pollution? Give a reason for your answer. [2 lines] *[2]*

(NICCEA)

OUTLINE ANSWERS

Question 1 (a) (i) The two major industries in the developing country were farming (fertilizer manufacture uses much of the sulphuric acid) and metal mining (metal ore processing used the next largest quantity of acid).

(ii) The chart should show at least one *new industry* such as plastics and fibres, *[1]* though it would not be expected to take such a big portion *[1]* of the total acid production as in a developed country at an early stage. Which particular new industry is chosen is not important.

(b) Gas A is sulphur dioxide.
Catalyst B is vanadium(V) oxide.
Liquid C is concentrated sulphuric acid.
Liquid D is water. *[1 mark] each*

Question 2 This question is mainly about the Contact process and its processes discussed in the text.

(a) Sulphur burns in the **oxygen** of the air *[1]*.

$$S(l) + O_2(g) \rightarrow SO_2(g)$$

sulphur + oxygen → sulphur dioxide

No sulphur trioxide is formed when sulphur burns in air.

(b) Most sulphur compounds will **burn** in air to give sulphur dioxide. H_2S, hydrogen sulphide, will burn to give sulphur dioxide *[1]*.

(c) The heat exchanger shown in the flow diagram absorbs heat from the waste gases before they are disposed of. It is an **economizing measure***[1]*.

(d) In the converter, sulphur dioxide is oxidized to sulphur trioxide. The catalyst is vanadium(V) oxide:

$$2SO_2(g) + O_2(g) \rightarrow 2SO_2(g)$$ *[1]*

(e) Sulphur trioxide reacts violently with water, producing a mist, *[1]* which is difficult to condense, and a considerable quantity of heat. Absorption in concentrated sulphuric acid reduces both these effects.

$$H_2SO_4(l) + SO_3(g) \rightarrow H_2S_2O_7(l)$$ *[1]*

(f) This will cut costs of transport, *[1]* reduce risks of accidents with the acid *[1]* and also will enable the sale of recovered heat energy to other plant operators if they are very close *[1]*.

(g) Sulphur dioxide is emitted by any coal-burning process *[1]*. Coal-fired power stations emit large amounts because they burn enormous quantities of coal per year. Crude oil often contains sulphur compounds and if burnt would also pollute the air.

(h) Acid rain is said to damage forests. It acidifies lakes and so kills fish and aquatic plants *[1]*.

Question 3 (a) From the equation, 2×14 (28 tonnes) *[1]* of nitrogen produces 2×17 (34 tonnes) of ammonia *[1]*. So 1 tonne of nitrogen will produce 34/28 tonnes *[1]* of ammonia = 1.21 tonnes *[1]*.

(b) The reaction occurs with a reduction in the number of molecules *[1]*. Le Chatelier's principle states that if pressure is increased, the position of equilibrium *[1]* will move to the side with the smaller number of molecules *[1]*.

(c) (i) Plants cannot take up fertilizer unless it is in solution *[1]*.
(ii) They get washed or leached into ditches/rivers *[1]* and produce excessive growth and decay of plants which deplete water of its oxygen *[1]* or cause **eutrophication** *[1]*.

Question 4 (a) (i) Vanadium(V) oxide/vanadium pentoxide *[1]*.
(ii) The catalyst speeds up the reaction *[1]* and makes the process more economic *[1]*.
(iii) $2SO_2(g) + O_2(g) \rightarrow 2SO_3(g)$ or $SO_2(g) + \frac{1}{2}O_2(g) \rightarrow SO_3(g)$
[1 for formulae; 1 for balance.]

(b) Battery acid or fertilizer manufacture or paint making *[1]*.

(c) (i) Diluting the acid with water gives out a lot of heat *[1]*. To ensure the heat is spread throughout the solution, acid is added to water *[1]*; otherwise water would float on the acid *[1]* if added to it and heat would concentrate in the top layer *[1]*, causing risk of spitting.
(ii) Water reacts to form hydrogen ions, H^+ *[1]*, which cause acidity *[1]*.

Question 5 This is a comprehension exercise. Apart from some chemical knowledge, you will need to keep looking to the text for information you may not have.

(a) The materials required are those needed to make the two acids, nitric and sulphuric, together with the imported raw material for phosphate production. There are *more than* four so *any four* will do. Note that *all materials* must be imported—brought in from abroad *[1]* × *4*.

(b) (i) and (ii) are connected. If (i) is not known (ii) can only be guessed at (see p. 130). (iii) is straightforward, leading to the ammonium salt, which is a dual-nutrient fertilizer.

(c) Remember that sulphuric acid has *two* hydrogen atoms to be replaced by ammonium ions.

(d) Another ammonium salt is required.

(e) (i) The brown gas is nitrogen dioxide, one of the chemicals formed in the manufacture of nitric acid. (Modern plants would not emit such pollution.)

(ii) You must give two pollutants *[2] and* two processes which produce them *[2]*. Look again at the map—do you see other sources of pollution?

(f) The effect of wind direction is important in factory siting. In this case, the prevailing wind is favourable—you must *say why*.

(g) (i) and (ii) are probably general knowledge. Remember that absence of cooling towers does not mean the local engineers have discovered a way of producing power without cooling!

(h) This question asks for your considered judgement about a situation you may not be familiar with. Marks are awarded in such questions for reasonable comments relevant to the problem rather than the 'correct answer'.

STUDENT ANSWER WITH EXAMINER'S COMMENTS

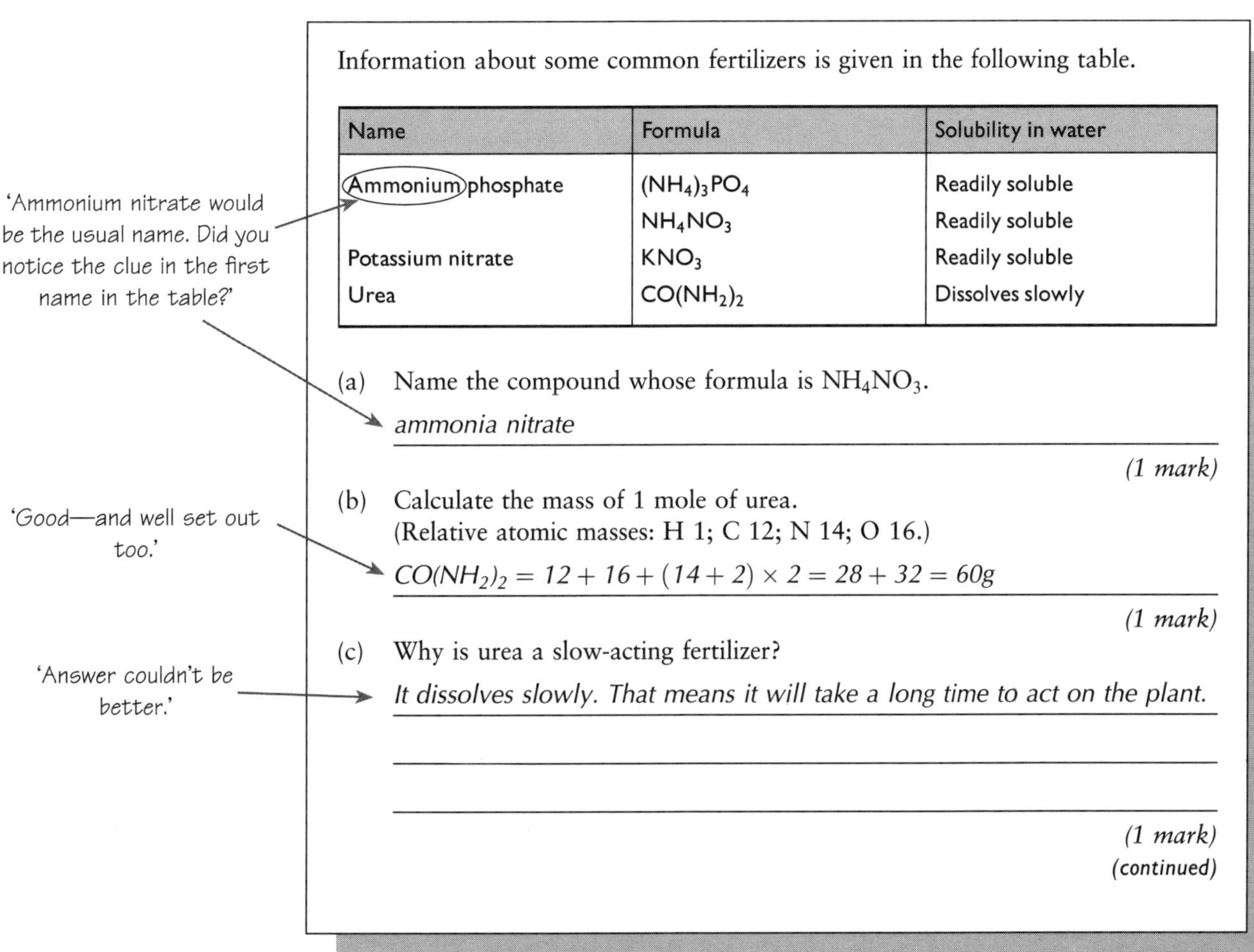

Information about some common fertilizers is given in the following table.

Name	Formula	Solubility in water
Ammonium phosphate	$(NH_4)_3PO_4$	Readily soluble
	NH_4NO_3	Readily soluble
Potassium nitrate	KNO_3	Readily soluble
Urea	$CO(NH_2)_2$	Dissolves slowly

(a) Name the compound whose formula is NH_4NO_3.

ammonia nitrate

(1 mark)

(b) Calculate the mass of 1 mole of urea.
(Relative atomic masses: H 1; C 12; N 14; O 16.)

$CO(NH_2)_2 = 12 + 16 + (14 + 2) \times 2 = 28 + 32 = 60g$

(1 mark)

(c) Why is urea a slow-acting fertilizer?

It dissolves slowly. That means it will take a long time to act on the plant.

(1 mark)

(continued)

'Ammonium nitrate would be the usual name. Did you notice the clue in the first name in the table?'
'Good—and well set out too.'
'Answer couldn't be better.'

(continued)

(d) How can good plant growth be maintained if chemical fertilizers like those in the table are not used?

I think the farmer would have to use manure from cows or pigs or waste from breweries—as they do near my home—phew!

'Nice to see you applying your experience! Yes natural manures often do smell!'

(2 marks)

(e) Another substance which may be added to soil is hydrated lime $Ca(OH)_2$.

(i) What is the chemical name for hydrated lime?

calcium hydroxide

'Good—you have "read" the formula (Ca for calcium, OH for hydroxide).'

(1 mark)

(ii) What is the main reason for adding hydrated lime to soil?

To make it alkaline.

'If you added a great deal it might do that, but the main reason is to *neutralize* acidity in the soil. This is usually caused by use of ammonium compounds as fertilizer.'

(1 mark)

(iii) Why should hydrated lime and ammonium phosphate *not* be applied to the soil at the same time?

ammonium phosphate would react with the lime.

'Yes it would. But TWO marks are given—and three lines for the answer. You could have guessed that TWO points should be made. "They react to form *ammonia gas which would escape and be lost to the crops*".'

(2 marks)

ISEG-Nuffield Alternative I

SUMMARY

Use this list to help you with your revision. Tick off the points as you revise them in the text.

- ▷ Nitrogen fixation is the conversion of the element nitrogen to nitrogen **compounds**.
- ▷ The nitrogen cycle shows how the element circulates in nature and how it moves from the air to the soil and back.
- ▷ **Ammonia** is manufactured from nitrogen and hydrogen in a **synthesis** reaction called the **Haber process**.
- ▷ The hydrogen is usually extracted from methane; the nitrogen from the **air**.
- ▷ The Haber process needs a temperature of **400 °C**, a pressure of more than **200 atmospheres** and an **iron catalyst**.
- ▷ The two main uses of ammonia are to make **fertilizers** and to make **nitric acid**.
- ▷ Fertilizers are **nitrogenous** compounds.
- ▷ The commonest nitrogenous fertilizer is **ammonium nitrate**, which contains **35% nitrogen** available to plants as a nutrient for growth.
- ▷ Nitric acid is made by **oxidizing** ammonia.
- ▷ Ammonium nitrate is made by **neutralizing** ammonia with nitric acid.
- ▷ Ammonia plant and nitric acid plant would be sited next to each other for **economic reasons**.
- ▷ The three major essential elements for plant growth are nitrogen (**N**), phosphorus (**P**) and potassium (**K**).
- ▷ The need for **protein**, which is manufactured by plants from nitrogenous compounds in the soil, has fostered the **worldwide use** of synthetic fertilizers.
- ▷ **Protein** is more likely to be deficient in the diet of people in underdeveloped countries than **fats** or **carbohydrates**.
- ▷ **Over-use** of any fertilizer can have a damaging effect on the environment, causing **eutrophication** of rivers and lakes.
- ▷ Eutrophication results in
- ▷ of oxygen in water, causing death of aquatic life. This is caused by **bacterial decomposition** of the **overabundance** of vegetation caused by the **excess** of fertilizer.
- ▷ **Sulphuric acid** is made from sulphur via sulphur dioxide, sulphur trioxide and oleum.
- ▷ Sulphur will burn in air to **sulphur dioxide** but not to sulphur trioxide.
- ▷ Sulphur dioxide is oxidized to **sulphur trioxide** at **450 °C** using a **vanadium(V) oxide** catalyst and **normal pressure**.
- ▷ This catalysed reaction is the **Contact** process.
- ▷ To make sulphuric acid, sulphur trioxide must be reacted with **water**.
- ▷ This reaction is carried out **indirectly** in two stages.
  - (i) Sulphur trioxide is reacted with concentrated sulphuric acid to form '**oleum**'—a 'superconcentrated' acid.
  - (ii) Oleum is then diluted with water to form concentrated sulphuric acid of **98% concentration**.
- ▷ Despite the fact that the reaction does not go to 100% completion, the **pollution** from the process is **very small**.
- ▷ All the reactions in the manufacture of sulphuric acid are **exothermic**. This allows the manufacturing company to **utilize waste heat to make electricity** and even to **sell it** to electrical supply companies.
- ▷ Two major uses of sulphuric acid are as **battery acid** and to make **fertilizer**.
- ▷ The main **fertilizer** made with sulphuric acid is calcium **superphosphate**.

Chapter

10 Electrochemistry

GETTING STARTED

One of the many ways of classifying substances is on their ability to pass an electric current. We can divide all known substances into two groups; conductors and non-conductors.

- A substance that allows electricity to pass through it is a **conductor**.
- Substances which do not allow electricity to pass through them are **non-conductors** or insulators.

The chemist's main interest is in conductors of a special type. These are called **electrolytes.** An electrolyte differs from other types of conductor in two major properties. An electrolyte is

- a compound of a metal with a non-metal, i.e. an ionic compound;
- **decomposed** if a **direct** current is passed through it (a.c. won't do!).
- only decomposed if the compound is **molten** or **dissolved in water**—the ions must be **free to move** in the electric current.

Electrolysis is the decomposition of a compound into its elements by passage of electricity.

The word *electrolysis* is derived from two Greek words *electro* and *lusis* meaning 'splitting by electricity'. Electrolysis is only useful for extracting elements if they form ionic compounds.

The elements usefully extracted by electrolysis are:

- aluminium from bauxite;
- chlorine from concentrated brine (sodium chloride from salt deposits);
- pure copper from impure copper;
- sodium metal from molten sodium chloride.

TOPIC CHART

LONDON	MEG	NEAB	NICCEA	SEG	WJEC	TOPIC	STUDY	REVISION 1	REVISION 2
✓	✓	✓	✓	✓	✓	Electrolysis			
✓	✓	✓	✓	✓	✓	The typical electrolysis circuit			
	✓	✓	✓	✓		The products of electrolysis			
✓	✓	✓	✓	✓	✓	Molten electrolytes			
	✓	✓	✓	✓		Aqueous electrolytes			
✓	✓	✓	✓	✓	✓	Summary of important electrolyses			
✓		✓				Other electrolytic processes			
	✓			✓		Electrolysis calculations			

WHAT YOU NEED TO KNOW

Electrolysis

Electrolysis is carried out by inserting two **electrodes** into the electrolyte and passing a **direct current** through it. A convenient direct current source is a battery or a lab-pack. A d.c. source will have a positive and a negative terminal. The electrodes are made of graphite (a fairly inert non-metal) or an inert metal such as stainless steel, platinum or titanium. Sometimes the electrode is required to dissolve away during the electrolysis in which case it will **not** be made of an inert metal (see p. 143). The material chosen for the electrodes must be unreactive to both the electrolyte and to the electrode products—unless it is convenient or economic to allow reaction to occur (see the electrolysis of alumina).

The electrolyte must contain freely moving ions. As the current passes through the electrolyte, the ions move to the electrode which has **a charge opposite to their own charge.**

The electrode connected to the positive terminal of the supply is called the **anode.** The anode attracts negatively charged ions called **anions.**

The electrode connected to the negative terminal of the supply is called the **cathode.** The cathode attracts positively charged ions called **cations.**

Ions from the electrolyte are **discharged** at both electrodes, forming products which are elements.

- The *cathode product* is always either a *metal* or *hydrogen.*
- The *anode product* is always a *non-metallic* element such as a halogen or oxygen.
- The *electrode product* may be a *deposit* of a solid element or it may be a gas, in which case the gas bubbles to the surface of the electrolyte and can be collected if required (see Fig. 10.2 below).

Note: The use of an alternating supply (mains a.c. supply) would cause the electrodes to alternate between being anodes and cathodes fifty times per second and **no electrolysis** would occur.

The typical electrolysis circuit

The main features of the circuit are:

(i) A d.c. supply to provide an electrolysing current with positive and negative electrodes when connected.
(ii) A and C are the anode (+) and cathode (−) in Fig. 10.1 below.
(iii) The electrolyte is a molten ionic compound or an aqueous solution of a salt, an acid or an alkali. The important requirement of an electrolyte is that it contains **mobile ions.**
(iv) The electrolysis is carried out in an electrolysis cell. This can be any vessel which will
  (a) contain the liquid electrolyte;
  (b) allow the insertion of the electrodes; and
  (c) allow the collection or removal of the products.

A beaker is best for electrolysis in which a metal is deposited on the cathode (Fig. 10.1). The types of apparatus shown in Fig. 10.2 below are better if gases are to be collected.

Fig. 10.1 Electrolysis of solutions

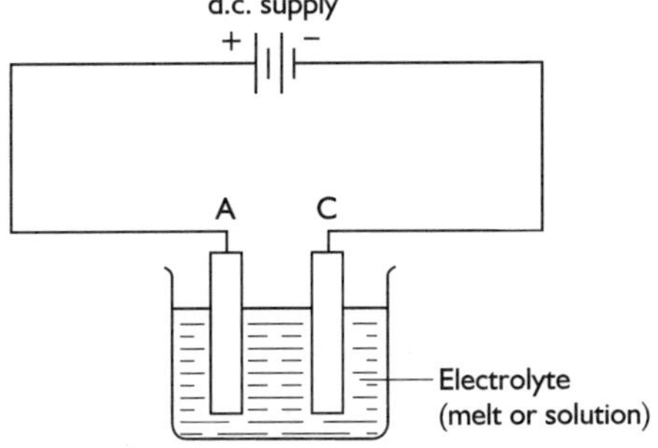

The products of electrolysis

Ionic compounds usually contain one metal and one or more non-metallic elements. If there is one metal and one non-metal present, the compound will be electrolysed to the metal at the cathode and the non-metal at the anode; for example, NaCl when molten will produce sodium at the cathode and chlorine at the anode.

Fig. 10.2

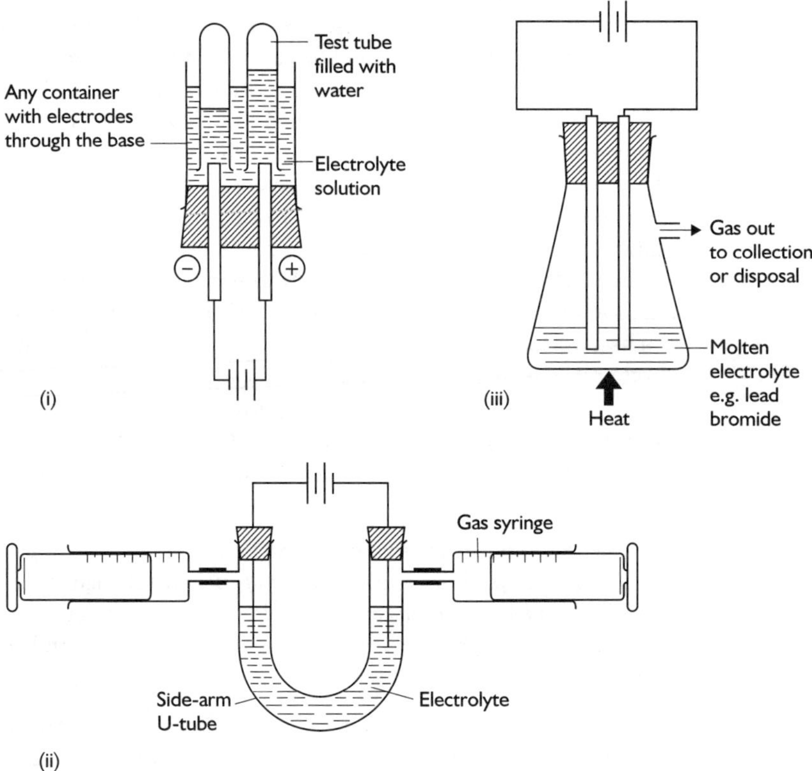

Molten electrolytes

At this level these will be simple binary compounds, i.e. they will contain only two elements—a metal and a non-metal. The **metal** will be the **cathode product**; the **non-metal** will be the **anode product**.

An example is the electrolysis of molten lead bromide, $PbBr_2(l)$. A carbon anode and a steel cathode are suitably **inert** electrodes (see Fig. 10.2(iii)).

At the anode (+)

Anodes are positively charged because they are **lacking in electrons**. Anions, on the other hand are negatively charged ions—they are atoms or groups of atoms with an **excess** of electrons. In this example the anode accepts one electron from each anion. We say the anion is *dis*charged at the anode:

$$2Br^-(l) - 2e^- \rightarrow Br_2(g)$$

2 bromide ions minus 2 electrons → 1 bromine gas molecule

Bromine gas is the product as the temperature of the molten lead bromide is above the boiling point of bromine.

Because the anion loses electrons to the anode the process is one of **oxidation** of the anion at the anode: anodic oxidation.

'The equations for the discharge of ions at the anode and cathode are often badly done in examination answers. Make the effort to understand them so that you do not lose marks on these easy equations.'

At the cathode (−)

Cathodes are negatively charged because they have an **excess of electrons.**

Cations are positively charged ions—they are atoms of groups of atoms with one or more electrons missing. They are electron **deficient.**

In this example the cathode gives two electrons to each lead cation. The lead cations are discharged at the cathode:

$$Pb^{2+}(l) + 2e^- \rightarrow Pb(l)$$

lead ion plus 2 electrons → lead metal atom

Molten lead is the product at the cathode since lead (m.p. 323 °C) is a liquid at the temperature of the molten lead bromide, m.p. 373 °C.

'Cathodic reduction'

Because the cation gains electrons from the cathode the process is one of **reduction** of the cation at the cathode: cathodic reduction.

Overall, the lead bromide is decomposed into the elements lead and bromine:

$$PbBr_2(l) \rightarrow Pb(l) + Br_2(g).$$

Revision: A useful exercise is to explain what happens when molten lithium chloride, LiCl, is electrolysed. Base your explanation on the two sections above. The same exercise should be done for zinc chloride $ZnCl_2$ for MEG candidates.

Aqueous electrolytes

These are really mixtures of **two** electrolytes—**the compound and water.** Water itself is a very weak electrolyte. It is slightly ionized:

$$H_2O(l) \rightleftharpoons H^+(aq) + OH^-(aq).$$

Because the hydrogen ions ($H^+(aq)$) and the hydroxyl ions ($OH^-(aq)$) are **in equilibrium** with water molecules in any aqueous solution, these ions will be replaced as quickly as they are removed. This means that these two ions from water behave **as if** they were present in large concentrations. They can be discharged as any other ions are discharged.

Predicting the electrolysis products for aqueous solutions

It is possible to understand why aqueous solutions produce the observed products by looking at the **'reactivity series'** for cations and anions as shown in Table 10.1. These are similar to reactivity series studied elsewhere in this book.

Table 10.1

Reactivity series for cations	Reactivity series for anions	
Potassium	Sulphate	These ions are *never* discharged
Sodium	Nitrate	
Calcium	Carbonate	
Magnesium		
Aluminium		
Hydrogen	Oxide/hydroxide	
Zinc	Chloride	
Tin	Bromide	
Lead	Iodide	
Copper		
Silver		

'Stable ions do not discharge'

The ion **lowest** in the tables above will be discharged at each electrode in preference to any other ion present. The **most reactive** metals **form the most stable ions**. Therefore, these ions will be difficult to convert back to metals. This will cause the least reactive metals to discharge instead. Similarly, the **least reactive non-metals** will be **most easily discharged.** By *listing* the ions present at each electrode and consulting the tables above, the main products can be found.

Using the table to understand the products of electrolysis

For example, consider the electrolysis of concentrated aqueous sodium chloride, NaCl(aq), using graphite (carbon) electrodes. When the current is switched on, one electrode becomes positively charged and the other becomes negatively charged. Negatively charged ions are attracted to the anode (+) and positively charged ions to the cathode (−).

At the anode (+)

The ions **attracted** will be OH^- (aq) from the water and Cl^-(aq) from the sodium chloride. Of the two ions, the chloride ion will be preferentially discharged since it is lower in the above table than the hydroxide ion.

$$2Cl^-(aq) - 2e^- \xrightarrow{\text{loss of 2 electrons to anode}} Cl_2(g)$$

At the cathode (−)

The ions **attracted** will be the H^+(aq) from water and the Na^+(aq) from the sodium chloride. Of the two, the lowest in the table will be preferentially discharged. This is the hydrogen ion.

$$2H^+(aq) + 2e^- \xrightarrow{\text{gain of 2 electrons from the cathode}} H_2(g)$$

It is a requirement of electrolysis that the same number of electrons should feature in both electrode equations. This is because the electrons that are picked up by the anode are passed round the circuit to the cathode where they are given to the discharging cations.

Overall reactions

$$2NaCl(aq) + 2H_2O(l) \rightarrow 2Na^+(aq) + 2OH^-(aq) + H_2(g) + Cl_2(g)$$

The ions that have not been discharged remain in solution and are equivalent to a solution of sodium hydroxide. The products of electrolysis of sodium chloride are therefore:

aqueous sodium hydroxide + hydrogen + chlorine

When carried out industrially, this process is the basis of the **chlor-alkali** industry. The most important products are the sodium hydroxide (the alkali) and chlorine. Huge tonnages of these are used annually all over the world.

Summary of some important electrolyses

Table 10.2 Some important electrolyses

Electrolyte	Anode product	Cathode product	Other observations
1. The manufacture of aluminium			
Molten aluminium oxide **Ions**: Al^{3+}(l) and O^{2-}(l)	Oxygen at carbon anode. Anode slowly oxidized to carbon dioxide	Molten aluminium at carbon cathode	Electrolyte is a mixture of alumina (aluminium oxide) with cryolite to lower its melting point
	Overall reaction: $2Al_2O_3(l) \rightarrow 4Al(l) + 3O_2(g)$		
2. The electrolysis of dilute hydrochloric acid			
Dilute hydrochloric acid **Ions**: H^+(aq) and Cl^-(aq) $H^+(aq) + OH^-(aq)$ from water	Chlorine at inert anode	Hydrogen at inert cathode	Equal volumes of the gases are produced
	Overall reaction: $2HCl(aq) \rightarrow H_2(g) + Cl_2(g)$		
If the acid is *very* dilute hydrogen and oxygen are produced.			
3. The electrolysis of water			
Dilute aqueous sulphuric acid **Ions**: H^+(aq) and SO_4^{2-}(aq) $H^+(aq) + OH^-(aq)$ from water	Oxygen at inert anode	Hydrogen at inert cathode	In effect, water is decomposed. Sulphuric acid remains unaffected
Overall reaction: $2H_2O(l) \rightarrow 2H_2(g) + O_2(g)$ water has been decomposed			

'One day this process may be used to produce hydrogen gas a a motor vehicle fuel. It will need a cheap source of electricity to become an acceptable fuel.'

Table 10.2 *(Continued)*

Electrolyte	Anode product	Cathode product	Other observations
4. The manufacture of chlorine and sodium hydroxide			
Concentrated aqueous sodium chloride	Chlorine at inert anode $OH^-(aq)$ ions accumulate around anode	Hydrogen at inert anode. $Na^+(aq)$ ions accumulate around cathode	The loss of hydrogen and chlorine leaves sodium hydroxide solution as product
Ions: $Na^+(aq)$ and $Cl^-(aq)$ $H^+(aq) + OH^-(aq)$ from water	**Overall reaction**: $2NaCl(aq) + 2H_2O(l) \rightarrow 2NaOH(aq) + H_2(g) + Cl_2(g)$		
5. The industrial refining of copper			
Aqueous copper(II) sulphate at copper electrodes	Copper anode dissolves	Copper deposits on cathode	Copper is transferred from anode to cathode. Electrolyte concentration remains constant
Ions: $Cu^{2+}(aq)$, $SO_4^{2-}(aq)$ $H^+(aq) + OH^-(aq)$ from water	**Overall reaction**: Cu (impure) $\rightarrow$ Cu (pure) Copper has been purified		

Other electrolytic processes

Electroplating

This is an electrolysis in which

(i) the **cathode** is an object to be **metal coated**; and
(ii) the electrolyte must contain **ions of the metal** to be coated onto the cathode.

The anode is usually a piece of the plating metal, e.g. a piece of silver for silver plating. Examples include the silver plating of trophies, jewellery and cutlery; gold plating of microprocessor connections; zinc plating of steel (galvanizing); chromium and nickel plating of parts for bicycles and cars.

A special example of an electroplating process is used to purify (refine) copper. This is called **copper refining**, see Table 10.2 above. In this process, the anode is a plate of impure copper (about 90% pure). The cathode is a very thin plate of pure copper. Before the electrolysis, the cathode is very lightly greased. Electrolysis is carried out in an aqueous solution of copper(II) sulphate.

During the electrolysis the copper present in the impure copper anode dissolves into the electrolyte and is then plated onto the original, pure copper cathode. When all the copper from the anode has deposited on the cathode, the anode and cathode are replaced and the process is repeated (see Table 10.3, p. 145).

Because of the light greasing of the original cathode, the deposited copper can be **peeled off** and the thin cathode reused. Pure copper of 'five-nines' (i.e. 99.999%) purity is used for electrical wires.

Anodizing

Whereas electroplating is a process which occurs on the cathode, anodizing occurs on the anode. **Anodizing** is the electrolytic process of coating objects made of aluminium with a very thin **oxide film** to protect the metal from corrosion and dulling of the surface shine.

Electrolysis calculations

By including an ammeter and a variable resistor in the circuit shown in Fig. 10.1, the **current** passing through an electrolyte can be controlled and measured. The **mass** of an element deposited in a **given time** at either electrode can be measured, usually by weighing the electrode before and after the electrolysis for metallic deposits.

Carrying out experiments like this, Michael Faraday discovered that:

The mass of an element deposited at an electrode is directly proportional to the quantity of electricity passed.

We can understand why this is by recognizing that every **atom** produced requires a definite number of electrons to be either added to or removed from the **ion** being *dis*charged. For example,

one Cu^{2+} ion *plus* 2 electrons → one Cu atom

or

one Cl^- ion *minus* 1 electron → one Cl atom

So, the more electrons passed (higher current for the same time or the same current for longer time) the more atoms are discharged and the greater the mass of the element produced. Faraday realized that the quantity of electricity was a measure of the number of electrons passing round the circuit.

Quantity of electricity

- The quantity of electricity passing during electrolysis is measured by **the quantity of electrical charge.**
- Quantity of charge is a measure of the **number of electrons** passed through the electrolyte.
- Quantity of electrical charge is calculated as

current in amps × time in seconds

- An important quantity of charge is the **charge on one mole of electrons**, called the faraday
- One Faraday is equal to 96 500 coulombs (amp seconds).

Looking at the discharge of copper ions in the electrolysis of aqueous copper salts, we write the cathode reaction as

$$Cu^{2+}(aq) \quad + \quad 2e^- \quad \longrightarrow \quad Cu(s)$$

1 mole of copper ions + 2 moles of electrons ⟶ 1 mole of copper atoms

Since 1 mole of copper weighs 63.5 g and 1 mole of electrons corresponds to 1 Faraday of charge, we see that

- 63.5 g copper results from 2 Faradays of charge passed;

so

- 63.5 g copper results from 2 × 96 500 coulombs passed.

Hence, for copper,

$$\text{ONE coulomb of charge produces } \frac{63.5}{2 \times 96\,500} \text{ grams of copper.}$$

So **for any element** this is equivalent to

$$\frac{\text{relative atomic mass } (A_r) \text{ of element}}{96\,500 \times \text{charge on the ion}}$$

As a general rule, then, the **total mass** of an element produced at an electrode by a known quantity of electricity is calculated by the expression

$$\text{mass discharged} = \frac{A_r \text{ of element} \times \text{coulombs passed}}{96\,500 \times \text{charge on the ion}}$$

An example will show the method in use.

A current of 2 amps was passed for 2 minutes through copper(II) chloride solution. What mass of (a) copper and (b) chlorine would be produced?

(a) Coulombs passed = amps × seconds = $2 \times 2 \times 60 = 240$
Charge on the copper ion is 2 (Cu^{2+})
Relative atomic mass of copper is 63.5
So

$$\text{Mass from } \mathbf{240} \text{ coulombs} = \frac{63.5 \times 240}{96\,500 \times 2} = \mathbf{0.079\,g\ of\ copper}$$

(b) Coulombs passed = 240 (the same for both products)
Charge on a chloride ion is 1 (Cl^-)
Relative atomic mass of chlorine is 35.5
So

$$\text{Mass from } \mathbf{240} \text{ coulombs} = \frac{35.5 \times 240}{96\,500 \times 1} = \mathbf{0.0883\,g\ of\ chlorine}$$

Note: that both calculations are based on the single equation shown boxed above.

Calculating volumes of gases given off at anodes

For gaseous products we would normally wish to know the **volume** and not the mass produced. In the calculation above, of the mass of chlorine produced at the anode, we could **convert** the mass to a volume as follows:

> **1 mole of molecules of any gas** occupies a volume of **24 000 cm^3** at room temperature and pressure

So for chlorine gas

$$Cl_2 = 2 \times 35.5\,g = 71\,g \text{ per mole of molecules}$$

Therefore

$$\mathbf{0.0883\,g\ of\ chlorine} \text{ is } \frac{0.0883}{71} = \mathbf{0.00124\ moles} \text{ of chlorine gas molecules}$$

The volume of chlorine will be 24 000 cm^3 × 0.00124 moles = 29.8 cm^3.

Table 10.3 Summary of useful substances produced by electrolysis

Cathode product required or formed	Anode product required or formed	Electrodes required	Electrolyte required
Aluminium *Cathode reaction:* $4Al^{3+}(l) + 12e^- \rightarrow 4Al(l)$	**Oxygen** *Anode reaction:* $6O^{2-}(l) - 12e^- \rightarrow 3O_2(g)$	Carbon cathode, carbon anode	MOLTEN aluminium oxide
Sodium: *Cathode reaction:* $2Na^+(l) + 2e^- \rightarrow 2Na(l)$	**Chlorine** *Anode reaction:* $2Cl^-(l) - 2e^- \rightarrow Cl_2(g)$	Steel cathode, carbon anode	MOLTEN sodium chloride
Sodium hydroxide and hydrogen: *Cathode reaction:* $2H^+(aq) + 2e^- \rightarrow H_2(g)$	**Chlorine** *Anode reaction:* $2Cl^-(aq) - 2e^- \rightarrow Cl_2(g)$	Titanium anode, nickel cathode	AQUEOUS sodium chloride
Pure copper: *Cathode reaction:* $Cu^{2+}(aq) + 2e^- \rightarrow Cu(s)$	None, copper dissolves *Anode reaction:* $Cu(s) - 2e^-(aq) \rightarrow Cu^{2+}(aq)$	Pure copper cathode, impure copper anode	AQUEOUS copper(II) sulphate

Taking it further

By **rearranging** the equation (shown boxed on p. 144) it is possible to measure

- the charge on an ion, or
- the quantity of charge passed round a circuit, or
- the relative atomic mass of the element discharged

if all the other values are known.

Electrical costs in metal production

In the last section we saw that the quantity of electricity to deposit 1 mole of a metal depends on the charge on the ion. It is for this reason that aluminium production by electrolysis is expensive. One mole of aluminium (27 g) times requires 3 (Al^{3+}) as much electrical charge as 1 mole of sodium (23 g) (Al^{3+}) and $1\frac{1}{2}$ times as much as 64 g of copper (Cu^{2+}).

EXAMINATION QUESTIONS

Question 1(F)

The apparatus shown below (Fig. 10.3) can be used to electrolyse sodium chloride solution.

Fig. 10.3

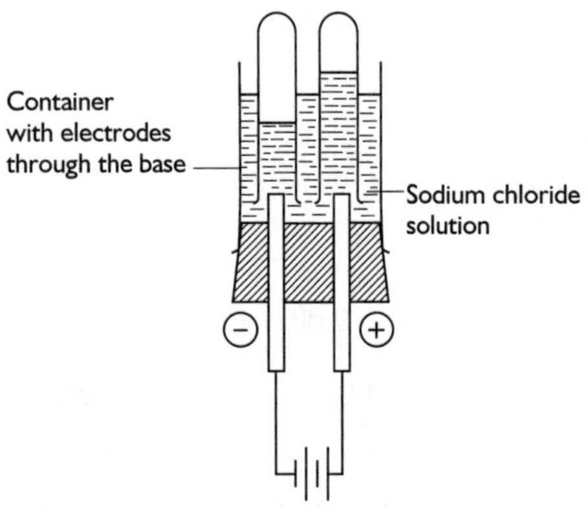

(i) Name the product formed at:
1. the positive electrode
2. the negative electrode *[2]*

(ii) Give *one* large-scale use of the product formed at the negative electrode. *[1]*

(iii) The final solution contains Na^+ ions and OH^- ions.
Name the useful chemical that could be obtained from this solution. *[1]*

[Total 4 marks]

Question 2(F)

As part of an investigation, a student passed electricity through dilute hydrochloric acid using the apparatus shown below (Fig. 10.4).

Fig. 10.4

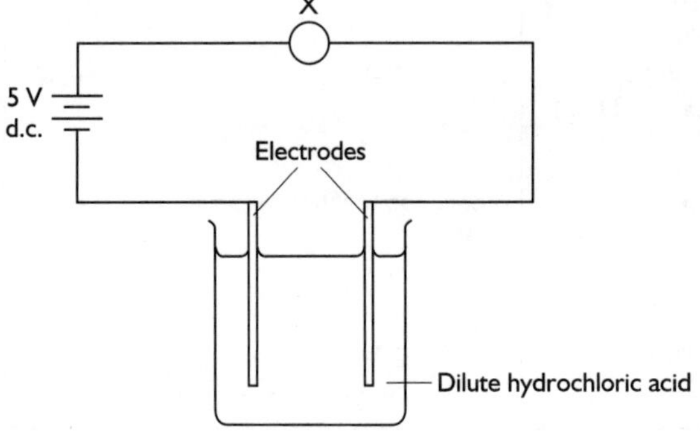

(a) (i) What piece of apparatus could be connected at X to show that the liquid is passing an electric current? [1]
(ii) Name a suitable material for the electrodes. [1]
(iii) What does the term *electrolysis* mean? [2 lines] [2]

(b) Two gases, **A**, and **B**, were formed during the electrolysis of dilute hydrochloric acid.
Gas **A** was green and bleached blue litmus.
Gas **B** was colourless and exploded at a flame.
Give the name for:

(i) Gas **A** ______________________ [1]

(ii) Gas **B** ______________________ [1]

(c) What gas would be given off at the anode if dilute sulphuric acid were used instead of hydrochloric acid? [1 line]

______________________ [1]

[Total 7 marks]

Question 3(H)

(a) A labelled diagram of a cell used to produce aluminium metal is shown below (Fig. 10.5).

Fig. 10.5

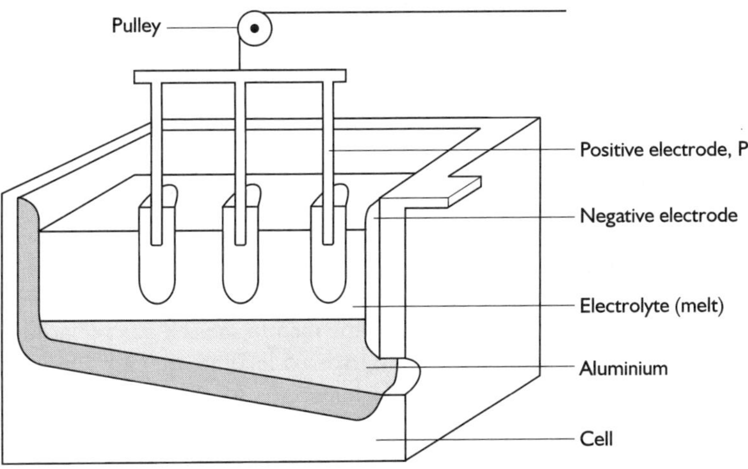

(i) What is the electrode P made from? [1]
(ii) Give a balanced ionic equation for the reaction which takes place at the cathode. [1]
(iii) Name the gas given off at the positive electrode. [1]
(iv) P is hung on a pulley so it can be moved. Suggest why P might have to be moved. [2 lines] [1]
(v) Why does the aluminium sink to the bottom of the cell? [2 lines] [1]

(b) High-purity copper is obtained by electrolysis using a crude copper anode and a thin, pure copper cathode in a solution of copper sulphate. A current of 100 amperes (A) is used for 12 hours. What mass of copper is formed at the cathode?

Include in your answer the equation for the reaction occuring at the cathode. Show now toy obtained your answer and give the unit.

(The faraday constant (F) is *96 500* coulombs per mole. The relative atomic mass of copper is 64.) [5 lines]

[Total 10 marks]

Question 4(H)

Sodium hydroxide (NaOH) is manufactured by the electrolysis of sodium chloride solution ($NaCl(aq)$). Hydrogen (H_2) and chlorine (Cl_2) are also formed. The equation below shows the overall reaction taking place.

$$2NaCl(aq) + 2H_2O(l) \rightarrow 2NaOH(aq) + H_2(g) + Cl_2(g)$$

The table below (Table 10.4) shows some of the uses of the products.

Table 10.4

Product	Use
Sodium hydroxide	Making detergents, soap, paper, bleach and artificial fibres
Chlorine	Making bleach, solvents, pesticides and plastics, and to sterilize water supplies
Hydrogen	Making margarine and ammonia

There are three main industrial processes for the electrolysis of sodium chloride solution. Information about these processes is shown in the table below (Table 10.5).

Table 10.5

Process	Information
Castner–Kellner	Produces a concentrated solution of sodium hydroxide but needs toxic mercury that can contaminate rivers. The process needs lots of energy.
Diaphragm	Produces a dilute solution of sodium hydroxide but the diaphragm needs replacing frequently. The diaphragm is made of asbestos, which may cause cancer.
Membrane	Produces a concentrated solution of sodium hydroxide but needs pure sodium chloride solution to start with. The process needs very little energy.

Read the information above and use it to answer the questions.

(a) Name the raw material needed for all three processes which make sodium hydroxide? *[1]*

(b) The Castner–Kellner cell used to be the most common process to make sodium hydroxide. In recent years the membrane cell has replaced the Castner–Kellner cell in the manufacture of sodium hydroxide. State *two* advantages of the membrane cell over the Castner–Kellner cell. [3 lines] *[2]*

(c) In the membrane process chlorine (Cl_2) is formed at the positive electrode (anode) from chloride ions (Cl^-)

(i) Write down the electrode reaction that occurs at the positive electrode. *[1]*

(ii) Hydrogen (H_2) is formed at the negative electrode (cathode).
The reaction that occurs at the negative electrode is

$$2H^+(aq) + 2e^- \rightarrow H_2(g)$$

How many moles of hydrogen molecules (H_2) are produced when 1 mole of electrons (1 Faraday) is passed through sodium chloride solution? *[1]*

(iii) The relative atomic mass (A_r) of hydrogen is 1.0.
What mass (in grams) of hydrogen is formed when 20 moles of electrons (20 Faradays) are passed through the solution? [3 lines] *[2]*

(iv) Sodium chloride solution can also be electrolysed in the laboratory.
Describe what you would *see* at the negative electrode. *[1]*

[Total 8 marks]

Question 5(F)

(a) Potassium bromide, KBr, is a salt which can be electrolysed when it is molten. During this process, what product would you expect to be formed

(i) at the positive electrode?

(ii) at the negative electrode? *[2]*

(b) Why does solid potassium bromide *not* conduct electricity? [2 lines] *[2]*

[Total 4 marks]

Question 6(H)

The following diagram (Fig. 10.6) shows a method of nickel plating an object using a solution of nickel(II) sulphate ($NiSO_4$).

Fig. 10.6

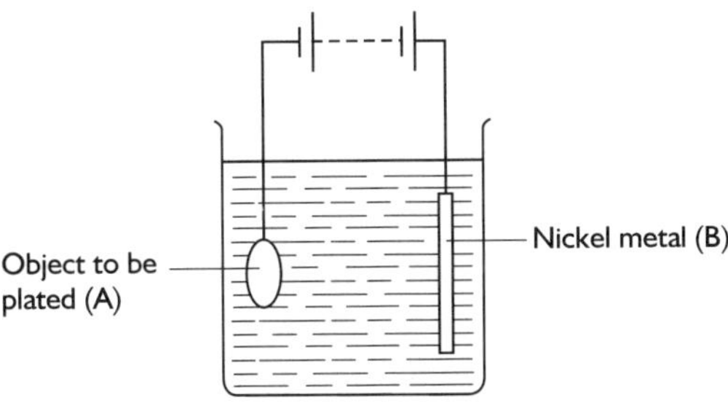

(i) State the names of the electrodes represented as A and B in the diagram. *[1]*

(ii) Give equations to represent the reactions occurring at A and B. [2 lines] *[2]*

(iii) If the object to be plated is made of plastic, it has to be painted with a suspension of graphite before the plating occurs. Explain the reason for this. *[1]*

[Total 4 marks]

Question 7(H)

The diagram below (Fig. 10.7) shows the electrolysis of sodium chloride solution.

Fig. 10.7

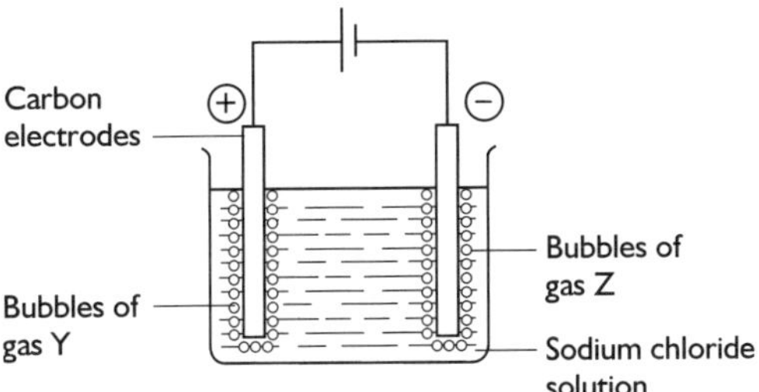

(a) Name the gases Y and Z. *[2]*

(b) If a few drops of universal indicator are added to the solution before electrolysis starts, the indicator is green. As electrolysis happens, the indicator gradually turns blue.

  (i) What is the pH of the solution when the indicator is green? [1 line] *[1]*

  (ii) Explain why the electrolysis causes the indicator to go blue. [3 lines] *[3]*

  (iii) Name a compound produced on an industrial scale by electrolysis of sodium chloride solution. [1 line] *[1]*

(c) In the electrolysis of copper(II) chloride solution the electron transfer at the negative electrode is shown by the following equation.

$Cu^{2+}(aq) + 2\ e^{-} \rightarrow Cu(s)$

  (i) What does (aq) stand for? [1 line] *[1]*

  (ii) What would you expect to see at the negative electrode during this electrolysis? [2 lines] *[2]*

(d) The table (Table 10.6) gives information about three substances A, B and C when they are solid and when they are molten.

  (i) Suggest possible identities for substances A and B. [1 line] *[2]*

  (ii) What type of bonding does solid B have? [1 line] *[1]*

  (iii) What type of bonding does solid C have? [1 line] *[1]*

  (iv) When the melted substance A conducts electricity what particles are carrying the current? [1 line] *[1]*

Table 10.6

	Solid substance		Molten substance		
Substance	Appearance of solid	Does the solid conduct electricity?	Does the melt conduct electricity?	Product at + electrode	Product at − electrode
A	White solid	No	Yes	Bromine	Lead metal
B	Yellow solid	No	No	(Does not conduct)	
C	Grey solid	Yes	Yes	None	None

(e) (i) Predict the products of electrolysis of an aqueous solution of aluminium sulphate using inert electrodes. Explain how you arrive at your answer. [4 lines] *[1]*

(ii) Why is cryolite added to aluminium oxide during the electrolytic manufacture of aluminium? [2 lines] *[1]*

[Total 17 marks]

OUTLINE ANSWERS

Question 1

(i) 1. Chlorine gas *[1]*.
2. Hydrogen gas *[1]*.

(ii) To hydrogenate vegetable oils in margarine manufacture *[1]*.

(iii) Sodium hydroxide *[1]*.

Question 2

(a) (i) Bulb or ammeter *[1]*.
(ii) Carbon or platinum *[1]*.
(iii) Decompose/split up/breakdown *[1]* by d.c. current *[1]*.

(b) (i) Chlorine *[1]*.
(ii) Hydrogen *[1]*.

(c) Oxygen *[1]*.

Question 3

(a) (i) Carbon *[1]*.
(ii) $Al^{3+}(l) + 3e^- \rightarrow Al(l)$ *[1]*.
(iii) Oxygen or carbon monoxide or carbon dioxide *[1]*.
(iv) 1 mark for any *one* of these:
Lowering:
- the carbon anodes slowly burn away;
- the level of electrolyte drops as the aluminium is removed.

Raising: to remove anodes for replacement.
(v) Because it is denser than the electrolyte *[1]*.

(b) The equation for copper deposit at the cathode:

$Cu^{2+}(aq) + 2e^- \rightarrow Cu(s)$ *[1]*

64 g of copper are formed by 2 × 96 500 coulombs *[1]*.
100 amps for 12 × 60 × 60 seconds = 4 320 000 coulombs *[1]*.

$$\text{Mass of copper formed} = \frac{64 \times 4\,320\,000}{2 \times 96\,500} \; [1] = 1432.5\,\text{g} \; [1].$$

[Correct answer only, no working shown, 4 marks.]

Question 4

(a) Sodium chloride *[1]*.

(b) Needs less energy *[1]*; uses no toxic /dangerous materials *[1]*.

(c) (i) $Cl^- - e^- \rightarrow \frac{1}{2}Cl_2$, or $2Cl^- - 2e^- \rightarrow Cl_2$ *[1]*.
(ii) Half a mole of hydrogen *[1]*.

(iii) 20 grams *[1]* because 20 moles of electrons discharge 20 hydrogen ions (unit positive charge) *[1]* each of mass 1 g.
(iv) Bubbles *[1]* of gas—hydrogen.

Question 5

(a) (i) Bromine gas would be expected at the positive electrode. Bromide ions are Br^-. They are negatively charged and will be attracted to the positive electrode, where they will give up electrons to become bromine molecules, Br_2 *[1]*.
(ii) Because there is no other positive ion present than the potassium ion, potassium metal is produced at the negative electrode *[1]*.
(b) Solid potassium bromide is an ionic compound *[1]* *but* its ions are *not free* to move *[1]* to the electrodes to be discharged.

Question 6

(i) The electrode names should be straightforward recall but metals are always plated on the cathode *[1]*.
(ii) **At A**. During the process of electroplating, the cathode is the object to be plated. Therefore, the equation here is for the formation of nickel. The solution contains nickel(II) ions. This is a clue to the electrode equation. It is similar to that for the plating of copper *[1]*.
At B. This is the nickel anode. It dissolves to supply the ions for plating the cathode. The reaction is the reverse of the cathode equation.
(iii) The coating of graphite is to make a non-conductor—the plastic—conduct, otherwise it could not be part of the circuit. Look up the reasons for this.

Question 7

To answer the question well, candidates require a good general understanding of qualitative aspects of electrolysis. The diagram is of an electrolysis of aqueous sodium chloride using carbon electrodes. The circuit is of a simple electrolysis.

(a) The gas Y is chlorine. Chlorine is more easily discharged than oxygen from aqueous solutions of chlorides; the electrode is the anode. The gas Z is hydrogen. Hydrogen is more easily discharged than sodium from aqueous solutions of sodium salts; the electrode is the cathode.
(b) (i) The starting solution is neutral (universal indicator green). Sodium chloride is a neutral salt. The pH is 7 *[1]*.
(ii) The change in pH indicated by the universal indicator turning blue (pH > 7) means that the solution has become alkaline *[1]*. Hydroxyl ions have built up in the electrolyte *[1]*. This is because of the two ions present in the solution from the ionization of water, OH^-(aq) and H^+(aq), the hydrogen ions have been discharged at the cathode to form hydrogen gas *[1]*. The hydroxyl ions are *not discharged* and their concentration increases, making the remaining solution alkaline.
(iii) This electrolysis produces two elements (hydrogen and chlorine) but one compound—sodium hydroxide. The compound sodium chlorate(I) could also form if the chlorine from the anode was reacted with the sodium hydroxide solution formed. Sodium chlorate(I) is common bleach *[1]*.
(c) This part is about a different electrolysis, that of aqueous copper(II) chloride.
(i) (aq) is short for aqueous. It means the solution is copper(II) chloride dissolved in water *[1]*.
(ii) The negative electrode is the cathode. Positive ions are discharged there. The electrode equation shown indicates that copper is discharged at the cathode. A pink–brown deposit would be seen when the electrolyte was removed *[1]*.
(d) (i) Substance A could be lead bromide because electrolysis produces lead and bromine (p. 140).
Substance B could be sulphur since it is a yellow molecular (i.e. non-ionic) substance. It could be *any* yellow, molecular substance in fact, but sulphur is the one most likely to be familiar to you *[1]*.

'Parts of (d) are not strictly within the scope of this chapter. They are answered here for completeness.'

(ii) B is not a metal—its solid form does not conduct electricity. It is not ionic—its melt does not electrolyse (conduct). So B must be molecular and its bonding must be *covalent [1]*.

(iii) C conducts in the solid form. It must be a metal. Its bonding is *metallic* (Chapter 7, p. 68).

(iv) Molten A must contain *ions* because it conducts only when liquid *[1]*.

(e) (i) Aqueous aluminium sulphate contains two cations—aluminium ions and hydrogen ions. Hydrogen ions discharge more easily than aluminium ions because they are lower in the reactivity series than aluminium ions, i.e. less stable. Hydrogen gas will form *[1]*. Of the two anions—sulphate ions and hydroxide ions—hydroxide ions discharge to form oxygen gas as in the electrolysis of sulphuric acid.

(ii) Electrolysis of aluminium oxide cannot occur unless it is molten or dissolved. Because the oxide is insoluble in water the only option is to melt it. It melts at 2070 °C! Adding cryolite lowers the melting point to a more reasonable temperature. Alternatively, the oxide can be considered to **dissolve** in the molten cryolite *[1]*.

STUDENT ANSWER WITH EXAMINER'S COMMENTS

The following results were obtained during the electrolysis of 500 cm^3 of aqueous copper(II) sulphate using carbon electrodes

Total mass of copper deposited on the cathode/g	Time current was passed/hour
0.70	$\frac{1}{2}$
1.40	1
2.75	2
3.00	$2\frac{1}{2}$
3.00	3
3.00	$3\frac{1}{2}$

(a) Draw a labelled diagram of the apparatus you could use, including the electrical circuit, in order to carry out this electrolysis. *(2 marks)*

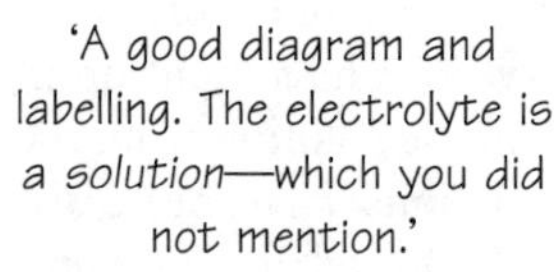

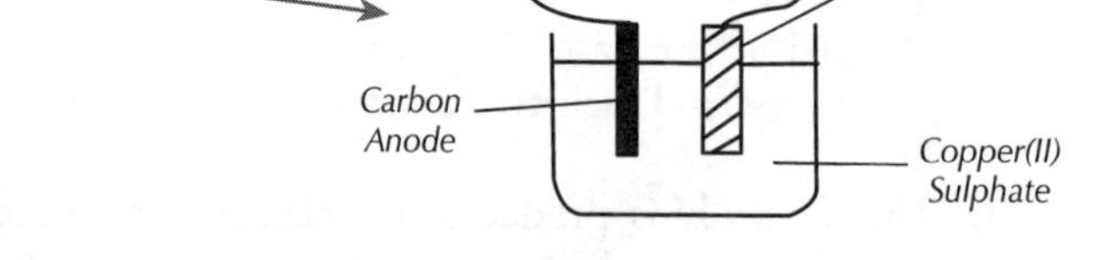

(b) (i) Plot the results on the graph below. *(2 marks)*

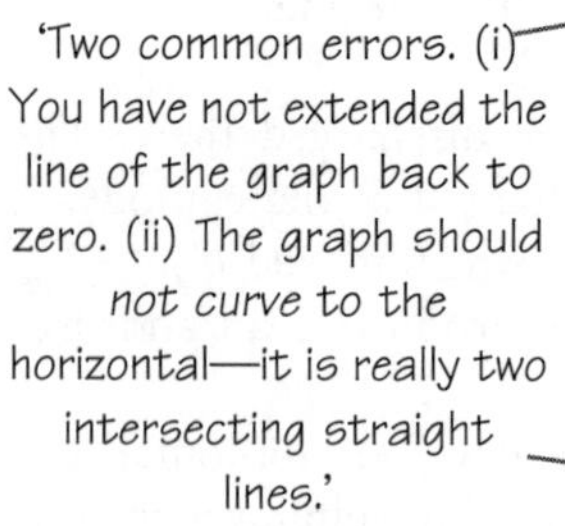

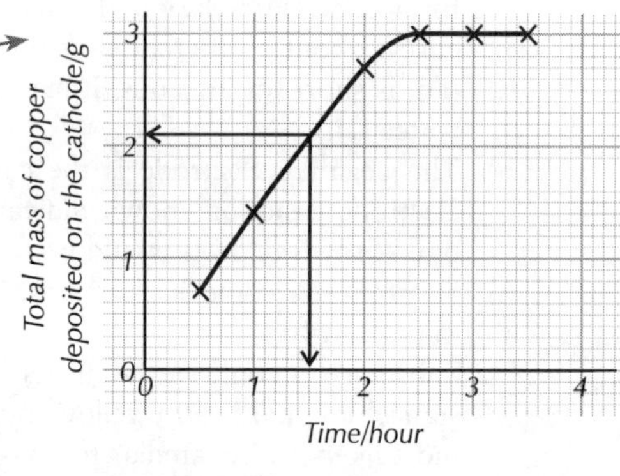

(continued)

(continued)

'Good—clearly showing on the graph how you got your answer.'

(ii) What is the total mass of copper deposited on the cathode after the current has passed for $1\frac{1}{2}$ hours?

2.1 g

'Apart from the error of using 2.1 g instead of 3.0 g (the whole of the copper deposited) your calculation is excellent. You would lose half a mark or possibly one out of the 5 marks for (iii). Also note that m means metres and not moles.'

(iii) Calculate the concentration, in mol/dm^3, of the original aqueous copper(II) sulphate.

relative atomic mass of copper = 64

2.1 g of copper = $\frac{24}{64}$ moles = 0.033 m

∴ 0.033 moles copper from 0.033 moles copper sulphate in 500 cm^3.

*The solution was **0.066 moles per dm^3***

(5 marks)

'Two good reasons.'

(iv) Suggest two reasons why some metal objects are copper plated.

1. plating stops rusting.

2. It makes objects look nicer.

(2 marks)

SUMMARY

Use this list to help with your revision. Tick off the points as you revise them in the text.

- ▷ Electrolysis is the splitting of ionic compounds into their **elements** by passage of a direct current.
- ▷ Electrolytes are **ionic compounds**, molten or in aqueous solution.
- ▷ Electrolysis is used on a large scale
  - ▷ to extract aluminium from molten aluminium oxide;
  - ▷ to purify copper;
  - ▷ to make chlorine from salt solution;
  - ▷ to extract sodium metal from molten common salt.
- ▷ The apparatus will be different for electrolysis
  - ▷ of molten electrolytes;
  - ▷ where gases are being collected;
  - ▷ where electrodes are being weighed.
- ▷ The anode is the **positive** electrode where **oxidation** occurs.
- ▷ The cathode is the **negative** electrode where **reduction** occurs.
- ▷ In aqueous solution electrolysis, the elements formed may come
  - ▷ entirely from electrolysis of the **water**, e.g. with dilute H_2SO_4; or
  - ▷ entirely from electrolysis of the ionic **solute**, e.g. conc. HCl; or
  - ▷ partly from **each component** of the solution, e.g. with $CuSO_4$.
- ▷ Water is split up into hydrogen and oxygen only if it contains an added compound to make it conduct electricity, e.g. a little H_2SO_4.
- ▷ The equations for the reactions at the electrodes must include **electrons**. For example,

  $Al^{3+} + 3e^- \rightarrow Al$ or $Na^+ + e^- \rightarrow Na$

  $Cl^- - e^- \rightarrow \frac{1}{2}Cl_2$ and $2O^{2-} - 4e^- \rightarrow O_2$

(continued)

(continued)

- The **number of electrons shown** in both electrode reactions must be the same.
- The fact that metals deposit on the **cathode** in electrolysis is the basis for **electroplating** with silver, chromium or nickel.
- The fact that oxygen is formed at the **anode** during electrolysis of dilute sulphuric acid is the basis for **anodizing** aluminium.
- The **numerical value** of the charge on an ion gives the number of **Faradays** of electric charge required to discharge **the atomic mass of the element** expressed in grams.
- Quantity of electric charge is expressed in **coulombs = amps × seconds**.
- The electricity costs of aluminium production are higher than for other metals produced by electrolysis because of the **high charge** and **low mass** of the aluminium ion.

Chapter

11 Representing reactions

GETTING STARTED

You must learn the symbols for the common elements; frequently they are the first two letters of the name but *not* always—beware.

Compounds are formed when elements or compounds chemically combine together—you must learn how to name compounds.

In this chapter you will learn how to write formulae and equations; make sure you understand the methods used. The reactants and products in equations have state symbols to indicate whether they are gases, liquids or solids. Ionic equations are equations which simply show the ions that take part in the reaction.

Finally, in this chapter there is a list of all the different types of reactions you are likely to meet.

TOPIC CHART

LONDON	MEG	NEAB	SEG	NICCEA	WJEC	TOPIC	STUDY	REVISION 1	REVISION 2
✓	✓	✓	✓	✓	✓	Naming compounds			
✓	✓	✓	✓	✓	✓	Writing formulae			
✓	✓	✓	✓	✓	✓	Writing equations			
✓	✓	✓	✓	✓	✓	State symbols			
✓	✓	✓	✓	✓	✓	Ionic equations			
✓	✓	✓	✓	✓	✓	Half equations			
✓	✓	✓	✓	✓	✓	Summary of types of reaction			

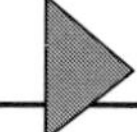

WHAT YOU NEED TO KNOW

Naming compounds

Compounds of **two elements** have an **-ide** ending. The metal is always written down first. Thus a compound of magnesium and oxygen is called magnesium **oxide** and a compound of sodium and chlorine is called sodium chlor**ide**. (Many metals end in the letters **-ium.**)

If the compound is made up of **two non-metals**, the non-metal that is either **lower down** the group (if they are in the same group), or **nearest to the left-hand side** of the periodic table, is placed **first**. Thus a compound of sulphur and oxygen is called **sulphur** dioxide and a compound of carbon and sulphur is called **carbon** disulphide.

If the compound is made up of **three elements**, one a **metal**, one a **non-metal** and the other **oxygen**, the compounds have **-ate** endings. A compound of copper, sulphur and oxygen is called copper sulph**ate** and a compound of calcium, carbon and oxygen is called calcium carbon**ate**.

If the compound contains a **metal, hydrogen** and **oxygen,** the compounds have a **hydroxide** ending. A compound of sodium, hydrogen and oxygen is called sodium **hydroxide** and a compound of calcium, hydrogen and oxygen is called calcium **hydroxide**.

Writing formulae

The **valency** of an element is a number which shows its combining power. In **ionic** compounds it is equal to the charge on the ions of the elements. In **covalent** compounds it gives the number of covalent bonds which the element can form.

Simple compounds

To write the formula of a simple compound, e.g. aluminium oxide:

- Write the valency of the element to the top right-hand side of each element:

  Al^3O^2

- Put the valency of the second element to the bottom right-hand side of the first element, and the valency of the first element to the bottom right-hand side of the second element:

  Al_2O_3

- Do not write down 'ones' and simplify the numbers if possible.
- Thus the formula of the compound between carbon and oxygen is

  $C^4O^2 \quad C_2O_4$

This can be simplified to CO_2. Some ions contain more than one element. However, the same rules still apply; e.g. for calcium hydrogencarbonate:

$Ca^2HCO_3^1 \quad Ca_1(HCO_3)_2$

The formula is

$Ca(HCO_3)_2$

'Do not forget the brackets. $PbNO_{32}$ means 1 atom of lead, 1 atom of nitrogen and 32 atoms of oxygen!'

Note: To show that there are two hydrogencarbonates, brackets are placed around the symbols. For lead(II) nitrate we have Pb^2 and NO_3^1, hence the formula is $Pb(NO_3)_2$.

Writing equations

Chemical reactions can be summarized by writing **equations**, either in words or by using symbols. The most important thing to remember is that it must represent a reaction that is known to take place. Sodium burns in chlorine to form sodium chloride. This can be stated as:

sodium + chlorine → sodium chloride

'Never write $NaCl_2$.'

The **arrow** indicates that a reaction takes place from left to right. The chemicals on the left of the equation are the reactants and those on the right are the products. The reaction can also be represented by **symbols:**

$Na + Cl_2 \rightarrow NaCl$

'This is important.'

- Each substance must be represented by its correct formula.
- Remember that gases that are elements are diatomic.
- We have seen that atoms cannot be created or destroyed, but in the above example there are two chlorine atoms on the left-hand side and only one chlorine on the right-hand side. To **balance the equation for chlorine atoms** we need to put a '2' in front of the NaCl:

  $Na + Cl_2 \rightarrow 2NaCl$

  We now have two sodium atoms on the right-hand side and only one on the left-hand side. To balance the sodium atoms we need to put a '2' in front of the Na:

  $2Na + Cl_2 \rightarrow 2NaCl$

  The equation is now said to be balanced.

Here are two further examples:

(i) iron(III) oxide + carbon monoxide → iron + carbon dioxide

Unbalanced: $Fe_2O_3 + CO \rightarrow Fe + CO_2$.
Balanced: $Fe_2O_3 + 3CO \rightarrow 2Fe + 3CO_2$.

'When balancing equations, never change the correct formula of a substance. Note that it is 2Fe not Fe_2.'

(ii) ammonia + copper(II) oxide → nitrogen + copper + water

Unbalanced: $NH_3 + CuO \rightarrow N_2 + Cu + H_2O$.
Balanced: $2NH_3 + 3CuO \rightarrow N_2 + 3Cu + 3H_2O$.

State symbols

When we look at the equations we have written, they only tell us that the reaction has occurred. They do not tell us the speed of the reaction or the **state** of the substances. This last point is easily dealt with because we can use **state symbols**. We add (s) to represent a solid, (l) to represent a liquid, (g) to represent a gas and (aq) for a substance dissolved in water (an aqueous solution). Thus our two examples become:

$Fe_2O_3(s) + 3CO(g) \rightarrow 2Fe(s) + 3CO_2(g)$

$2NH_3(g) + 3CuO(s) \rightarrow N_2(g) + 3Cu(s) + 3H_2O(g)$

Note that in this last reaction water is formed as water vapour.

Ionic equations

When iron is added to copper(II) sulphate solution, copper and iron(II) sulphate are formed:

iron + copper(II) sulphate → copper + iron(II) sulphate

$Fe(s) + CuSO_4(aq) \rightarrow Cu(s) + FeSO_4(aq)$

If we write this equation in terms of **ions** we get

$Fe(s) + Cu^{2+}(aq) + SO_4^{2-}(aq) \rightarrow Cu(s) + Fe^{2+}(aq) + SO_4^{2-}(aq)$.

We can see that the sulphate ions are unaffected by the reaction and therefore they can be left out. They are called **spectator ions**.

$Fe(s) + Cu^{2+}(aq) \rightarrow Fe^{2+}(aq) + Cu(s)$.

'Check that both the number of atoms and the number of charges balance.'

This is called an **ionic equation**. It balances in both the number of atoms and the number of charges on each side of the equation. Another example of an ionic equation is

$CO_3^{2-}(s) + 2H^+(aq) \rightarrow CO_2(g) + H_2O(l)$

This is the reaction between a solid carbonate and an acid to form carbon dioxide, water and a salt; for example, if calcium carbonate were added to hydrochloric acid the products would be carbon dioxide, water and, in this case, the salt calcium chloride. **The spectator ions are calcium ions and chloride ions.**

Half equations

Half equations are usually written for reactions occurring at the electrodes during electrolysis. At the anode, the ions lose electrons and become neutral. At the cathode, the ions accept electrons and become neutral. The following are some examples of half equations.

- Chloride ions losing electrons and becoming chlorine molecules:

  $2Cl^-(aq) - 2e^- \rightarrow Cl_2(g)$

- Aluminium ions gaining three electrons and forming aluminium atoms:

  $Al^{3+}(l) + 3e^- \rightarrow Al(l)$

- Hydroxyl ions losing electrons are becoming oxygen molecules and water molecules

  $4OH^-(aq) \rightarrow O_2(g) + 2H_2O(l)$

Summary of types of reaction

There are many types of chemical reactions.

- **Addition**
  When two or more compounds react together to form one compound:

  ethene + bromine → dibromoethane

- **Cracking**
  The breaking down of an organic molecule into smaller molecules:

  butane → ethane + ethene

- **Dehydration**
  The removal of the elements of water from a compound:

  ethanol → ethene + water

- **Displacement**
  When one element displaces another:

  zinc + copper(II) sulphate → copper + zinc sulphate

  potassium iodide + chlorine → potassium chloride + iodine

- **Electrolysis**
  When molten compounds or solutions are decomposed by an electric current. Anode reactions are oxidations, cathode reactions are reductions
  Electrolysis of brine gives

  at the anode $2Cl^-(aq) - 2e^- \rightarrow Cl_2(g)$

  at the cathode $2H^+(aq) + 2e^- \rightarrow H_2(g)$

- **Equilibrium**
  When a reversible reaction reaches a balance of reactants and products:

  sulphur dioxide + oxygen ⇌ sulphur trioxide

- **Exothermic**
  When energy is given out in a chemical reaction; ΔH is negative:

  methane + oxygen → carbon dioxide + water + heat

- **Endothermic**
  When energy is taken in during a chemical reaction; ΔH is positive:

  oxygen + energy from UV light → ozone − heat

- **Fermentation**
  When sugar solutions are converted by enzymes to ethanol:

  glucose → ethanol + carbon dioxide

- **Hydration**
  When water is added to a compound:

  anhydrous copper(II) sulphate + water → hydrated copper(II) sulphate

Hydrolysis
When water reacts with a compound:

aluminium chloride + water → aluminium hydroxide + hydrogen chloride

Neutralization
When an acid reacts with a base:

hydrochloric acid + sodium hydroxide → sodium chloride + water

Oxidation
When an element or compound accepts oxygen, gives up hydrogen or loses electrons. It is the opposite of reduction. Oxidation and reduction usually occur together. The underlined substance is oxidized in the following equations:

<u>hydrogen</u> + oxygen → water
<u>ammonia</u> + oxygen → nitrogen + water
<u>chloride ions</u> minus electrons → chlorine molecules

Polymerization
When many small molecules link up to form a very large molecule:

ethene → poly(ethene)

Precipitation
When two soluble compounds react to form an insoluble compound:

'Remember the state symbols'

sodium sulphate(aq) + barium chloride(aq) → barium sulphate(s)
+ sodium chloride(aq)

Redox
A redox reaction is a reaction where reduction and oxidation simultaneously take place (this is nearly always the case):

iron + copper(II) ions → copper + iron(II) ions

$Fe(s) + Cu^{2+}(aq) \rightarrow Cu(s) + Fe^{2+}(aq)$

Copper(II) ions have gained two electrons to become copper—it has been reduced.
Iron has lost two electrons to become an iron(II) ion—it has been oxidized.
Oxidation and reduction can be remembered by the acronym OILRIG.
oxidation is loss of electrons; reduction is gain of electrons

Reduction
When an element or compound accepts hydrogen, loses oxygen or gains electrons. It is the opposite of oxidation. Reduction and oxidation usually occur together. The underlined substance is reduced in the following equations:

<u>copper oxide</u> + hydrogen → copper + water
<u>nitrogen</u> + hydrogen → ammonia
<u>hydrogen ions</u> + electrons → hydrogen molecules

Reversible
A reaction that can go in either direction:

hydrated copper sulphate ⇌ anhydrous copper sulphate + water

Synthesis
A reaction in which a compound is made from its elements. The compounds often have -ide endings:

magnesium + oxygen → magnesium oxide

$2Mg(s) + O_2(g) \rightarrow 2MgO(s)$

iron + sulphur → iron(II) sulphide

$Fe(s) + S(s) \rightarrow FeS(s)$

'When a substance thermally decomposes it does NOT react with oxygen!'

- **Thermal decomposition**
  A compound breaks down on heating into simpler substances which do not recombine on cooling:

  sodium nitrate → sodium nitrite + oxygen

- **Thermal dissociation**
  A compound breaks down on heating into simpler substances which recombine on cooling:

  ammonium chloride ⇌ ammonia + hydrogen chloride

EXAMINATION QUESTIONS

Question 1(F) Complete the following word equations.

(a) magnesium + oxygen → .... *[1]*
(b) sodium hydroxide + hydrochloric acid → .... + ... *[1]*
(c) aluminium + copper oxide → .... + ... *[1]*

Question 2(F) Complete the following symbol equations.

(a) Fe(s) + S(s) → .... *[1]*
(b) MgO(s) + 2HCl(aq) → .... + ... *[1]*
(c) $CaCO_3$ + $2HNO_3$(aq) → .... + ... + ... *[1]*
(d) H^+(aq) + ... (aq) → H_2O(l) *[1]*

Question 3(F) Choosing *only* from the list below, which word can be used to describe each of the following reactions:

cracking	**polymerization**
displacement	**precipitation**
fermentation	**synthesis**
neutralization	

(a) hydrochloric acid + sodium hydroxide → sodium chloride + water
(b) glucose → ethanol + carbon dioxide
(c) ethene → poly(ethene)
(d) magnesium + oxygen → magnesium oxide
(e) chlorine + potassium iodide → iodine + potassium chloride
(f) hexane → ethene + butane
(g) barium chloride + sodium sulphate → barium sulphate + sodium chloride *[7]*

Question 4(H) Write a word equation and a balanced chemical equation for each of the following reactions. The first one has been done for you.

(a) gas + gas → liquid

hydrogen + oxygen → water

$2H_2(g) + O_2(g) \rightarrow 2H_2O(l)$

(b) solid + solid → solid
(c) solid + gas → gas
(d) solid + gas → solid
(e) gas + gas → gas
(f) solid + aqueous solution → gas + aqueous solution
(g) aqueous solution + aqueous solution → solid + aqueous solution
(h) solid + aqueous solution → solid + aqueous solution
(i) gas + aqueous solution → solid + water *[8]*

Question 5(H) Write ionic equations for the following reactions:

(a) $Mg(s) + CuSO_4(aq) \rightarrow Cu(s) + MgSO_4(aq)$
(b) $HCl(aq) + NaOH(aq) \rightarrow NaCl(aq) + H_2O(l)$
(c) $Na_2CO_3(aq) + H_2SO_4(aq) \rightarrow Na_2SO_4(aq) + H_2O(l) + CO_2(g)$
(d) $Zn(s) + H_2SO_4(aq) \rightarrow H_2(g) + ZnSO_4(aq)$
(e) $Ca(HCO_3)_2(aq) + Na_2CO_3(aq) \rightarrow CaCO_3(s) + 2NaHCO_3(aq)$ *[5]*

Question 6(H) Write half equations for the discharge of the following ions during electrolysis.

(a) hydrogen from hydrogen ions
(b) oxygen from oxide ions
(c) chlorine from chloride ions
(d) copper from copper ions
(e) aluminium from aluminium ions
(f) oxygen from hydroxyl ions *[6]*

OUTLINE ANSWERS

Question 1

(a) Magnesium oxide.
(b) Sodium chloride + water.
(c) Copper + aluminium oxide.

Question 2

(a) $FeS(s)$.
(b) $MgCl_2(aq) + H_2O(l)$.
(c) $Ca(NO_3)_2(aq) + H_2O(l) + CO_2(g)$.
(d) $OH^-(aq)$.

Question 3

(a) Neutralization.
(b) Fermentation.
(c) Polymerization.
(d) Synthesis.
(e) Displacement.
(f) Cracking.
(g) Precipitation.

Note that the following equations are only examples—there are many other reactions that would fit the descriptions.

Question 4

(b) iron + sulphur → iron sulphide
$Fe(s) + S(s) \rightarrow FeS(s)$
(c) carbon + oxygen → carbon dioxide
$C(s) + O_2(g) \rightarrow CO_2(g)$
(d) magnesium + oxygen → magnesium oxide
$2Mg(s) + O_2(g) \rightarrow 2MgO(s)$
(e) carbon monoxide + oxygen → carbon dioxide
$2CO(g) + O_2(g) \rightarrow 2CO_2(g)$
(f) magnesium + hydrochloric acid → hydrogen + magnesium chloride
$Mg(s) + 2HCl(aq) \rightarrow H_2(g) + MgCl_2(aq)$
(g) barium chloride + sodium sulphate → barium sulphate + sodium chloride
$BaCl_2(aq) + Na_2SO_4(aq) \rightarrow BaSO_4(s) + 2NaCl(aq)$
(h) zinc + copper sulphate → copper + zinc sulphate
$Zn(s) + CuSO_4(aq) \rightarrow Cu(s) + ZnSO_4(aq)$
(i) carbon dioxide + calcium hydroxide → calcium carbonate + water
$CO_2(g) + Ca(OH)_2(aq) \rightarrow CaCO_3(s) + H_2O(l)$

Question 5
(a) $Mg(s) + Cu^{2+}(aq) \rightarrow Cu(s) + Mg^{2+}(aq)$
(b) $H^+(aq) + OH^-(aq) \rightarrow H_2O(l)$
(c) $CO_3^{2-}(aq) + 2H^+(aq) \rightarrow H_2O(l) + CO_2(g)$
(d) $Zn(s) + 2H^+(aq) \rightarrow H_2(g) + Zn^{2+}(aq)$
(e) $Ca^{2+}(aq) + CO_3^{2-}(aq) \rightarrow CaCO_3(s)$

Question 6
(a) $2H^+(aq) + 2e^-\ lH_2(g)$
(b) $2O^{2-} - 4e^- \rightarrow O_2(g)$
(c) $2Cl^-(aq) - 2e^- \rightarrow Cl_2(g)$
(d) $Cu^{2+}(aq) + 2e^- \rightarrow Cu(s)$
(e) $Al^{3+}l + 3e^- \rightarrow Al(s)$
(f) $4OH^-(aq) - 4e^- \rightarrow O_2(g) + 2H_2O(l)$

STUDENT ANSWER WITH EXAMINER'S COMMENTS

When magnesium burns in air, one of the products is magnesium oxide.

(a) Write the symbol equation for the formation of magnesium oxide including state symbols.

'Oxygen is diatomic O_2' → *Mg(s) + O(g) → MgO(s)*

(3 marks)

(b) Explain why this reaction is an example of:

(i) oxidation

Addition of oxygen

(1 mark)

(ii) synthesis

'Look up the definition at the end of this chapter. You are thinking of synthetic' → *When something is made from something else that can be used instead of natural substances*

(2 marks)

(c) When magnesium burns in air it gives out heat. What is the name given to this type of reaction?

Exothermic

(1 mark)

(d) When magnesium burns in air another product of the reaction is magnesium nitride (Mg_3N_2). When water reacts with magnesium nitride a gas is given off that turns damp litmus papers blue.

(i) Name the gas given off.

'Ammonia!' → *hydrogen nitride*

(1 mark)

(ii) What name is given to the reaction between water and a compound?

'Bad luck, it should be hydrolysis' → *hydration*

(1 mark)

(continued)

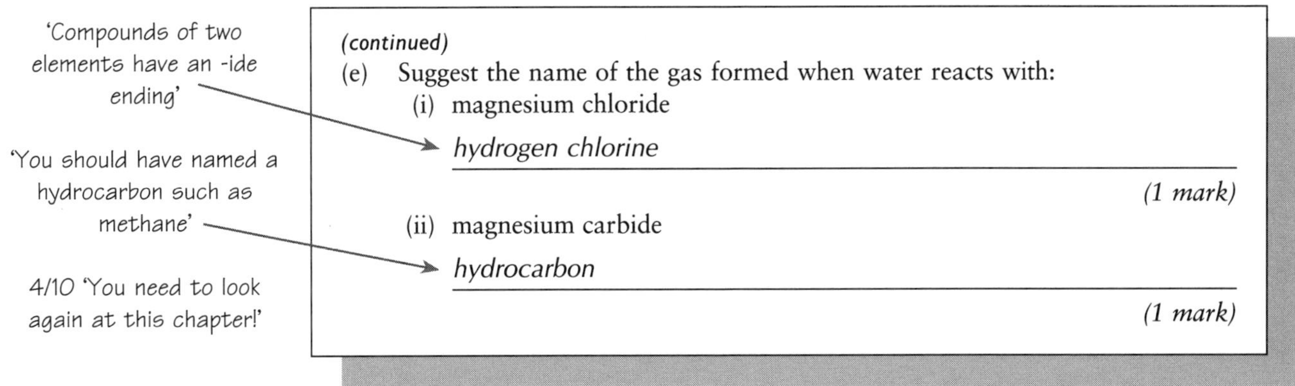

'Compounds of two elements have an -ide ending'
'You should have named a hydrocarbon such as methane'
4/10 'You need to look again at this chapter!'
(continued)
(e) Suggest the name of the gas formed when water reacts with:
(i) magnesium chloride
hydrogen chlorine
(1 mark)
(ii) magnesium carbide
hydrocarbon
(1 mark)

SUMMARY

Use this list to help with your revision. Tick off the points as you learn them

▷ Make sure you know the symbols for all the common elements.

Metals		**Non-metals**	
Al	aluminium	Ar	argon
Ba	barium	Br	bromine
Ca	calcium	C	carbon
Cu	copper	He	helium
Fe	iron	H	hydrogen
Pb	lead	I	iodine
Mg	magnesium	Ne	neon
K	potassium	N	nitrogen
Na	sodium	O	oxygen
Zn	zinc	S	sulphur

▷ Compounds of two elements usually have an **-ide** ending:

$CaBr_2$ calcium bromide
Mg_3N_2 magnesium nitride
Al_2O_3 aluminium oxide

▷ Compounds containing oxygen generally have an **-ate** ending:

$CaCO_3$ calcium carbonate
$NaNO_3$ sodium nitrate
$KClO_3$ potassium chlorate

▷ Remember how to write formulae—this means learning the combining power of various elements and radicals. Here are a few for you to learn:

Table 11.1

Combining power			
1	2	3	4
Potassium	Barium	Aluminium	Carbon
Sodium	Calcium	Nitrogen	Silicon
Bromine	Copper(II)	Iron(III)	
Chlorine	Iron(II)		
Hydrogen	Lead		
Iodine	Magnesium		
Nitrate	Zinc		
Hydrogencarbonate	Oxygen		
Hydroxide	Carbonate		
	Sulphate		

(continued)

(continued)

Thus the formula of zinc iodide can be obtained from Zn^2I^1 cross over ZnI_2 and aluminium hydroxide, $Al^3(OH)^1$ cross over to $Al(OH)_3$.

- When you write equations, make sure that there are equal numbers of atoms on each side of the equation.
- Remember the state symbols: (s) solid; (l) liquid; (g) gas and (aq) aqueous.
- Ionic equations must balance so that each side has the same number of atoms *and* the same number of charges.
- Finally, learn the different types of reactions.

Chapter

12 Quantitative chemistry

GETTING STARTED

Do not be afraid of calculations. You will find that if you work through the examples in this chapter, and practise with other types of calculations, they will become much easier.

The easiest way to tackle any chemistry problem is to understand **the mole**. Just remember that a **mole** is a number—a very large number. It is in the region of: 600 000 000 000 000 000 000 000 which is abbreviated to 6×10^{23}. You do *not* have to remember this number—it is called Avogadro's number. A mole of anything contains Avogadro's number of that thing. Thus a mole of copper atoms has 6×10^{23} atoms; a mole of oxygen molecules has 6×10^{23} oxygen molecules (O_2); and a school containing a mole of students would have 6×10^{23} pupils. All the definitions in this chapter are based on a mole of carbon-12 atoms. Carbon-12 is a particular **isotope** of carbon.

TOPIC CHART

LONDON	MEG	NEAB	SEG	NICCEA	WJEC	TOPIC	STUDY	REVISION 1	REVISION 2
✓	✓	✓	✓	✓	✓	Relative atomic mass			
✓	✓	✓	✓	✓	✓	Relative formula mass			
✓	✓		✓	✓	✓	The mole			
✓	✓	✓	✓	✓	✓	Empirical formula			
	✓					Molecular formula			
✓	✓		✓	✓	✓	Calculations from equations			
✓	✓	✓	✓	✓		Avogadro's law			
	✓					Incomplete reactions			
✓	✓		✓	✓	✓	Molar solutions			
✓	✓	✓	✓	✓	✓	Calculations in titrations			
✓	✓	✓	✓			Calculations in electrolysis			
	✓		✓			Quantity of electricity (faraday)			

WHAT YOU NEED TO KNOW

Relative atomic mass

Relative atomic mass (A_r) is a way of measuring how heavy an **atom** is. Carbon-12 (an isotope of carbon) is given a relative atomic mass of 12.00. The masses of all other atoms are compared with this value. The atoms of magnesium are twice as heavy as carbon atoms, they have a relative atomic mass of 24. The mass of the oxygen atom is one and one-third that of carbon, i.e. 16.

Relative formula mass

Relative formula mass (RFM) is similar to relative atomic mass, but in this case it applies to **compounds**, i.e. it is the sum of the relative atomic masses in a formula on a scale on which the mass of one atom of carbon-12 is 12 units. It applies to all compounds, even if they are ionic. Thus, relative formula mass is calculated by adding together the relative atomic masses of all the elements present. The relative formula (molecular) mass (M_r) of carbon dioxide (CO_2) is $12 + (2 \times 16) = 44$; the M_r of sodium carbonate (Na_2CO_3) is $(2 \times 23) + 12 + (3 \times 16) = 106$.

To find the percentage of an element in a compound

The following examples will help you to work out the percentage of an element in a compound. Make sure you understand the calculations. You are not expected to remember the relative atomic masses of the elements, but you may have to work out the formula of a compound.

(a) What is the percentage of magnesium in magnesium oxide MgO (A_r Mg = 24; A_r O = 16)?

The relative formula mass (RFM) of MgO is $24 + 16 = 40$.

24 parts of the RFM are magnesium, so the percentage of magnesium is

$$\frac{24 \times 100}{40} = 60\%$$

Multiplying by 100 converts the figures to a percentage (60%).

This tells us that 60% of magnesium oxide is magnesium.

(b) What is the percentage of oxygen in aluminium oxide (A_r Al = 27) to the nearest whole number?

The formula of aluminium oxide is Al_2O_3.

Relative formula mass of aluminium oxide is $2 \times 27 + 3 \times 16 = 102$.

48 parts of the RFM are oxygen, so the percentage of oxygen in aluminium oxide is

$$\frac{48 \times 100}{102} = 47\%$$

This tells us that 47 per cent of aluminium oxide is oxygen.

(c) What is the percentage of carbon in ethane (C_2H_6) (A_r C = 12; A_r H = 1)?

Relative formula mass of ethane is $2 \times 12 + 6 \times 1 = 30$.

Because there are two carbon atoms in ethane, then 24 parts of the RFM are carbon so the percentage of carbon in ethane is

$$\frac{24 \times 100}{30} = 80\%$$

The mole

The **mole** is the amount of a substance that contains the same number of particles as there are atoms in 12.00 grams of carbon-12. This number of atoms is 6×10^{23} and it is called the **Avogadro constant** or **number.**

Since relative atomic mass and relative molecular mass are based on carbon-12, then the relative atomic mass of an element and the relative molecular mass of an element or compound must contain Avogadro's number of particles. Thus the following all contain the same number of particles: 44 grams of carbon dioxide (molecules); 18 grams of water (molecules); 23 grams of sodium (atoms) and 100 grams of calcium carbonate. 100 grams of calcium carbonate contains 1 mole of calcium atoms (40 grams), 1 mole of carbon atoms (12 grams) and 3 moles of oxygen atoms (48 grams). You must make sure that you state the type of particles you are talking about; thus 1 mole of oxygen atoms has a mass of 16 grams and the mass of 1 mole of oxygen molecules is 32 grams.

Empirical formula

The simplest formula which shows the ratio of each type of atom in a compound is called its **empirical formula.** Using the idea of moles, it can be calculated, for all compounds, from experimental results.

Example

4.14 g of lead is found to react with 3.20 g of bromine. What is the formula of lead(II) bromide? (A_r Pb = 207; A_r Br = 80)

Moles of lead $= \frac{4.14}{207} = 0.02$ mole of lead atoms.

Moles of bromine $= \frac{3.20}{80} = 0.04$ mole of bromine atoms.

1 mole of lead atoms (Pb) reacts with 2 moles of bromine atoms (Br).

Formula of lead(II) bromide is $PbBr_2$.

To determine the formula of magnesium oxide

Weigh a crucible and its lid empty. Clean about 15 cm of magnesium ribbon (to remove its oxide layer). Coil the magnesium and place it in the crucible. Put the lid on the crucible and weigh again. The difference in these two masses gives the mass of magnesium used. Heat the crucible strongly until the magnesium catches fire. Keep lifting the crucible carefully (so that no magnesium oxide escapes) until the reaction has finished. Allow the crucible containing the magnesium oxide to cool down and weigh it (not forgetting the lid).

Typical results are:

mass of crucible + lid	23.45 g
mass of crucible + lid + magnesium	23.63 g
mass of crucible + lid + magnesium oxide	26.75 g

From these results it can be seen that:

0.18 g of magnesium (23.63–23.45) reacted with 0.12 g (26.75–23.63) of oxygen.

Number of moles of magnesium atoms = 0.18/24 = 0.0075.

Number of moles of oxygen atoms = 0.12/16 = 0.0075.

Since 0.0075 mole of magnesium atoms react with 0.0075 mole of oxygen atoms, then 1 mole of magnesium atoms react with 1 mole of oxygen atoms.

The formula of magnesium oxide is MgO.

Molecular formula

The **molecular formula** shows how many of each type of atom are present in a molecule. If the relative molecular mass (M_r) is known, it is possible to work out the molecular formula.

Example

A compound X contains 6 g of carbon and 1 g of hydrogen. The relative molecular mass of X is 56. What is the molecular formula of X?

Moles of carbon $= \frac{6}{12} = 0.5$.

Moles of hydrogen $= \frac{1}{1} = 1$

1 mole of carbon reacts with 2 moles of hydrogen.

Empirical formula is CH_2.

'M_r' of empirical formula $= 12 + (2 \times 1) = 14$.

$\frac{56}{14} = 4$. Therefore there must be four 'CH_2' in the molecular formula.

Molecular formula of X is C_4H_8.

Calculations from equations

(a) What mass of calcium oxide can be formed by heating 10 g of calcium carbonate until it all decomposes?
There are two ways of tackling this problem, but both involve writing the equation first:

calcium carbonate → calcium oxide + carbon dioxide

$CaCO_3(s) \rightarrow CaO(s) + CO_2(g)$

Method 1

RFM of $CaCO_3$ is $40 + 12 + 3 \times 16 = 100$.

RFM of $CaO = 40 + 16 = 56$.

Thus from the equation:

100 g of calcium carbonate will produce 56 g of calcium oxide, thus

10 g of calcium carbonate will produce $\frac{56 \times 10}{100} = 5.6$ g.

Method 2

From the equation we can see that:

1 mole of calcium carbonate produces 1 mole of calcium oxide.

We have seen from method 1 that the RFM of calcium carbonate is 100, and thus the number of moles used $= 10/100$ which is 0.1 mole.

Hence 0.1 mole of calcium oxide must be formed.

The RFM of calcium oxide is 56 and thus the mass of calcium oxide formed is $0.1 \times 56 = 5.6$ g.

(b) What mass of silver will be displaced if 1.6 g of copper is added to an excess of silver nitrate solution (A_r Cu = 64; A_r Ag = 108)?
An excess of silver nitrate means that all the copper will react with the silver nitrate solution and leave some silver nitrate over (the excess).
The equation is

copper + silver nitrate → silver + copper nitrate

$Cu(s) + 2AgNO_3(aq) \rightarrow 2Ag(s) + Cu(NO_3)_2(aq)$

Method 1

64 g of copper will displace $2 \times 108 = 216$ grams of copper.
1.6 grams of copper will displace $\frac{216 \times 1.6}{64} = 5.4$ g.

Method 2

From the equation, 1 mole of copper displaces 2 moles of silver.

Moles of copper used $= 1.6/64 = 0.025$.

Moles of silver formed $= 2 \times 0.025 = 0.050$.

Mass of silver formed $= 0.050 \times 108 = 5.4$ g.

Avogadro's law

Avogadro's law states that **equal volumes of all gases** under the same conditions of temperature and pressure **contain the same number of molecules.** It follows from this law that 1 mole of any gas under the same conditions of temperature and pressure must occupy the same volume. At room temperature and pressure this volume is 24 dm^3 and it is called the **molar gas volume.**

(a) What volume of carbon dioxide is required to reduce 1.60 g of iron(III) oxide at room temperature and pressure?
The equation for the reaction is

iron(III) oxide + carbon monoxide → iron + carbon dioxide

$$Fe_2O_3(s) + 3CO(g) \rightarrow 2Fe(s) + 3CO_2(g)$$

Method 1

RFM of iron(III) oxide is $2 \times 56 + 3 \times 16 = 160$.

160 g of iron(III) oxide is reduced by $3 \times 24 = 72\,dm^3$ of carbon monoxide.

1.6 g of iron(II) oxide will be reduced by $\frac{72 \times 1.6}{160} = 0.72\,dm^3$.

Method 2

1 mole of iron(III) oxide is reduced by 3 moles of carbon monoxide.

Moles of iron(III) oxide used $= 1.6/160 = 0.01$ mole.

Moles of carbon monoxide required $= 3 \times 0.01 = 0.03$ mole.

Volume of carbon monoxide required $= 0.03 \times 24 = 0.72\,dm^3$.

Incomplete reactions

Sometimes reactions do not go to completion. It is possible to calculate either how much of the reactant has reacted or how much of the product has been formed.

Example

The reaction between nitrogen and hydrogen to form ammonia is reversible:

$$N_2(g) + 3H_2(g) \rightleftharpoons 2\,NH_3(g)$$

What is the percentage yield of ammonia, at room temperature and pressure, if 12 dm³ of hydrogen react to give 2 dm³ of ammonia?

Moles of hydrogen used $= 12/24 = 0.5$.

3 moles of hydrogen produce 2 moles of ammonia if the reaction goes to completion.

Moles of ammonia that should be formed $= 0.5 \times \frac{2}{3} = \frac{1.0}{3}$ mole.

Volume of ammonia that should be formed $= \frac{1.0}{3} \times 24 = 8\,dm^3$.

Percentage yield $= \frac{2}{8} \times 100 = 25\%$.

Molar solutions

If a solution contains **one mole** of substance dissolved in **one litre** of solution it is called a **molar solution.** The units of molar solution are mol dm^{-3} or mol l^{-1} or mol per litre.

A one molar solution (1 M) contains 1 mole of the solute in 1 litre of solution.

The RFM of sodium hydroxide (NaOH) $= 23 + 16 + 1 = 40$; thus a molar solution of sodium hydroxide contains 40 g of sodium hydroxide in 1 litre of solution.

The RFM of hydrogen chloride (HCl) is $35.5 + 1 = 36.5$. If 1 litre of a solution contains 71 g of hydrogen chloride it is said to be 2 M (two molar).

The RFM of sulphuric acid (H_2SO_4) is $2 \times 1 + 32 + 4 \times 16 = 98$. A 0.1 M ('point one molar') solution of sulphuric acid will contain 9.8 g of sulphuric acid in 1 litre of solution.

Calculations in titrations

Titrations can be used to work out the concentrations of acids or alkalis.

Suppose that 25.00 cm³ of 2.0 M sodium hydroxide was exactly neutralized by 20.00 cm³ of sulphuric acid solution. Calculate the concentration of the sulphuric acid.

sodium hydroxide + sulphuric acid → sodium sulphate + water

$2NaOH(aq) \quad + \quad H_2SO_4(aq) \quad \rightarrow \quad Na_2SO_4(aq) \quad + H_2O(l)$

From the equation we can see that 2 moles of sodium hydroxide react with 1 mole of sulphuric acid.

Moles of sodium hydroxide used $= \dfrac{25.0 \times 2}{1000} = 0.05$ mole.

Number of moles of sulphuric acid in 20.00 cm^3 = 0.05/2 = 0.025 mole.

If 20 cm^3 of sulphuric acid solution contains 0.025 mole then

1000 cm^3 (1 litre) contains $\dfrac{0.025 \times 1000}{20} = 1.25$ mol per litre

Hence the sulphuric acid is 1.25 M.

Calculations in electrolysis

You may either be given the half equation for a reaction at an electrode or be expected to know it.

What mass of chlorine and what volume of chlorine (at normal temperature and pressure) can be obtained by the electrolysis of 234 g of molten sodium chloride?

RFM of sodium chloride NaCl = 23 + 35.5 = 58.5 g.

The number of moles of sodium chloride used = 234/58.5 = 4 moles.

$NaCl(s) \rightarrow Na^+ + Cl^-$

That is, 1 mole of sodium chloride produces 1 mole of chloride ions.

During electrolysis 2 moles of chloride ions lose 2 moles of electrons to form 1 mole of chlorine gas:

$2Cl^- - 2e^- \rightarrow Cl_2(g)$

From these two equations it can be seen that

2 moles of sodium chloride produces 1 mole of chlorine gas on electrolysis.

Hence 4 moles of sodium chloride will produce 2 moles of chlorine gas.

(i) Mass of 1 mole of chlorine (Cl_2) is 35.5 × 2 = 71.
Mass of chlorine formed = 2 × 71 = 142 g.

(ii) Volume of 1 mole of chlorine gas at room temperature and pressure = 24 dm^3.
Volume of chlorine formed = 2 × 24 = 48 dm^3.

Quantity of electricity (faraday)

The mass of substance discharge at an electrode depends upon:

- the amount of current; and
- the time the current flows.

Thus the higher the current and the longer the current flows, the greater the amount of substance discharged.

An electric current is the movement of charge through a conductor. The unit of charge is the coulomb.

A coulomb is the amount of electricity equivalent to one ampere flowing for one second.

If a current of 3 amperes is passed for 30 minutes, then the number of coulombs equals 3 × 30 × 60 = 5400 coulombs. (We multiply by 60 to convert the minutes to seconds.)

A faraday is 96 500 coulombs and it is the amount of electricity carried by a mole of electrons.

The following examples illustrate the meaning of a faraday:

- To discharge a mole of sodium ions (Na^+) requires 1 faraday.

- To discharge a mole of copper ions (Cu^{2+}) requires 2 faradays.
- To discharge a mole of oxide ions (O^{2-}) requires 2 faradays, and to discharge a mole of oxygen molecules (O_2) requires 4 faradays.

The greater the charge on the ion, the greater the number of faradays required to discharge the same mass of the ion.

EXAMINATION QUESTIONS

Question 1(F) Ammonium nitrate, NH_4NO_3, is a common fertilizer. It is very soluble in water.

(a) Calculate the relative formula mass of ammonium nitrate. *[2]*
(b) Other than the cost of ammonium nitrate, suggest and explain
  (i) one advantage of using ammonium nitrate as a fertilizer;
  (ii) one disadvantage of using ammonium nitrate as a fertilizer. *[2]*

Question 2(F) You are given the following relative atomic masses: H = 1; O = 16; Mg = 24; Al = 27; S = 32; Ca = 40; Cu = 64.

(a) Calculate the relative formula masses of the following compounds:
  (i) CaS
  (ii) Al_2O_3
  (iii) $Mg(OH)_2$
  (iv) $CuSO_4.5H_2O$ *[4]*
(b) A metal compound has the formula MCl_4 and has a relative formula mass of 261. If the relative atomic mass of chlorine is 35.5, what is
  (i) the relative atomic mass of M? *[2]*
  (ii) the metal M? *[1]*

Question 3(F) The equation shows the burning of ethane in air to form water and carbon dioxide:

$$2C_2H_6(g) + 7O_2(g) = 4CO_2(g) + 6H_2O(l)$$

$$[A_r(C) = 12;\ A_r(H) = 1;\ A_r(O) = 16]$$

(a) (i) Calculate the mass of 1 mole of carbon dioxide. *[1]*
  (ii) Calculate the mass of carbon dioxide that is formed from 30 g ethane. *[1]*
(b) Draw a diagram showing how you could collect some of the water formed during the burning. *[2]*
(c) How could you prove that the liquid collected was water. *[1]*

Question 4(H) Magnesium sulphate crystals ($MgSO_4.7H_2O$) can be made by adding excess magnesium oxide (MgO), which is insoluble in water, to dilute sulphuric acid.

(a) Why is the magnesium oxide added in excess? *[1]*
(b) The apparatus shown below (Fig. 12.1) could be used to separate the excess magnesium oxide from the solution. Label the diagram by putting the correct words in each of the spaces below. *[4]*

Fig. 12.1

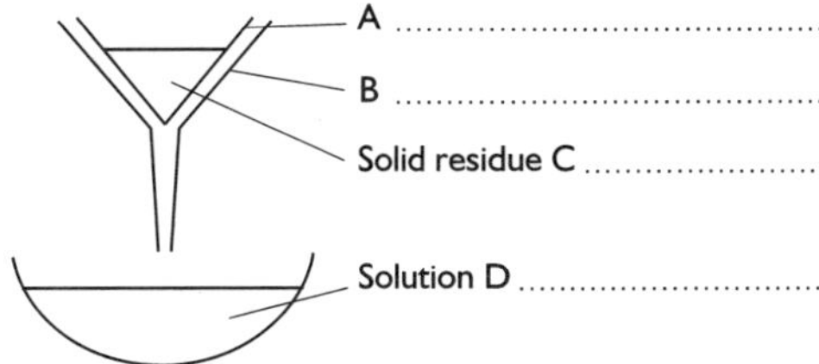

(c) Given the relative atomic masses: H = 1, O = 16, Mg = 24, S = 32, calculate the relative formula mass of
  (i) Magnesium oxide, MgO
  (ii) Magnesium sulphate crystals, $MgSO_4.7H_2O$ *[3]*
(d) Use your answers in (c) to calculate the maximum mass of magnesium sulphate crystals that could be obtained from 2.0 g of magnesium oxide. *[2]*
(e) Describe how you would obtain pure, dry crystals of magnesium sulphate from magnesium sulphate solution. *[4]*

Question 5(H)

You determined the concentration of an aqueous solution of barium hydroxide solution by using a titration method. Barium hydroxide is poisonous. You placed 25.0 cm^3 of 0.100 mol dm^{-3} hydrochloric acid in a conical flask and titrated it against barium hydroxide solution. You found that 20.5 cm^3 of the alkali was required to neutralize the acid.

(a) Name a suitable indicator for this reaction. What would be the colour of the indicator at the end of the reaction? *[1]*
(b) What would you see if you added a solution of sulphuric acid to barium hydroxide solution? *[1]*
(c) What piece of apparatus is used to measure exactly 25.0 cm^3 of hydrochloric acid? *[1]*
(d) What is the name of the apparatus in which you placed the barium hydroxide solution? *[1]*

The equation for the reaction is

$$Ba(OH)_2(aq) + 2HCl(aq) \rightarrow BaCl_2(aq) + 2H_2O(l)$$

(e) (i) Calculate the number of moles of hydrochloric acid in 20.5 cm^3 of the 0.100 mol dm^{-3} HCl.
  (ii) Calculate the number of moles of barium hydroxide in 25.0 cm^3 of solution and hence find the number of moles in 1 dm^3.
  (iii) Calculate the relative formula mass of barium hydroxide and hence calculate the concentration of the barium hydroxide solution in g dm^{-3} to one decimal place. *[7]*

Question 6(H)

To find the formula of a compound formed between copper and bromine, copper was heated with an excess of liquid bromine in the apparatus shown below (Fig. 12.2). The experiment was carried out in a fume cupboard.

Fig. 12.2

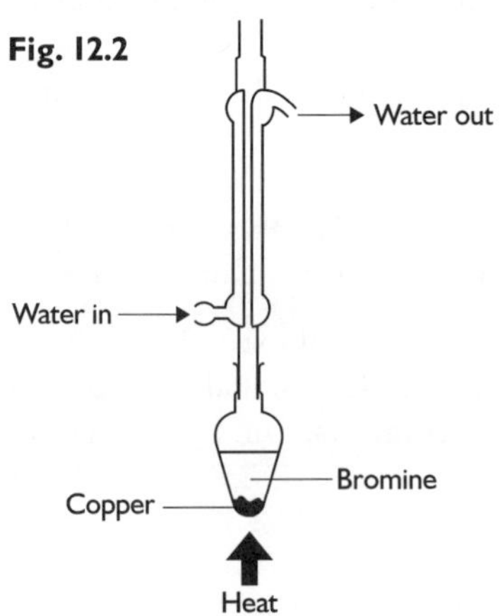

After the reaction was over, any bromine which had not been used was removed, leaving the compound behind. From the readings made, the mass of bromine which had combined with the copper was calculated.

The experiment was repeated starting with different masses of copper.

(a) Why is a reflux condenser used in the apparatus? *[1]*
(b) Explain what should be done to remove the unreacted bromine. *[2]*

(c) Complete the list below, which gives the readings that need to be taken in order to calculate the masses of bromine and copper which have combined.

(i) mass of empty flask

(ii) ______________________________

(iii) ______________________________

[2]

The results from some of the experiments are shown plotted on the graph below (Fig. 12.3).

Fig. 12.3

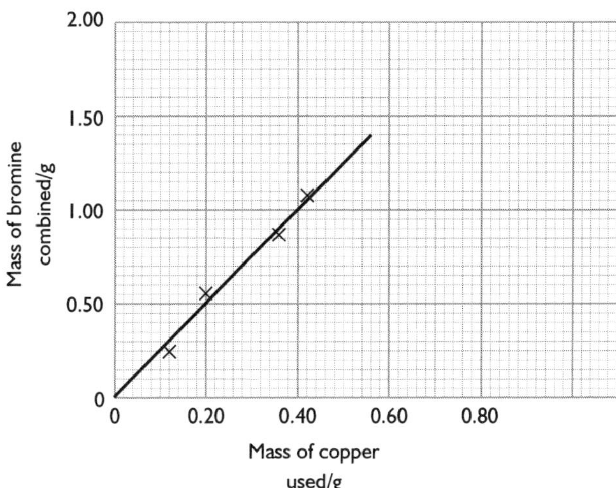

(d) Use the graph to find out

(i) what mass of bromine would combine with 0.30 g of copper; *[1]*

(ii) what mass of compound would be formed from 0.50 g of copper. *[1]*

(e) A further experiment found that 0.64 g of copper combined with 1.60 g of bromine

(i) Plot this result on the graph. *[1]*

(ii) How many grams of bromine would combine with 64 g of copper? *[1]*

(iii) How many moles of bromine would combine with 1 mole of copper? (relative atomic masses: Cu 64; Br 80.) *[1]*

(iv) Write the formula of the compound formed between copper and bromine in these experiments. *[1]*

(v) Name the compound formed in these experiments. *[2]*

Question 7(H)

An electric current was passed through molten potassium iodide and an aqueous solution of potassium iodide using the apparatus shown (Fig. 12.4).

(a) The solution around the anode in beaker B turned brown. What was being formed at this electrode? *[1]*

Fig. 12.4

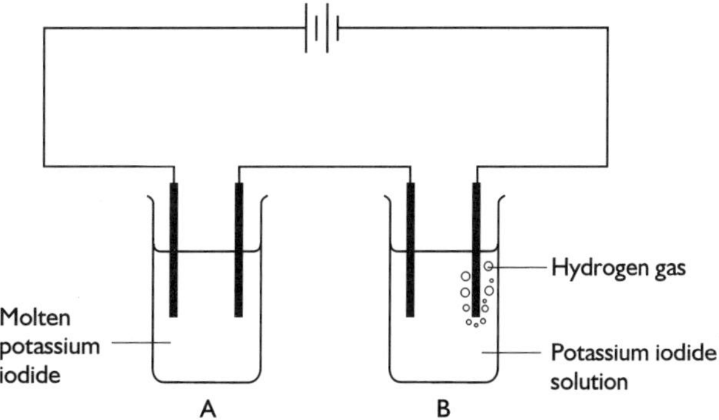

(b) A purple vapour was seen around the anode in beaker A. What was being formed at this electrode? *[1]*
(c) Hydrogen gas was formed at the cathode in the aqueous potassium iodide? Describe the test for hydrogen *[1]*
(d) A metal that rapidly tarnished is formed at the cathode in beaker A. What metal is being formed? *[1]*

A current of 0.1 ampere was passed for 16 minutes.

(e) If 1 faraday = 96 000 coulombs, how many faradays were passed? *[1]*

12 cm^3 of hydrogen gas were produced at the cathode in B. One mole of gas occupies 24 000 cm^3 under the conditions of this experiment.

(f) How many moles of hydrogen were given off? *[1]*
(g) Using your answers to questions (e) and (f), how many faradays are required to produce one mole of hydrogen. What does this tell you about hydrogen gas?

OUTLINE ANSWERS

Question 1

(a) $14 + 4 \times 1 + 14 + 3 \times 16 = 80$.
(b) (i) It is very soluble in water.
(ii) It is explosive.

Question 2

(a) (i) 72; (ii) 102; (iii) 58; (iv) 250.
(b) (i) $261 - 4 \times 35.5 = 119$; (ii) tin.

Question 3

(a) (i) 44 g; (ii) 88 g.
(b) See Fig. 12.5.

Fig. 12.5

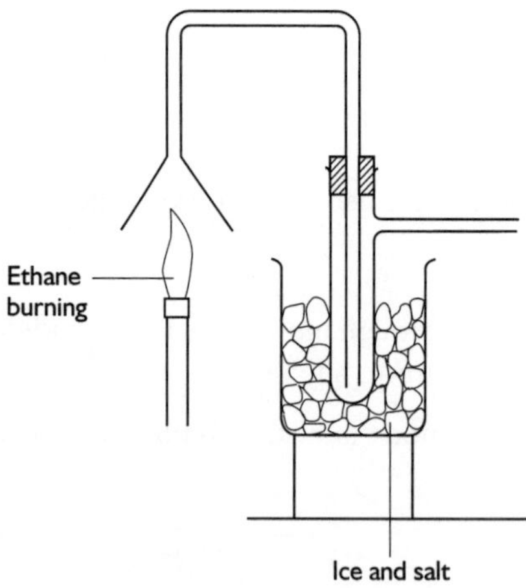

(c) Measure the melting point and boiling point of the liquid; it should be 0 °C for the melting point and 100 °C for the boiling point.

Question 4

(a) To make sure that all the sulphuric acid is used up.
(b) A, filter paper; B, filter funnel; C, magnesium oxide; D, magnesium sulphate solution.
(c) (i) 40; (ii) 246.
(d) Since 40 g of MgO gives 246 g of $MgSO_4.7H_2O$ then 2 g of MgO will give $246 \times 2/40 = 12.3$ g.
(e) See p. 36.

Question 5

(a) Methyl orange; yellow.
(b) A white precipitate (of barium sulphate).
(c) Pipette.
(d) Burette.
(e) (i) 0.00205 mole.
(ii) Number of moles of barium hydroxide in 25 cm^3 is $\frac{1}{2} \times 0.00205 = 0.001025$ moles in 1000 cm^3 (1 dm^3) $= 1000 \times 0.001025/25 = 0.041$.
(iii) Relative formula mass of barium hydroxide is $137 + 2 \times 17 = 171$; concentration $= 0.041 \times 171 = 7.0\,g\,dm^{-3}$.

Question 6

(a) To prevent the volatile bromine liquid from escaping.
(b) Remove the condenser and heat the mixture gently in a fume cupboard.
(c) (ii) Mass of flask + copper; (iii) mass of flask + copper bromide.
(d) (i) 0.75 g; (ii) $1.25 + 0.50 = 1.75$ g.
(e) (i) See graph.
(ii) 160 g; (iii) $160/80 = 2$ moles of bromine atoms; (iv) $CuBr_2$
(v) copper bromide.

Question 7

(a) Iodine; (b) iodine; (c) burns with a 'pop'; (d) potassium.
(e) $0.1 \times 16 \times 60$ (to convert to seconds) $= 96$; $96/96\,000 = 0.001$ faraday.
(f) $12/24\,000 = 0.0005$.
(g) 2 faradays; hydrogen must be diatomic, H_2.

STUDENT ANSWER WITH EXAMINER'S COMMENTS

Pure zinc reacts slowly with dilute sulphuric acid to produce hydrogen. Addition of copper(II) sulphate solution increases the speed of the reaction because zinc displaces copper from copper(II) sulphate solution. The copper formed acts as a catalyst. The graph below plots the volume of hydrogen obtained when various volumes of 1.0 mol/dm^3 copper(II) sulphate were added to excess dilute sulphuric acid and x g of zinc. The volume of hydrogen was measured at room temperature and pressure (r.t.p.) and the same mass of zinc (x g) was used each time.

Fig. 12.6

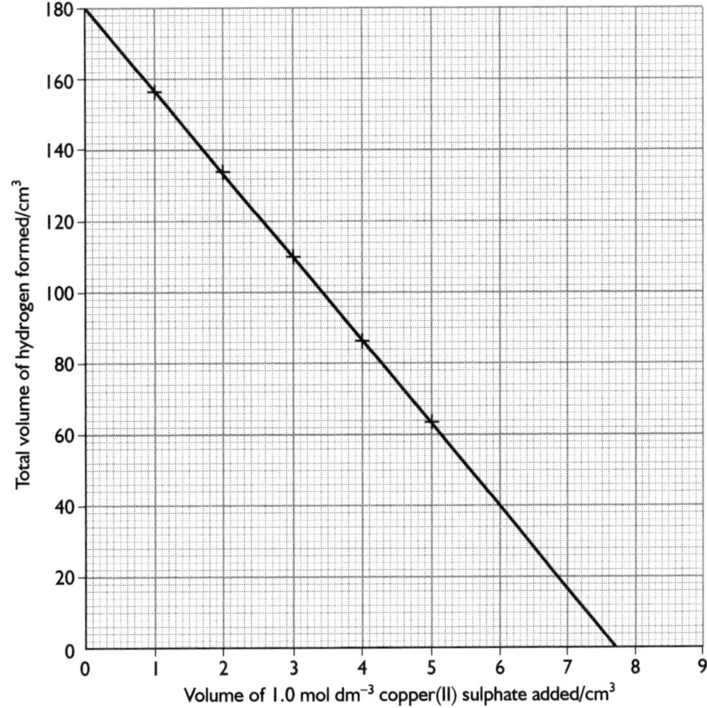

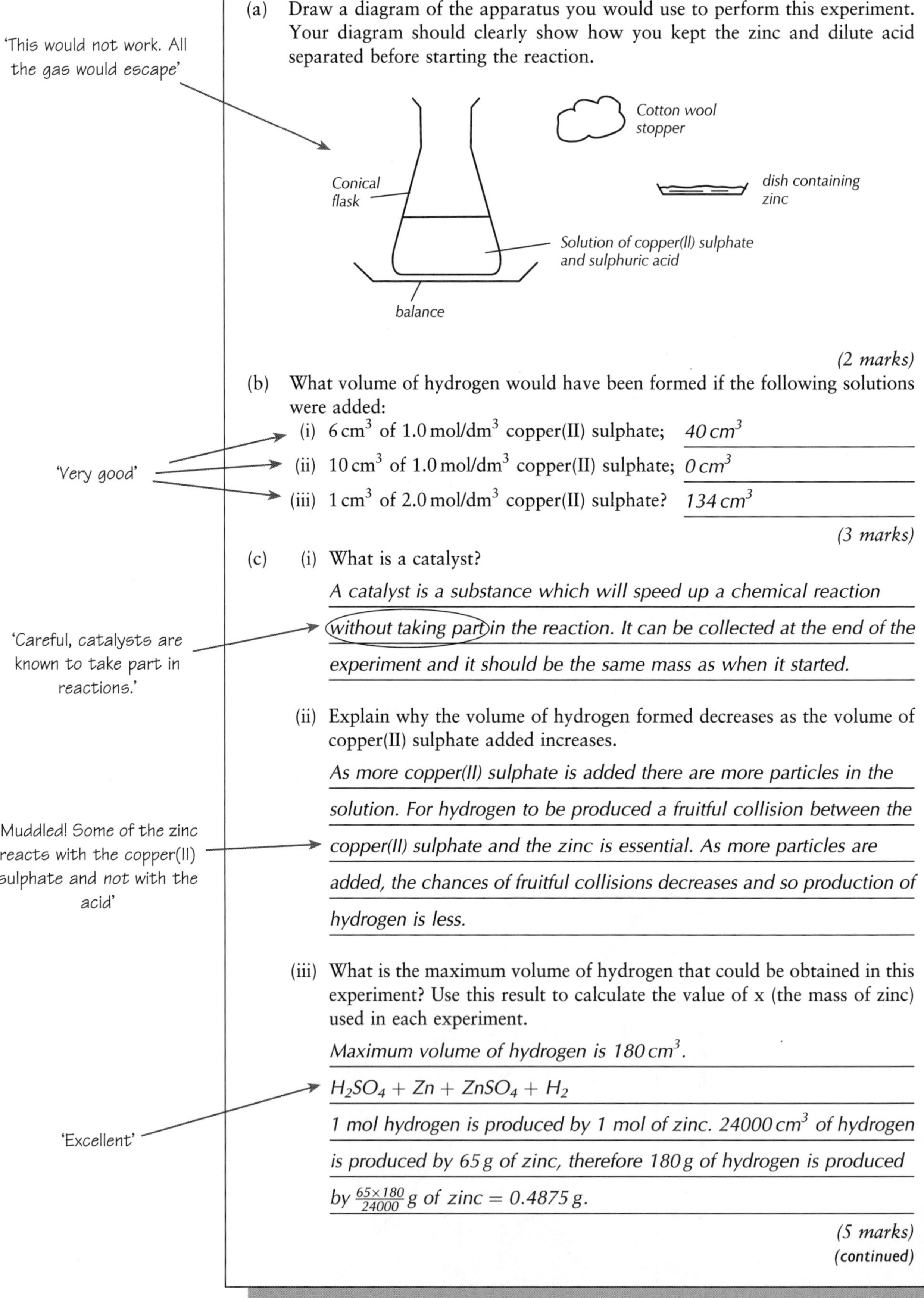
'This would not work. All the gas would escape'
Cotton wool stopper
Conical flask
dish containing zinc
Solution of copper(II) sulphate and sulphuric acid
balance
'Very good'
'Careful, catalysts are known to take part in reactions.'
'Muddled! Some of the zinc reacts with the copper(II) sulphate and not with the acid'
'Excellent'

(a) Draw a diagram of the apparatus you would use to perform this experiment. Your diagram should clearly show how you kept the zinc and dilute acid separated before starting the reaction.

(2 marks)

(b) What volume of hydrogen would have been formed if the following solutions were added:

(i) 6 cm^3 of 1.0 mol/dm^3 copper(II) sulphate; *40 cm^3*

(ii) 10 cm^3 of 1.0 mol/dm^3 copper(II) sulphate; *0 cm^3*

(iii) 1 cm^3 of 2.0 mol/dm^3 copper(II) sulphate? *134 cm^3*

(3 marks)

(c) (i) What is a catalyst?

A catalyst is a substance which will speed up a chemical reaction without taking part in the reaction. It can be collected at the end of the experiment and it should be the same mass as when it started.

(ii) Explain why the volume of hydrogen formed decreases as the volume of copper(II) sulphate added increases.

As more copper(II) sulphate is added there are more particles in the solution. For hydrogen to be produced a fruitful collision between the copper(II) sulphate and the zinc is essential. As more particles are added, the chances of fruitful collisions decreases and so production of hydrogen is less.

(iii) What is the maximum volume of hydrogen that could be obtained in this experiment? Use this result to calculate the value of x (the mass of zinc) used in each experiment.

Maximum volume of hydrogen is 180 cm^3.

$H_2SO_4 + Zn + ZnSO_4 + H_2$

1 mol hydrogen is produced by 1 mol of zinc. 24000 cm^3 of hydrogen is produced by 65 g of zinc, therefore 180 g of hydrogen is produced by $\frac{65 \times 180}{24000}$ g of zinc = 0.4875 g.

(5 marks)

(continued)

'Silver would act as a catalyst, but zinc does not displace magnesium.'

'Silver is below hydrogen in the reactivity series.'

'This equation is nonsense!'

'Overall, I was impressed by your answers to parts (b) and (c). You went astray in (d) (iii). From your equation in (d) (i) one mole of zinc displaces two moles of silver. Thus, this is equivalent to adding 2 cm^3 of 1.0 mol/dm^3 of copper(II) sulphate. Answer 134 cm^3. (This was a very hard question!) Score 9/15'

(continued)

(d) The order of reactivity of the metals used in this experiment is magnesium (most reactive), zinc, copper, silver (least reactive).

(i) Write the equation for the reaction between zinc and aqueous silver nitrate.

$Zn + 2AgNO_3 \rightarrow Zn(NO_3)_2 + 2Ag$

(ii) Suggest why the use of silver nitrate in this experiment in place of copper(II) sulphate affects the volume of hydrogen given off, but the use of magnesium sulphate has no effect on the volume of hydrogen given off.

This is because the valency of silver is one whereas the valency of copper and magnesuim is two. Two moles of silver are produced when zinc nitrate is formed. The silver reacts with the acid and so more hydrogen is produced than with the other two metals

(iii) Calculate the volume of hydrogen formed if x g of zinc were added to 4 cm^3 of 1.0 mol/dm^3 aqueous silver nitrate and excess dilute sulphuric acid.

$Zn + 2AgNO_3 + H_2SO_4 \rightarrow Zn(NO_3)_2 + Ag_2SO_4 + H_2$.

1 mol of zinc reacts with 2 mols silver nitrate to form 1 mol of hydrogen.

(5 marks)

SUMMARY

Use this list to help with your revision. Tick off the points as you learn them.

- The relative atomic mass RAM (A_r) of an atom is the mass of an atom on a scale where an atom of carbon-12 is 12.00.
- The relative formula mass (RFM) of a chemical is the mass of the chemical on a scale where an atom of carbon-12 is 12.00. (The chemical can be a covalent element, a covalent compound or an ionic compound.) You should be able to work out that the RFM of Na_2CO_3 is 106.
- A mole is the amount of substance that contains the same number of particles as there are atoms in 12.00 grams of carbon-12.
- A mole contains 6×10^{23} particles—it is called Avogadro's number.
- The number of moles of an element can be calculated by dividing the mass of the element by its relative atomic mass. You should be able to work out that 32 grams of oxygen is 2 moles of oxygen atoms.
- The number of moles of a compound can be found by dividing the mass of the compound by its relative formula mass. You should be able to show that 255 grams of sodium nitrate ($NaNO_3$) is 3 moles of sodium nitrate.
- Avogadro's law states that 'equal volumes of all gases under the same conditions of temperature and pressure contain the same number of molecules'.
- One mole of any gas under the same conditions of temperature and pressure occupy the same volume.
- The concentration of a solution can be found by dividing the number of grams of the solution in 1 litre of the solution by the relative formula mass of the solute.
- You should be able to show that if 1 litre of a solution contains 126 grams of nitric acid (HNO_3) then it is two molar (2 M).
- A molar solution (M) contains 1 mole of solute in 1 litre of solution.
- A faraday is a mole of electrons.
- The unit of charge is a coulomb.
- A coulomb is the amount of electricity equivalent to one ampere flowing for one second. You should be able to show that if a current of 1.5 amperes flows for 45 minutes, the number of coulombs used is equal to 4050.

Chapter

13 Earth and its atmosphere

GETTING STARTED

The Earth as we know it has evolved over a period of 4500 million years. What has happened to the Earth in that time is still largely unknown. The study of rocks (**geology**) and of fossils of plants and animals has given many clues about the processes that have occurred.

In this chapter we shall look at the history and continuing evolution of:

- The **atmosphere**, which has changed from one completely without oxygen—consisting mainly of **carbon dioxide, methane** and **ammonia**—to one mainly of **nitrogen** and **oxygen.**
- The **oceans,** which formed first as almost pure water, to the present-day **saline** mixture containing every known element, mostly as their salts.
- **Rocks,** initially composed of solid particles from space but evolving through **igneous** rock to form **sedimentary** and then **metamorphic** rocks.
- **Continents,** which are believed to have formed from a single large land mass (**Pangaea**) through **continental drift** which has occurred by a process involving **plate tectonics.**

TOPIC CHART

LONDON	MEG	NEAB	NICCEA	SEG	WJEC	TOPIC	STUDY	REVISION 1	REVISION 2
✓	✓	✓		✓	✓	The evolution of the Earth and its atmosphere			
		✓				The structure of the Earth			
✓	✓	✓		✓	✓	Formation of rocks and rock types			
✓	✓	✓		✓	✓	The rock cycle			
✓	✓	✓		✓	✓	Rocks—identification and uses			
✓	✓	✓		✓	✓	Plate tectonics			

WHAT YOU NEED TO KNOW

The evolution of the Earth and its atmosphere

There is no direct evidence of the early history of the evolution of the Earth and its atmosphere. We do have a knowledge of the atmosphere of planets in the solar system that resemble the Earth in size and structure. From this and other information from rock and fossil studies we can build up a picture of the possible changes that occurred in the first few billion years of the planet's existence. A possible sequence of events is as follows:

- When the Earth first formed it would not have had an atmosphere at all, because the particles of dust which stuck together to form the Earth came from space where there is no gas other than minute concentrations of **hydrogen** and **helium**!
- As dust particles collected and the planet grew, great **heat** would have been generated (see Note 1 below).
- Heat within the planet caused **volcanic activity** on a huge scale.
- The planet would become covered with **igneous rock**.
- The volcanoes would also spew out huge quantities of steam, oxides of carbon, methane, ammonia and hydrogen sulphide from chemical reactions in the hot interior (this process continues today).
- When the planet's surface eventually cooled to below 100 °C, the steam would condense to water and the **first seas** would form—about 3.8 billion years ago.
- Water-soluble gases like ammonia and carbon dioxide would dissolve in the seas.
- Heavy rain would **erode** and dissolve the igneous rock crust.
- The first **sediments** would form and seas would become **salty**.
- Life developed in the sea or in dust clouds. The first living organisms may have been bacteria capable of living on the **carbon compounds** and **ammonia** from the atmosphere, producing waste products which might fertilize future plant life or be converted to nitrogen gas (by denitrifying bacteria).
- Ultraviolet radiation in sunlight, and also lightning, decomposed water vapour into hydrogen and **oxygen** and ammonia into **nitrogen** and hydrogen. Hydrogen would be lost into space.
- As life evolved, photosynthetic algae and plants evolved and the **oxygen** concentration of the atmosphere increased.
- Plankton in the sea locked up carbon dioxide in their shells (44% of $CaCO_3$ is carbon dioxide) and, on death, deposited shell remains on sea bed—atmospheric carbon dioxide decreased (about 2 billion years ago).
- Plant life proliferated, increasing the amount of oxygen in the atmosphere. Coal and oil deposits formed (60–90% carbon), locking up even more carbon dioxide as 'fossil fuels' (see Note 2).

Note 1: Heat is generated when gravity pulls large masses of matter together into a planet. More heat is generated by radioactive decay in the body of the Earth.

Note 2: Huge quantities of carbon dioxide were removed from the atmosphere by the formation of deposits of fossil fuel and carbonates (now mainly limestone). It is estimated that the carbon dioxide in carbonate rock alone would, if released, increase the present concentration by a factor of 150 000!

Summary We see that this possible sequence of events would remove most of the carbon dioxide from the original atmosphere; replacing some of it with oxygen, locking the rest up in carbonate deposits such as limestone. Nitrogen would have formed by decomposition of the original ammonia and by bacterial activity. Once oxygen formed, the remaining methane would have been oxidized to carbon dioxide and water (see Table 13.1).

Table 13.1 Composition of the atmosphere now and 4 billion years ago

Gases in present atmosphere		Gases in atmosphere 4 billion years ago
Nitrogen	78%	Carbon dioxide and carbon monoxide
Oxygen	21%	Water vapour
Argon	0.9%	Ammonia
Carbon dioxide	0.04%	Methane
Water vapour	small and variable percentage	Hydrogen sulphide

The structure of the Earth

The Earth is a globe with a structure rather like an apple. Like an apple, it is found to be made up of recognizable layers:

- an invisible outer layer we call the **atmosphere**;
- a thin skin we call the **crust**;
- a middle layer called the **mantle** (composed of **upper** and **lower** parts).
- central part we call the **core** (composed of an **outer** and an **inner** part).

The rocks that we can see, that we use for building and as a source of chemicals; the rocks that have weathered to form soil on which we grow crops—all these are a very small part of the whole Earth.

The Earth is a sphere which is very slightly flattened at the poles. Figure 13.1 shows a cross section through the centre of the Earth illustrating its layered structure.

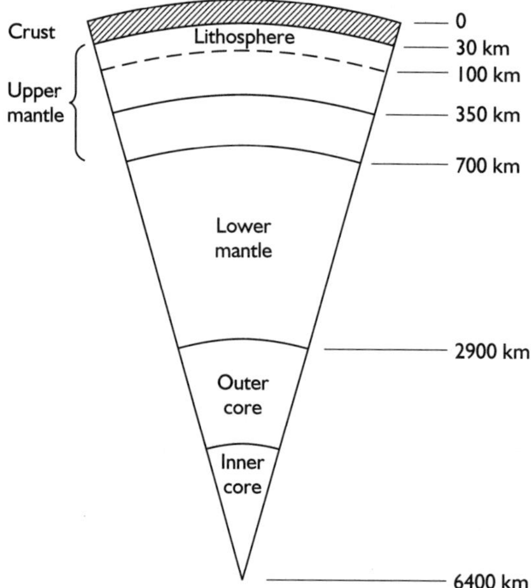

Fig. 13.1 A section of the Earth showing its layers

Above the crust sit the oceans and the atmosphere. The highest point of the crust is the top of mount Everest at about 9000 metres above sea level. The deepest part of the oceans is 11 000 metres below sea level. The thickness of the atmosphere cannot be so easily measured because there is no obvious upper boundary. However, most of the atmosphere is held in the lower 30 000 metres from the surface. The atmosphere (and the changes that go on in it) is of such importance in our daily lives that we shall look at this region first. Table 13.2 presents some interesting facts about the Earth.

The oceans

When the young Earth had cooled sufficiently for the steam in its atmosphere to condense, ocean(s) formed. This mass of water would quickly begin to dissolve any water-soluble components of the atmosphere—such as ammonia and carbon dioxide. Conditions would develop for living organisms to thrive in the sea. Even today, vast quantities of carbon dioxide are dissolved in the Earth's oceans, reducing the 'greenhouse' effect of this gas.

We believe that eons ago rainfall was greater than today. Rain dissolves gases and would react with and dissolve much of the exposed surface of the planet. The oceans became the reservoirs of the salts which were washed off the surface. Today's oceans are the result of billions of years of erosion and chemical activity.

The present-day atmosphere

The present-day atmosphere is the result of the effects of the interaction of the parallel evolution of the Earth and organic life on its surface. Volcanic activity has spewed great quantities of steam, oxides of carbon, methane, hydrogen sulphide and ammonia into the atmosphere over the past 4000 million years. Some of these gases have been removed by

Table 13.2 Some interesting facts about the Earth

Mass	6000 million, million, million, million grams (6×10^{27} g)
Volume	1100 million, million, million, million cm^3 (1.1×10^{27} cm^3)
Density	5.5 g cm^{-3} (mass divided by volume)

Its radius is about 6400 kilometres
Its circumference around the Equator is about 40 000 kilometres
Its diameter pole-to-pole is about 20 kilometres shorter than its diameter across the equator
Total surface area 500 million square kilometres
Land area is 30% of the total surface area
Ocean area is 70% of the total surface area
Largest continent—Eurasia—36% of the total land area
Largest ocean—Pacific—50% of the total ocean area
Highest point on land—top of Mount Everest at 8848 metres above sea-level
Lowest point under the sea—bottom of the Marianas Trench, 11 033 metres below sea-level
Age of the Earth—about 4600 million years
First solid crust—about 4000 million years ago
First surface water—about 3800 million years ago
First life on Earth—bacteria and blue/green algae about 3000 million years ago
Oxygen appeared on Earth—about 2000 million years ago
The first green algae appeared on Earth—about 1000 million years ago
Animals appeared on Earth—about 1000 million years ago
First land plants appeared—about 400 million years ago
Coal forests appeared 300 million years ago
Age of the dinosaurs—about 200 million years ago
Flowers evolved—about 150 million years ago
Humans appeared on Earth—about 2 million years ago
The Earth is a great magnet. Its magnetic poles are close to the geographical N- and S-poles at present, but they have wandered about the globe in times past.

reaction with oxygen, others by dissolving in the oceans or reaction with the rocks of the crust. The oxygen concentration has been increased by photosynthesis and the carbon dioxide concentration has decreased mainly as a result of the process of growth of vegetation and fossilization of plant remains. These latter processes lock-up large quantities of carbon dioxide in the form of forests, coal and oil deposits and sedimentary carbonate rock.

Now that the composition of the atmosphere has reached a reasonably steady state, see Table 13.1, the balance of gases in the atmosphere is largely controlled by the cycles of formation and removal that we study as

- the nitrogen cycle;
- the carbon cycle;
- the water cycle.

Details of these cycles are given below.

The nitrogen cycle

The nitrogen cycle (Fig. 13.2) shows how a balance can be achieved between processes which add nitrogen to the atmosphere and those that remove it. For example, nitrogen is 'fixed' in compounds by lightning and by nitrogen-fixing bacteria. The reverse process occurs through denitrifying bacteria which convert nitrogen compounds back to nitrogen. Synthetic nitrogen fixation by the Haber process is described in Chapter 9. The proportion of nitrogen in the atmosphere does not seem to be as critical as that of oxygen or carbon dioxide. There are no real concerns about possible changes in this proportion of nitrogen brought about by human activity on the planet.

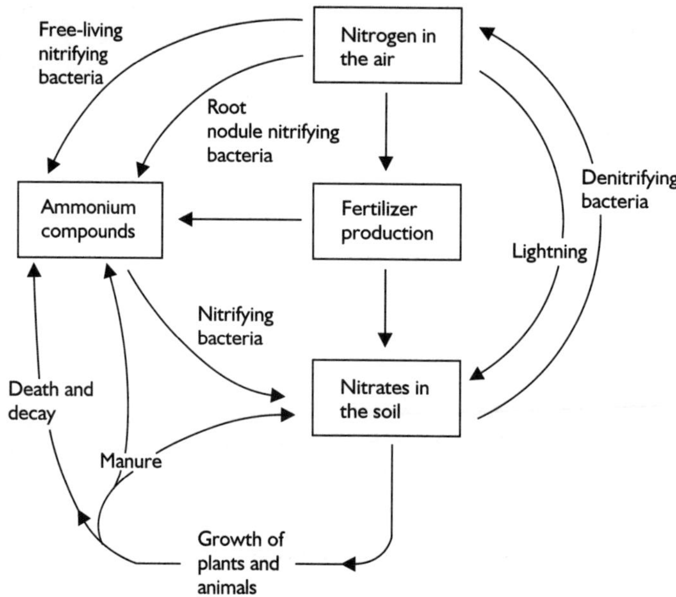

Fig. 13.2 The nitrogen cycle

The carbon cycle

Millions of years ago the concentration of carbon dioxide was very high. The percentage in the atmosphere in recent times has been comparatively constant at about 0.028–0.038%. Figure 13.3 shows how the processes of formation and removal of carbon dioxide keep the present-day balance. It is not difficult to see how the reduction in carbon dioxide could have come about in past ages. For example, consider that 300 million years ago the climate favoured prolific growth of plant life. When much of this plant life died, it fell into swamps and did not decay by the normal processes back to carbon dioxide. Over millions of years these deposits of undecomposed plant remains formed coal (oil deposits formed in a similar way from sea creatures). The carbon cycle diagram shows that this coal-forming process would have taken a large amount of carbon dioxide *out* of the atmosphere and the processes which would normally *reverse* this—burning and decomposition—would not be occurring fast enough to balance the removal. Nowadays, we are burning fossil fuels much more rapidly than natural processes are forming them. This has caused the percentage of carbon dioxide to rise from about 0.028% to 0.038% over the past century. Since we cannot speed up fossil-fuel making processes, we must reduce the production of carbon dioxide if we are to keep the concentration at its present level. If you study the carbon cycle diagram you may see other possible processes for achieving an overall reduction.

Fig. 13.3 The carbon cycle

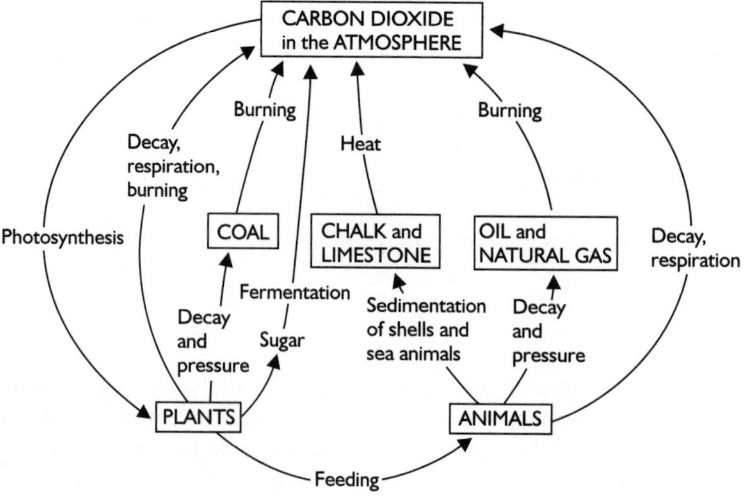

The water cycle

The proportion of water vapour in the atmosphere is controlled by temperature rather than by the abundance of water on the planet. The water vapour concentration of the air varies with temperature and the availability of liquid water. Only by a rise in average global temperatures could the water vapour concentration increase. This is not to say that water vapour in the atmosphere is not important—it is in fact a 'greenhouse gas'. However, its concentration is not easily affected by human activity (see Fig. 13.4).

Fig. 13.4 The water cycle

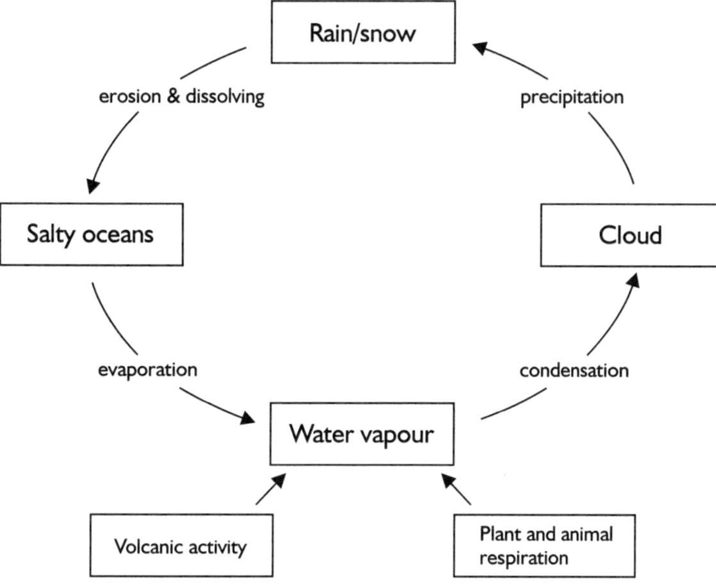

The Earth's crust (thickness 8–35 km)

The oldest rocks date back some 4000 million years. As time went by, volcanic activity would have continually changed the appearance of the surface crust. Many cycles of mountain building and erosion may have occurred over this time. More recently—the past one thousand million years—change has been slower and the crust has taken on an appearance that we would recognize. There is clear evidence, however, that continents and oceans have been changing in size and shape even during this period.

The present continents and oceans are now believed to have formed from a single very large land mass called **Pangaea** which had formed about 275 million years ago and began to break up about 200 million years ago. Surrounding Pangaea was a single very large ocean. The break-up of Pangaea created the present-day continents and oceans, although the process took some 50 million years.

The present crust is of two different types called **oceanic** and **continental**.

- Oceanic crust is formed below oceans and is relatively thin—only about 8 km deep.
- Continental crust is much deeper and is between 20 and 70 km thick.

The differences are summarized in Table 13.3.

Table 13.3 The Earth's layered structure

Layer	Average thickness/km	Density compared with water	Composition	Temperature/°C	Age/millions of years
Crust	Oceanic 8 Continental 35	Oceanic 3.0 Continental 2.7	Solid basalt Solid granite	10–600	0–200 3–500
Mantle	2900	3.5–5.5	Semi-plastic Rocky material	600–1200	} 4500
Outer core	} 3400	10–12	Liquid iron/nickel		
Inner core		12–18	Solid–mainly iron with some nickel	} 3000	

- Rocks of the continental crust are granite and sedimentary rocks such as sandstones or shales. These are composed of oxides of silicon with aluminium and some iron in the form of silicates. They are low-density rocks.
- Rocks of the oceanic crust are the denser basalts—silicates. Oceanic crust rock is denser than continental crust rock. No oceanic crust older than 220 million years is known.
- The crust of the Earth is itself very thin by comparison with the Earth as a whole. The crust is thickest over the land masses where mountains have arisen and thinnest where it has formed beneath oceans.

The mantle (thickness 2900 km)

Beneath the crust is the region called the **mantle**. The mantle material is subdivided by its strength into two layers. The Earth's crust floats and moves about on the mantle. During volcanic eruptions the material of the mantle bursts through the crust to the surface. The release of pressure causes the mantle material to liquefy and this fluid is called magma.

The core (thickness 3400 km)

The central part of the Earth is its **core**. This is the densest part: 12 to 18 times denser than the crust. It is believed to be composed mainly of iron and some nickel. The core contains an inner and an outer sphere.

- The outer part is liquid because of the high temperature and the lower pressure there.
- The inner part is solid because of the higher pressure, but temperatures of 3000 °C plus may exist in this region.

(Unlike water, the melting points of most other substances increase with increase in pressure.)

Temperature and pressure inside the Earth

The temperature and pressure increase from surface to core. The source of heat is believed to be the radioactive decay of uranium, potassium and thorium isotopes contained in the material of the mantle. The pressure increase arises from the weight of material pressing on the inner layers.

Magnetic field of the Earth

The liquid outer core is possibly the source of the Earth's magnetic field. The exact cause is not known, but it has been suggested that the motion of the fluid caused by the Earth's rotation might account for the observed magnetism.

The Earth's magnetic field has been recorded in solid rock whenever molten material reaches the surface and crystallizes. By analysing rock from many places on Earth and of many different ages, geologists have found that the magnetic field of the Earth has changed in intensity and in direction many times during its history. Magnetic field measurements (and other evidence) in Britain show that this country was situated in an equatorial region 200 million years ago!

Formation of rocks and rock types

The Earth's crust is 75% igneous, 20% metamorphic and 5% sedimentary rock. At the surface it is 75% igneous and 25% sedimentary rock. Figure 13.5 presents an outline of rock formation.

- The earliest rocks would have been igneous or metamorphic. They would have formed while the Earth was still too hot for liquid water to exist.
- When seas did eventually form, erosive processes would have caused sedimentary deposits to form in the ocean.
- Some of these sedimentary rocks, subjected to high pressure and/or high temperature would have formed metamorphic rock.
- The formation of sedimentary and metamorphic rock from weathered igneous rock is part of a cycle called the rock cycle (see Fig. 13.6).

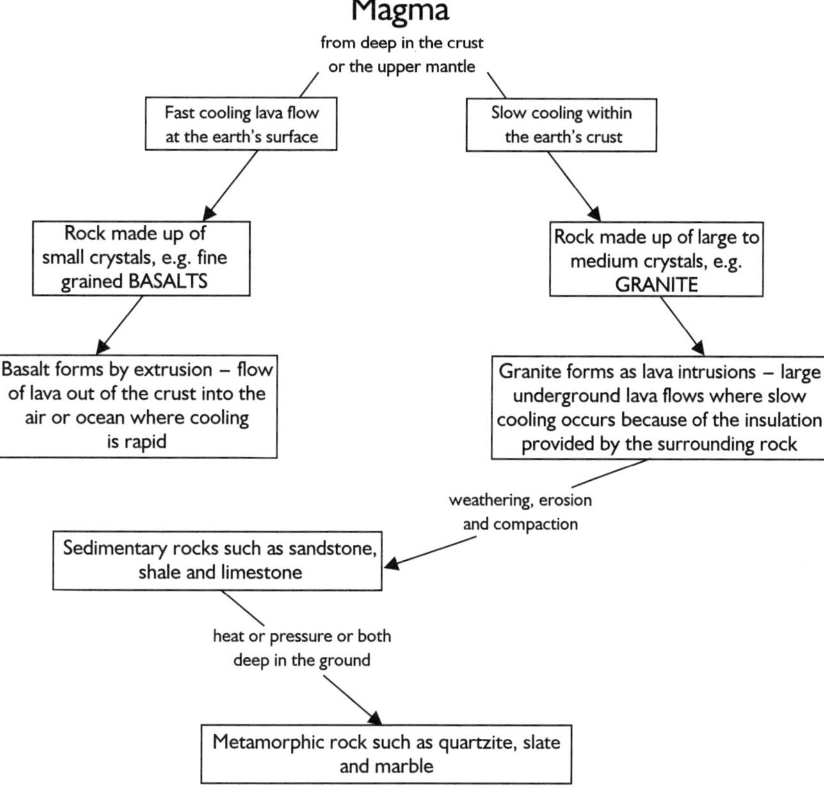

Fig. 13.5 Major rock types in the Earth's crust

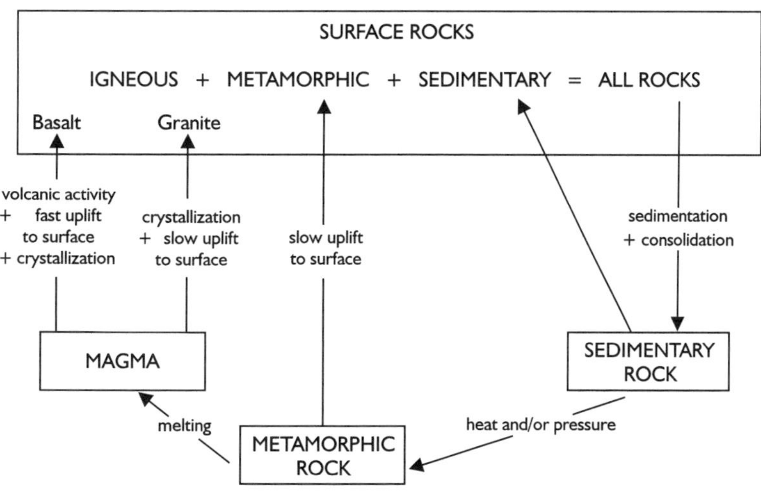

Fig. 13.6 The rock cycle

The processes shown in the rock cycle are: (i) **metamorphosis**—a change of crystalline state caused by *heat* and/or *pressure*; (ii) **sedimentation**—weathering/erosion/transportation/deposition/cementation and consolidation under pressure.

A summary of the major rock types whose formation is detailed in Fig. 13.5 is given in Table 13.4 below.

Table 13.4 Major rock types and examples

Rock	Examples	Conditions for formation
Igneous	Basalt (dark colour)—small crystals	Erupted magma cooling quickly
	Granite (light colour)—large crystals	Extruded magma cooling slowly
Sedimentary	Limestone Sandstone Shale	Sediments compacted and cemented under pressure*
Metamorphic	Marble (from limestone) Slate (from shale)	Sedimentary rock subjected to heat and/or pressure*

*These processes take millions of years.

The rock cycle

Igneous rock (Latin ignis *= fire)*

There are two main types of **igneous rock** associated with volcanic activity, see Fig. 13.7.

- **Extrusive**—formed by extrusion (pushing out) of magma through vents in the Earth's crust into the air or into the ocean. If cooling is rapid, crystals are small and the resulting rock is *basalt* (under the ocean) or *obsidian* (a glass) on land. *Pumice*, also land-formed, is solid volcanic froth with bubbles inside making it light enough to float on water.
- **Intrusive**—formed when magma from below the crust forces it way **upwards** into
  - *vertical* fractures (forming *dikes*). The resulting rock is granite.
  - *sideways* between existing horizontal rock strata (forming *sills*).

Where a huge mass of intrusive magma makes a space for itself, a dome shaped mass forms on cooling: this is a granite *batholith*.

Intrusions cool slowly, have large crystals and are granites.

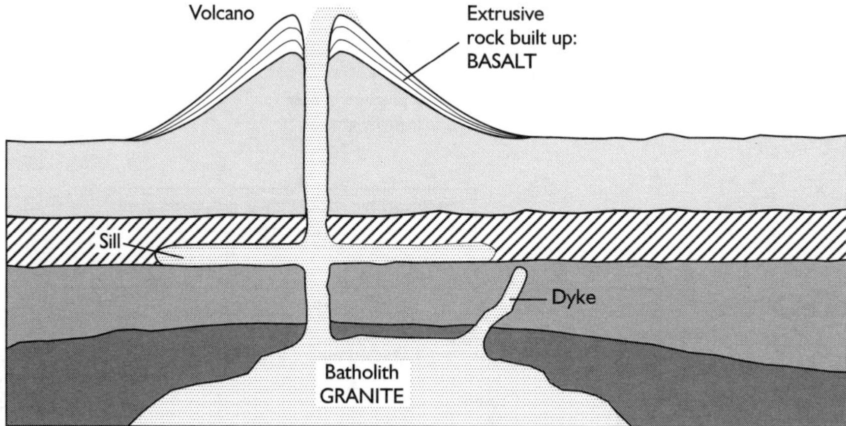

Fig. 13.7 A cross section through a volcano showing formation of granite and basalt

Sediments and sedimentary rock (Latin sedimentum *= settling)*

Sedimentary rock is formed by compaction and cementation of sediments. Sediments are collections of small particles resulting from the erosion of weathered igneous rock or from deposits of dead shelled sea creatures.

Fossils found in sedimentary rocks provide evidence of the age of the rock.

Weathering of rock

Chemical weathering—decomposition Igneous rock was the first type of rock formed in the Earth's crust. Because of the conditions under which it is formed, this type of rock is unstable under the conditions **at the Earth's surface** where temperature and pressure are much lower. Chemical weathering occurs largely due to the action of carbon dioxide dissolved in water. The unstable igneous rock reacts relatively easily with the acidic rain water. Part of the rock dissolves and the remainder is weakened by the process and erodes more readily.

Physical weathering—disintegration This is the result of a number of processes.

- **Freeze–thaw weathering.** At low temperatures, cracks in the rock can fill with water which then freezes. On freezing, water expands and forces the rock apart. This eventually fragments the rock and exposes it to more rapid weathering by other processes.
- **Exfoliation.** It is possible that daily heating also fragments rock in a similar way to freeze–thaw weathering.

Where weathered rock forms on slopes, the mineral grains are washed away rapidly, exposing more rock to the weathering process.

Biological weathering—disintegration and decomposition The growth of roots of shrubs and trees in rock crevices is capable of forcing the rock apart, causing fracture and fragmentation.

Further weathering occurs due to organic matter which produces acidic products which attack rock as described above.

Erosion

Sediments form by erosion—wearing down—of weathered rock by moving water or ice, wind or waves. Unweathered rock—fresh igneous rock, for example—is not easily eroded. The process of **weathering** softens igneous rock allowing fragments to be more readily **swept clear by the eroding forces**. The weathered particles eventually find their way into rivers, lakes and the sea.

Transport of sediment

This is by water (rivers), wind, or ice (glaciers). Whichever process has occurred, the fragments become sorted, en route, according to size. The largest particles settle out first and the finest particles last. If a river has deposited sediments in a large lake, for example, the coarsest bits of rock will be near the shore and the fine mud will be much farther out, with sand in between.

When these sediments finally form rock, the rocks will be:

- conglomerate—coarse particles;
- sandstone—sand particles;
- shale or mudstone—very fine mud or clay particles.

A similar 'assortment' is evident where all the sediment is forced to pile into a small area of deep water. Here the coarsest layer is on top and the finest at the bottom.

Quarrying for material to make concrete is usually done in such sedimentary rock sites. The coarse material produces gravel; finer material is used for concrete, and sand is used to make mortar.

Compaction and cementation—the final stage

Sedimentary rock is formed when sediments are subject to high-pressure compaction.

- Thick piles of sediments are produced by erosion of weathered rock.
- Compaction under pressure occurs lower down in the pile expelling water and air due to the weight of material above.
- In time the sediment becomes cemented together forming a solid aggregate called sedimentary rock.
- The commonest cause of the cementation is via minerals deposited from solutions present in the layers.
- A feature of sedimentary rock is its layered structure. It is most often found on top of igneous and metamorphic rocks and may contain *fossils*.
- The texture of most sedimentary rocks formed in this way indicates particles bound together by cementing material.

Sedimentary rocks not formed by weathering and erosion

Limestone, chalk, rock-salt and coal are sedimentary rocks. The formation of these sedimentary rocks is different from the process described above.

- **Limestone** is compacted sediment formed from the dead bodies of countless millions of shelled sea creatures. The internal structure of the body has long since decayed but the shell material remains and has become rock. Limestone is mainly calcium carbonate—the chemical of the shells.
- **Chalk** is a finer-grained rock than limestone but has the same calcium carbonate composition. The calcium carbonate that formed chalk arose from the remains of tiny sea plants whose dead bodies form a white mud of almost pure calcium carbonate (calcite).
- **Rock-salt** has formed from a mixture of sediments with the salts deposited from evaporated sea-water. The process of compaction described above hardens the sediment into a rock.
- **Coal** began forming two hundred million years ago from plant and tree remains in swamp conditions. Such conditions slow down the natural decay of the organic material which eventually becomes covered in mud and sand. Compaction by pressure converts

the soft deposits to harder coal; the mud and sand also become compacted, to mudstone and sandstone, and these sedimentary rocks are always found with coal deposits.

*Metamorphic rock (Greek—***meta** *= after,* **morphe** *= form)*

Metamorphic rock forms from sedimentary rock under any of the following conditions:

- **Limestone to marble**—the rock is close to a high-temperature granite intrusion. The heat from the intrusion changes the form of the sedimentary rock. (Sandstone into quartzite is another example.)
- **Mudstone or shale to slate**—the rock is subject to high pressure.
- **Shale to schist**—the rock is subject to high pressure and high temperature. **Shale becomes schist** in such a process and **gneiss** (pronounced 'nice') is formed in a similar manner but from granite.

Metamorphic rocks are to be found in present-day and ancient mountain ranges because of the high temperatures and pressures in the mountain-building process.

The formation of all types of rock other than those formed by extrusion of lava from volcanoes has taken many tens of millions of years (see **plate tectonics** below).

The age of rocks

Radioactive decay

The age of rock can be estimated with reasonable accuracy from a knowledge of the rate of decay of its radioactive components. The technical details are beyond the scope of this chapter, but in principle, any radioactive element found in rock will have been decaying since the rock formed. If the decay products and the remaining radioactive element are both collected, it is possible to calculate how long the element has been in the rock, i.e. the age of the rock.

The fossil record

Fossils are the petrified (made into rock) remains of animals and plants preserved in sediments at the time of their death. Rocks containing the same fossils can reasonably be regarded as being of the same age or in the same age-range. Also, if particular fossils are found in widely separated parts of the world, then either the living organism must have been widely distributed or else the separated parts of the globe were at one time joined together. Fossil evidence of this sort supports the theory of **continental drift**.

Magnetic field

Reversals of the magnetic field of the Earth can be used to date rocks. Since the dates of magnetic reversals are known, the sequence of these found in the oceanic rocks formed outwards from a spreading centre at a mid-ocean ridge has been used to date the oceanic crust. The oldest such crust is 165 million years.

Rock sequence

- The oldest rocks are igneous.
- Metamorphic rocks are younger than the sedimentary rocks they are formed from.
- An intrusive igneous rock formation must be younger than the surrounding rocks.

Rocks—identification and uses

Identification

The features of rocks which help in their identification include:

- **chemical reactivity**, e.g. limestone fizzes when treated with dilute hydrochloric acid;
- **colour**—basalt is a dark igneous rock, whereas granite is a light colour;
- **hardness**—rocks that have been subjected to high temperatures and/or high pressures are hard. Hardness can be tested by scratching with a steel blade or stylus;
- **fossils**—fossils form in sediments and so can only exist in sedimentary rocks;

- **layers of grains or fragments** show sedimentary origin;
- **bands** of interlocking crystals show metamorphosed rock of sedimentary origin;
- **randomly arranged** interlocking crystals show igneous origin.

Figure 13.8 is one of many keys for identifying rock types.

Some details of the appearance of rocks and their type can be found in Table 13.5.

Fig. 13.8 Identifying rock types

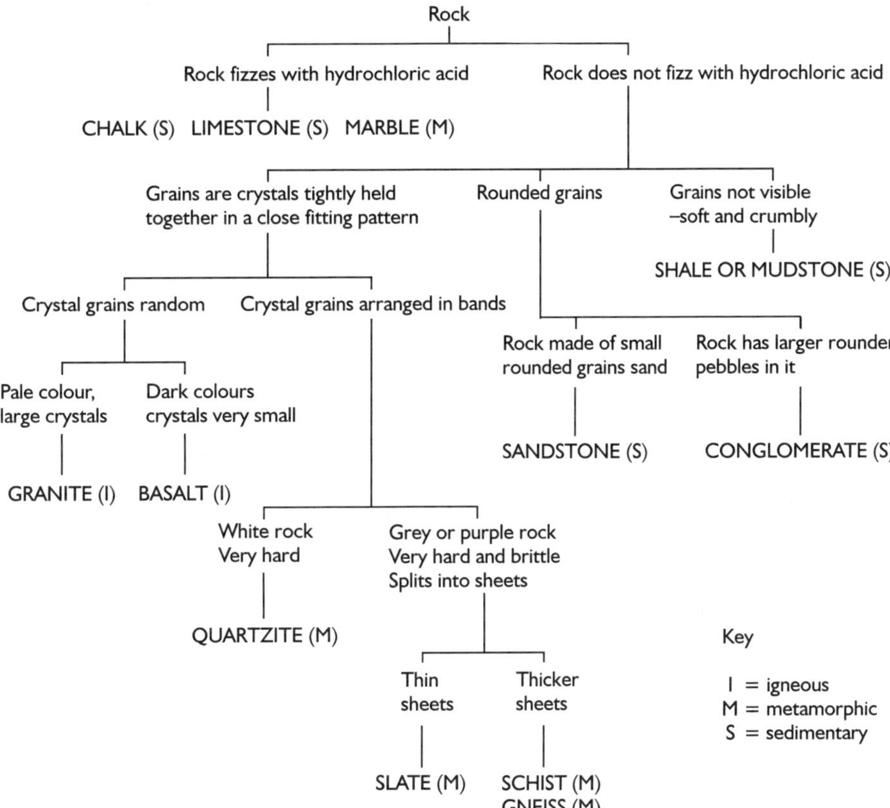

Table 13.5 Common rocks and their type

Rock type	Examples	Mineral content	Visible characteristics
Igneous	Granite	Quartz, feldspar and mica	Random interlocking crystals—crystal size depends on cooling rate, see Rock Cycle
Sedimentary	Sandstone	Quartz, haematite	Layered structure
	Limestone	Calcite	Many contain fossils
Metamorphic	Marble	Calcite	Bands of interlocking crystals
	Slate	Clay	Fine-grained

Uses of rocks

The common rocks mentioned often in this chapter are useful in many ways:

- **Granite, limestone** and **sandstone** are used as building block material. Broken into small lumps they are used as 'metalling'—the coarse foundation of roads.
- **Slate** is used as a roofing material.
- **Marble** and **Slate** are used commonly as headstones on graves.
- **Limestone** and **clay/shale** mixtures, when strongly heated, form cement. Cement, mixed with lime, **sand** and water forms mortar.

Limestone—a commercially important sedimentary rock

Limestone is almost pure calcium carbonate—the compacted remains of the shells of countless sea creatures. It has been used for many centuries to make quicklime and slaked lime.

When heated to 1000 °C, calcium carbonate loses carbon dioxide and becomes calcium oxide (quicklime)

$$CaCO_3(s) \rightarrow \underset{\text{quicklime}}{CaO(s)} + CO_2(g)$$

This is carried out in a lime kiln (Fig. 13.9).

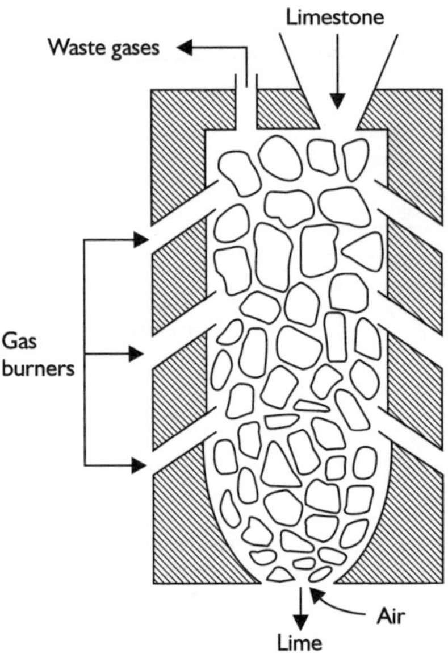

Fig. 13.9 Preparation of calcium oxide

Quicklime is dangerous: if brought into contact with water it becomes very hot. For safety reasons, it is usually sold already treated with water—called *slaked lime.*

$$CaO(s) + H_2O(e) \rightarrow Ca(OH)_2(s)$$

Uses of limestone

- In lumps as foundations for roads and motorways.
- Mixed with coal and iron ore to make iron and steel.
- Mixed with clay and powdered, cement is formed on strong heating.
- Mixed with sand and soda ash (sodium carbonate) and heated—glass forms.

Uses of lime

- Farmers use it to cure excess acidity in their soil.
- Most lime is used in steelmaking, where it serves the same purpose as limestone in iron smelting: it removes acidic impurities as slag.
- Water companies use it to remove excess hardness from water supplies.
- Bricklayers mix lime with cement and sand to produce mortar.

Plate tectonics

Continental drift

It is believed that 200 million years ago, there was a single large supercontinent surrounded by sea (Fig. 13.10). This land-mass is called **Pangaea** ('all lands'). When this land-mass broke up, the parts separated into what we see as the present continents (Fig. 13.11). The break-up and separation of the fragmented supercontinent is thought to have occurred by a process known as **continental drift.**

The evidence for continental drift is in several parts:

(i) The shapes of the present-day continents, especially South America and Africa, are distinctive enough to have prompted the idea that the two were once joined together.

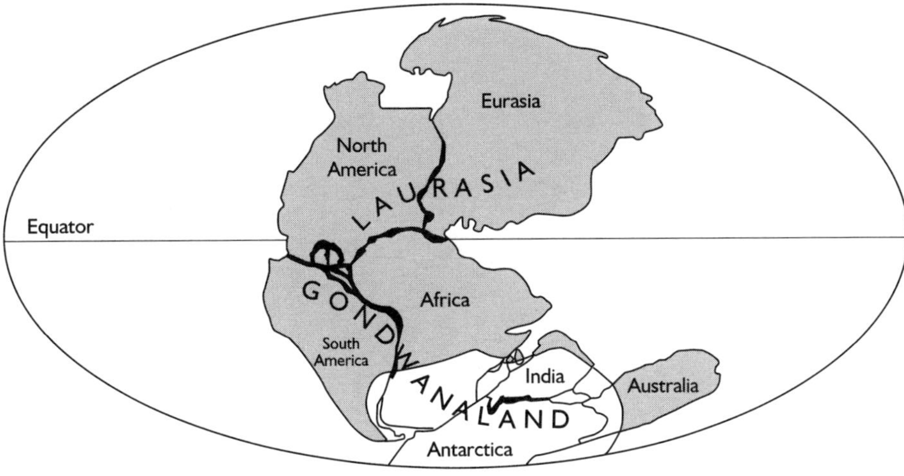

Fig. 13.10 The major continents 200 million years ago—Pangaea. Key: White area is the position of ancient ice cover. Shaded areas show the overlap of present-day land shapes used in this reconstruction

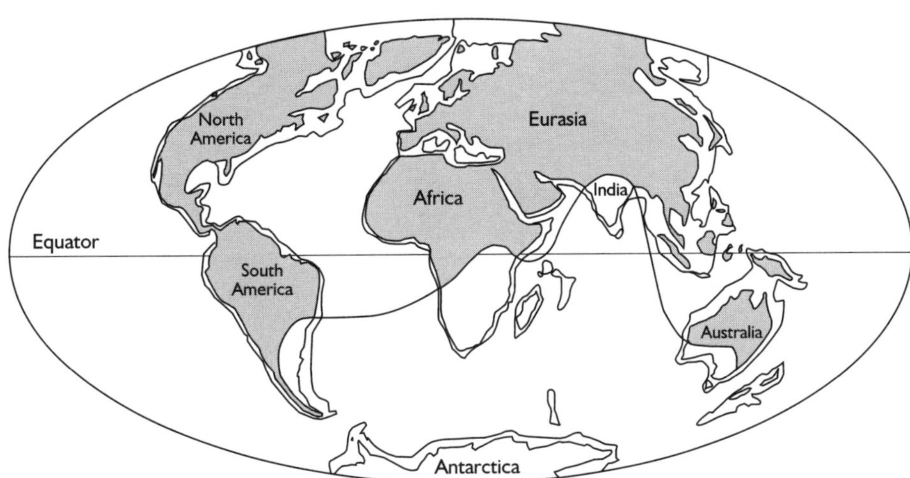

Fig. 13.11 Present-day continents—the result of continental drift from the original Pangaea. Key: White areas show the ice-covered areas of ancient Pangaea. Continent outlines show the position of the continental shelf

(ii) Fossils found in Africa are also found in parts of the world very far away—in S. America, India and Australia in fact.

(iii) The magnetic record stored in rock as it solidified shows that all the southern continents were located close together about 150–200 million years ago.

That continental drift was possible is explained by the modern theory of plate tectonics. If we were able to run the geological record backwards over 200 million years, we believe we would find the present continents moving in reverse to their positions when they were joined in one supercontinent—Pangaea. The fit is only approximate at the coastal boundaries but is better at the continental shelf boundaries (see Fig. 13.10 above).

*Plate tectonic theory (from Greek—***tecton** *means a builder)*

The theory assumes that the present Earth's crust consists of six large and several smaller **plates**. The **crustal plates** are of lower density than the mantle and so float on it. It helps to visualize this situation to think of the whole crust as if it were a sheet of ice covering the surface but broken into six large and several small, irregular, sheets.

The map in Fig. 13.12 shows these plates and their direction of movement. The position of these plates is deduced from the volcanic and earthquake activity where plates meet at the plate margins.

Plate movement is only a few centimetres a year but can now be measured from satellites by laser beams. The present continents and the surface features such as mountains and volcanoes are believed to be the result of movement of these plates over many millions of years.

The theory of **plate tectonics** therefore explains **continental drift**. It also explains more observable phenomena such as volcanic and earthquake activity, sea-floor spreading and crustal structures—in a single unifying theory.

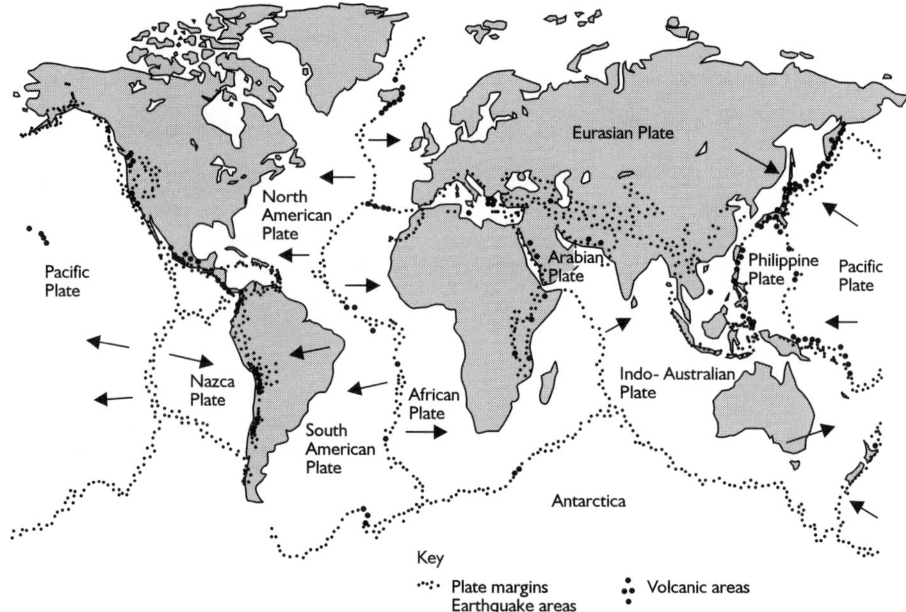

Fig. 13.12 The major plates of the Earth, showing active plate margins. Key: arrows indicate direction of movement of the plates

The plate tectonics theory states that:

- The surface of the Earth is covered by a series of thin, rigid plates. The total surface area of these plates is believed to be constant, which means that if some crust is destroyed in one place an equal area must be formed elsewhere.
- Plate motion is believed to be driven by convection currents in the mantle driven by heat released by natural radioactive decay processes.
- The plates are always in motion.
- At the plate margins, the movement causes **volcanic** and **earthquake** activity and sometimes **mountain building** and **oceanic trench formation.**

The effects of tectonic plate movements

When two plates interact a **plate margin** results and a change in the appearance of the crust results.

Plates may move in any of three ways, producing three types of plate margin:

1. **They may slide past each other.** This is happening along the coast of the USA in California. There, on the **San Andreas Fault**, two continental plates are sliding past each other producing earthquakes but **no volcanoes**; see Fig. 13.13.

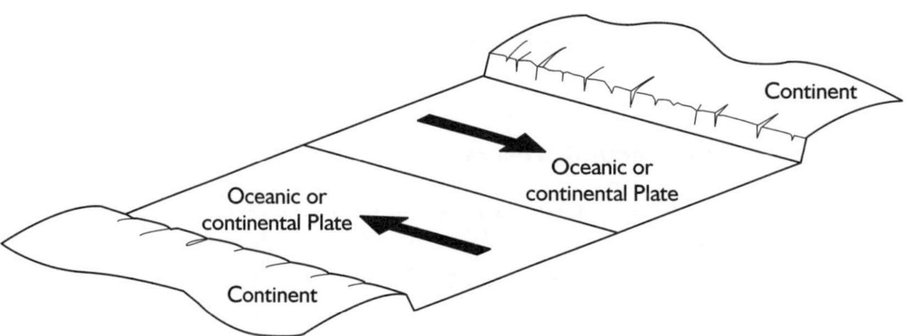

Fig. 13.13 Plates sliding past each other, e.g. San Andreas fault

2. **They may move towards each other**. Here crusts are colliding. There are two types of colliding plates: (i) an oceanic plate colliding with a continental plate; (ii) a continental plate colliding with another continental plate.

   In (i) the oceanic plate, being thinner and denser, is **driven down** (subducted) under the thicker, less dense continental plate, Fig. 13.14. The consequences are that

   - an **ocean trench** forms;
   - during the subduction, much **frictional heat** is produced which melts surrounding rock forming magma which results in **volcanic activity;**

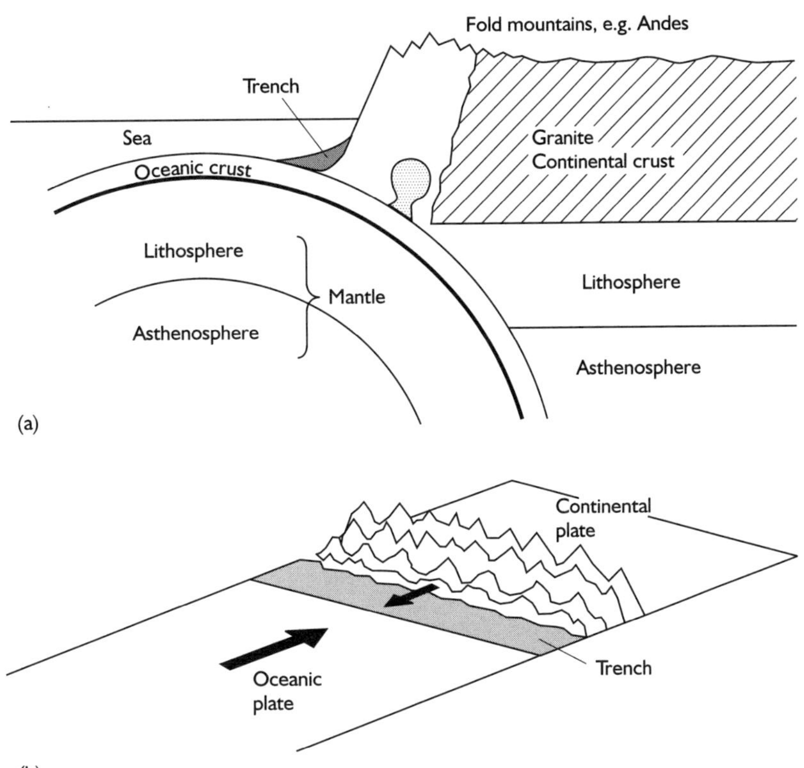

Fig. 13.14 Plates in collision: formation of the Andean mountain range and ocean. (a) Section. (b) Schematic

- a **mountain** of ocean-crust sediment is scraped up at the edge of the continental crust. The **Andes** mountain range has formed in this way.

In (ii) the collision of two continental plates has created the **Himalayas.**

3. **They may move away from each other**. Here plates are diverging. There are two types of divergent plate margin: (i) when both plates are oceanic plates, a ridge forms; (ii) when both plates are continental plates, a rift-valley forms.

   In (i) the **ocean widens** and the gap produced is filled by rising **magma**. The rapid cooling of this magma causes the igneous rock called **basalt** to pile up into a ridge. The **Mid-Atlantic Ridge** is forming in this way; see Fig. 13.15. **Earthquake** and **volcanic** activity occur along the Mid-Atlantic Ridge.

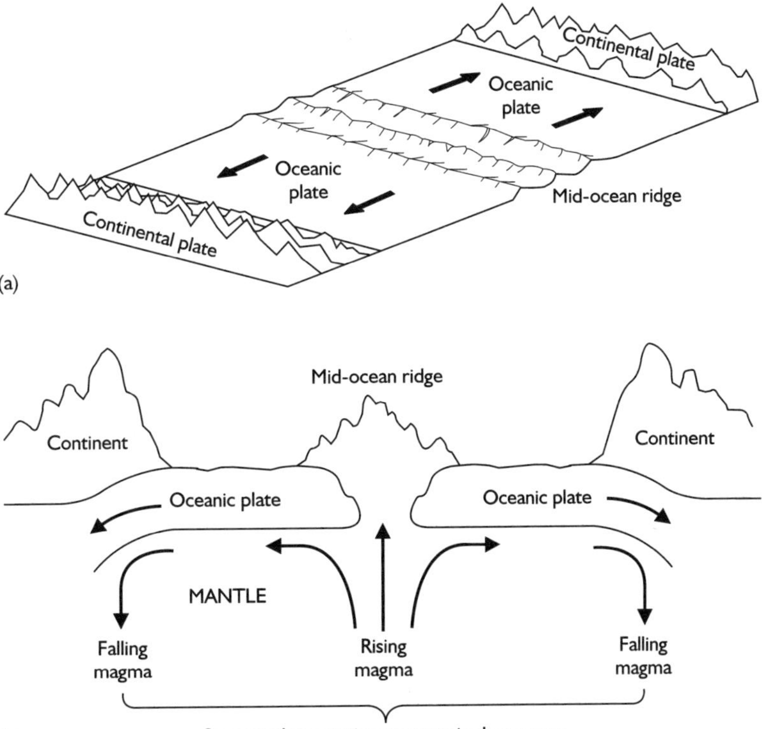

Fig. 13.15 Sea-floor spreading and ridge formation, e.g. Mid-Atlantic Ridge. (a) Schematic. (b) Section

In (ii) two continental plates moving apart create a rift valley as in the African Rift valley. There is **earthquake and volcanic** activity here also.

Continental drift, where parts of the single ancient continent Pangaea have moved apart, is largely the result of sea-floor spreading. Examination of the sea floor to both sides of the Mid-Atlantic Ridge shows the sea floor to be made up of bands of rock running parallel with the ridge. In these bands of iron-rich rock, the Earth's **magnetic field** is recorded exactly as it was when the magma solidified. The rocks show bands with **alternately reversed magnetic fields.** Exactly the same pattern is seen on both sides of the ridge. Because we know that throughout time the Earth's magnetic field has reversed many times, these records in the rocks of the floor of the Atlantic Ocean are evidence that it was formed by sea floor spreading.

Rock recycling

It is evident that the process of **subduction** takes old rock formations into the mantle whereas **sea-floor spreading** creates new rock. In this way the Earth's rocks are recycled. Each volume of new rock is equal to the volume of old rock removed from the crust. Convection currents in the mantle cause mixing and circulation of magma.

Volcanoes (from Vulcan*—Roman god of fire)*

Volcanic activity is common at plate margins. There are currently about 500 active volcanoes in the world. Igneous rocks are formed from molten rock (magma) which comes from the mantle at temperatures around 1000 °C. Volcanoes also give out large volumes of gases such as hydrogen sulphide (H_2S), sulphur dioxide (SO_2) and hydrogen chloride (HCl) as well as nitrogen, carbon dioxide and water vapour.

Volcanoes are the origin of two main types of igneous rock—extrusive and intrusive (see The rock cycle, p. 186).

Thermal springs and geysers

These are sited over old volcanoes. An extinct volcano can take a million years to cool, deep below the surface. If ground water enters the fissures in the hot rock, nearly boiling water can rise to the surface. If steam is produced also, the hot water is ejected from the ground fissure with spectacular effect. Bath, in Avon, has hot springs known for at least two thousand years. The geysers of Iceland are located over a recently active volcanic area on the Mid-Atlantic Ridge.

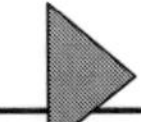

EXAMINATION QUESTIONS

Question 1

(a) Explain what is meant by the following terms:
  (i) igneous rock [2 lines]
  (ii) sedimentary rock [2 lines]
  (iii) metamorphic rock [2 lines] *[6]*

(b) Explain how sedimentary rock can be recycled as igneous rock. *[4]*

(c) A student examined two samples of the same type of igneous rock using a microscope at the same magnification.
She made the drawing below (Fig. 13.16).

Fig. 13.16

Sample A

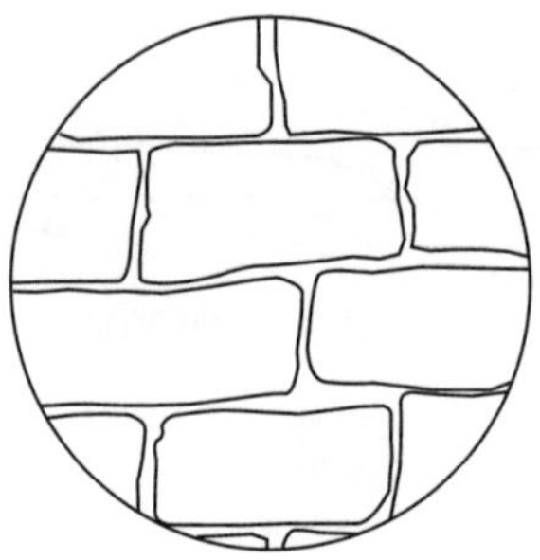

Sample B

What difference in the origin of the two samples is likely to have caused this difference in appearance? [2 lines] *[2]*

[Total 12 marks]

Question 2

The diagram below (Fig. 13.17) shows part of the rock cycle.

(a) (i) What is rock type A? [1 line] *[1]*

(ii) What changes take place to the magma to form rock type B? [1 line] *[1]*

Fig. 13.17

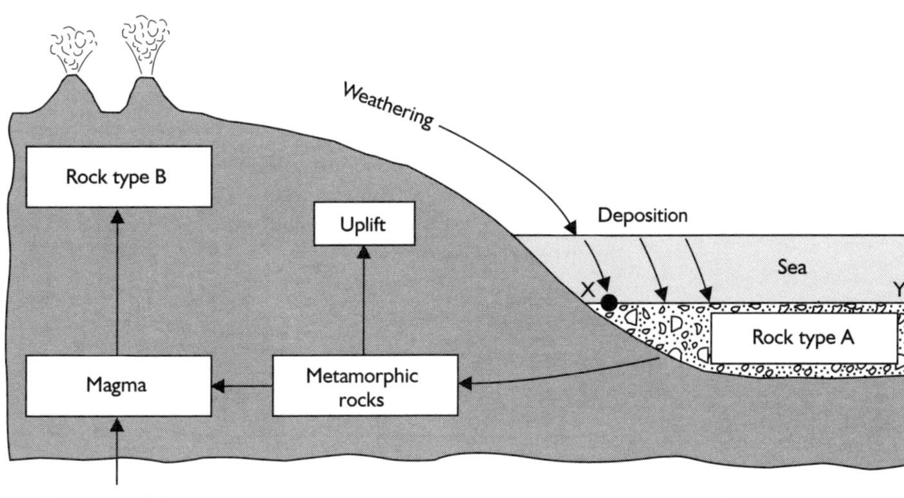

(iii) Suggest *one* way that rain can act as a weathering agent on exposed rocks. [1 line] *[1]*

(iv) What happens to rock type A while it is changing to metamorphic rock? [1 line] *[2]*

(v) Suggest *one* difference between sediments found at X and Y on the diagram. [1 line] *[1]*

[Total 6 marks]

Question 3

The map below (Fig. 13.18) shows two of the continents bordering the Atlantic Ocean. It is believed that 150 million years ago these two continents were joined.

Fig. 13.18

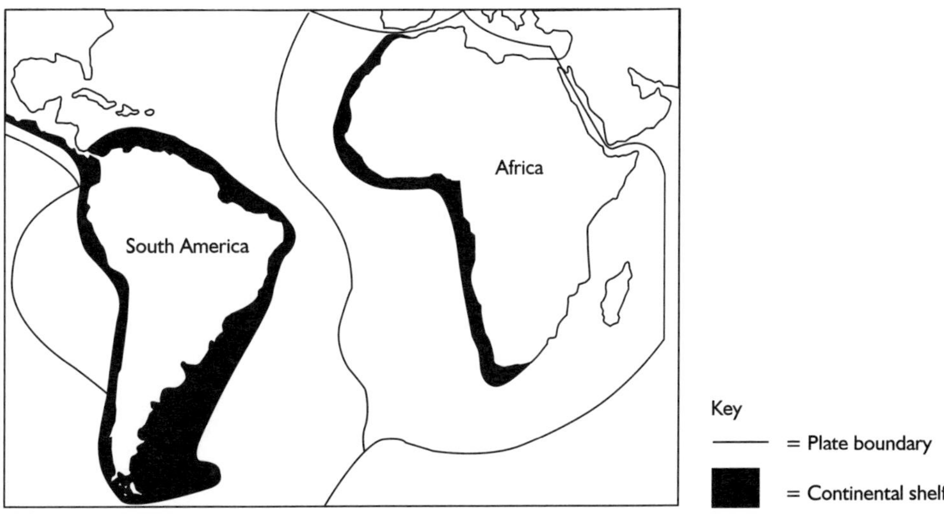

Use the theory of plate tectonics to explain how these continents could have moved apart to reach their present positions. You may use diagrams if you wish. [7 lines]

[Total 7 marks]

Question 4(F)

(a) The early atmosphere of the Earth may have contained methane and carbon monoxide but very little oxygen. At that time the temperature was high and there were many electrical storms in the atmosphere. Why is it unlikely that oxygen would have been present in large amounts if methane and carbon monoxide were present? [2 lines] *[1]*

(b) As plant life developed, the amount of oxygen in the atmosphere increased.
   (i) Name the process by which plants add oxygen to the atmosphere? [1 line] *[1]*
   (ii) What gas is removed from the atmosphere by the same process? [1 line] *[1]*

(c) What temperature conditions must have existed on Earth for oceans to form? Explain your answer. [2 lines] *[2]*

(d) The amount of carbon dioxide in the atmosphere is partly controlled by the oceans.
   (i) How does this happen? [3 lines]
   (ii) Why is carbon dioxide affected by this process more than other gases in the atmosphere? [3 lines] *[3]*

(e) A, B and C (Fig. 13.19) represent plates of the Earth's crust moving in the directions of the arrows.

Fig. 13.19

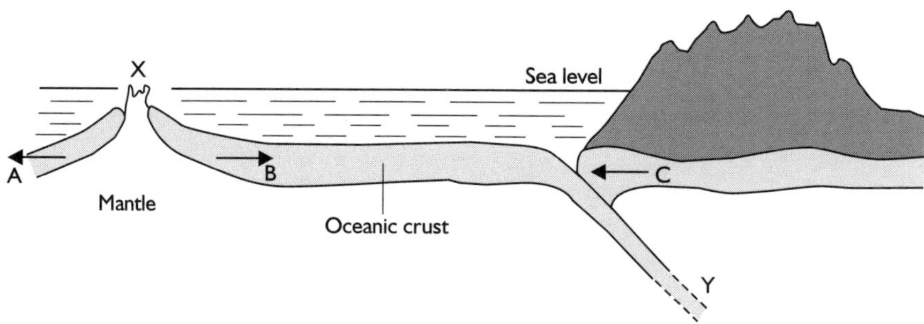

   (i) Give one natural occurrence, often disastrous, which can happen at plate boundaries. [1 line] *[1]*
   (ii) Why would you expect igneous rock to form at plate boundary X? [3 lines] *[3]*
   (iii) Metamorphic rock forms at Y. Give *two* conditions which must exist at Y. [2 lines] *[2]*

[Total 14 marks]

Question 5(F)

This key (Fig. 13.20) can be used to identify some common rocks.

(a) Use the key to describe *three* features of the rock called schist. [3 lines] *[3]*

(b) Which other rock shown in this key is *most* like schist? *[1]*

[Total 4 marks]

Question 6(H)

Until fairly recently scientists thought that the continents had always been in the same positions.

Fig. 13.10 shows where scientists now think the continents were 200 million years ago. Fig. 13.11 shows the positions of the continents today.

(a) The theory of crustal movements states that the continents have moved apart over the last 200 million years. Give *two* pieces of evidence for the movement [4 lines] *[2]*

(b) The crust of the Earth includes several tectonic plates. What causes tectonic plates to move? [4 lines] *[3]*

(c) The tectonic plate labelled T in diagram 1 eventually collided with an oceanic tectonic plate. Describe what happens to continental tectonic plates when they collide with oceanic plates. [4 lines] *[4]*

[Total 9 marks]

Fig. 13.20

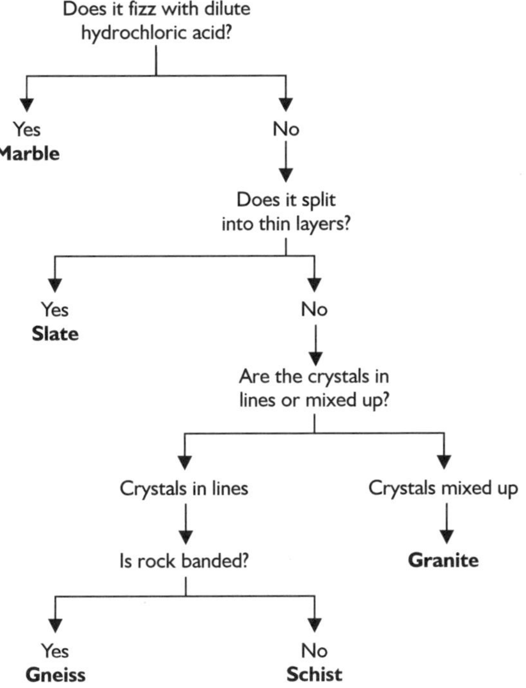

Fig. 13.21

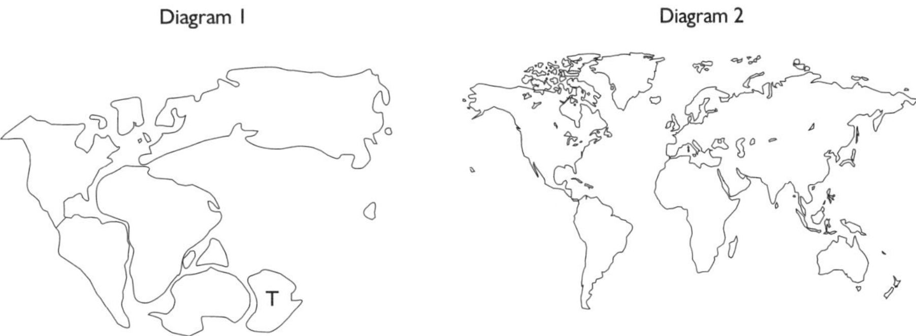

OUTLINE ANSWERS

Question 1

(a) (i) Igneous rock is rock formed by crystallization *[1]* of magma from the mantle *[1]*.

(ii) Sedimentary rock is rock formed on the Earth's surface by the effect of pressure *[1]* on the materials resulting from the breakdown of surface rock *[1]*.

(iii) Metamorphic rock is rock formed by the effect of heat and pressure *[1]* on other types of rock—without melting *[1]*. It forms beneath the crust.

(b) Sedimentary rock which is part of an ocean plate can be pushed down (subducted) by tectonic movement *[1]* into the mantle *[1]* where it melts *[1]* and may be reformed in volcanic activity as igneous rock *[1]*. (See Fig. 13.14.)

(c) Sample A has smaller crystals than sample B. Sample A has crystallized at a faster rate than B *[1]*. Rapid cooling produces small crystals; slow cooling produces large crystals *[1]*.

Question 2

(a) (i) Rock type A is sedimentary *[1]*.

(ii) Rock type B is formed from magma on cooling *[1]* as it moves to the Earth's surface.

(iii) Rain contains dissolved carbon dioxide and reacts chemically with certain rock components, dissolving them *[1]*. The material that does not react fragments.

(iv) Rock type A is sedimentary. Under pressure and at high temperature it forms metamorphic rock.

(v) Sediments carried by water to the sea are made up of particles with a range of sizes. On entering the sea the **larger particles** deposit on the bottom near the shore whilst the smaller particles travel further out. The difference is therefore in size or diameter *[1]*.

Question 3

(i) Look back to the section on Plate tectonics, and especially Figs 13.10 and 13.11. The following indicates some of the points you might make.

150 million years ago the African and S. American continents were joined at their continental shelf boundaries. Since then they have been moving apart by ocean spreading *[1]*. The plate boundary shown (also called a plate margin) is the line of activity of a divergent margin *[1]*. Here magma wells up from the mantle *[1]*, causing the formation of new ocean crust on either side of the margin *[1]*. Year by year the distance apart of the continental shelf boundaries increases as more magma emerges *[1]*. The margin is also the scene of the formation of a mid-atlantic ridge *[1]* and volcanic activity *[1]* is evident. A diagram such as Fig. 13.15(a) could also be used to illustrate this answer.

Question 4

(a) Methane and carbon monoxide are both **flammable** gases. They would burn in oxygen *[1]*.

(b) (i) Photosynthesis *[1]*.
(ii) Carbon dioxide *[1]*.

(c) Less than 100 °C *[1]*, since water is a vapour above that temperature *[1]*.

(d) (i) Oceans absorb carbon dioxide *[1]*. They also give carbon dioxide off *[1]*.
(ii) Carbon dioxide is more soluble in water than the other atmospheric gases *[1]*.

(e) (i) Volcanoes or earthquakes *[1]*.
(ii) Magma *[1]* from the mantle *[1]* pushes up and solidifies *[1]*, forming an oceanic ridge *[1]* [*Any three points.*]
(iii) Metamorphic rock is sedimentary rock being strongly heated *[1]* and put under high pressure *[1]*.

Question 5

(a) From the key, schist does not fizz (react) with dilute hydrochloric acid *[1]*; it does not split into thin layers *[1]*; its crystals are in lines *[1]* and it is not banded *[1]*. [*Any three points score.*]

(b) Gneiss is most like schist *[1]*.

Question 6

(a) Land masses have shapes that fit together *[1]*; similar fossils are found in places now far apart *[1]*; similar rocks are found far apart *[1]*. [*Any 2 points.*]

(b) Movement of magma in the mantle *[1]*—convection currents *[1]* caused by radioactive heating *[1]*.

(c) The oceanic plate *[1]* is pushed under the continental plate (subducted) *[1]*; the oceanic plate melts *[1]* and the continental plate is pushed up to form mountains *[1]*.

STUDENT ANSWER WITH EXAMINER'S COMMENTS

The diagram below represents the structure of part of the Earth's crust and mantle.

Fig. 13.22

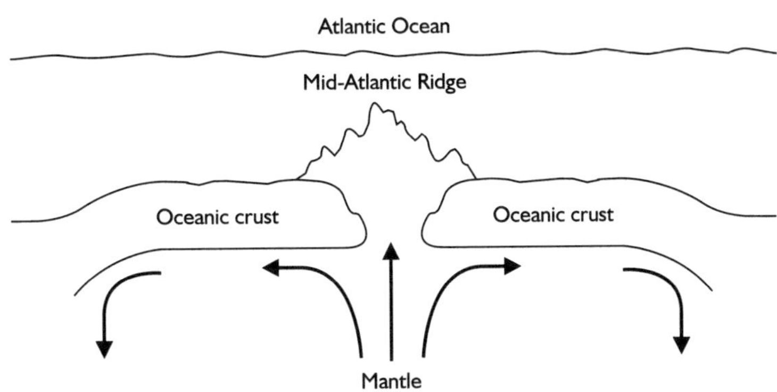

(a) (i) What type of rock forms the Mid-Atlantic-Ridge?

Igneous rock—it will be basalt rather than granite.

'A good start. Igneous rock would be sufficient for the mark. Your further comment shows your deeper knowledge'

(ii) Explain your answer to (i) *(3 marks)*

Molten magma flows out and cools quickly in the sea. This gives basalt because crystallization is quick and small crystals form.

'Again a good answer.'

(b) State two pieces of evidence that oceanic plates are still actively moving along the Mid-Atlantic Ridge. *(2 marks)*

There are volcanoes on the ridge and it is known that the ocean is getting wider year by year.

'Active volcanoes show active movement.'

(c) The positions of the Earth's continents have changed over the past 200 million years.

(i) How could these changes have occurred?

By continental drift. The continents are on plates which have moved apart over the years. The movement is caused by convection currents in the mantle.

'Yes—not just a name of the process but a concise description of it is required for full credit.'

'Convection currents in the magma of the mantle would be better.'

(ii) What might happen to the continents over the next 200 million years? *(4 marks)*

They will probably move further apart and more mountains and volcanoes may form.

'The volcanoes would be active initially—of course.'

(Total 9 marks)

'A near perfect answer to a higher level question, 8/9.'

SUMMARY

Use this list to help you with your revision. Tick off the points as you revise them in the text.

- ▷ The Earth's atmosphere 4500 million years ago contained no **oxygen**.
- ▷ The gases which formed the atmosphere initially came from **volcanoes**.
- ▷ These early gases are thought to be **carbon dioxide, water vapour, ammonia** and **methane**.
- ▷ Eventually ultraviolet **radiation** would have split some ammonia and water vapour into nitrogen, hydrogen and **oxygen**.
- ▷ The first life would have lived in an atmosphere with very little oxygen (in fact **oxygen would have been toxic** to it) but could have **photosynthesized** oxygen.
- ▷ Eventually **oxygen built up** and the other gases decreased in proportion, especially **carbon dioxide**.
- ▷ The atmosphere now is more or less **balanced**—gases are entering and leaving in equal amounts—with the exception of **carbon dioxide** which has increased by about **30%** over the past century.
- ▷ The carbon, nitrogen and water cycles show **reversible changes** in action keeping atmospheric composition constant.
- ▷ The Earth has three solid layers—**crust, mantle** and **core**. The oceans and atmosphere make up the rest of the planet.
- ▷ The crust is **thin** and made up of a number of **discrete plates**.
- ▷ The main groups of rocks are **igneous, sedimentary** and **metamorphic**.
- ▷ **Igneous** rock forms as **magma** from **intrusions** and **extrusions** cools.
- ▷ Magma **extrusion** produces **basalt** by **rapid cooling** on the surface of the Earth.
- ▷ Magma **intrusion** produces **granite** by **slow cooling** inside the Earth.
- ▷ Basalt is **darker** and has **smaller crystals** than granite.
- ▷ Fast crystallization produces small crystals; slow crystallization gives large crystals.
- ▷ The first rock was igneous, since volcanoes existed before seas.
- ▷ Material from eroded igneous rock is transported by rain and wind into lakes and seas where it forms deposits of **sediment** which becomes **compacted** and **cemented** into **sedimentary rock**.
- ▷ Where sedimentary rock in the crust is **subducted** it is **heated strongly** and/or comes under **high pressure**; this metamorphoses it (changes its form) into **metamorphic rock**.
- ▷ Any **fossils** in the original sedimentary rock are destroyed in this process.
- ▷ Examples of igneous rock are **basalt** and **granite**.
- ▷ Examples of sedimentary rock are **limestone, chalk, sandstone, mudstone** and **shale**.
- ▷ Examples of metamorphic rock are **marble, quartzite, slate, schist** and **gneiss**, formed, respectively, from the sedimentary rocks shown in bold type above.
- ▷ The age of rocks can be determined by measurements of **radioactive decay**.
- ▷ **Plate tectonic theory** explains how the present continents have formed from one giant land mass **200 million years ago**.
- ▷ Plates are believed to move because of the **convection currents** in the magma of the mantle.
- ▷ Plates may move towards each other (colliding plates) or they may move away from each other (diverging plates).
- ▷ Colliding plates form **mountains** and **ocean trenches** (continental + oceanic) with **volcanoes/earthquakes** or just mountains (two continental plates).
- ▷ Diverging plates may form **ocean ridges** (both oceanic) or rift valleys (both continental) with **volcanoes/earthquakes**.
- ▷ Plates **sliding past** each other cause **earthquakes** with no lift or subduction.
- ▷ Igneous and metamorphic rocks are formed in these plate movements.

Chapter

14 The periodic table

GETTING STARTED

The elements of the periodic table are arranged in order of their proton (atomic) numbers, from 1 to 107. This arrangement is, roughly, also the order of increasing relative atomic masses of the elements.

The simplest classification of elements is the metal/non-metal classification. This classification fits well into the broader classification of the periodic table.

The structure of the table was first devised by the Russian chemist Dimitrii Mendeleyev in 1869. At that time there were only about 60 elements known and attempts to bring order to them had not previously been very successful.

The table used today is much the same as Mendeleyev's table. The gaps he left have now been filled and the table has been extended by the addition of a group of noble gases which Mendeleyev knew nothing of, and more elements beyond bismuth, which had the highest relative atomic mass known to him.

The modern periodic table consists of horizontal rows of elements, called **periods**, and vertical columns, called **groups**.

There are eight groups and seven periods. The reasons for arranging the elements in groups and periods lies in the electron structure of their atoms and has been discussed in Chapter 6.

TOPIC CHART

LONDON	MEG	NEAB	NICCEA	SEG	WJEC	TOPIC	STUDY	REVISION 1	REVISION 2
✓	✓	✓	✓	✓	✓	Classification of the elements			
✓	✓	✓	✓	✓	✓	Group 1 elements—the alkali metals			
			✓		✓	Group 2 elements—the alkaline earth metals			
✓	✓	✓	✓	✓	✓	Group 7 elements—the halogens			
✓	✓	✓	✓	✓	✓	Group 0 elements—the noble gases			
✓	✓	✓		✓	✓	The transition elements—heavy metals			

WHAT YOU NEED TO KNOW

Classification of the elements

Early attempts to classify elements

The periodic table arose from a careful and detailed study of the 63 elements then known by Dimitrii Mendeleyev and Lothar Meyer in the years 1869–71. They have a joint claim to be discoverers of the law of periodicity* but Mendeleyev is credited with devising the arrangement of the elements in the form called the periodic table.

However, Mendeleyev was not the first person to attempt a classification. The English chemist John Newlands (1863–6) saw that when the known elements were arranged in atomic mass order, every eighth element was similar. He called this the 'Law of Octaves', comparing this pattern with the musical octave in which every eighth note is similar. This same periodic trend is a feature of Mendeleyev's periodic law. Unfortunately, at the time Newlands suggested this law, it could be seen to apply only to the first 16 elements. His idea was ridiculed at the time but his contribution to chemistry was later recognized with the award of the Davy Medal by the Royal Society.

Earlier still than this, in 1829, Johann Dobereiner had described certain groups of *three* elements, chosen for their similar properties, whose atomic masses were such that the atomic mass of the middle element was the average of the masses of the first and third. These became known as 'Dobereiner's triads'. A 'triad' that you can test for yourself is *lithium*, *sodium* and *potassium*. Look up their relative atomic masses and show that the value for sodium is midway between the values for lithium and potassium.

The periodic table is useful to students of chemistry because it helps us to remember the properties of elements and also explains why elements have these properties.

*The modern periodic law states that the chemical and physical properties of the elements are periodic functions of their atomic numbers. In this sense the word *periodic* applies to the fact that similar properties recur at regular 'atomic number intervals'.

Metals and non-metals

A simple classification of elements is into **metals** and **non-metals**. These are fairly clearly separated within the periodic table as shown in Fig. 14.1.

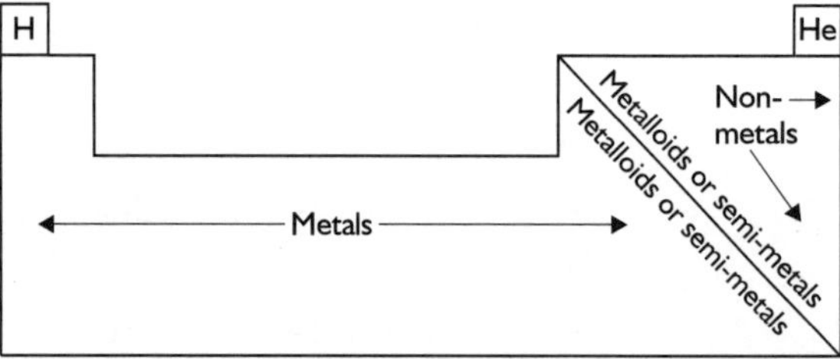

Fig. 14.1 The periodic table, showing the division into metals and non-metals

Semi-metals or metalloids

The class of elements which lies on the borderline between metals and non-metals is often classified as **semi-metals** or **metalloids** (see Fig. 6.1). This class includes elements such as silicon. The differences between metals and non-metals are shown in Table 14.1.

Table 14.1 Table of elements showing the properties of metals and non-metals

Metals	Non-metals
Good conductors of heat and electricity	Poor conductors of heat and electricity
Shiny	Dull
Malleable	Brittle
Strong	Weak
React with oxygen to form basic oxides	React with oxygen to form acidic oxides
Usually high density	Usually low density
Usually high melting points except alkali metals	Usually low melting points except carbon
Many react with dilute acid to produce hydrogen	No reaction with dilute acid

The periodic table

We can start by looking at the change in properties of elements as their atomic number increases in single units. This sequence is a **period** and we refer to the changes in properties as **trends.**

Trends in properties across a period

These trends are clearest across the second and third periods, that is elements Li—Ne and Na—Ar.

Table 14.2 The elements of the third period showing the electronic structures and valency

Element	Na	Mg	Al	Si	P	S	Cl	Ar
Metal/non-metal*	m	m	m	n/m	n/m	n/m	n/m	n/m
Valency	1	2	3	4	3 or 5	2 or 6	1 or 7	0
Outer shell electrons	1	2	3	4	5	6	7	8
Inner shell electrons	2,8	2,8	2,8	2,8	2,8	2,8	2,8	2,8

*m = metal; n/m = non-metal.

The information in Table 14.2 shows the following trends.

Going across Table 14.2 from left to right:

1. **The elements change from metals to non-metals.**
   This is easily shown by testing the elements for electrical conductivity using the apparatus of Fig. 14.2. **Metals** conduct and the bulb lights, **non-metals** do not conduct and the bulb does not light.
2. **A particular shell (energy level) is filling with electron 5.**
3. **The number of electrons in the outer electron shell increases from 1 to 8.**
4. **The number of outer electrons equals the group number.**
5. **The valency of the elements increases from 1 to 4 in single units for the elements in the first four groups and then decreases by single units from 4 to 1 for the elements of groups 4–7.**
   The reason for this is discussed in Chapter 6.

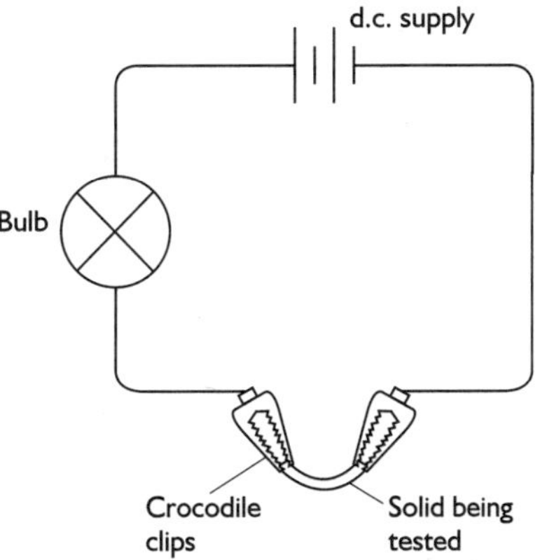

Fig. 14.2 Electrical conductivity testing apparatus

Trends in properties down a group

The phrase 'down a group' is a short way of saying that the change being considered is from the top element to the bottom element in the group. The groups studied in detail at GCSE level are groups 1, 2, 7 and 0. The electron arrangements of these groups are shown in Table 14.3.

The most obvious feature of the above electron structures is the presence of **the group number** of electrons in the outer shell.

The elements react in such a way as to achieve an **outer shell electron arrangement of the nearest noble gas (group 0 element).**

Trends common to all groups 'down the group'

1. **The atom gets larger: its diameter increases.**
   This is caused by the addition of an extra electron **shell** for each step down the group. The number of such shells corresponds to the number of the period in which the element is placed. For example, sodium is in period 3 and so has three shells containing electrons—its electron structure is 2 8 1. Its atoms will be smaller than those of potassium, the element below it in the same group, because potassium atoms have four shells and an electron structure of 2 8 8 1.
2. **The number of electrons in the outer shell is always equal to the group number.**
   See Table 14.3. All the elements in the same group have the same number of electrons in the outer shell.

Table 14.3 Electron structures of selected groups of elements

Group 1		**Group 2**	
Lithium	2 1	Beryllium	2 2
Sodium	2 8 1	Magnesium	2 8 2
Potassium	2 8 8 1	Calcium	2 8 8 2
Rubidium	2 8 18 8 1	Strontium	2 8 18 8 2
Caesium	2 8 18 18 8 1	Barium	2 8 18 18 8 2
Group 7		**Group 0**	
Fluorine	2 7	Helium	2
Chlorine	2 8 7	Neon	2 8
Bromine	2 8 18 7	Argon	2 8 8
Iodine	2 8 18 18 7	Krypton	2 8 18 8
		Xenon	2 8 18 18 8

3. **The atoms lose their outer electron(s) more easily.**
   The effect of this is to make metals more reactive down the group and non-metals less reactive. This is because, to react, **metal** atoms must **lose** their outer electrons and form positive ions. The farther from the **attracting** nucleus the outer electrons are the more easily they can be lost (transferred) to another atom.
   The opposite is the situation for **non-metals**. They are the elements that **gain** electrons to achieve a full outer electron shell. In doing so they must attract electrons to the outer shell. This attraction is stronger the closer the outer shell is to the attracting nucleus of the atom, i.e. the smaller the atom. So the most reactive non-metal elements are at the top of their groups, in contrast to the metals.
   This difference in reactivity trend between metals and non-metals is the result of the basic difference between atoms of metals and atoms of non-metals. Metal atoms will always lose electrons in their chemical reactions; non-metal atoms will gain electrons when forming stable ions.
4. **The density of the element increases.**
   The densest elements in Table 14.4 are towards the bottom of each group.
5. **The melting point and boiling point of the elements changes.** For metals it decreases; for non-metals it increases (Table 14.5).

Table 14.4 A summary of group trends

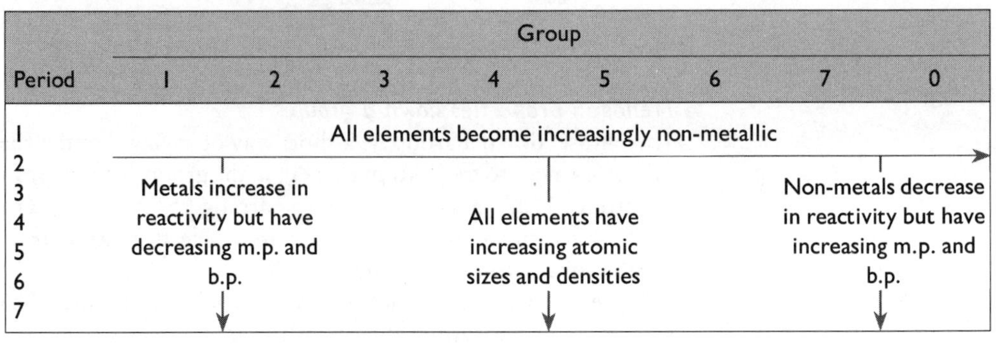

Table 14.5 Trends in melting points and boiling points of group 1 and group 7 elements

Group I			Group 7		
	m.p.*	b.p.*		m.p.*	b.p.*
Li	454	1615	F	53	85
Na	371	1156	Cl	172	238
K	336	1033	Br	266	332
Rb	312	959	I	387	457

*Temperatures are in degrees kelvin. To convert to degrees Celsius subtract 273. This will sometimes give temperatures below zero Celsius.

Groups and their properties

The elements of a **group** have similar properties. This fact is related to the similar electron structures of the atoms of the elements of the group. If every atom in a group had the same number of electron shells as well as the same number of electrons in the outer shell, then all elements in that group would have **identical properties. They would, of course, be one and the same element.**

What makes elements of the same group similar but not identical is the different number of electron shells but the same number of electrons in the outer one. Some groups show family properties better than others. These are the groups studied at GCSE level. They are groups 1, 2, 7 and 0.

Hydrogen

Hydrogen is often placed in the middle at the top of the periodic table. However, it is also placed at the top of group 1. So, which group is it in? The answer is that hydrogen does not readily fit into any group.

It is sometimes shown in group 1 because:

- It has a valency/oxidation number of 1, e.g. it forms HCl, H_2O.
- It forms ions with a single positive charge, compare Na^+ with H^+.
- Like the alkali metals its atom has one electron in its outer shell.

It is not always placed in group 1 because:

- It is not a metal like group 1 metals.
- It forms mostly covalent compounds whereas metals form ionic compounds.
- It is a gas at normal temperatures, the alkali metals are all solids.
- It does not have any of the metallic properties elements of group 1.

It could be placed in group 7 with the halogens on the basis of its atomic structure. Its atom has one electron less than a full shell. However, hydride ions (H^-) of the same charge as the halide ions are rare and do not exist in aqueous solution.

Hence hydrogen is best placed in the middle of the table at the top where it stands alone because of its unique properties.

The periodic table as a useful tool for chemists

The periodic table is a useful tool that chemists use to summarize their knowledge and understanding of the chemistry of the elements. As you become more familiar with it you will be able to use it in the same way.

Group I elements—the alkali metals

The elements lithium, sodium, potassium, rubidium, caesium and francium are the **most reactive** metals in the periodic table. They are soft metals, easily cut with a knife to reveal a shiny cut surface which quickly tarnishes. Their softness is mainly due to their low melting points. In this property, and in their low densities, they differ from most other metals.

Because these metals are so reactive they must be kept out of contact with any of the substances they can react with. These include all non-metals except the noble gases, and most compounds containing these non-metals. For this reason they are usually stored under a liquid **hydrocarbon** such as paraffin oil. This keeps the metal out of contact with oxygen, water vapour and carbon dioxide.

If alkali metals come into contact with **water or its vapour** the following reaction occurs:

$$2Na(s) + 2H_2O(l) \rightarrow 2Na^+OH^-(aq) + H_2(g)$$

sodium + water → sodium hydroxide + hydrogen

With **oxygen or air**, the reaction is

$$4Na(s) + O_2(g) \rightarrow 2Na_2^+O^{2-}(s)$$

sodium + oxygen → sodium oxide

Sodium hydroxide and sodium oxide are both white solids. These white solids are also alkalis and will react further with carbon dioxide in the air to form, finally, sodium carbonate as the end-product of the reaction. The rapid tarnishing of a cut surface of any of these metals is caused by reaction with oxygen, water vapour and carbon dioxide in the air.

As we have seen, the reactivity of these elements increases **down the group**. Lithium is the least reactive and francium is the most reactive. Francium is in fact a synthetic element and has only been made in minute quantities. Even so, its reactions have been found to be exactly as predicted from our knowledge of the group trend.

The reaction of the alkali metals with **water** is perhaps the most interesting of the reactions of alkali metals. Lithium, sodium and potassium all float on water—they are all less dense than water itself.

Explanation of the trend in reactivity of the alkali metals

Each alkali metal atom must lose one electron to achieve a noble gas electron structure of eight outer electrons; see Table 14.3 for the electron arrangements in atoms of group 1 elements. They do this by transferring the single outer electron to atoms of other elements—usually non-metallic elements. The outer electron is more easily lost the farther away from the attracting nucleus it is. An outer electron is shielded from the attraction of the positively charged nucleus by any intervening shells of electrons. The outermost electron in a caesium atom has five full shells separating it from its nucleus and so is subject to a smaller attractive force than the outer electron of the atoms of the other alkali metals. The lithium atom, on the other hand, has its outer electron separated from the nucleus by only a single full shell of electrons. Its outer electron is poorly shielded from the nucleus and consequently is more strongly held in the atom. So, the ease of electron loss follows exactly the trend in reactivity.

Reactions of sodium

If we take the reaction of **sodium** with water as a starting point we can compare the reaction of the others with it. A small piece of sodium can be cut easily with a knife from a larger lump. When placed on water it immediately melts, forming a small ball of metal and moves about the surface of the water making a hissing sound. It rapidly becomes smaller as it reacts with the water and eventually disappears, sometimes with a bang! What has happened?

Sodium reacts with water to form sodium hydroxide which dissolves in the water. Hydrogen gas is also formed but is not noticed because it is given off into the air from *above* the water level. To collect the gas and identify it as hydrogen would require the sodium to be held under water to fill a test tube of water with the gas.

This can be a dangerous procedure if not done with care. It can be done using a 'sodium spoon'—a special metal gauze container at the end of a long handle (Fig. 14.3). Water can react with the sodium and hydrogen can escape through the holes in the gauze.

The reaction is

$$2Na(s) + 2H_2O(l) \rightarrow 2Na^+OH\text{-}(aq) + H_2(g)$$

sodium + water → sodium hydroxide + hydrogen

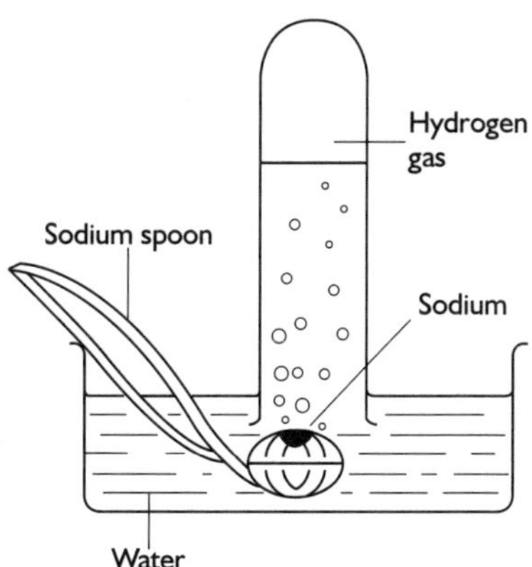

Fig. 14.3 The use of a sodium spoon in collecting hydrogen from the reaction of sodium or lithium with water

With air

Sodium burns with a yellow flame if heated in air. Sodium oxide is formed. Testing the residue with damp indicator paper will confirm the alkaline nature of the oxide:

sodium + oxygen → sodium oxide

$$4Na(s) + O_2(g) \rightarrow 2Na_2^+O^{2-}(s)$$

With chlorine

Sodium burns strongly in chlorine with a bright yellow flame:

sodium + chlorine → sodium chloride

$$2Na(s) + Cl_2(g) \rightarrow 2Na^+Cl^-(s)$$

The products of all these reactions are **ionic** compounds.

Substituting the symbol of **any other alkali metal for that of sodium** in the above equation gives the corresponding equation for the reaction of that element with water.

Reactions of lithium and potassium

From the reactions and properties of sodium given above it is possible to **predict**—to foretell—the reactions of other alkali metals:

(i) **Lithium** will be **harder** than sodium; **potassium** will be **softer**—because the melting points decrease down the group and the lower the melting point the softer the metal.
(ii) For the same reason as in (i), **lithium** does **not melt** on reaction with water, whereas **potassium** will form a **globule** like sodium. **Both** will **float.**
(iii) **Potassium** will be **more reactive** than sodium; **lithium** will be **less reactive** than sodium. In fact, potassium catches fire or, rather, the hydrogen given off catches fire over potassium. A lilac flame is seen.
(iv) **Both** will produce **alkaline solutions** of the metal hydroxide and also hydrogen gas as shown by the equation above. Lithium hydroxide has the formula LiOH, and potassium hydroxide, KOH.
(v) **Both** will **burn in air** to form alkaline oxides of formula Li_2O and K_2O.
(vi) **Both** will **burn in chlorine,** producing white solid chlorides of formulae LiCl and KCl.

Alkali metals below potassium are more dense than water and much more reactive than potassium. We would predict them to be extremely violent in their reactions with any of the substances that lithium, sodium and potassium react with.

Compounds of the alkali metals and their properties

These metals react strongly with the halogens and oxygen as we have seen above. The resulting compounds are alkali metal halides and oxides. In their reactions, alkali metal atoms lose their single outer electron. See Table 14.3 for the electron arrangements of group 1 elements.

Solubility—all alkali metal compounds are soluble in water.

Members of each set of compounds have similar formulae and properties:

- The **chlorides:** LiCl, NaCl, KCl, etc., are all **ionic** salts which can be electrolysed when molten to give the alkali metal at the cathode and chlorine at the anode.
- The **hydroxides:** LiOH, NaOH, KOH, etc., are all strong alkalis and ionic.
- The **oxides:** Li_2O, Na_2O, K_2O, etc., are all strong alkalis which form the hydroxides when they react with water. All are ionic.

The **group** is called the **alkali metals** because of the alkalis formed by reaction with air or water. The pure metals themselves are not alkalis.

The general reactions of alkali metals involve the transfer of one electron from each metal atom with the formation of a singly positively charged cation: e.g.

$$Na \rightarrow Na^+ + e^-$$

Uses of compounds of the alkali metals

- Sodium chloride—common salt, as a preservative and flavouring agent in food
- Sodium carbonate—soda or washing soda, used to make glass and as a water softener
- Sodium hydrogencarbonate—'bicarb' as a raising agent in cakes and as an antacid
- Potassium iodide—to add iodine to salt and cattle salt-licks to prevent iodine deficiency in humans and farm animals
- Potassium chloride—mixed with sodium chloride in low-sodium salt

Group 2 elements—the alkaline earth metals

'NICCEA and WJEC only'

The only members of this group studied at this level are **magnesium** and **calcium**. Examination questions will probably be set on the prediction of the properties and reactions of other metals in the group where these are **similar** to those of magnesium and calcium.

These metals are not as reactive as the alkali metals and also are harder, so that they are difficult to cut with a knife. Their hardness compared with alkali metals can be seen to be connected with their higher melting points. Melting points **decrease** going **down the group** as with all groups of metals. **Density** also increases **down the group**.

Reactions of group 2 metals

- These atoms lose two electrons from their outer electron shell, gaining a double positive charge in the process; see Table 14.3 for the electron arrangements in group 2 atoms.
- The metals tarnish in air but more slowly than group 1 metals.
- Their reaction with water is much slower and they are all denser than water. The products of reaction with water are hydrogen and a metal oxide or hydroxide.
- With the exception of magnesium, they are also kept under paraffin oil to stop reaction with water vapour, oxygen and carbon dioxide from the air.

The reactions of calcium

Calcium is a very reactive metal. It is kept under oil to reduce its reaction with air or water vapour. It reacts quickly with air to form a white oxide coating. It burns strongly in air or oxygen with a red flame:

$$2Ca(s) + O_2(g) \rightarrow 2CaO(s)$$

calcium + oxygen → calcium oxide (quicklime)

Calcium oxide is a base. It reacts with water to form its hydroxide, which is an alkali, $Ca(OH)_2$, common name **slaked lime**:

$$CaO(s) + H_2O(l) \rightarrow Ca(OH)_2(s)$$

calcium oxide + water → calcium hydroxide (slaked lime)

'Compare this with the behaviour of sodium. Group 1 elements float on water, group 2 elements sink.'

A small piece of calcium will **sink** as it reacts with water. A steady stream of gas bubbles is produced and a white residue appears in the water. The equation for the reaction is

$$Ca(s) + 2H_2O(l) \rightarrow Ca(OH)_2(s) + H_2(g)$$

calcium + water → calcium hydroxide + hydrogen

The gas can be collected in an upturned test tube full of water as with sodium. The gas will explode if put to a flame, showing it to be **hydrogen.** If the resulting solution is filtered and the filtrate is shaken with some carbon dioxide gas, a milky precipitate forms:

$$Ca(OH)_2(aq) \quad + \quad CO_2(g) \quad \rightarrow \quad CaCO_3(s) \quad + H_2O(l)$$

calcium hydroxide + carbon dioxide → calcium carbonate + water

The filtrate is lime-water (calcium hydroxide solution). Calcium hydroxide is a strong alkali but is not very soluble in water.

Reactions of other alkaline earth metals

From its position in the group, **magnesium** would be expected to be less reactive than calcium. **Strontium,** which is just below calcium, would be expected to be more reactive than calcium. This proves to be so.

Magnesium is a light silvery metal. Its uses are given in Chapter 8. Magnesium does **not** react with **cold water** unless it is finely powdered (surface area effect on the rate of reaction). Even then, the reaction takes days rather than minutes.

Magnesium **will** react **with steam:**

$$Mg(s) \quad + H_2O(g) \rightarrow \quad MgO(s) \quad + \quad H_2(g)$$

magnesium + steam → magnesium oxide + hydrogen

Magnesium also **burns in air** or oxygen to form the oxide

$$2Mg(s) \quad + \quad O_2(g) \quad \rightarrow \quad 2MgO(s)$$

magnesium + oxygen → magnesium oxide

Magnesium **reacts rapidly** with **dilute** solutions of hydrochloric and sulphuric acids to form magnesium salts and hydrogen gas:

$$Mg(s) \quad + \quad H_2SO_4(aq) \quad \rightarrow \quad MgSO_4(aq) \quad + \quad H_2(g)$$

magnesium + sulphuric acid → magnesium sulphate + hydrogen

A **similar reaction** occurs with **dilute hydrochloric acid,** HCl(aq); the salt magnesium chloride ($MgCl_2$) is formed. Try working out the equation.

Strontium should react more rapidly with water, producing a fast stream of hydrogen and forming an alkaline solution which will be cloudy. It should burn in air or oxygen, but more vigorously than either magnesium or calcium. This is, in fact, what happens.

The reactions of **barium** can be predicted in the same way. Which is the most reactive metal in group 2?

Try constructing equations for the reactions of barium with water or dilute hydrochloric acid.

Compounds of alkaline earth metals and their properties

These metals react less strongly than the alkali metals do with the halogens and with oxygen. Members of each set of compounds have similar formulae and properties.

The **chlorides** $MgCl_2$, $CaCl_2$, etc., are all ionic salts which, when electrolysed in the molten state, give the metal at the cathode and chlorine at the anode. These metals are produced industrially by this process.

The **oxides,** MgO, CaO, etc., are all bases. Calcium oxide and the oxides of the more reactive elements in the group react **exothermically** with water to form hydroxides:

$$CaO(s) \quad + H_2O(l) \rightarrow \quad Ca(OH)_2(s)$$

calcium oxide + water → calcium hydroxide + heat

Glass manufacture

Glass is a supercooled liquid. It is a mixture of silicates. Many different types of glass are in use. For example, everyday glass is mainly a mixture of calcium and sodium silicates. Other types of glass contain potassium silicates and boron compounds (Pyrex glass) or lead silicates (crystal glass). Pure silica forms silica glass, a glass with a high melting point which resists cracking even when plunged, red-hot, into cold water!

Glass is made by mixing sand (silica), limestone and soda ash (sodium carbonate) together with broken glass added to speed up the melting. The mixture reacts to form a mixture of sodium and calcium silicates. This mixture is made into bottles and sheets of glass. Plate-glass used for high-quality windows is made by floating molten glass onto a bath of liquid tin. The molten glass settles as a film of even thickness. The absolutely smooth surface of the molten tin gives the solidifying glass the same polished surface.

'Float-glass process'

Group 7 elements—the halogens

These are the **reactive** non-metals **fluorine, chlorine, bromine** and **iodine.**

- The elements are all **diatomic**—they have two atoms per molecule, F_2, Cl_2, Br_2 and I_2.
- The elements are **coloured.** Fluorine and chlorine are green gases, bromine is a brown liquid, and iodine a grey solid which forms a purple vapour on heating.
- Unlike the groups of metal elements just discussed, non-metals have the **most reactive** elements at the top of the group. The most reactive is fluorine, the least reactive is iodine.

Fluorine is much too dangerous to use in a school laboratory, which gives a hint as to its extreme reactivity.

Explanation of the trend in reactivity of the halogens

Each halogen must **accept** an electron to achieve a noble gas electron structure of eight electrons in its outer shell; see Table 14.3 for the electron arrangements in atoms of group 7 elements. This it does by either:

(i) accepting an electron by **transfer** from a metal atom; or
(ii) accepting a **share** of an electron from another non-metal atom.

In either case the electron which is being accepted is most strongly held if it enters an electron shell close to the nucleus, which strongly attracts electrons. So the element with its outer shell of electrons closest to the nucleus—fluorine—will most readily form compounds and will be the most reactive. The reactivity will decrease down the group as the outer shell of electrons gets further from the nucleus.

'Note that the melting point and boiling points of group 1 elements decrease down the group, whereas the melting and boiling point of groups 7 and 0 increase down the group.'

The trend in the melting points of these elements is also in the opposite direction to that with groups of metals. The melting point of fluorine is lowest and that of iodine the highest. Fluorine and chlorine are gases, bromine is a liquid and iodine a solid **at room temperature.**

Reactions of the halogens

These are best studied using **chlorine** as an example. Chlorine is toxic and the following reactions should be carried out in a fume cupboard.

Reaction with metals, e.g. sodium

The reaction of sodium with chlorine is very vigorous and forms the ionic salt sodium chloride—common salt:

$$2Na(s) + Cl_2(g) \rightarrow 2Na^+Cl^-(s)$$

sodium + chlorine → sodium chloride

It is useful to consider the differences between chlorine and sodium and the resulting salt, sodium chloride. Whereas chlorine is a poisonous green gas, and sodium a very reactive soft metal, when reacted together the product is a tasty, non-poisonous, stable white solid. Why is this?

It is because each chlorine atom has accepted one electron from a sodium atom. The **atoms** of the two elements no longer exist as atoms and are now in fact **ions**—sodium and chloride ions. Obviously, the presence of **one more** or **one less** electron has had a tremendous effect on the properties of the atoms.

'Chemical reaction creates new properties'

A similar change of properties occurs with the other halogens when they become halides, and other metals when they become metal salts.

Such is the nature of the **chemical reaction!**

Reaction of halogens with water

There is no strong reaction with water, with the exception of the reaction of fluorine with water.

Chlorine, bromine and iodine react to decreasing extents, forming an acidic, bleaching solution. The bleaching power of these solutions decreases as the reactivity of the halogen decreases.

'Chemical test for chlorine: it bleaches damp u.l paper'

The usual **chemical test** for chlorine depends upon the formation of acid and bleach on reaction with water. A piece of **damp** universal indicator paper will first turn red and then colourless with chlorine. This also happens with bromine and iodine, but more slowly:

$$Cl_2(g) + H_2O(l) \rightarrow HCl(aq) + HOCl(aq)$$

chlorine + water → hydrochloric acid + chloric(I) acid (bleach)

Reactions with non-metallic elements

Halogens react also with other non-metallic elements such as hydrogen, phosphorus and sulphur. However, the compounds formed are not ionic—they are molecular. For example, hydrogen will burn in chlorine, forming hydrogen chloride. Hydrogen chloride is a colourless gas. The hydrogen and chlorine atoms are joined by a covalent bond into a simple molecule containing two atoms.

The reaction can be represented as

$$Cl{-}Cl(g) + H{-}H(g) \rightarrow 2H{-}Cl(g)$$

1 molecule 1 molecule 2 molecules

'Refer to p. 65 for properties of molecules'

The fact that hydrogen chloride is a gas at room temperature indicates to us that it has a low boiling point and is therefore composed of molecules and not ions (which would give it much higher melting and boiling points).

Displacement reaction of halogens with halides

Just as metals are able to displace each other from solutions of their ions (see p. 257), so non-metals can do the same. A more reactive non-metal can displace a less reactive non-metal from a salt of the latter.

Remember—the more reactive halogen is higher in the group!

Chlorine can displace bromine from **ionic** bromides and iodine from **ionic** iodides:

$$Cl_2(g) + 2Br^-(aq) \rightarrow 2Cl^-(aq) + Br_2(aq)$$

chlorine + bromide ions → chloride ions + bromine

If sodium bromide is the salt used, the equation could also be written

$$Cl_2(g) + 2NaBr(aq) \rightarrow 2NaCl(aq) + Br_2(aq)$$

chlorine + sodium bromide → sodium chloride + bromine

The reaction of chlorine with **iodides** is similar—iodine is displaced:

$$Cl_2(g) + 2KI(aq) \rightarrow 2KCl(aq) + I_2(aq)$$

chlorine + potassium iodide → potassium chloride + iodine

The iodide used above could have been **any soluble metal iodide.**

▶ Try constructing an equation, containing ions, for the iodine displacement. It should look something like the first equation given above with the symbol for iodine in place of the symbol for bromine.

- Try also writing an equation for the reaction between bromine and potassium iodide. Will a displacement occur?
  (Note that all halide ions have a single negative charge.)

Fluorine

The study of **fluorine** is not on any GCSE syllabus. However, questions may be asked about its properties where these can be **predicted** from a knowledge of the properties of the other halogens and an understanding of the group reactivity trend.

Fluorine is at the **top** of the group.

- It would be expected to be a gas at room temperature because its boiling point should be lower than that of chlorine, which is also a gas.
- It would be expected to be the most reactive element in the group and will therefore react vigorously with sodium to form sodium fluoride.
- It should displace chlorine, bromine and iodine from their ionic compounds.

Can you predict some of the properties of the synthetic halogen astatine which is below iodine in the group?

Uses of the halogens and their compounds

The elements

- Chlorine is a disinfectant. It is used to sterilize tap water and swimming-pool water.
- Bromine is used to make antiknock for leaded petrol.
- Iodine is an antiseptic used in alcoholic solution.

The compounds

- Fluorides are used in some toothpastes and also to fluoridate some domestic water supplies.
- Sodium chloride is common salt, used as flavouring, to de-ice roads, and to regenerate the resins in water-softeners.
- Sodium hypochlorite—a solution of chlorine in sodium hydroxide—is domestic bleach (5%) and is also used in swimming-pool sterilization.
- Potassium iodide is put into 'iodized table salt' and cattle licks to combat iodine deficiency.
- Silver bromide and silver iodide are the light-sensitive chemicals in photographic film.

Group 0 elements—the noble gases

The elements helium (He), neon (Ne), argon (Ar), krypton (Kr) and xenon (Xe) make up the group of almost totally unreactive gases called the **noble gases**.

They are all **monatomic** gases. That is, their molecules contain a single atom. This is because they have no need to combine with any other atom to achieve a full outer shell of electrons–they already have one!

They are all gases at room temperature because of the very small attractive forces between their molecules. Helium has the smallest molecule of the noble gases. Its molecules attract each other least and so the melting and boiling points of helium are the lowest in the group. Radon, with the largest molecules, has the highest melting and boiling points of the group. (Radon is the noble gas element below xenon; it is a radioactive element and is not studied at GCSE level. Its properties can, however, be predicted in the usual way from a knowledge of the properties of the other noble gases.)

Occurrence

These gases occur in the air, though only argon, at about 1% of the air, is common. Apart from helium, which is found in natural gas in some parts of the world, the gases are obtained by the fractional distillation of liquid air.

Group trends—physical properties

The trend **down the group** is to higher melting points and boiling points and higher densities, as with other non-metals (Table 14.6).

Table 14.6 Some physical properties of the noble gases

Noble gas	Density/g litre^{-1}	Melting point/K	Boiling point/K
Helium	0.17	1	4
Neon	0.84	25	27
Argon	1.66	84	87
Krypton	3.46	116	121
Xenon	5.45	161	166

Note: Temperature values in degrees K (kelvin) are 273 degrees larger than temperatures in degrees Celsius (°C).

Chemical reactivity

The lack of reactivity of the noble gases is caused by the inability of their atoms to transfer or share electrons. Each noble gas element has atoms with the outer electron shell full. For helium this is the first shell and contains just two electrons. The electron structures of the noble gases are shown in Table 14.3.

Noble gas atoms do not need to react with other atoms—not even with their own atoms—to achieve a full outer shell of electrons. They are therefore **inert** to other substances.

Until the early 1960s, no compounds of these elements had been prepared. At that time xenon was found to be capable of reacting with fluorine, the most reactive non-metal known. A knowledge of these reactions is not required for GCSE examinations.

The ability of xenon to form compounds illustrates very well the increased ability of electrons to be lost from the outer shell of the atom towards the bottom of a group. The most reactive noble gases are low down in the group—krypton, xenon and radon.

Uses of the noble gases

The word 'noble' as used to describe these gases means **not very reactive**. This 'nobility' is very useful to chemists when they require the use of a non-reactive gas, for instance as an inert atmosphere to exclude reactive gases from a reaction vessel.

'It is a common error to believe that helium is used in "hot air balloons"!'

Helium is a non-flammable substitute for hydrogen in balloons and 'airships'. It is not used in 'hot air' balloons!

Helium mixed with oxygen is supplied to deep-sea divers. It prevents an unpleasant and sometimes fatal affliction called 'the bends'. Nitrogen in air dissolves in the blood as a diver descends and 'undissolves' forming gas bubbles in the capillaries as the diver ascends—resulting in great pain. Helium does not do this. It does, however, give the diver a squeaky voice while it is being breathed!

Neon is used in red illuminated signs and is also the 'starter' gas in sodium street lamps. Its tell-tale red glow is visible when these lamps are first turned on. The electric current conducted by the neon warms up the lamp, which vaporizes the solid sodium inside. When the sodium is fully vaporized it conducts the current, giving a yellow glow which mixes with the red of the neon to give the typical orange light of the sodium street lamp. A common laser gas is a helium–neon mixture.

Argon is the main gas filling ordinary electric light bulbs. Its purpose is to prevent the tungsten filament from vaporizing too rapidly and becoming weakened.

Argon is the commonest of the noble gases and is available cheaply to industry. It is used wherever a non-reactive atmosphere is required cheaply; one such application is in welding, where the melted metal might react with oxygen in the air and cause failure of the weld. Here the argon is directed onto the metal being welded and keeps out air.

Krypton and **xenon** are also used as fillings for light bulbs. Krypton is used in miners' head-lamp bulbs which are much brighter, for the same size, than ordinary lamp bulbs; xenon is in the brightest bulbs in use—in lighthouses! These two gases prevent the filament in the bulb vaporizing away and therefore allow the filament to be run at a much higher temperature, producing more intense light.

The transition elements—heavy metals

These metals are **not a group** of the periodic table—they do not all have the same number of electrons in the outer shell of their atoms. They are, in fact, a block of dense metals in the middle of the periodic table with many properties in common. They could be called a 'family' of elements.

Only some of the elements in the first row of this block will be considered.

Properties of transition metals

'Students often believe that *all* metals have high melting points. This is untrue. Alkali metals, for instance, have very low melting points.'

(i) **Metallic nature.** All are metals but they are harder than the alkali metal and have very little reaction with water—with the exception of iron.

(ii) **High densities.** Unlike the alkali metals, none of them floats on water. Densities vary from about 3 to 9 $g\,cm^{-3}$ for elements 21–30.

(iii) **High melting and boiling points.** Melting points range from 420 °C to 1900 °C and boiling points from 900 °C to 3400 °C.

(iv) Many of these elements are used as **catalysts** to speed up chemical reactions. Iron is the catalyst in the **Haber** process, nickel in the hydrogenation of vegetable oils to make margarine and vanadium(V) oxide the **Contact process.** Manganese(IV) oxide catalyses the decomposition of hydrogen peroxide solution in the laboratory preparation of oxygen.

(v) The compounds of most of the elements of this block are coloured in **aqueous solution,** e.g. copper(II) ions, $Cu^{2+}(aq)$, are blue and iron(II) ions, $Fe^{2+}(aq)$, are green.

(vi) The atoms of each of these elements can exist in **several different valencies** or **oxidization states,** e.g. iron(II) and iron(III) compounds which have different colours.

(vii) These elements are used in a number of important alloys (see p. 102).

The place of transition elements (heavy metals) in the periodic table is shown in Fig. 14.4.

Fig. 14.4 Position of the transition elements in the periodic table

Some uses of transition metals

- Titanium is light and strong: it is used in aircraft and submarine construction.
- Chromium plating gives a polished silver finish to steel.
- Iron is used to manufacture steels.
- Nickel plating of copper and brass improves appearance.
- Copper is used for electrical wire, water and heating pipes, brassware and coinage.
- Zinc is a component of brass and is used as a coating for steel to prevent rusting.

EXAMINATION QUESTIONS

Questions 1–4(F)

Questions 1 to 4 concern the periodic table as shown in Fig. 14.5 where the letters A–E represent elements.

Select the letter which represents:

1. A metal which produces hydrogen at a steady rate when added to water.
2. A metal which floats and reacts vigorously with water.

Fig. 14.5

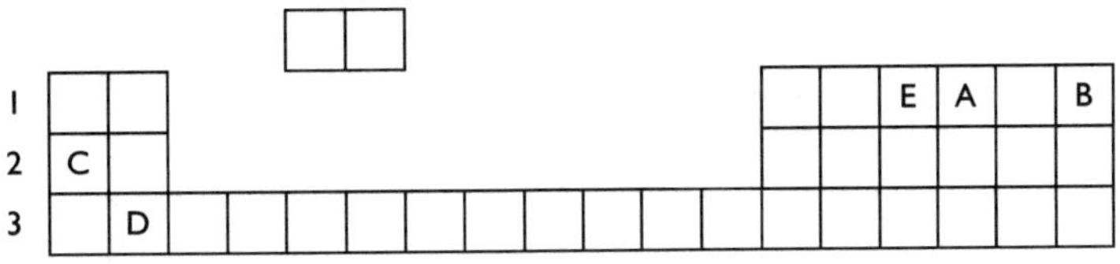

1															E	A		B
2	C																	
3		D																

3. A gas that forms no compounds.
4. A gas that is an oxidizing agent.

(WJEC)

Questions 5–8(F)

Questions 5 to 8 concern the structure of an alkali metal atom (Fig. 14.6).

Fig. 14.6

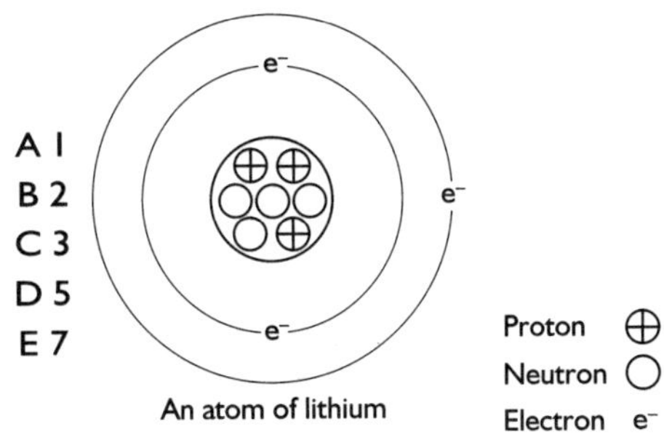

Match the numbers lettered A–E with the statements in questions 5 to 8. Each letter may be used once, more than once or not at all.

5. The mass number of the atom.
6. The valency of the atom.
7. The atomic number of the atom.
8. The positive charge on the ion formed from the atom.

[1] each

Question 9(F)

An element X forms an ion X^{2-}.

(a) To which group of the Periodic Table does the element X belong? [1 line] *[1]*

(b) Write the formula of the compound formed between caesium and X. (Caesium has symbol Cs and is in group 1 of the Periodic Table.) [1 line] *[1]*

(c) The ion X^{2-} contains 54 electrons. How many protons are present in the nucleus of an atom of X? [1 line] *[1]*

[Total 3 marks]

(SEG)

Question 10(F)

This question is about the Periodic Table (Fig. 14.7).

Fig. 14.7

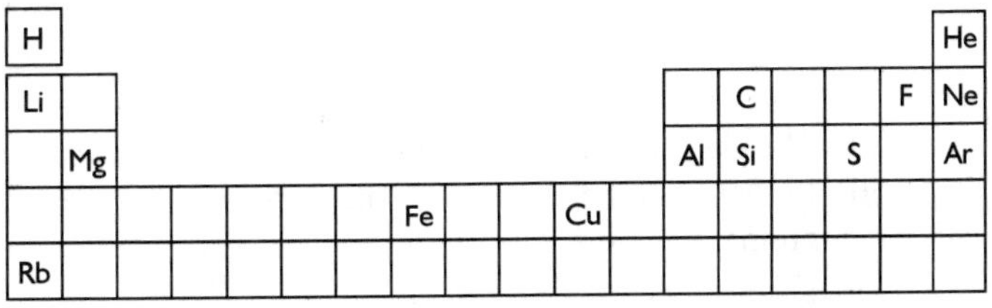

H																	He
Li													C			F	Ne
	Mg											Al	Si		S		Ar
							Fe			Cu							
Rb																	

(a) Using *only* the symbols in the table, give the symbol for:
  (i) an element which is in group 3 of the Periodic Table;
  (ii) an element which is in the same period as carbon (C);
  (iii) a non-metal used in computer hardware;
  (iv) a metal that is used in light alloys;
  (v) an element that is used in illuminated signs;
  (vi) an element which forms an ion with a 2+ charge;
  (vii) the element that reacts most violently with fluorine (F). *[7]*

(b) Place the symbol for each of the following elements (Table 14.7) in its correct place in the Periodic Table of Fig. 14.7. *[3]*

Table 14.7

Element	Symbol	Atomic number
Oxygen	O	8
Calcium	Ca	20
Bromine	Br	35

[Total 10 marks]
(ULEAC)

Question 11 (H)

The positions of the first twenty elements in the Periodic Table are shown below (Fig. 14.8).

Fig. 14.8

						H											He
Li	Be											B	C	N	O	F	Ne
Na	Mg											Al	Si	P	S	Cl	Ar
K	Ca																

(a) In 1869, Dimitrii Mendeleyev published a table on which this Periodic Table has been based. He stated that 'when elements are arranged in order of atomic mass, similar properties recur at intervals'. Discuss whether or not this historical statement is acceptable now. [6 lines] *[3]*

(b) Group 1 contains the elements lithium, sodium, potassium, rubidium and caesium. Why do these elements have similar chemical properties? [2 lines] *[1]*

(c) The diagram (Fig. 14.9) shows a small piece of sodium placed on water. The water contains a small amount of a pH indicator.

Fig. 14.9

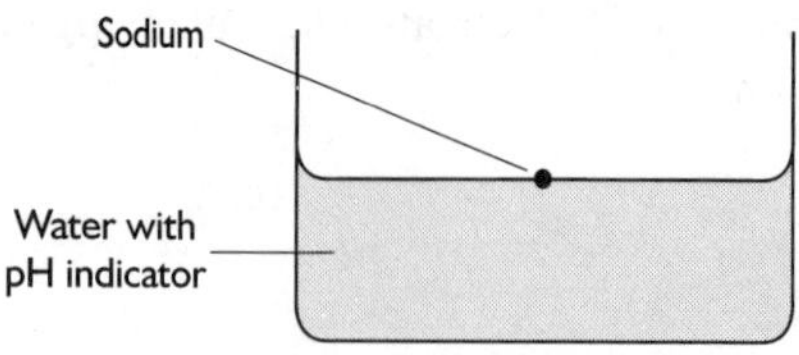

  (i) What observation shows that sodium has a low density? [1 line] *[1]*
  (ii) The reaction causes the pH indicator to change colour. What has happened to the pH of the solution to cause this colour change? Explain your answer. [3 lines] *[3]*
  (iii) Why is a flame produced when potassium reacts with water but not when sodium reacts with water. Explain why. [3 lines] *[2]*

(d) (i) The elements helium, neon and argon are *unreactive*. Explain why. [3 lines] *[2]*
  (ii) In the space below draw a diagram to show the electron arrangement of a neon atom. *[1]*

[Total 13 marks]

Question 12(H)

(a) (i) How does the reactivity of the elements change going down group 1? [1]
(ii) Name the products of the reaction between sodium and water. [1]
(iii) What happens to the electrons in the outer shell of the atoms when elements of group 1 react? [1]

(b) (i) Write down the symbol and electronic structure of fluorine atom. [1]
(ii) How does the reactivity of the elements change going down group 7? [1]
(iii) Give a reason for this change in reactivity. [2]

(c) Predict whether radon (Rn) will react with fluorine. Give your reasons. [3]

[Total 10 marks]

Question 13(H)

'A periodic table is given on p. 311'

Use your periodic table and your knowledge of more familiar elements to *suggest* answers to the following questions.

You are not expected to *know* about the chemistry of rubidium, bromine and selenium.

(a) Rubidium, Rb, has the atomic number 37.
(i) In what group of the periodic table is rubidium? [1]
(ii) Name the *two* products you would expect when rubidium reacts with water. [2]
(iii) Suggest *two* observations which you might *see* during the reaction. [2]

(b) Bromine, Br, has the atomic number 35. It reacts with hydrogen to form a gas, hydrogen bromide.

$$H_2 + Br_2 \rightarrow 2HBr$$

Hydrogen bromide is very soluble in water.
(i) Name a common laboratory liquid you would expect to behave like hydrogen bromide solution. [1]
(ii) What *two* products would you expect to be formed when magnesium reacts with hydrogen bromide solution? [2]
(iii) Suggest *two* observations which you might *see* during the reaction. [2]

[Total 10 marks]

OUTLINE ANSWERS

Questions 1–4

1. D. Any group 2 metal other than magnesium will react with cold water to produce hydrogen at a 'steady rate'.
2. C. Alkali metals float on water and react very vigorously with it.
3. B. The noble gases at the top of the group form no compounds. They are helium, neon and argon.
4. A. This is oxygen, at the top of group 6.

Questions 5–8

5. E. Mass number is the number of protons + neutrons in the nucleus of an atom.
6. A. The valency is the number of electrons in the outer shell of this atom.
7. C. The number of protons in the nucleus.
8. A. The atom will lose its single outer electron to become an ion.

Question 9

(a) The ion has two negative charges. It has been formed from an atom by gaining two electrons. The original atom must have had *two* electrons in its outer shell *less* than the number needed for stability—eight. This identifies its group number as group 6.

(b) Here candidates are asked to predict a formula of a compound containing an element they will never have seen or studied. One of the values of a knowledge of the periodic table is that such predictions are not difficult. Caesium is in group 1—we are told. It will have *one* outer electron. Atoms of element X have two electrons less than an octet—(a) above. Therefore, caesium atoms will transfer electrons to atoms of X until X has a full outer shell and each caesium atom also has a full outer shell. Each caesium atom can only donate *one* electron for its outer shell to be a full shell (loss of the outer single electron makes the *next shell* inwards *the new outer shell*). Each X atom must accept *two* electrons for a full outer shell. The formula is worked out by this kind of reasoning. Try it.

(c) Protons are positively charged particles in the nucleus of an atom. Because every atom is neutral in charge, overall, there must be as many negative charges as there are positive charges. Each electron has a single negative charge, so 54 of them will need to be balanced by 54 positive charges. However, since the ion has a charge of 2−, the number of protons must be 52.

Question 10 A diagram of the periodic table is provided. Only those elements marked on the table can be used to answer the questions.

(a) (i) Group 3 is not marked as such. It is the third vertical column from the left *omitting the transition element block*. The element is Al, aluminium. The symbol is required.

'Don't confuse same period with same group'

(ii) Lithium, fluorine and neon are elements in the same period as carbon: any one of the symbols for these will be acceptable.

(iii) Computer hardware means computers themselves. Si, silicon is used in their manufacture.

(iv) Mg, magnesium or Al, aluminium are used in light alloys.

(v) Ne, neon is used as the gas filling for illuminated sign tubes.

(vi) A 2+ charge would be found on an ion of a group 2 metal: Mg is an answer. However, Cu and Fe also have ions with 2+ charges and these answers would be equally acceptable even though they are transition metals.

(vii) Fluorine is the most reactive non-metal; rubidium is the most reactive metal shown on the table provided. Rb is the answer. Note, however, that caesium is even more reactive but is not one of the symbols on the table and *would not be accepted as the answer to the question.*

(b) This part is testing your knowledge of the structure of the periodic table. Elements are arranged in *atomic number order*. Count the numbers out starting at hydrogen = 1. Oxygen will come just before F; calcium immediately under Mg (as a check, Ca *is* a group 2 metal like Mg); Br is a halogen and in case, by now, you are finding difficulty counting to 35, it will be the third halogen down, two spaces below F.

Question 11 (a) In the modern periodic table it is the atomic (proton) number that increases. So the statement is not acceptable now *[1]*.

Since similar properties do recur at intervals, for example group 1 elements have similar properties, this part of the statement is acceptable *[2]*.

(b) They each have the same number of outer electrons—one *[1]*.

(c) (i) It floats on water *[1]*.

(ii) The solution has become alkaline *[1]*. The product of the reaction, sodium hydroxide *[1]* has a pH of 12–14 *[1]*.

(iii) The reaction is more exothermic *[1]* and the hydrogen released ignites *[1]*.

(d) (i) All have a full outer shell of electrons *[1]*. They have no tendency to gain or lose electrons *[1]*.

(ii) 2,8 is the electron structure of neon *[1]*.

Question 12 (a) (i) Reactivity increases down the group *[1]*.

(ii) Sodium hydroxide and hydrogen *[1]*.

(iii) The single outer electron is lost, leaving a singly positively charged ion *[1]*.

(b) (i) Symbol F, structure 2,7 *[1]*.

(ii) Reactivity *decreases* down group 7 *[1]*.

(iii) Down the group the outer electron shell gets farther from the nucleus (increased shielding) *[1]*. This produces an ever-weaker attraction for the incoming electron the atom must accept to become an ion *[1]*.

(c) The farther down the group we go the more likely the element is to lose an electron *[1]*. Fluorine must gain an electron *[1]*. Therefore the lower elements of the group of noble gases are the most likely to react with fluorine—radon is the lowest in the group and may react *[1]*.

Question 13

(a) (i) Group 1 *[1]*.
(ii) Rubidium hydroxide *[1]* and hydrogen *[1]*.
(iii) Flames, metal sinks, metal melts *[any two for 2 marks.]*

(b) (i) Hydrochloric acid *[1]*, but any mineral acid would do.
(ii) Magnesium bromide *[1]* and hydrogen *[1]*.
(iii) Fizzing *[1]* magnesium dissolves *[1]*.

STUDENT ANSWER WITH EXAMINER'S COMMENTS

																F
Na																
						Mr										Kr
															I	

This question is about elements in the Periodic Table. Using only the symbols shown in the Periodic Table above, give symbols for

(a) two elements in the same group of the Periodic Table;
fluorine and *Iodine*
(1 mark)

'The elements are correct. The symbols were requested not the names, but you have shown you know what a group is. F is fl<u>uo</u>rine'

(b) two elements in the same peroid of the Periodic Table;
flourine and *sodium*
(1 mark)

'You probably misread the table here. Use a straight edge to confirm that the elements in the same horizontal row (period) are Kr and Mn.'

(c) two metallic elements;
sodium and *magnesium*
(2 marks)

'Na is sodium but Mn is manganese. If you had read the question more carefully and so used symbols you would have gained the second mark here!'

(d) the element which forms ions with a single positive charge;
sodium
(1 mark)

'Good. The ion is, of course, Na^+ from group 1.'

(e) the element whose atoms contain the largest number of protons;
krypton
(1 mark)

'Wrong, I'm afraid. Did you choose this because it is in the group, with the *biggest group number*? The most protons are contained in the atom with the highest atomic number I.'

(f) the element with most atoms in a 10 g sample
iodine
(1 mark)

'You did not understand this. The answer is F. 10 g of F is *more moles* than 10 g of I because the RAM of F is less than the RAM of I.'

(ULEAC) *(Total 7 marks)*

SUMMARY

Use this list to help you with your revision. Tick off the points as you revise them in the text.

- ▷ Early attempts to **classify** elements include those by Newlands (**'octaves'**) and by Dobereiner (**'triads'**).
- ▷ The number of electrons in the **outer shell** gives the **group number**.
- ▷ The **number of shells** in an atom gives its **period number.**
- ▷ Elements change from **metals to non-metals** across a period.
- ▷ Trends in properties **down** groups:
  - (i) Metals become **more reactive**, denser, have **lower m.p.** and **b.p.**
  - (ii) Non-metals become **less reactive**, denser, have **higher m.p. and b.p.**
- ▷ Elements of groups 1 and 2 are **all metals** and
  - ▷ react with **air** to form oxides, e.g. Na_2O;
  - ▷ react with **water** or **steam** to form oxides/hydroxides and hydrogen, e.g. $Mg + H_2O \rightarrow MgO + H_2$;
  - ▷ form **ionic compounds**, e.g. Na^+Cl^-.
- ▷ Group 1 elements are softer than group 2 elements, and can be **cut with a knife**—potassium is the softest, lithium the hardest of these three.
- ▷ Group 1 metals, Li, Na and K, **float on water** and react very quickly—potassium catches **fire**.
- ▷ Group 2 metals, magnesium and calcium, **sink in water** and **react slowly**—calcium much faster than magnesium.
- ▷ **All salts** of the group 1 metals are **soluble in water**.
- ▷ **Group 2** metals are **less reactive** than group 1 metals.
- ▷ Elements of **group 7**
  - ▷ react with metals to form salts—fluorides, **chlorides, bromides** and **iodides**—which are **ionic**;
  - ▷ react with non-metals to form **molecular compounds** such as hydrogen halides—HCl, HBr and HI.
- ▷ The **uses of halogens** include
  - ▷ chlorine as a **bactericide** and disinfectant;
  - ▷ bromine to make **anti-knock**;
  - ▷ iodine as an **antiseptic**.
- ▷ Elements of **group 0** are unreactive—they lack reactivity because they have stable electron structures which include an outer **octet** of electrons, so they have **no tendency to give up or accept electrons**.
- ▷ **Transition elements** have similar properties such as:
  - ▷ **high m.p.** (about 1000 °C plus);
  - ▷ **high density**, e.g. mostly 5–9 $g\,cm^{-3}$;
  - ▷ **resistance to corrosion**, e.g. chromium, nickel;
  - ▷ **catalytic activity**, e.g. iron in the Haber process;
  - ▷ **coloured compounds**, e.g. copper compounds are blue;
  - ▷ **electrical conductivity**, e.g. copper.
- ▷ Transition metals find uses wherever the above properties are essential: electrical wiring, parts for jet engines, catalysts in industry, coloured pigments for paints and plastics, electroplating and building, vehicle and railway construction. **Make a note of one or more transition elements for each use.**

Chapter

15 Acids, bases and salts

GETTING STARTED

Nearly all compounds of elements other than carbon fall into the categories of acid, base or salt.

Acids are recognized by their **acidity**. One well known property of acids is their **sourness**. Unripe apples, for example, taste sour because they contain an excess of malic acid. However, identifying acids by their sour taste would be dangerous practice and so chemical tests have been developed from the known properties of acids.

Acids show themselves in the following ways:

- They turn litmus or universal indicator solution red.
- They fizz with reactive metals, e.g. magnesium, zinc or iron, giving off hydrogen which explodes at a flame.
- They fizz with carbonates or hydrogencarbonates, giving off carbon dioxide which turns lime-water milky.
- They neutralize bases and alkalis, forming salts and giving out heat.

Bases and **alkalis** have complementary properties to acids:

- They turn red litmus or universal indicator solution blue/purple.
- They neutralize acids, forming salts and giving out heat.

Salts are formed by neutralization of acids and bases:

- They are ionic compounds.
- They contain a metal and one or more non-metal atoms.
- They include common compounds such as common salt, copper sulphate and potassium nitrate.

TOPIC CHART

LONDON	MEG	NEAB	NICCEA	SEG	WJEC	TOPIC	STUDY	REVISION 1	REVISION 2
✓	✓	✓	✓	✓	✓	Testing for acidity and alkalinity			
✓	✓	✓	✓	✓	✓	Properties of acids and bases			
✓	✓	✓	✓	✓	✓	Salts			
✓	✓	✓	✓	✓	✓	Acid–base neutralization			
✓	✓	✓	✓	✓	✓	Strong and weak acids			
✓	✓	✓	✓	✓	✓	Acids in the laboratory			
✓	✓	✓	✓	✓	✓	Acids in the environment			
✓	✓	✓	✓	✓	✓	Practical methods of preparing salts in the laboratory			
✓	✓	✓	✓	✓	✓	Uses of salts			

WHAT YOU NEED TO KNOW

Testing for acidity and alkalinity

'Although litmus is a good indicator for distinguishing an acid from an alkali it has limitations. Unlike universal indicator, litmus will not measure pH nor will it indicate that a substance is neutral.'

'Even *strong* alkalis can have pHs of 8–12 if they are in *dilute* solution. The distinction between *strong* and *weak* in alkalis, as with acids, is in the *proportion of molecules* which are ionized in solution'

The pH scale

The pH scale is a numerical scale which is used as a measure of the acidity or alkalinity of a solution. The scale ranges from 0 to 14.

- A pH of 0 represents the strongest acid.
- A pH of 14 the strongest alkali.
- A pH of 7 is neutral.

Fig. 15.1 The pH scale

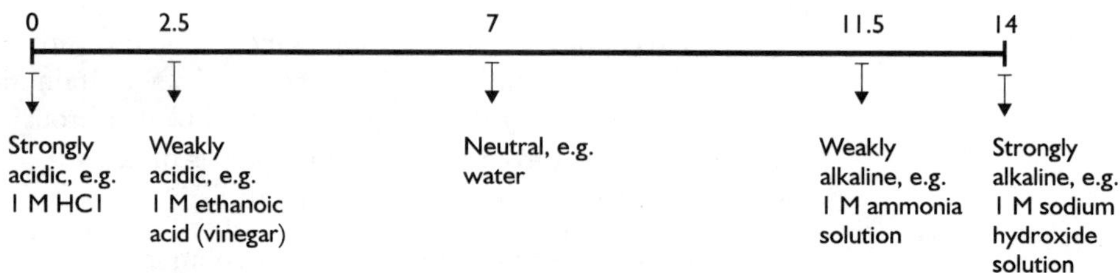

The pH of a solution can be measured in two ways:

- adding universal indicator solution or paper to the solution and reading the pH from the colour chart for the indicator;
- reading from a pH meter with the probe dipping into the solution.

The pH meter usually gives the more accurate value.

Properties of acids and bases

Properties of acids

Table 15.1 gives a detailed summary of the important properties of aqueous solutions of acids.

Table 15.1 Properties of aqueous solutions of acids

Reagent	Reaction	Comments
Magnesium or any metal **above copper** in the reactivity table	The acid gives off **hydrogen** gas and leaves a solution of the salt of the metal.	Any pure, grey powder which fizzes in acid will almost certainly be a metal.
Calcium carbonate or any other carbonate or hydrogencarbonate	**Carbon dioxide** is given off from the carbonate or hydrogencarbonate.	This reaction is also used as a test for carbonates or hydrogencarbonates.
Any **base** or **alkali** e.g. copper(II) oxide or sodium hydroxide	**Neutralization** occurs: heat is produced.	pH of solution will rise. A neutral solution is formed if **no excess** of alkali is added.

Procedure to carry out these simple tests for acids

- To a solution suspected of being an acid add a piece of magnesium metal. The mixture should **fizz** if an acid is present. The hydrogen produced can be collected by loosely closing the tube with a bung or thumb. Hydrogen will explode if the mouth of the tube is put to a flame. The explosion is louder if air is allowed to mix with the gas before testing.
- The above test can be repeated using a marble chip in place of the magnesium. Fizzing will again occur but this time the gas produced is carbon dioxide. The test for carbon dioxide is to bubble the gas through lime-water. Lime-water turns milky if carbon dioxide is present.

Any of the reactions given in the table can be used as a **test** for acidity. Equations for the reactions occurring in these tests **using hydrochloric acid as an example of an acid** are given in Table 15.2.

Table 15.2 Balanced equations for the reactions of acids

Metal	magnesium	+ hydrochloric acid	→	**magnesium** chloride	+	hydrogen gas		
	$Mg(s)$	+ $2HCl(aq)$	→	$MgCl_2$	+	$H_2(g)$		
Carbonate	calcium carbonate	+ hydrochloric acid	→	**calcium** chloride	+	carbon dioxide	+	water
	$CaCO_3(s)$	+ $2HCl(aq)$	→	$CaCl_2(aq)$	+	$CO_2(g)$	+	$H_2O(l)$
Base	copper(II) oxide	+ hydrochloric acid	→	**copper(II)** chloride	+	water		
	$CuO(s)$	+ $2HCl(aq)$	→	$CuCl_2(aq)$	+	$H_2O(l)$		
Alkali	sodium hydroxide	+ hydrochloric acid	→	**sodium** chloride	+	water		
	$NaOH(aq)$	+ $HCl(aq)$	→	$NaCl(aq)$	+	$H_2O(l)$		

The common factor in all of the reactions shown in Table 15.2 is that a hydrogen atom of the acid has been replaced by a metal atom.

The role of water in creating acidity

'Hydrogen ions and also protons'

All acids produce hydrogen ions ($H^+(aq)$ or $H_3O^+(aq)$) when dissolved in water. Consider the common acid, hydrochloric acid. Hydrochloric acid is a solution of hydrogen chloride gas in water. When hydrogen chloride gas is added to water a reaction occurs and heat is given out:

$$HCl(g) + H_2O(l) \rightarrow H_3O^+(aq) + Cl^-(aq) \quad \text{(exothermic)}$$

more often written as:

$$HCl(g) + aq \rightarrow H^+(aq) + Cl^-(aq) \quad \text{(exothermic)}$$

The fact that heat is given out tells us that hydrogen chloride is not simply dissolving in water but is actually reacting with it! The product contains two ions that were not present in the reactants. The ion $H_3O^+(aq)$ is called the **hydroxonium ion** and is equivalent to $H^+(aq)$ which is called the hydrated **hydrogen ion.** This is the ion responsible for all **acidic** properties. Similar reactions occur when other **mineral acids** are added to water. (Mineral acids are the common acids of the laboratory, hydrochloric, nitric and sulphuric acids made from minerals found in rocks.) Try to construct the equation for the reaction of nitric acid, HNO_3, with water—remembering that H_3O^+ or $H^+(aq)$ must be one of the two products!

The properties of bases/alkalis

(i) The property common to all bases/alkalis is that they produce hydroxide ions ($OH^-(aq)$) when dissolved in water. Three examples illustrate this:

$$NaOH(s) + aq \rightarrow Na^+(aq) + OH^-(aq)$$

$$CaO(s) + H_2O(l) \rightarrow Ca^{2+}(aq) + 2OH^-(aq)$$

$$NH_3(g) + H_2O(l) \rightarrow NH_4^+(aq) + OH^-(aq)$$

In the first example the OH^- ion is present in the solid alkali and is *released* into the solution as the sodium hydroxide dissolves. In the second and third examples, the $OH^-(aq)$ ion is formed by *reaction* of the added compound with the water.

(ii) An alkali is a water-soluble base. So alkalis can be recognized by their effect on damp pH paper—they turn it any colour between blue–green (pH 8) and purple (pH 12–14). Using the indicator paper **damp** allows some of the alkali to dissolve in the water and the dyes in the paper respond more quickly.

(iii) A base which does not dissolve in water will not affect universal indicator paper. It will, however, neutralize an acid.

Whether **a solid substance** is a base is shown in the following test. Put a small amount of acid solution in a beaker. Add a few drops of a pH indicator; the indicator will turn red. Now, add **the substance** a little at a time to the acid. If the pH, as measured by the indicator,

rises—the indicator colour changes from red to green—then the substance being added is a base. The pH will eventually rise to 7 as the acid becomes completely neutralized.

In this reaction the base reacts with the acid forming a soluble salt and so a **solution** will be formed. Most salts are soluble in water, so most bases dissolve completely in acids.

Salts

The salts formed by neutralization of acids

Salts from the three mineral acids:

- hydrochloric acids produces chlorides;
- nitric acid produces nitrates;
- sulphuric acid produces sulphates (or hydrogensulphates if the acid is half neutralized).

The process of neutralization of an acid can be carried out in three different ways:

1. by bases or alkalis as explained above;
2. by reaction with a metal, e.g. magnesium;
3. by reaction with a carbonate or a hydrogencarbonate, e.g. $CaCO_3$ or $NaHCO_3$.

Salts produced by the neutralization of alkalis/bases

The commonest alkalis are

- sodium hydroxide, NaOH, which produces sodium salts;
- calcium hydroxide (slaked lime, $Ca(OH)_2$), which produces calcium salts;
- ammonia solution, $NH_3(aq)$ (ammonium hydroxide, NH_4OH), which produces ammonium salts.

Acid–base neutralization

The acid–base neutralization process

The acidity of acids and the alkalinity of alkalis are destroyed in the process of neutralization. This is seen by considering the reaction between hydrochloric acid and sodium hydroxide solution. Written simply this is

$$HCl(aq) + NaOH(aq) \rightarrow NaCl(aq) + H_2O(l)$$

However, because acids contain hydroxonium ions and alkalis contain hydroxide ions, the process can be written

$$\underset{\text{hydroxonium ion}}{H_3O^+(aq)} + Cl^-(aq) + Na^+(aq) + \underset{\text{hydroxide ion}}{OH^-(aq)} \rightarrow Na^+(aq) + Cl^-(aq) + \underset{\text{water}}{H_2O(l)}$$

or

$$\underset{\text{hydrogen ion}}{H^+(aq)} + Cl^-(aq) + Na^+(aq) + \underset{\text{hydroxide ion}}{OH^-(aq)} \rightarrow Na^+(aq) + Cl^-(aq) + \underset{\text{water}}{H_2O(l)}$$

By crossing out all the particles that **do not change in** the process, i.e. that are the same on both sides of the equation, we get the **nett** reaction:

$$H_3O^+(aq) + OH^-(aq) \rightarrow H_2O(l) + H_2O(l)$$

or

$$H^+(aq) + OH^-(aq) \rightarrow H_2O(l)$$

We discover that neutralization is simply the reaction of hydrogen ions (or hydroxonium ions) from acids with hydroxide ions from alkalis! The only new product is water, a *neutral* compound. The salt solution which also forms is a mixture of the ions from the acid and alkali which did not change in the process. (Ions which do not change during a chemical reaction, such as the $Cl^-(aq)$ and the $Na^+(aq)$ in the above example, are called **spectator ions.**)

Applications of neutralization

Most plants and animals, including humans, require near-neutral conditions for normal existence.

The everyday use of alkalis to correct excessive acidity is illustrated by the following.

- The use of antacids (commonly calcium carbonate, $CaCO_3$ or sodium hydrogencarbonate, $NaHCO_3$) to relieve excess stomach acidity, a common cause of indigestion:

  $$CaCO_3(s) + \underset{\text{stomach acid}}{2HCl(aq)} \rightarrow CaCl_2(aq) + H_2O(l)$$

- The use, by farmers of lime ($Ca(OH)_2$) or limestone ($CaCO_3$) to correct the pH of soil. Soil acidity is often caused by application of acidic fertilizers such as ammonium nitrate. Most plants require a pH of 6–8 for optimum growth; lime is applied when the pH drops below 6.
- Application of lime to lakes in Scandinavian countries helps to overcome the effects of acid rain.
- Ammonia solution—or any weak alkali—will neutralize a bee sting or a jellyfish sting.

The everyday use of acids is illustrated by the following:

- The 'lime scale' that forms on kettle elements can be dissolved by vinegar or by commercial products which contain formic, phosphoric or sulphamic acids.
- Cars and other manufactured articles made from steel are 'pickled' in dilute sulphuric or hydrochloric acid to remove rust before painting.
- Cake mixes contain tartaric acid or acid phosphates and sodium hydrogencarbonate which react on addition of water (remember that water makes the acid acidic!). The resulting chemical reaction produces carbon dioxide gas which helps the mixture to 'rise'.
- The acidity of colas, lemonade and wines is caused by acids.
- Vinegar/lemon juice will neutralize a wasp sting or a sea-urchin sting.

Strong and weak acids

It was shown earlier in this chapter that acids produce hydrogen ions (hydroxonium ions) when added to water. The difference between a strong acid and a weak acid lies in the **concentration of hydrogen ions** formed in this process.

Consider two solutions, one a solution of ethanoic acid (vinegar) and the other hydrochloric acid, both containing the **same number of moles of acid per cubic decimetre**, say $1\,mol\,dm^{-3}$. Measuring the pH of these two solutions, we find that hydrochloric acid has a pH of 0–1 whereas ethanoic acid solution (vinegar) has a pH of 2–3.

How is this difference explained?

- The pH of 0 for hydrochloric acid shows the *hydrogen ion* concentration of the hydrochloric acid to be $1\,mol\,dm^{-3}$, which is the same as the acid concentration.
- The *hydrogen ion* concentration of the ethanoic acid is about $0.01\,mol\,dm^{-3}$ (pH about 2 units greater) which is a *hundred times less* than the $1\,mol\,dm^{-3}$ concentration of ethanoic acid molecules.
- The reason for the difference in pH lies in the different reactions of the two types of acid with water.
- Hydrochloric acid ionizes *completely* in water producing a hydrogen ion concentration which is the same as its molar concentration. **Every hydrogen chloride molecule has reacted to form a hydrogen ion:**

  $$HCl(g) + H_2O(l) \rightarrow H_3O^+(aq) + Cl^-(aq)$$

- Ethanoic acid, in contrast, ionizes *incompletely* in water, producing a hydrogen ion concentration which is a hundred times lower than its molar concentration.

  $$CH_3CO_2H(l) + H_2O(l) \rightleftharpoons H_3O^+(aq) + CH_3CO_2^-(aq)$$

  The ethanoic acid solution, after reaction, contains 99 molecules of unreacted ethanoic acid for every one that has reacted. **Remember**, it is only the hydrogen ion concentration that is measured by the pH value, not the unreacted acid concentration.

Acids in the laboratory

The mineral acids

The usual laboratory acids are the **mineral acids**:

- hydrochloric acid;
- sulphuric acid;
- nitric acid.

These acids, **even in dilute solution**, are strong acids.

Of the three mineral acids, sulphuric acid is preferred as a laboratory acid because

- it is the cheapest;
- it gives off no irritating fumes even when concentrated;
- it has other useful properties than simply as an acid.

The properties of sulphuric acid

Reaction with water

The reaction is strongly exothermic. Because sulphuric acid is much denser than water the mixing must be done **correctly** to be done **safely**. Water added to the acid will float on the acid. Reaction between the acid and water will occur in the top layer which will boil vigorously. Sulphuric acid and water will spit out. Acid in the eyes or on the skin is harmful and corrosive.

'The safe way of mixing sulphuric acid and water'

The correct method of mixing is to add the denser acid to water. In sinking through the water, the acid mixes thoroughly and heat is spread throughout the mixture, which gets hot but does not boil.

$$H_2O(l) + H_2SO_4(l) \rightarrow H_3O^+(aq) + HSO_4^-(aq)$$

The product of the reaction is dilute or aqueous sulphuric acid, $H_2SO_4(aq)$.

As a dehydrating agent

Because of its reaction with water, sulphuric acid will extract water from

(a) hydrated salts, e.g. $CuSO_4.5H_2O(s)$; and
(b) compounds in which the elements of water are present, e.g. carbohydrates such as sugar and starch.

An example of (a) is the **dehydration** of copper(II) sulphate crystals, which are blue, with the acid. The product is white, anhydrous copper(II) sulphate and dilute sulphuric acid:

$$CuSO_4.5H_2O(s) + H_2SO_4(l) \rightarrow CuSO_4(s) + H_2SO_4(aq)$$

An example of (b) is the dehydration of sugar (sucrose) which produces carbon and dilute sulphuric acid.

$$C_{12}H_{22}O_{11}(s) + H_2SO_4(l) \rightarrow 12C(s) + H_2SO_4(aq)$$

In each example sulphuric acid reacts with water and itself becomes dilute sulphuric acid. The reactions are exothermic.

As a drying agent

Sulphuric acid can be used to dry moist gases, e.g. chlorine, oxygen and nitrogen, provided the gas does not react with the acid. E.g. ammonia cannot be dried this way.

As a typical acid

All the properties of typical acids apply to dilute sulphuric acid. It will:

- neutralize bases and alkalis;
- give hydrogen with reactive metals;
- give carbon dioxide with carbonates (with the exception of those which, like calcium carbonate, form an insoluble coating with the acid); and
- turn universal indicator red.

Hydrogen gas is usually prepared in the laboratory by the action of dilute sulphuric acid on zinc:

$$Zn(s) + H_2SO_4(aq) \rightarrow ZnSO_4(aq) + H_2(g)$$

Pure sulphuric acid, however, is **not acidic.** It does not have any of the properties of a typical acid. The reason for this unusual situation is the absence of **hydrated protons** in the pure acid. Addition of water produces hydrated protons (hydrated hydrogen ions), which have all the properties of acids. Thus:

$$H_2SO_4(l) + H_2O(l) \rightarrow H_3O^+(aq) + HSO_4^-(aq)$$

$$H_2SO_4(l) + \text{water} \rightarrow H^+(aq) + HSO_4^-(aq)$$

The same reaction occurs when concentrated sulphuric acid removes water from hydrated salts, sugars and gases. The reaction shown above explains why concentrated sulphuric acid is less corrosive to some metals than the dilute acid. Metals that will react with hydrated hydrogen ions (hydrated protons) will not always react with the concentrated acid, which contains none; for example, lead and steel can withstand attack by concentrated sulphuric acid.

Acids in the environment

Acid rain

Many gases that exist in the environment form acidic solutions when dissolved in water.

- **Carbon dioxide** dissolves in rain to produce a solution of pH about 5.5. This dilute solution is called carbonic acid (although there is no evidence for the existence of the *molecule*, formula H_2CO_3, usually considered to be carbonic acid).
  The reaction produces hydrogen ions:

  $$H_2O(l) + CO_2(g) \rightleftharpoons H^+(aq) + HCO_3^-(aq)$$

- **Sulphur dioxide**, produced naturally and as an industrial pollutant, dissolves in rain to form a solution known as sulphurous acid. Its presence in rain causes the pH to drop below 5.5 and become 'acid rain'. The reaction is

  $$H_2O(l) + SO_2(g) \rightarrow H^+(aq) + HSO_3^-(aq)$$

- **Nitrogen oxides**, usually a mixture of NO and NO_2, dissolve in rain to form a mixture of nitric and nitrous acids, e.g.

  $$H_2O(l) + 2NO_2(g) \rightarrow 2H^+(aq) + NO_3^-(aq) + NO_2^-(aq)$$

Practical methods of preparing salts in the laboratory

Salts are formed as products of neutralization of acids and bases. The methods of preparation of salts in laboratories or in industry, however, are not confined to neutralization reactions.

Table 15.3 Solubilities of salts and methods of preparation

Salts	Solubility	Method of preparation
Carbonates	All insoluble *except* sodium, potassium and ammonium	Precipitation if insoluble, e.g. $CaCO_3$ or $CuCO_3$
Sulphates	All soluble *except* barium, calcium and lead sulphates	Dilute sulphuric acid on metal, metal oxide or metal carbonate for soluble salts; precipitation for insoluble sulphates
Nitrates	All soluble	Dilute nitric acid on metal, metal oxide or metal carbonate
Chlorides	All soluble *except* silver and lead chlorides	Dilute hydrochloric acid on metal, metal oxide or metal carbonate; precipitation for insoluble chlorides

Methods of preparing salts in the laboratory

The method of preparation of any salt depends on the solubility in water of the substances used to make it and on the solubility of the salt itself (Table 15.3).

The methods of preparation can be divided into four classes:

- direct reaction between the elements, e.g. sodium chloride; called synthesis.
- precipitation method for insoluble salts;
- metal, metal oxide or metal carbonate with acids for all soluble salts;
- titration method for sodium and potassium salts.

Synthesis

Direct reaction has been illustrated elsewhere in the text (see Chapter 15, p. 207). The process is called **synthesis.** Compounds formed by this method include iron(III) chloride, sodium chloride and iron(II) sulphide:

sodium + chlorine → sodium chloride

iron + sulphur → iron(II) sulphide.

'All salts are *ionic* compounds and so have high melting and boiling points and can be electrolysed when molten or when dissolved in water'

'Try writing the ionic equations for these reactions.'

Precipitation reactions for making insoluble salts

This involves the mixing of two solutions. One solution should contain the chosen *metal* ions and the other the chosen *non-metallic* ions. The salt forms immediately on mixing and can be filtered off, washed with water and dried in a warm oven:

lead(II) nitrate + sodium chloride → lead(II) chloride + sodium nitrate

$$Pb(NO_3)_2(aq) + 2NaCl(aq) \rightarrow PbCl_2(s) + 2NaNO_3(aq)$$

silver nitrate + hydrochloric acid → silver chloride + nitric acid

$$AgNO_3(aq) + HCl(aq) \rightarrow AgCl(s) + HNO_3(aq)$$

barium chloride + sodium sulphate → barium sulphate + sodium chloride

$$BaCl_2(aq) + Na_2SO_4(aq) \rightarrow BaSO_4(s) + 2NaCl(aq)$$

Reactions between an acid and a metal, metal oxide or metal carbonate

These three types of reaction are very similar. They rely upon the fact that the three types of solid reactants are *not soluble in water*, but react with acid to form soluble salts and other products.

The method is almost identical for all three and so will be described as one method.

(1) The acid to be used is first chosen:
   - dilute sulphuric acid will form sulphates;
   - dilute nitric acid will form nitrates;
   - dilute hydrochloric acid will form chlorides.

(2) The metal-containing compound is then chosen:
   - **metals** will react with acid to produce **hydrogen gas** and the salt solution required;
   - **metal oxides** react with the acid with **no gas production** to form the salt solution required;
   - **metal carbonates** react with acids to give **carbon dioxide** and the salt solution required.

(3) A quantity of the acid is measured into a beaker. The powdered chosen solid is then added, a little at a time **until no more will react.** In the cases of the metal and the metal carbonate, this will be shown by no further fizzing of the mixture (Fig. 15.2).

(4) The acid has now been neutralized and excess solid has only water to dissolve in. **Since none of these solids dissolve in water,** the excess will remain as a **residue.** The mixture is **filtered.** The **filtrate** is a solution of the required salt (Fig. 15.3).

(5) The pure crystalline salt can be obtained from the solution by concentrating it until it becomes **saturated** with the salt. This is done by careful evaporation to drive off **most of the water,** but not all. The solution is saturated when a sample taken out and cooled

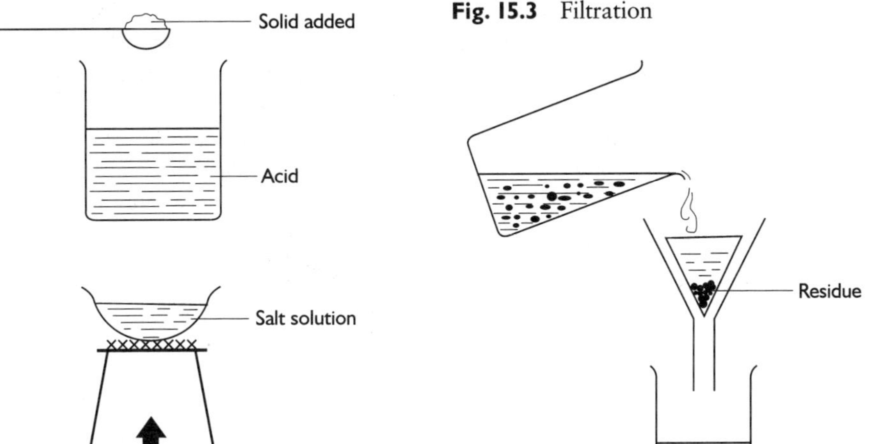

Fig. 15.2 Adding the solid in excess

Fig. 15.3 Filtration

Fig. 15.4 Evaporating to crystallization

gives crystals. When this occurs, the rest of the solution can be cooled and will deposit crystals (Fig. 15.4).

(6) The salt can be filtered from the mixture and the crystals on the filter paper **washed** with a little distilled water and finally dried with **tissue**. Pure crystals should not be wet!

'Dry with tissue'

Salts prepared in this way include hydrated copper(II) sulphate, hydrated magnesium sulphate and hydrated iron(II) sulphate.

Copper(II) sulphate crystals cannot be made by reacting the **metal** with acid because copper metal is not reactive enough to dissolve in dilute sulphuric acid. Instead the oxide or carbonate is used:

$$CuO(s) + H_2SO_4(aq) \rightarrow CuSO_4(aq) + H_2O(l)$$

copper(II) oxide + sulphuric acid → copper(II) sulphate + water

$$CuCO_3(s) + H_2SO_4(aq) \rightarrow CuSO_4(aq) + CO_2(g) + H_2O(l)$$

copper(II) carbonate + sulphuric acid → copper(II) sulphate + carbon dioxide + water

Magnesium salts can be prepared from magnesium metal, the oxide or the carbonate. All react with acids to give the salt and water as the only products left after filtration, e.g.

$$Mg(s) + H_2SO_4(aq) \rightarrow MgSO_4(aq) + H_2(g)$$

magnesium + sulphuric acid → magnesium sulphate + hydrogen

The equations for the reaction of the oxide and carbonate are similar to those for the copper compounds above.

Drying crystals of salts The drying process must be done at a **low temperature** and not by heating using a burner. This is because many salts contain **water of crystallization**, that is, they are **hydrated crystals**. If such crystals are heated to dryness they will **decompose** into the **anhydrous** salt, containing no water of crystallization, and **water vapour**. Usually, the hydrated salt is the required product.

If, for example, copper(II) sulphate crystals are dried by heating the following **dehydration** reaction occurs:

$$CuSO_4.5H_2O(s) \rightarrow CuSO_4(s) + 5H_2O(g)$$

hydrated copper(II) sulphate → copper(II) sulphate + steam

The result is a **white powder** instead of **blue crystals**. White **anhydrous copper sulphate** is formed.

Drying is quite easily done by soaking up excess liquid from the crystals with tissue and leaving them in a warm place to dry.

A crystalline salt which does not have water of crystallization, such as sodium chloride, *can* be heated to dryness to obtain a product.

Titration method

All compounds of sodium and potassium are soluble in water. For this reason it is **not possible** to add one reagent in excess and to filter the excess off in order to obtain a solution of the required salt, as in method (iii).

To overcome this difficulty, exact quantities of the two reacting compounds are mixed by **titrating** one into the other using an **indicator** to show when the correct reacting amount has been added. These reactions are usually between an acid and an alkali: see Fig. 15.5.

acid + alkali → salt + water

For example,

hydrochloric acid + sodium hydroxide → sodium chloride + water

$HCl(aq) + NaOH(aq) \rightarrow NaCl(aq) + H_2O(l)$

The reaction can be followed by watching the colour of an indicator in the mixture. Acid is added, a little at a time from a burette to a flask containing a measured volume of alkali containing two drops of an acid–base indicator. When the colour of the indicator **just** changes, the titration is stopped. The correct volume of acid to neutralize the alkali has been found.

If the transition is now **repeated without the indicator** but using the volume of acid measured in the first titration, a salt solution will have been made **free from indicator.** Evaporation to crystallization will give pure crystals of the salt. The crystals can be separated and dried by the method described above which, for sodium chloride, can be by heating.

'this is a more advanced method than that using an indicator'

An alternative method for finding the end-point of an acid–alkali titration is to monitor the conductivity of the mixture in the flask. (Conductivity is measured by a pair of electrodes in circuit with a battery and an ammeter. As the concentration of ion between the electrodes changes, so does the current measured by the ammeter.)

- The alkali in the flask at the beginning of the titration will show a **high conductivity** due to the presence of a high concentration of **hydroxide ions.**
- On adding acid, hydroxide ions react with the added **hydrogen ions** from the acid, forming **non-conducting** water molecules. This lowers conductivity.
- The volume of acid added to obtain the **lowest conductivity** is the required **titre.** This shows that all the alkali has been neutralized. (The electrical conductivity reaches a *minimum* but not zero. This is because the neutral solution contains ions from the salt (which conduct) as well as the non-conducting water molecules.)
- On addition of an excess of acid just beyond the end-point, the conductivity will be seen to *rise*.

Fig. 15.5 Titration

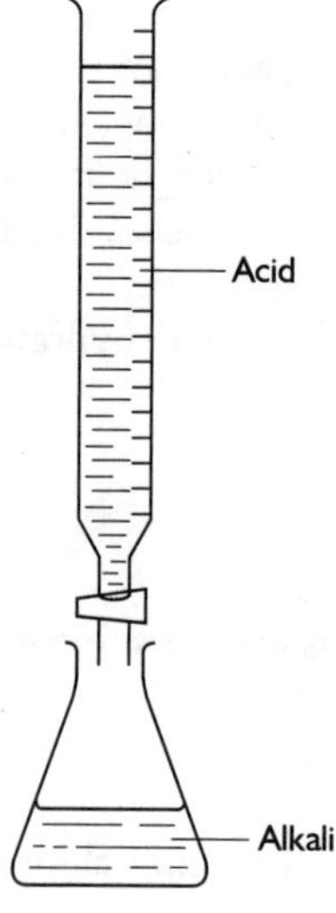

Titration as a method of finding the concentration of an acid or an alkali

The titration method used to prepare a salt can also be used to determine the unknown concentration of an acid or an alkali.

We shall take the results of a typical titration to show how this is done.

$25.00\,cm^3$ of a solution of sodium hydroxide of known concentration, $2\,mol\,dm^{-3}$, is placed in a $250\,cm^3$ conical flask. A burette is filled with hydrochloric acid of unknown concentration x moles dm^{-3}. Two drops of phenolphthalein indicator are added to the flask of alkali (see Fig. 15.5).

Suppose that $23.50\,cm^3$ of the acid is needed to change the colour of the indicator from pink to colourless. This volume of acid just neutralizes the alkali in the flask. The concentration of the acid may now be calculated.

The equation for the reaction is:

$NaOH(aq) + HCl(aq) \rightarrow NaCl(aq) + H_2O(l)$

1 mole **1 mole**

The equation tells us that equal numbers of moles of acid and alkali have reacted. Hence

moles of acid = moles of alkali

$$\left.\begin{array}{l} \text{Moles of alkali} = \dfrac{25.00 \times 2}{1000} \\ \text{Moles of acid} \;\; = \dfrac{23.50 \times x}{1000} \end{array}\right\} \text{These two must be equal}$$

$$\text{Therefore } \frac{25.00 \times 2}{1000} = \frac{23.50 \times x}{1000}$$

$$\text{Leading to } \frac{25.00 \times 2 \times 1000}{23.50 \times 1000} = x$$

$$\text{and } x = \frac{25.00 \times 2}{23.50} = 2.12\,\text{mol}\,\text{dm}^{-3}$$

The concentration of the hydrochloric acid is $2.12\,\text{mol}\,\text{dm}^{-3}$.

For another calculation see pp. 169–170.

Uses of salts

Many of the most useful substances are salts. A few examples are given in Table 15.4, others will be discussed as their chemistry is studied elsewhere in the text.

Table 15.4 Uses of salts

Salt	Use
Aluminium sulphate	To acidify soil for acid-loving plants
Ammonium salts	Fertilizers
Barium sulphate	'Barium meal' before a stomach X-ray
Calcium sulphate	Gypsum wall plaster: plaster of Paris for setting broken limbs
Iron(II) sulphate	'Iron tablets' for anaemia
Magnesium sulphate	A laxative in some 'health salts'
Silver chloride	Photographic film emulsion
Sodium carbonate	Water softener

EXAMINATION QUESTIONS

Question 1 (F)

The diagram (Fig. 15.6) shows a pH scale.

Fig. 15.6

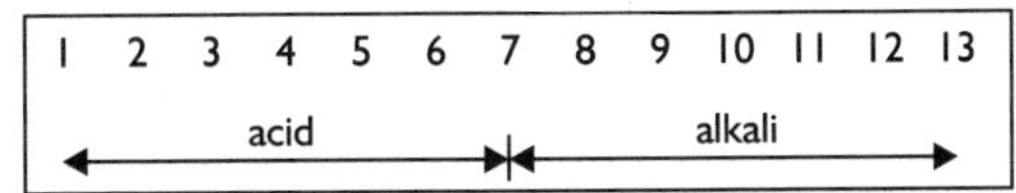

(a) (i) Which *one* of the following could be used to find the pH of a substance? *[1]*

litmus limewater starch universal indicator

(ii) What problem would you have finding the pH of strawberry jam using this? *[1]*

(b) The table (Table 15.5) shows the pH of solutions of five oxides, A, B, C, D and E. Complete the table by writing in the description of the pH. Two have been done for you. *[3]*

Table 15.5

Oxide	pH	Description
A	1	Strong acid
B	6	
C	7	
D	9	Weak alkali
E	13	

(c) The treatment for stings usually involves neutralization with a weak acid like lemon juice or a weak alkali like dilute ammonia. This stops the pain.
The information below (Fig. 15.7) was found in a holiday guide.

Fig. 15.7

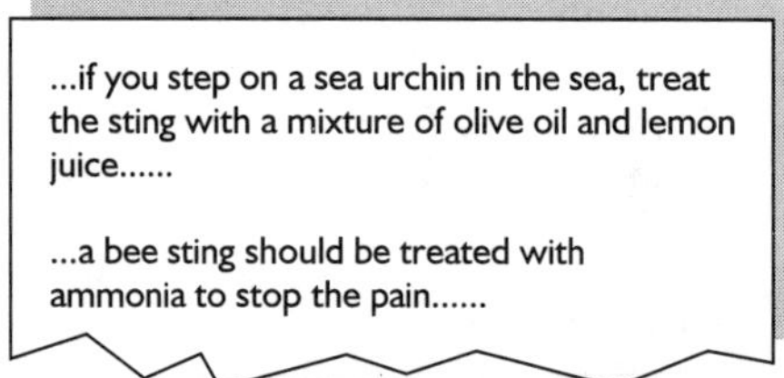

...if you step on a sea urchin in the sea, treat the sting with a mixture of olive oil and lemon juice......
...a bee sting should be treated with ammonia to stop the pain......

What does this information tell you about the pH of the stings of
- (i) sea urchins? *[1]*
- (ii) bees? *[1]*

[Total 7 marks]

Question 2(F)

The graph (Fig. 15.8) shows how the temperature changes when an alkali is added to exactly 20.0 cm^3 of acid. The acid and alkali used have the same concentrations in moles dm^{-3}.

Fig. 15.8

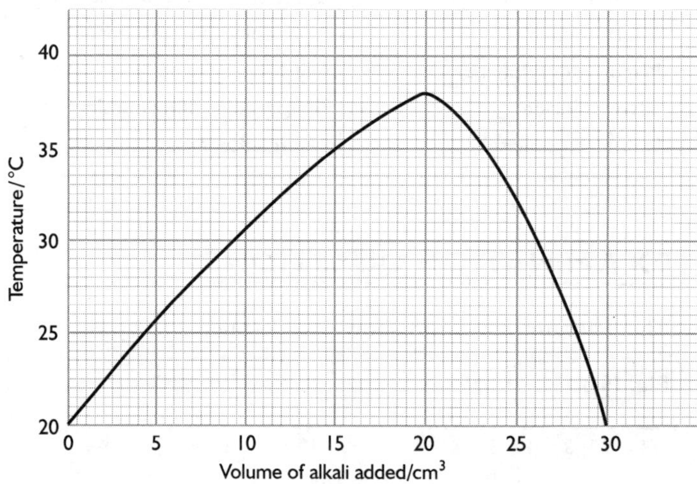

(a) Use the graph to help you answer the following questions.
- (i) What was the temperature of the acid at the beginning of the experiment? *[1]*
- (ii) How much alkali was added to just neutralize the acid? *[1]*

(b) (i) After 30 cm^3 of the alkali had been added, the solution was tested with universal indicator. Universal indicator is red in acidic solution, green in neutral solution and blue in alkaline solutions. What colour would you expect the indicator to turn? *[1]*
- (ii) Give a reason for your answer to (i). [2 lines] *[2]*

(c) If the experiment were done with a more concentrated alkali, what *two* differences would this make? [2 lines] *[2]*

[Total 7 marks]

Question 3(H)

The salt sodium hydrogen phosphate, (Na_2HPO_4) is used as a softening agent in processed cheese. The salt can be made by reacting phosphoric acid (H_3PO_4) with an alkali.

(a) Complete the name of an alkali that could react with phosphoric acid to make sodium hydrogen phosphate.

_______________________ hydroxide *[1]*

(b) What name is given to a reaction in which an acid reacts with an alkali to make a salt? *[1]*

(c) (i) What ions are present when any acid is dissolved in water? *[1]*

(ii) What ions are present when any alkali is dissolved in water? *[1]*

(iii) Write a chemical equation for the reaction that takes place between the ions named in (i) and (ii). *[1]*

Question 4(H)

A student experimented with aqueous ammonia ('ammonium hydroxide solution'), aqueous sodium hydroxide (both of concentration 1.0 mol dm^{-3}) and water. He measured the pH and the electrical conductivity. His results are shown in the table (Table 15.6).

Table 15.6

Substance	pH	Electrical conductivity
Aqueous ammonia	10.5	0.035
Aqueous sodium hydroxide	13	2.75
Water	7	0.001

'See p. 230'

Electrical conductivity is a measure of the ability of a liquid to conduct an electric current.

(a) (i) How might the student have found the pH values? [1 line] *[1]*

(ii) Suggest why both the pH and conductivity of the sodium hydroxide are higher than for the aqueous ammonia although they are of the same concentration. [2 lines] *[2]*

(b) Calculate the volume, in cm^3:

(i) of hydrochloric acid, concentration 1.0 mol dm^{-3} required to neutralize 50 cm^3 of sodium hydroxide, concentration 1.0 mol dm^{-3}. [3 lines] *[2]*

(ii) of sulphuric acid, concentration 0.5 mol dm^{-3} required to neutralize 50 cm^3 of aqueous ammonia, concentration 1.0 mol dm^3. [3 lines] *[2]*

[Total 7 marks]

Question 5(F)

Complete the table below (Table 15.7) which describes the preparation of some salts. *[6]*

(SEG)

Table 15.7

Reactants				Products		
magnesium oxide	+		→	magnesium sulphate	+	
	+		→	zinc chloride	+	hydrogen
	+	sodium sulphate	→	lead sulphate	+	

Question 6(H)

This question is about acids and their reactions.

(a) When a dilute acid reacts with a metal a gas is produced. What is the name of this gas? *[1]*

Name of gas _______________________

(b) Put names in the boxes below to form a word equation describing one reaction between a dilute acid and a metal. *[1]*

Fig. 15.9

Sodium hydroxide solution reacts with dilute sulphuric acid.

(c) What type of substance is sodium hydroxide? [1 line] *[1]*
(d) What is this sort of reaction called? [1 line] *[1]*
(e) Write a word equation for this reaction. [1 line] *[2]*
(f) Write a symbol equation for this reaction. [1 line] *[2]*
(g) Describe how you would use this reaction in the laboratory to prepare a dry crystalline sample of the salt formed. Include all of the stages necessary to obtain the final product. [8 lines] *[5]*
(h) Vinegar is a mixture of ethanoic (acetic) acid and water. Vinegar is sometimes made from wine. What is it in the wine which is changed into ethanoic acid to make the vinegar? [1 line] *[1]*

'p. 168 gives the method'

(i) 'Heartburn' is a sensation caused by the presence of too much acid in the stomach. Name one substance often used to reduce the amount of acid and cure the heartburn. [1 line] *[1]*
(j) Aluminium nitrate is formed when aluminium hydroxide is dissolved in nitric acid. How much aluminium nitrate is produced when 7.8 g of aluminium hydroxide is completely dissolved in nitric acid?

$$Al(OH)_3 + 3HNO_3 \rightarrow Al(NO_3)_3 + 3H_2O$$ *[3]*

(Relative atomic masses: Al = 27, O = 16, N = 14, H = 1.)

Answer ______________________________ g.

[Total 18 marks]
(NICCEA)

Question 7(H) Cadmium (Cd) is an element in the same group of the periodic table as zinc. Cadmium carbonate is insoluble in water and reacts in the same way as zinc carbonate with dilute acids. Cadmium sulphate is soluble in water and crystallizes as a salt hydrate.

(i) Give the formulae of cadmium carbonate and cadmium sulphate. [1 line] *[1]*
(ii) Describe the preparation of a dry, crystalline sample of hydrated cadmium sulphate from cadmium carbonate. [8 lines] *[5]*

(WJEC)

Question 8(F) The four substances listed in the table below are all chemicals used in the home. The table shows the results expected for each substance in each of three simple tests.

Table 15.8

Substance	Add water then indicator	Action of gentle heat on sample	Action of acid on substance
Sodium carbonate	Alkaline	No reaction	Odourless gas
Sodium hydrogencarbonate	Alkaline	Gas evolved	Odourless gas
Citric acid	Acidic	No reaction	No reaction
Calcium chlorate(I)	Alkaline	No reaction	Gas with a strong smell

Devise an identification key which will show how this information could be used to identify as unknown solid as one of these substances. *[5 marks]*

OUTLINE ANSWERS

Question 1

(a) (i) Universal indicator *[1]*.
(ii) It is coloured and the colour would blend with the colour of the indicator giving a false reading *[1]*.

(b) B—weak acid (nearly neutral) *[1]*.
C—neutral *[1]*.
E—strong alkali (or base) *[1]*.

(c) (i) The sting is alkaline *[1]*.
(ii) The sting is acidic *[1]*.

Question 2

The graph (Fig. 15.8) shows how the temperature changes when an alkali is added, a little at a time, to 20.0 cm^3 of acid. The acid and alkali used have the same concentration in moles dm^{-3}.

(a) (i) 20 °C *[1]*.
(ii) 20 cm^3 *[1]*.

(b) (i) Blue *[1]*.
(ii) The solution is now alkaline *[1]* because, for equal concentrations of this acid and alkali, *equal volumes would neutralize each other*. There is more than 20 cm^3 of alkali added, therefore the alkali is in excess *[1]*.

(c) The maximum temperature would be reached at a lower volume of alkali *[1]*; the maximum temperature would have been higher *[1]* (same heat energy in a smaller total volume of solution).

Question 3

(a) Sodium (hydroxide) *[1]*.

(b) Neutralization *[1]*.

(c) (i) Hydrogen ions or hydroxonium ions or H^+ or H_3O^+ *[1]*.
(ii) Hydroxyl ions or hydroxide ions or OH^- *[1]*.
(iii) $H^+ + OH^- \rightarrow H_2O$ *[1]* or $H_3O^+ + OH^- \rightarrow 2H_2O$ *[1]*.

Question 4

(a) (i) Using a pH meter or universal indicator *[1]*.
(ii) Sodium hydroxide is a strong base, ammonia is a weak base—sodium hydroxide is therefore fully dissociated into ions but ammonia is only partly dissociated *[1]*. There are more ions in the sodium hydroxide solution to conduct the current *[1]*.

(b) (i) The acid and alkali react in the molar ratio 1:1 *[1]*
or

$$HCl + NaOH \rightarrow NaCl + H_2O \quad [1]$$

Therefore for equal concentrations *equal volumes* will be required—50 cm^3 of hydrochloric acid *[1]*
or

$$x\,cm^3 \times 1\,M = 50\,cm^3 \times 1, \text{ so } x = 50\,cm^3 \quad [1]$$

(ii) The reaction of sulphuric acid with ammonia is different,

$$H_2SO_4 + 2NH_4OH \rightarrow (NH_4)_2SO_4 + 2H_2O(1)$$

or acid and alkali react in the ratio of 1:2 *[1]*.

However, since the number of moles of ammonia for neutralization is *twice* the number of moles of sulphuric acid, neutralization is obtained with half the volume of acid if the concentrations are the same *or* with the same volume if the acid is half the alkali concentration—*which it is*. So the volume of sulphuric acid is 50 cm^3 *[1]*.
Or

$$x\,cm^3 \times 0.5 \times 2 = 50\,cm^3 \times 1, \; x\,cm^3 = \frac{50 \times 1}{0.5 \times 2} = 50\,cm^3 \quad [1]$$

Question 5 Salt preparations are discussed on p. 227 and summarized in Table 15.3. This question can be answered from the information in these references.

Question 6

(a) The gas is **hydrogen**. Hydrogen is produced by the reaction of **any metal which is higher in the reactivity series than hydrogen** with dilute sulphuric or hydrochloric acids.
(b) Any metal more reactive than copper will do. Do not choose dilute nitric acid, it does not produce hydrogen with metals.
(c) Sodium hydroxide is a **strong alkali.**
(d) Neutralization occurs.
(e) Sodium hydroxide + sulphuric acid → sodium sulphate + water.
(f) $H_2SO_4(aq) + 2NaOH(aq) \rightarrow Na_2SO_4(aq) + 2H_2O(l)$.

Note that **two moles** of sodium hydroxide neutralizes **one** mole of **sulphuric acid. This is because each molecule of sulphuric acid has two hydrogen atoms capable of becoming hydrogen ions.** Each of these hydrogen ions will react with **one** hydroxide ion from sodium hydroxide—hence two moles of sodium hydroxide are needed for every mole of sulphuric acid.

(g) The method is exactly as described on p. 230, but the acid and alkali chosen are as required by the question. There are five steps, for one mark each.
(h) Ethanoic acid is formed when ethanol is oxidized by bacterial action. It is oxygen from the air and enzymes from the bacteria that cause the oxidation or 'souring' of wine.
(i) 'Heartburn' or 'acid indigestion' may be cured by neutralizing excess acid in the stomach with a **weak alkali,** e.g. sodium hydrogencarbonate.
(j) The equation must be 'read' here. It shows that **one mole of aluminium hydroxide** reacts with **three moles of nitric acid** to form **one mole of aluminium nitrate** and **three moles of water.**

In this reaction all the aluminium hydroxide will dissolve because **all nitrates are soluble in water.**

The mass of aluminium nitrate depends on the mass of aluminium hydroxide dissolved. Remember to 'read' the equation. **The calculation concerns only the aluminium hydroxide and the aluminium nitrate formed from it.** One mole of aluminium hydroxide forms one mole of aluminium nitrate.

Formula mass of $Al(OH)_3$ is $27 + (16 + 1) + (16 + 1) + (16 + 1) = 78\,g$.

Formula mass of $Al(NO_3)_3$ is $27 + 3 \times (14 + 16 + 16 + 16) = 213\,g$.

So 78 g of aluminium hydroxide gives 213 g of aluminium nitrate. Therefore 7.8 g (exactly one-tenth of a mole—for ease of calculation!) will produce 21.3 g of aluminium nitrate.

There are two marks for the two formula mass calculations and one mark for the final answer.

What happens if you make a mistake? It is easy to make an arithmetical error in a calculation like the one above. An examiner does not give marks *only* for the correct answer. **If you carry through your mistakes but use the correct method of solving the problem you will gain credit for all correct steps other than the one you made your mistake in!** This could get you full marks minus one.

Question 7

(a) (i) Cadmium is a metal which is *not directly studied* for the examination. For this reason, candidates are *given* information about it which should *enable them* to answer the questions that follow.

The 'message' is that cadmium is **like zinc** in its chemistry. This should give the formulae of the two cadmium salts to a candidate who knows, or can work out, the formulae of the corresponding zinc salts. Zinc forms ions with **two positive charges.** The formulae of its compounds are similar to those of group two metals such as magnesium and calcium. The same will be true, therefore, of cadmium salts. **$CdCO_3$ and $CdSO_4$ are the salts in question.**

(ii) The salt preparation asked for here is of a **soluble salt from an insoluble compound.** The crystals must be dry and are in fact **hydrated,** so the drying method is important. The five marks will be for *five distinct steps*. The first step has been taken for you—the reactants have been chosen!

Question 8

There is more than one possible scheme to be suggested here. Remember that you are not being tested on your memory of having done this in the course! You should be able to work out a scheme for yourself using the information given.

One possible scheme is:

Three of the substances are alkaline, the fourth acidic. A test with damp indicator paper will immediately identify the 'odd-one-out'—the acid—which will turn the paper orange, showing it to be a weak acid. This is citric acid.

Gentle heating will produce a gas with one of the remaining three substances, but no gas with the other two. The substance which gives a gas on heating is sodium hydrogencarbonate (bicarbonate of soda).

'Chlorine is the strong smelling gas.'

Adding an acid produces a strong-smelling gas with one of the **remaining** two substances, but an odourless gas with the other. The substance producing the strong-smelling gas is calcium chlorate(I); the other solid must be sodium carbonate as it is the only solid not so far identified.

The question asks for a key. One way of arranging a key is to ask questions about the results of the tests to which the answer is yes or no.

We could do the three suggested tests and ask the questions:

(1)	Is the pH of the solution less than 7?	Yes—Citric acid No—Do the next test
(2)	Is a gas produced on heating?	Yes—Sodium hydrogencarbonate No—Do the next test
(3)	Is a strong-smelling gas formed on reaction with an acid?	Yes—Calcium chlorate(I) No—Sodium carbonate

Another way is to display the results in the form of a pyramid as shown in Fig. 15.10.

Fig. 15.10

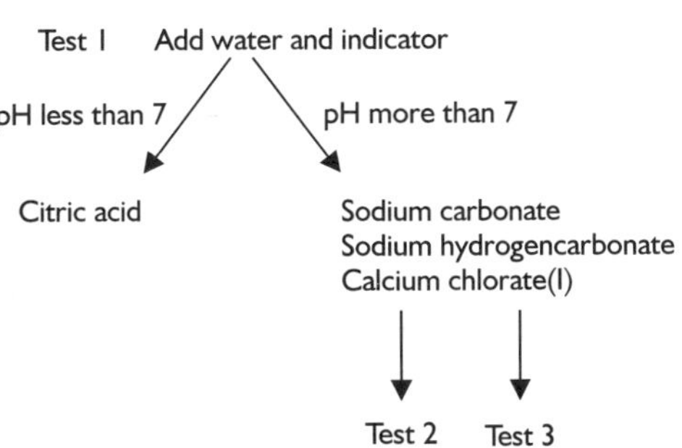

You should try to devise for yourself what test you would use as 2 and 3.

STUDENT ANSWER WITH EXAMINER'S COMMENTS

25.0 cm^3 of sodium hydroxide solution was neutralized by 37.5 cm^3 of 0.10 M hydrochloric acid.

(a) Write the symbol equation for the reaction.

$NaOH + HCl \rightarrow NaCl + H_2O$

'Good'

(1 mark)

(b) Calculate the molar concentration of the sodium hydroxide solution.

$25\,cm^3 \times M\ NaOH \equiv 37.5\,cm^3\ 0.10\,M\ HCl$

$x = \frac{37.5 \times 0.1}{25} = 0.15\,M$

'Good, units could be $mol\,dm^{-3}$'

(2 marks)

(c) Calculate the concentration of the sodium hydroxide solution in grams/litre using the relative atomic masses given in the Data Book.

$Na = 23 \quad O = 16 \quad H = 1$

$NaOH = 23 + 16 + 1 = 40.$

$0.15\,M = 0.15 \times 40\,g = 6.0\,g$ per litre.

'Good'

(2 marks)

(d) What would you use to find the end point of the titration and how would you know when the end point had been reached?

You would use indicator (phenolphthalin) in the titration flask. This changes to colourless when the end point is reached.

(2 marks)

(e) Describe how you would adapt the method to prepare pure crystals of the salt formed.

I would adopt this method as follows:-

Add the acid from the (burrete) to the sodium hydroxide in a flask. At the end point stop. Put the solution into an evaporating basin and evaporate nearly all the liquid away. Then set the basin on a window ledge to form crystals.

'Not quite an answer to the question. The word *adapt* means change. You did not understand it and missed the main point. If an *indicator* is used in the titration it will contaminate the salt crystals which you—*quite correctly*—prepare. You must repeat the titration with *no indicator*. Finally, you would have to remove the crystals and dry them to get them *pure*.'

(3 marks)

(Total 10 marks)

(NEAB)

'8/10–good'

SUMMARY

Use this list to help you with your revision. Tick off the points as you revise them in the text.

- ▷ The **pH** scale is a measure of acidity or alkalinity.
- ▷ **Acids** have pH values between **0 and 6.9**: **alkalis** have pH values between **7.1 and 14**.
- ▷ **Water must be present** for an acid to show acidity. Aqueous solutions of acids contain the hydroxonium (**$H_3O^+(aq)$**) or hydrated hydrogen ion (**$H^+(aq)$**): aqueous alkalis contain the hydroxide ion (**$OH^-(aq)$**).
- ▷ Acids and alkalis/bases **neutralize** each other, forming **salts**.
- ▷ Acids are useful in our daily lives: **vinegar** as a condiment and for putting on wasp stings; fruit juices; and acids for removing **lime scale**.
- ▷ Acidic gases in the atmosphere cause **acid rain—sulphur dioxide** and **nitrogen oxides**.
- ▷ **Salts** form when acids react with metals, metal oxides and carbonates. These reactions are used to make salts in the laboratory.
- ▷ Examples of salts of common acids are **chlorides**, **nitrates** and **sulphates**.
- ▷ All **salts of the alkali metals** and ammonia are **soluble** in water.
- ▷ **All nitrates** are **soluble** in water.
- ▷ Examples of salts of common alkalis are **sodium**, **calcium and ammonium** salts.
- ▷ Acid–base **neutralization** occurs by reaction of hydrogen ions (hydroxonium ions) with hydroxide ions by the equation

  $$H_3O^+(aq) + OH^-(aq) \rightarrow H_2O(l) + H_2O(l)$$

  or

  $$H^+(aq) + OH^-(aq) \rightarrow H_2O(l)$$

- ▷ The concentration of an aqueous acid or an aqueous alkali can be determined by **titration** of one against a solution of known concentration of the other using an **indicator** to find the **end-point**.
- ▷ The difference between strong acids and weak acids lies in their different **degrees of reaction with water** (called **dissociation**).
- ▷ The weak acid ethanoic acid reacts to the extent of only 1% with water.
- ▷ Sulphuric acid is the most common laboratory acid. It is made from concentrated sulphuric acid by adding the **acid to water** slowly—**much heat** is given out so great care and eye protection are vital!
- ▷ **Concentrated sulphuric** acid is a powerful **dehydrating agent** and will cause blisters on the skin. It will **dehydrate sugar** to pure **carbon**.
- ▷ Many salts are useful in our daily lives: **sodium chloride** is common salt used as a flavouring and to de-ice roads; **ammonium nitrate** and **potassium chloride** are fertilizers.

Chapter

16 Aqueous chemistry

GETTING STARTED

Water is the most abundant substance on the surface of our planet. It is essential for all forms of life. You may be familiar with the **water cycle**. The heat of the sun causes water to evaporate from the oceans, rivers and lakes. The water vapour forms clouds. The clouds cool and rise higher into the atmosphere and produce rain to feed the rivers, which in turn feed the oceans and lakes.

Water is vital to our everyday needs, just think what life would be like without water. You may have experienced a drought in your area.

Water is one of the most important raw materials in industry.

Water is sometimes known as the 'universal solvent' because it has the property of dissolving many chemicals. It is the main solvent in the home and school laboratories.

When certain chemicals dissolve in water it causes the water to become 'hard'. Hard water causes many problems that are costly to put right.

TOPIC CHART

LONDON	MEG	NEAB	SEG	NICCEA	WJEC	TOPIC	STUDY	REVISION 1	REVISION 2
✓	✓	✓	✓	✓	✓	The importance of water			
	✓	✓		✓	✓	Pure water			
✓	✓	✓		✓	✓	Drinking water			
	✓			✓		Reactions of water			
✓	✓	✓	✓	✓	✓	Hardness of water			
				✓		Stalactites and stalagmites			
✓	✓	✓		✓		Solubility			
✓	✓	✓		✓		Solubility curves			
✓	✓	✓	✓	✓	✓	Solubility of salts			
✓	✓					Tests for ions			
✓	✓					Analysis of ions			
	✓					Extraction of chemicals from the sea			

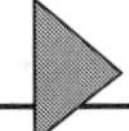

WHAT YOU NEED TO KNOW

The importance of water

Water, together with sodium chloride, calcium carbonate, coal, oil and air, is one of the most important basic raw materials and has many uses including the manufacture of sulphuric acid, the use of its solvent properties and its use as a coolant

About 80% of the world's surface is covered with water. It is therefore no surprise to find that water is the most common compound. It is present in almost all forms of living things. About 70% of you is water!

Water is a covalent molecule (Fig. 16.1). It is a liquid at room temperature because there are bonds holding water molecules to other water molecules; these bonds are called **hydrogen bonds**.

Fig. 16.1

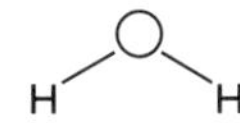

Water as a solvent

Water is often said to be the universal solvent. This is not true, of course, but many substances do dissolve in it.

(i) Oxygen dissolves in water. Without dissolved oxygen aquatic plants and animals could not survive. Gases dissolve less well in hot water than in cold water. For this reason aquatic animals have difficulty obtaining their oxygen supplies if the water is warm. Power stations emit warm water to rivers. Aquatic life disappears from the river section where the temperature is high enough to reduce the available oxygen. Fish will sometimes die in a garden pond that has become overheated in summer for the same reason.

(ii) Carbon dioxide dissolved in aqueous solutions of sugar and flavouring makes a refreshing drink—lemonade or cola; these drinks become flat if warmed.

(iii) Ionic solids, such as salts, dissolve well in water. The sea is a solution of many ionic compounds. The main compounds present are sodium chloride, magnesium and potassium sulphates with small amounts of compounds of calcium, bromine and carbon (as carbonate). The oceans contain about 3.5% dissolved solids. Some inland seas, like the Dead Sea, contain more.

(iv) Limestone or chalk dissolved in rain water produces the hard water characteristic of areas where such rocks underlie the surface.

Pure water

Distillation of water leaves all dissolved compounds behind and produces pure water. Pure water freezes at 0 °C and boils at 100 °C. These tests are used to show that a colourless liquid is pure water. The presence of water can be shown by adding:

- anhydrous copper(II) sulphate solid: colour change white to blue;
- anhydrous cobalt chloride paper: colour change blue to pink.

Drinking water

Water must be **purified** in order to make it fit for drinking. The water is first filtered through sand filter beds. The layers of sand become finer towards the bottom of the beds. The filtering process removes organic and inorganic debris. The water leaving the filter beds is relatively clear but it still contains fine particles. These are removed by adding potassium aluminium sulphate (potash alum) which causes the fine particles to settle. This process is called **sedimentation**. The clear water still contains harmful bacteria. Carefully controlled amounts of chlorine are added to kill the bacteria. Ozone is sometimes used instead of chlorine. It leaves no smell or flavour in the water. Bacteria can also be killed by boiling water but this is uneconomical on a large scale.

Sometimes fluorine is added to water in the form of **fluorides** to help strengthen our teeth. Some people are opposed to this because they feel that *they* should decide on what they drink and not the water authority.

Reactions of water

- Reactive metals such as sodium and potassium react with cold water to form hydrogen and an alkali:

  sodium + water → hydrogen + sodium hydroxide

  $2Na(s) + 2H_2O(l) \rightarrow H_2(g) + 2NaOH(aq)$

- Less reactive metals such as magnesium react with steam to form hydrogen and an oxide:

  magnesium + steam → hydrogen + magnesium oxide

  $Mg(s) + H_2O(g) \rightarrow H_2(g) + MgO(s)$

- Some compounds react with water to form acidic or alkaline solutions:

  ammonia + water → ammonium ions + hydroxyl ions

  $NH_3(g) + H_2O(l) \rightarrow NH_4^+(aq) + OH^-(aq)$

  This solution is alkaline because of the presence of $OH^-(aq)$.

  hydrogen chloride + water → hydrated hydrogen ions + chloride ions

  $HCl(g) + H_2O(l) \rightarrow H_3O^+(aq) + Cl^-(aq)$

  This solution is acidic because of the presence of $H_3O^+(aq)$.

- Some chemicals, such as sodium hydroxide solid, absorb water from the air and form a solution of sodium hydroxide.

Hardness of water

Rain water is a very weak solution of carbonic acid. It has a pH of 5 or 6:

water + carbon dioxide ⇌ carbonic acid

$H_2O + CO_2 \rightleftharpoons H_2CO_3$

When rain water falls on areas of the Earth that contain calcium carbonate or magnesium carbonate, a reaction occurs and the rock dissolves. This reaction produces calcium hydrogencarbonate or magnesium hydrogencarbonate. Both these compounds are very slightly soluble in water:

carbonic acid + calcium carbonate → calcium hydrogencarbonate

$H_2CO_3(aq) + CaCO_3(s) \rightarrow Ca(HCO_3)_2(aq)$,

carbonic acid + magnesium carbonate → magnesium hydrogencarbonate

$H_2CO_3(aq) + MgCO_3(s) \rightarrow Mg(HCO_3)_2(aq)$.

Other compounds present in the Earth also dissolve in water. These compounds prevent water from forming a lather easily with soap. The water is said to be **hard**. There are two types of hardness: **permanent hardness** and **temporary hardness.**

Hardness in water is caused by the presence of calcium ions and magnesium ions. Compounds present in hard water containing these ions are calcium hydrogencarbonate, magnesium hydrogencarbonate, magnesium sulphate, magnesium chloride, calcium sulphate and calcium chloride.

When calcium hydrogencarbonate and magnesium hydrogencarbonate are heated, they decompose and form insoluble carbonates. The calcium ions and magnesium ions are removed from the water. Since the ions are removed by heating water, they are said to cause temporary hardness:

calcium hydrogencarbonate → calcium carbonate + water + carbon dioxide

$Ca(HCO_3)_2(aq) \rightarrow CaCO_3(s) + H_2O(l) + CO_2(g)$

magnesium hydrogencarbonate → magnesium carbonate + water + carbon dioxide

$Mg(HCO_3)_2(aq) \rightarrow MgCO_3(s) + H_2O(l) + CO_2(g)$

The precipitation of calcium carbonate and magnesium carbonate causes **furring** in kettles and **scaling** in boilers. This fur can be removed using a weak acid such as ethanoic acid, citric acid, sulphamic acid or phosphoric acid. A strong acid would react with the metal kettle or boiler.

The other compounds that cause hardness in water, such as calcium sulphate, are not deposited by heating the water. They are said to cause *permanent* hardness.

The calcium ions and magnesium ions can be removed by:

(i) **Distillation.** The compounds are left behind in the distillation flask. Water formed by this process is very pure and is known as **distilled water.**

(ii) **Ion exchange water softening resins.** These are used in industry and are also found in dishwashers. The process is described by the equation which applies equally to magnesium ions.

$$Ca^{2+}(aq) + \begin{matrix}\text{sodium-form of}\\ \text{ion-exchange resin}\end{matrix} \rightleftharpoons 2Na^{+}(aq) + \begin{matrix}\text{calcium-form of}\\ \text{ion-exchange resin}\end{matrix}$$

When the ion-exchange resin no longer has any sodium ions to exchange for calcium ions it must be recharged: this is a reversal of the above process. Sodium chloride solution is run through the spent resin and the reaction shown above reverses. The calcium ions are flushed away in solution.

Water formed in these processes is called **soft water.** Soft water easily forms a lather with soap.

(iii) **Sodium carbonate.** Water can also be softened by adding sodium carbonate (washing soda). This precipitates calcium ions and magnesium ions as insoluble carbonates:

calcium chloride + sodium carbonate → calcium carbonate + sodium chloride

$$CaCl_2(aq) + Na_2CO_3(aq) \rightarrow CaCO_3(s) + 2NaCl(aq)$$

magnesium sulphate + sodium carbonate → magnesium carbonate + sodium sulphate

$$MgSO_4(aq) + Na_2CO_3(aq) \rightarrow MgCO_3(s) + Na_2SO_4(aq)$$

The advantages of hard water

Hard water is healthier to drink (it is thought to prevent heart attacks) and hardness gives water a pleasant taste. It provides calcium compounds that help the development of strong teeth and bones.

The disadvantages of hard water

(i) When it is heated it deposits calcium carbonate in pipes, boilers and kettles. This makes them less efficient and they might become blocked.

(ii) When it is added to soap it forms a scum which floats on the surface of the water. Scum is a calcium or magnesium compound of the soap; e.g. calcium stearate or calcium oleate.

(iii) The above two factors adds to the cost of living in a hard-water area. More soap is required and the deposits of scale and fur means that more energy is required to heat up the system.

Comparison of temporary and permanent hardness in water

Some water supplies have temporary hardness, some permanent hardness and others a mixture of the two. To determine which type is present the following test investigation is carried out.

Titration with soap solution

Titration with soap solution is done to discover how much soap reacts with the calcium or magnesium ions in the water sample. The more soap used, the higher the concentration of the calcium and magnesium ions. An indication that all these ions have reacted is seen when the water plus soap sample, shaken for 10 *seconds*, supports a froth which lasts for 1 *minute.*

Procedure

(i) $10\,cm^3$ of each water sample is titrated with soap solution. The sample is shaken after each $0.5\,cm^3$ addition of soap. The volume of soap solution needed to create the required lather is recorded. The results are noted.

(ii) $100\,cm^3$ of each water sample is boiled for 20 minutes to remove temporary hardness.

(iii) 10 cm^3 of each 'boiled water sample' is titrated with soap solution and the results are again noted.

Results

Consider the set of results shown in Table 16.1.

Table 16.1

Sample number	Volume of soap solution in unboiled sample/cm^3	Volume of soap solution in boiled sample/cm^3	Temporary hardness as a fraction of total hardness
1	0.1	0.1	0
2	2.4	1.6	1/3
3	4.0	4.1	0

Interpretation of the results

- **Permanent hardness is unaffected by boiling the water.** Calcium sulphate is a cause of this.
- **Temporary hardness is removed by boiling.** Calcium hydrogencarbonate is a cause of this.

With these guidelines we can interpret the results to mean:

(i) Sample 1 has little *or no* hardness.
The 0.1 cm^3 is the smallest volume of soap solution that can be added. If may not have been needed. **This is probably distilled water.**

(ii) Sample 2 loses one third of its hardness on boiling. This sample is hard water with 1/3 temporary hardness and 2/3 permanent hardness.

(iii) Sample 3 loses no hardness on boiling and is the hardest sample tested. Its hardness is all permanent hardness. The difference of 0.1 cm^3 is experimental error.

Stalactites and stalagmites

When rain water passes slowly through the roof of a limestone cave, it reacts to form calcium hydrogencarbonate solution, in the same way that hardness in water is formed. The drops of calcium hydrogencarbonate cling to the roof of the cave in droplets. The water droplets lose water and carbon dioxide, leaving solid calcium carbonate. Over a period of thousands of years a large column is built. The columns hanging from the roof of the cave are known as **stalactites.** Some of the solution also lands on the floor of the cave, and columns grow upwards. These are called **stalagmites.** Sometimes the stalactites and stalagmites join together. The columns are often coloured because they contain **transition metal** compounds.

One way of remembering which is which is that stalactites have to hold on 'tight' so that they do not fall from the roof and stalagmites contains a 'g' for 'ground'.

Solubility

Gases

Many gases are soluble in water. As you might expect, the solubility of gases increases with increase in pressure. Carbonated water and fizzy drinks are made by dissolving carbon dioxide in water under high pressure. When you unscrew the cap of a fizzy drink, you release the pressure and bubbles of carbon dioxide escape. The increase in solubility of gases with pressure can cause serious damage to deep-sea divers. Gas dissolves in their blood and if the divers rise to the surface too quickly they will suffer from the 'bends'.

Unlike soluble solids, gases are less soluble in cold water than in hot water. You may have noticed that when you leave a glass of water in a heated room, small bubbles appear in the water. These are bubbles of dissolved air escaping from the water.

Dissolved oxygen is essential for aquatic life. Water normally contains about 10 parts per million by mass of dissolved oxygen. The amount dissolved varies with temperature and pressure. The higher the temperature, the smaller the amount of oxygen present. Thus we would expect there to be less oxygen dissolved in water in summer than in winter. Sometimes water gets polluted by industrial waste or sewage or even by hot water from cooling plants.

Under these conditions bacteria multiply and use up the oxygen faster than it can be replaced. Such water is said to have a high **biochemical oxygen demand** (BOD), causing aquatic life to die. This collapse of the natural cycle is known as eutrophication. There are very strict rules about the type and amount of waste that can be dumped into lakes and rivers.

Chlorine dissolves in water to form chlorine water. Chlorine water is used as a bleaching agent and for sterilizing. It is often added to swimming pools to kill off bacteria.

Solids

Most ionic compounds are soluble in water, whereas most covalent compounds are insoluble. Covalent compounds tend to dissolve in organic solvents such as ethanol.

A **solute** is a substance that dissolves in a **solvent** to make a **solution**.

A **solvent** is a liquid which can be used to dissolve substances. Water is the commonest solvent. Water is often referred to as the universal solvent because it dissolves almost everything, so much so that it is difficult to obtain pure.

A **solution** is a uniform mixture of two or more substances. A solution is a special type of mixture; it is impossible to see any difference between the different substances even using a microscope.

solute + solvent → solution

Solutes can be made to dissolve in solvents more quickly by

- heating the solvent;
- increasing the surface area of the solute;
- stirring the solvent;
- adding more solvent.

Table 16.2 gives examples of various solutes, solvents and solutions and their uses.

Table 16.2

Solute	Solvent	Solution	Use
Sodium chloride	Water	Brine	Preservative
Cellulose	Amyl ethanoate	Nail varnish	Painting nails
White plastic	1,1,1-Trichloroethane*	Tipp-Ex	Covering unwanted ink
Fragrances	Ethanol	Perfumes	Cosmetic
Shellac	Ethanol	Liquid polish	Preserving furniture
Rubber	Benzene*	Rubber solution	Mending tyres
Pigments	White spirit	Paint	Covering surfaces

*These substances are hazardous and must be treated with care.

The solvent properties of various liquids are used to remove stains. Thus, a dry cleaning solvent such as 1,1,1-trichloroethane is used to remove grease and oil stains.

A **saturated solution** is a solution that has dissolved as much of the **solute** as it can at a particular temperature. No more solute will dissolve unless the temperature is increased. Cooling a hot saturated solution gives crystals of the solute. An **aqueous solution** is a solution of a solute in water.

Solubility curves

The solubility of a solute in water (or any other solvent) is given in the number of grams of solute per 100 grams of water (or solvent) to form a saturated solution. The solubility of most solutes increases as the temperature increases, as can be seen from the figures in Table 16.3.

You will notice that sodium chloride is only slightly more soluble in hot water than in cold water. If these figures are plotted on a graph the curve obtained is called a solubility curve (Fig. 16.2). We can see that at 80 °C, 100 g of a saturated solution of potassium nitrate contains 170 g of potassium nitrate. At 20 °C, less potassium nitrate dissolves to form a saturated solution; only 30 g. If a hot saturated solution of potassium nitrate at 80 °C is

Table 16.3

Solute	Temperature:	Solubility/g per 100 g				
		10 °C	20 °C	40 °C	60 °C	80 °C
Hydrated copper sulphate		17	21	29	40	55
Potassium nitrate		21	30	44	110	170
Sodium chloride		35.8	36.0	36.6	37.3	38.4

Fig. 16.2

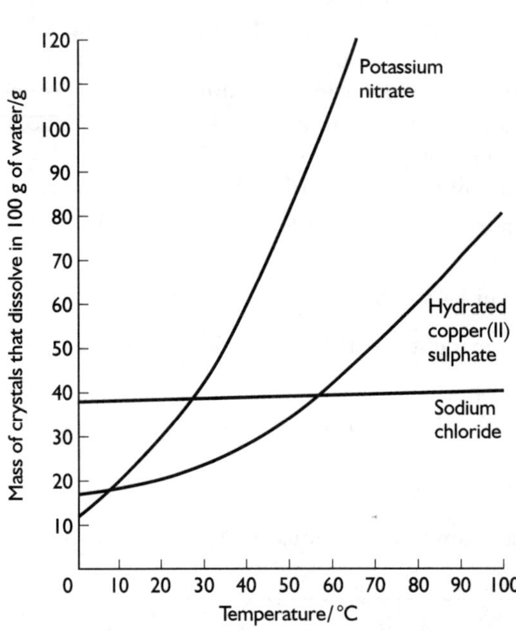

cooled to 20 °C, then 140 g (170 −30) of potassium nitrate solid will be deposited as crystals. This process is known as crystallization. The slower the cooling takes place, the larger the crystals.

Solubility of salts

The following general rules will help you to discover whether or not a salt is soluble in water.

- All **ammonium, sodium potassium and nitrate salts** are **SOLUBLE**.
- All **chlorides** are **SOLUBLE** except silver chloride and lead chloride.
- All **sulphates** are **SOLUBLE** except lead sulphate, barium sulphate and calcium sulphate.
- All **carbonates** are **INSOLUBLE** except ammonium carbonate, sodium carbonate and potassium carbonate.

The keys in Fig. 16.3 will help you to determine whether a salt is soluble or insoluble. Using these rules you can work out that

- potassium carbonate is **SOLUBLE**;
- lead sulphate is **INSOLUBLE**;
- magnesium chloride is **SOLUBLE**.

Also from this information you can write precipitation reactions. To form an insoluble salt, you must find two soluble salts that contain the appropriate **anion** and **cation**. To make the insoluble salt calcium sulphate you could react together calcium nitrate and sodium sulphate:

calcium nitrate + sodium sulphate → calcium sulphate + sodium nitrate

$$Ca(NO_3)_2(aq) + Na_2SO_4(aq) \rightarrow CaSO_4(s) + 2NaNO_3(aq)$$

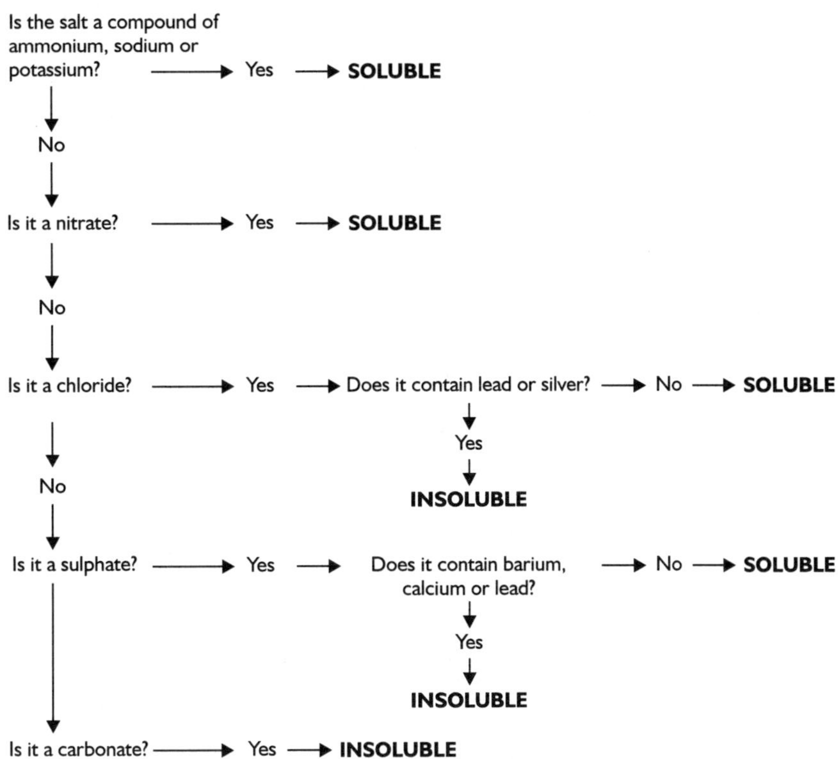

Fig. 16.3 Scheme to determine whether a salt is soluble or insoluble

When we say that salts are insoluble, they are in fact very sparingly soluble. If calcium sulphate solid was added to water and the mixture was shaken, it could be shown that the water contained small amounts of calcium sulphate.

Tests for ions

The insolubility of salts together with other tests can be used to identify ions in solution.

The simplest way to test for metal ions in solution is to divide the solution in two. To one portion add sodium hydroxide solution until it is present in excess. To the other sample add ammonia solution until it is present in excess.

Table 16.4

Metal ion		Observation with sodium hydroxide	Observation with ammonia solution
Aluminium	Al^{3+}	White precipitate soluble in excess to form colourless solution	White precipitate insoluble in excess
Calcium	Ca^{2+}	Faint precipitate insoluble in excess	No observable change
Copper	Cu^{2+}	Pale blue precipitate insoluble in excess	Pale blue precipitate soluble in excess to form blue solution
Iron(II)	Fe^{2+}	Dirty, blue-green precipitate insoluble in excess	Dirty, blue-green precipitate insoluble in excess
Iron(III)	Fe^{3+}	Brown precipitate insoluble in excess	Brown precipitate insoluble in excess
Lead	Pb^{2+}	White precipitate soluble in excess to form colourless solution	White precipitate insoluble in excess
Zinc	Zn^{2+}	White precipitate soluble in excess to form colourless solution	White precipitate soluble in excess to form colourless solution

Analysis of ions

Analysis of salts

All salts contain **cations** and **anions**. The following figures summarize the reactions of cations and anions found in the most common salts. Using the reagents shown and noting the results of the tests should allow the identification of the cation and anion in any simple salt.

First dissolve the unknown solid in water to make a solution. To identify the **cation** in the salt, use the scheme shown in Fig. 16.4. This scheme will identify the cations included in all **non-Nuffield** syllabuses. Some Nuffield syllabuses do not require cation analyses. However, study your own syllabus carefully before using this scheme and the one below. No one syllabus requires all these ions to be identified.

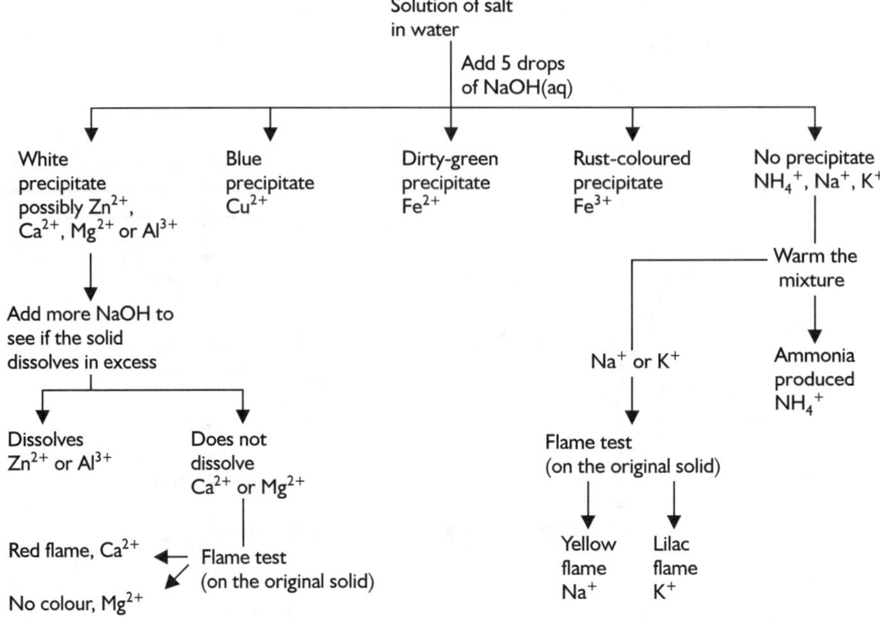

Fig. 16.4 Scheme to identify the *cation* in a salt

Flame tests

Very few metal ions produce flame colours. Those that do, however, can easily be identified. The **flame test** is usually done on the solid salt. Dip a new piece of **nichrome wire** into some **concentrated** hydrochloric acid. **Next dip the end of the wire into the solid to be tested.** This procedure produces a small amount of the **chloride of the metal** on the wire tip. This chloride will vaporize in the flame when the tip of the wire is put into it. If a coloured flame is seen, Table 16.5 below will help to identify the metal present. Flame tests are not used to identify non-metal ions.

Table 16.5

Metal ion	Flame colour
Sodium	Persistent yellow
Copper	Blue/green
Calcium	A 'flash' of red
Potassium	Faint purple/lilac

To identify the **anion** in the salt, use the scheme in Fig. 16.5.

Where **iodides** and **chlorides** are to be identified a better test is to make a solution of the salt and to add a solution of lead nitrate made acidic with dilute nitric acid. The chloride and iodide of lead are distinctly different. Lead chloride is a white precipitate and lead iodide a brilliant yellow precipitate:

$$Pb^{2+}(aq) + 2Cl^-(aq) \rightarrow PbCl_2(s)$$

lead ions + chloride ions → white precipitate of lead chloride.

$$Pb^{2+}(aq) + 2I^-(aq) \rightarrow PbI_2(s)$$

lead ions + iodide ions → yellow precipitate of lead iodide.

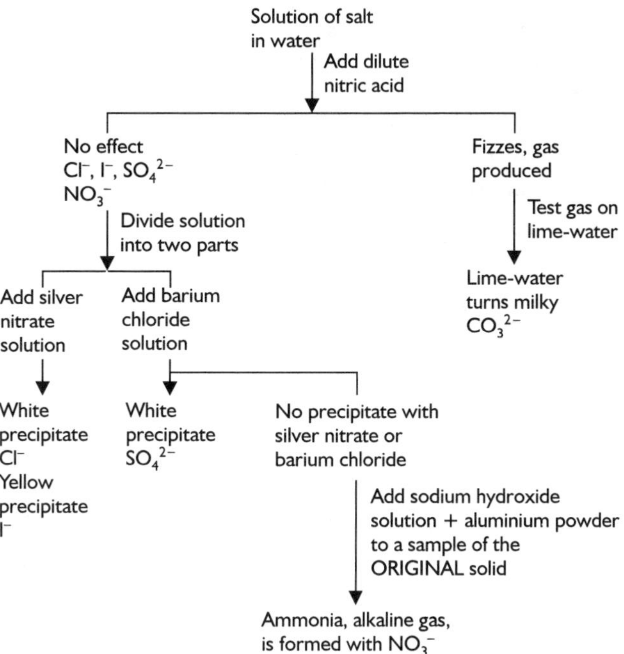

Fig. 16.5 Scheme to identify the *anion* in a salt

Extraction of chemicals from the sea

Sea salt

In very hot parts of the world, sea salt is obtained by trapping sea water in large shallow pools called salt pans. Heat from the sun evaporates the water leaving sea salt. Sea salt contains mainly sodium chloride, but it also contains other salts including magnesium chloride.

Bromine

Bromine is also extracted from sea water. Sea water contains a relatively high concentration of bromide ions. Sulphuric acid is added to sea water to lower the pH of the water to about 3.5. Chlorine is bubbled into the acidified solution to displace bromine:

chlorine + bromide ions → bromine + chloride ions

$$Cl_2(g) + 2Br^-(aq) \rightarrow Br_2(aq) + 2Cl^-(aq)$$

Bromine vapour is driven out of the sea water by blowing hot air through the mixture. The bromine vapour is condensed to a liquid. The process is relatively cheap because the raw materials—sea water, chlorine, sulphuric acid and air—are relatively cheap. In order to make the process more economic, extraction of bromine normally takes place near the manufacture of sulphuric acid (**Contact process**).

EXAMINATION QUESTIONS

Question 1 (F)

The information below (Table 16.6) was on a bottle of water. Some of the information had been removed.

Table 16.6

Ions present		Concentration/g l^{-1}
Calcium	Ca^{2+}	0.12
	Mg^{2+}	0.02
Potassium		0.01
Sodium	Na^+	0.01
Chloride	Cl^-	0.01
Hydrogencarbonate	HCO_3^-	0.27
Sulphate	SO_4^{2-}	0.04

(a) (i) Name the element that forms the ion Mg^{2+}.
(ii) What is the symbol for the potassium ion? [2]
(b) A sample of the water was evaporated to dryness and a white solid was left. When hydrochloric acid was added to the solid it gave off carbon dioxide. Name one substance that might have been formed. [1]
(c) How would you show that the water was hard water? What would be the result of your test? [2]
(d) Describe one method that could be used to soften the water. How does this method work? [3]
(e) Give one advantage and one disadvantage of hard water. [2]

Question 2(F) (a) (i) What is meant by the word '*aqueous*'?
(ii) What name is given to a solution that cannot dissolve any more solute at a given temperature? [2]

A student wanted to find the solubility of potassium chloride in water at room temperature (25 °C). The student weighed an evaporating dish empty and then with a solution of potassium chloride in water. (This solution could not dissolve any more potassium chloride.) The student carefully evaporated the solution to dryness. Once the evaporating dish was cold, it was weighed again, together with the solid residue.

(b) (i) How would you evaporate a solution slowly to dryness?
(ii) How would you show that the residue was dry? [3]
The following results were obtained in the student's experiment:

mass of dish empty	60.0 g
mass of dish + solution at 25 °C	94.0 g
mass of dish + potassium chloride	69.0 g

(c) (i) What mass of potassium chloride solution was used?
(ii) What mass of potassium chloride was left in the evaporating dish?
(iii) What mass of water was present in the potassium chloride solution?
(iv) What is the solubility of potassium chloride in water at 25 °C in g per 100 g of water? [4]
(d) Explain why the solubility of ammonium chloride cannot be found by this method. [2]

Question 3(F) Using chemical tests only, how would you distinguish between the following pairs of chemicals? In each case you must state the test you would carry out. You must give the result of the test for each substance.

(a) water and dilute hydrochloric acid
(b) water and ethanol
(c) sodium carbonate solution and sodium sulphate solution
(d) aluminium nitrate and zinc nitrate. [12]

Question 4(H) The solubility of copper sulphate crystals was investigated at various temperatures. The data obtained is shown in the table below (Table 16.7).

Table 16.7

Solubility (g per 100 g water)	14.4	20.8	28.6	40.1	55.2	75.6
Temperature (°C)	0	20	40	60	80	100

(a) Plot these results on graph paper. [4]
(b) Use the graph to find the solubility of copper(II) sulphate at 30 °C. [2]
(c) What mass of copper sulphate will crystallize from a saturated solution containing 50 g of water, if the solution is cooled from 100 °C to 30 °C? [2]
(d) A solution containing 100 g of water and 33 g of copper sulphate is kept at 50 °C. Is this solution saturated or not? Give reasons for your answer. [2]

Question 5(H)

(a) (i) How is filtration of reservoir water carried out? [1]
(ii) What is the purpose of this filtration? [1]

(b) (i) How may a sample of pure water be obtained from sea water? [1]
(ii) Explain the process of evaporation in terms of movement of molecules. [3]
(iii) Why does the salt in sea water not circulate through the atmosphere in the way the water does? [1]

(c) (i) Name one pollutant of river water other than an agricultural fertilizer. [1]
(ii) State the source of this pollutant and describe its effect. [2]

(d) (i) Why is chlorine added to water supplies? [1]
(ii) Tap water usually contains chloride ions rather than chlorine itself. Describe chemical tests that would show:
(I) that tap water does not contain chlorine,
(II) that tap water does contain chloride ions.
(In each case you should name the substances you would use and describe what you would observe.) [6]
(iii) Explain in terms of electron transfer what happens when chlorine is converted into chloride ions. [2]

Question 6

(a) From the reactivity series in Chapter 17 choose
(i) an element that can occur uncombined in the Earth's crust. [1]
(ii) an element that reacts vigorously with cold water. [1]

(b) A gas may be made by passing steam over heated zinc using the apparatus shown below (Fig. 16.6).

Fig. 16.6

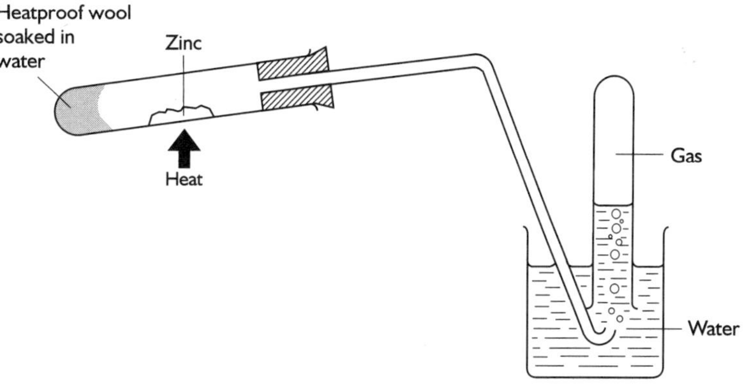

(i) Name the gas collected. [1]
(ii) Name the other product of the reaction. [1]
(iii) Write an equation for the reaction. [1]
(iv) Name one metal that should not be reacted with steam in this way. Explain your choice. [2]

OUTLINE ANSWERS

Question 1

(a) (i) Magnesium; (ii) K^+.
(b) Calcium carbonate or potassium carbonate or sodium carbonate.
(c) Shake it with soap solution; it would be difficult to form a lather.
(d) Add sodium carbonate; calcium ions remove as calcium carbonate; ions left do not cause hardness (other methods are described in this chapter).
(e) Advantages: provides calcium ions. Disadvantages: causes 'fur' in kettles.

Question 2

(a) (i) A solute dissolved in water; (ii) saturated.
(b) (i) gentle heating; (ii) reheat, cool and weigh again—no change in mass indicates that it was dry.

(c) (i) 34.0 g; (ii) 9.0 g; (iii) 25 g; (iv) 36 g.
(d) Ammonium chloride would dissociate into ammonia and hydrogen chloride and hence there would be no residue left in the evaporating basin.

Question 3

(a) Add pH paper; water pH 7 (green); dilute HCl about 1 (red).
(b) Add cobalt chloride paper; water will turn it from blue to pink; ethanol will have no effect.
(c) Add dilute acid (hydrochloric); sodium carbonate will give off carbon dioxide; sodium sulphate will give no reaction.
(d) Add dilute ammonia solution; aluminium nitrate will give a white precipitate insoluble in excess ammonia solution; zinc nitrate will give a white precipitate soluble in excess ammonia solution.

(There are other tests that are suitable—check them with your chemistry teacher.)

Question 4

(a) Your graph should look like the solubility curve for copper sulphate drawn in Fig. 16.2.
(b) Your answer should be in the region of 25.0 g.
(c) If 100 g used then 75.6 – 25.0 = 50.6; since 50 g used then 50.6/2 = 25.3 g.
(d) No; to be saturated it would have to contain 35 g (see your graph).

Question 5

(a) (i) Filter through filter beds made of sand.
(ii) To remove inorganic and organic debris.
(b) (i) Distillation.
(ii) Molecules in a liquid are in a continuous state of movement. Some of these molecules have sufficient energy to escape from the surface of the liquid and go into the air. This process is known as evaporation.
(iii) Salt (sodium chloride) is a high melting point solid and hence it is not volatile.
(c) (i) Phosphates from (ii) washing powders. They cause algae to grow in water, which eventually leads to a shortage of oxygen and then fishes die.
(d) (i) To sterilize or kill bacteria.
(ii) (I) Add pH paper; if paper is not bleached, then no chlorine is present.
(II) Add nitric acid and silver nitrate. A white precipitate (of silver chloride) shows that chloride ions are present.
(iii) Chlorine molecule gains two electrons and becomes two chloride ions:

$$Cl_2 + 2e^- \rightarrow 2Cl^-$$

Question 6

(a) (i) Gold or silver because of their lack of reactivity.
(ii) Sodium or potassium.
(b) (i) Hydrogen.
(ii) Zinc oxide.
(iii) zinc + steam → zinc oxide + hydrogen

$$Zn(s) + H_2O(g) \rightarrow ZnO(s) + H_2(g)$$

(iv) Sodium should not be reacted in this way. It is a very reactive metal and the reaction with steam would be explosive.

STUDENT ANSWER WITH EXAMINER'S COMMENTS

Hard water is water which has passed over rocks such as limestone. It contains certain dissolved substances.

(a) What is the chemical name for limestone?

calcium carbonate

(1 mark)

(b) Describe a simple experiment to show that a sample of hard water contains dissolved substances.

boil the water

'You should have answered "carefully to dryness".'

(1 mark)

(c) Table 1 compares the properties of sodium carbonate and sodium hydrogen-carbonate.

	Solubility in water	pH of aqueous solution
Sodium carbonate	Readily soluble	11
Sodium hydrogencarbonate	Not very soluble	8

Give one disadvantage of using bath salts containing

(i) sodium carbonate,

it is fairly alkaline (ph11)

'Good'

(1 mark)

(ii) sodium hydrogencarbonate

it takes away the natural oils.

'It tells you in the question that it is *not very soluble*.'

(1 mark)

Table 2 gives the volume of solution required to give a lasting lather with different samples of water.

Experiment	Volume of soap solution/cm^3
25 cm^3 distilled water	1.0
25 cm^3 of water sample A	7.0
25 cm^3 of water sample A which is boiled before adding soap solution.	4.0
25 cm^3 of water sample A after addition of bath salts.	1.0

(d) Name a piece of apparatus suitable for

(i) measuring out 25 cm^3 of distilled water, *measuring cylinder.*

'For accurate work you would use a pipette.'

(1 mark)

(ii) adding soap solution *burette*

'Correct'

(1 mark)

(iii) Give the name and formula of the dissolved substance that causes hardness in water.

calcium hydrogen carbonate

'The question also asks for the formula $Ca(HCO_3)_2$'

(1 mark)

(continued)

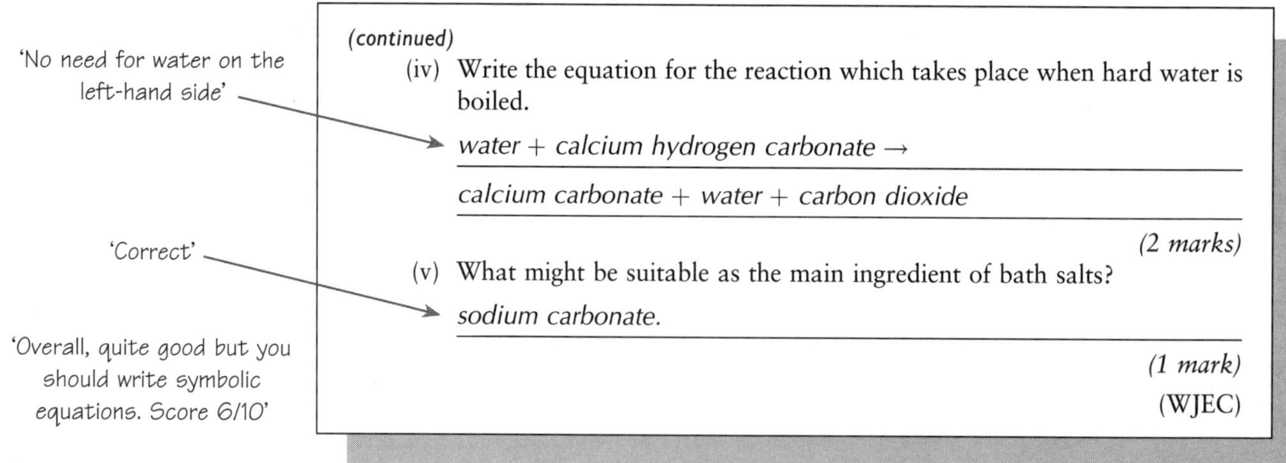

'No need for water on the left-hand side'
'Correct'
'Overall, quite good but you should write symbolic equations. Score 6/10'
(continued)
(iv) Write the equation for the reaction which takes place when hard water is boiled.
water + calcium hydrogen carbonate →
calcium carbonate + water + carbon dioxide
(2 marks)
(v) What might be suitable as the main ingredient of bath salts?
sodium carbonate.
(1 mark)
(WJEC)

SUMMARY

Use this list to help you with your revision. Tick off the points as you learn them.

- ▷ The test for pure water is that it freezes at 0 °C and boils at 100 °C.
- ▷ Water is an excellent solvent; ionic compounds tend to dissolve in water; covalent compounds tend not to dissolve (unless they react).
- ▷ The presence of water can be shown by adding:
  - ▷ anhydrous copper(II) sulphate solid: colour change white to blue;
  - ▷ anhydrous cobalt chloride paper: colour change blue to pink.
- ▷ Water must be purified before you can drink it safely.
- ▷ Temporary hardness can be removed by boiling; it is caused by calcium hydrogencarbonate and magnesium hydrogencarbonate.
- ▷ Permanent hardness cannot be removed by boiling; it is caused by calcium sulphate and magnesium sulphate.
- ▷ Hardness in water may be removed by:
  - ▷ distillation
  - ▷ ion exchange
  - ▷ adding sodium carbonate
- ▷ A **solute** is a substance that dissolves in a **solvent** to make a **solution**.
- ▷ A **solvent** is a liquid which can be used to dissolve substances.
- ▷ A **solution** is a uniform mixture of two or more substances.
- ▷ Solute + solvent → solution
- ▷ The solubility of solids increases with temperature.
- ▷ The solubility of gases decreases with temperature.
- ▷ A **saturated solution** is a solution that has dissolved as much of the **solute** as it can at a particular temperature.
- ▷ An **aqueous solution** is a solution of a solute in water.
- ▷ Important chemicals such as sodium chloride and bromine can be extracted from the sea

Chapter

17 Reactions of metals, non-metals and their compounds

GETTING STARTED

The essential chemical differences between a metal and a non-metal are that:

- a metal forms positive ions by losing electrons;
- a non-metal forms negative ions by gaining electrons.

Metals have the following general properties:

- their oxides are basic;
- their chlorides are ionic;
- they tend to be reducing agents;
- they react with acids to give hydrogen.

Some metals are more reactive than others and a reactivity series for metals can be produced. From reactions of an unknown metal you will be able to predict its position in the reactivity series.

The less reactive metals such as silver and gold occur in the free state as the pure metal. The reactive metals always occur as their compounds.

Iron is a very common metal but, unfortunately, it rusts in the presence of air and water. There are a number of ways of preventing rusting. Aluminium, on the other hand, is a very stable metal because it forms a stable oxide layer.

Non-metals have the following general properties:

- their oxides are acidic;
- their chlorides are covalent;
- they tend to be oxidizing agents;
- in general they do not react with acids.

Some non-metals are more reactive than others and a reactivity series for non-metals can be produced. Sulphur is an unreactive non-metal and sometimes is found in its free state as pure sulphur.

TOPIC CHART

LONDON	MEG	NEAB	SEG	NICCEA	WJEC	TOPIC	STUDY	REVISION 1	REVISION 2
✓	✓	✓	✓	✓	✓	Reactivity series of metals			
✓	✓	✓	✓	✓	✓	Corrosion of metals—rusting and anodizing			
✓	✓	✓	✓	✓	✓	Preparation and properties of some non-metals and their compounds			
✓	✓	✓	✓	✓	✓	Reactivity series of non-metals			
✓	✓	✓	✓	✓	✓	Tests to identify gases			
✓	✓	✓	✓	✓	✓	Uses of non-metals			
✓	✓	✓	✓	✓	✓	Uses of compounds			
			✓	✓	✓	Allotropy			

The properties of gases indicate to you how to collect the gases. If, for example, a gas is soluble in water you would *not* collect it over water.

Non-metals and non-metal oxides tend to be oxidizing agents, but note that hydrogen and carbon are reducing agents.

Nitrogen is unreactive because there is a triple covalent bond between the two nitrogen atoms. The noble gases are unreactive because they have a completed outer electron shell—they do not want to gain or lose electrons.

Carbon and sulphur both show allotropy.

WHAT YOU NEED TO KNOW

Reactivity series of metals

Anyone experimenting with metals soon notices that **they are not all equally reactive.** Some metals react extremely vigorously with other substances; others are quite difficult to 'persuade' to react.

The **reactivity series (reactivity table)** of metallic elements is a list or table in which the most reactive metal is placed at the top of the series and the least reactive metal is placed at the bottom. It is an **order of reactivity.**

The types of experimental results which need to be obtained in order to place metals in a reactivity order are discussed in the following pages.

Reaction with dilute acids to produce salts and hydrogen

Only metals **above copper** in the reactivity series react in this way:

$$Zn(s) + 2HCl(aq) \rightarrow ZnCl_2(aq) + H_2(g)$$

zinc + hydrochloric acid → zinc chloride + hydrogen

$$Fe(s) + 2HCl(aq) \rightarrow FeCl_2(aq) + H_2(g)$$

iron + hydrochloric acid → iron(II) chloride + hydrogen

Similar reactions occur with dilute sulphuric acid to produce metal sulphates and hydrogen.

- Dilute nitric acid does not react with metals in this way.
- Copper will not react with dilute acids in this way.

The usual method for producing hydrogen in the laboratory is by reacting zinc with dilute hydrochloric *or* dilute sulphuric acid.

Reaction with oxygen to form metal oxides

The most reactive metals burn, less reactive metals do not. Both types are oxidized, e.g.

$$2Mg(s) + O_2(g) \rightarrow 2MgO(s)$$

magnesium + oxygen → magnesium oxide

Only metals such as gold and platinum do not oxidize when heated in air.

Reaction with water to form hydrogen and a metal oxide or hydroxide

Where there is reaction, metals displace hydrogen and form hydroxides or oxides. (The results of a series of metals reacting with water are shown in Table 17.3.)

Cold water, e.g. sodium or calcium

$$2Na(s) + 2H_2O(l) \rightarrow 2NaOH(aq) + H_2(g)$$

sodium + water → sodium hydroxide + hydrogen

$$Ca(s) + 2H_2O(l) \rightarrow Ca(OH)_2(aq) + H_2(g)$$

calcium + water → calcium hydroxide + hydrogen

Fig. 17.1 The action of steam on metals

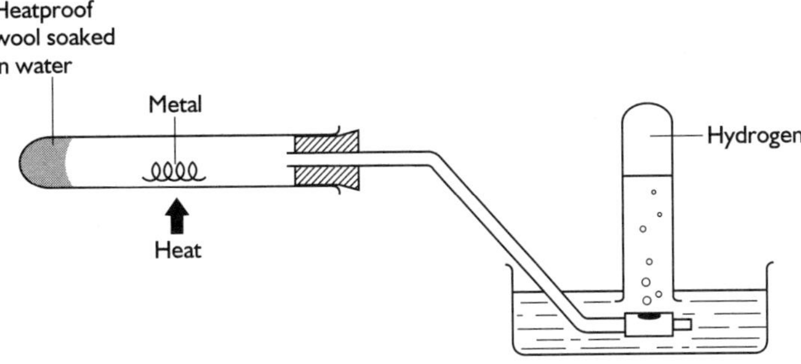

Steam, e.g. magnesium, zinc and iron (see Fig. 17.1)

$$Mg(s) + H_2O(g) \rightarrow MgO(s) + H_2(g)$$

magnesium + steam → magnesium oxide + hydrogen

Low down the reactivity series, at iron, the reaction with steam becomes reversible—an indication that metals less reactive than iron will not be reactive to steam:

iron + steam ⇌ iron(II)diiron(III) oxide + hydrogen

$$3Fe(s) + 4H_2O(g) \rightleftharpoons Fe_3O_4(s) + 4H_2(g)$$

There are three common oxides of iron: FeO, Fe_2O_3 and Fe_3O_4. They are named iron(II) oxide, iron(III) oxide and iron(II)diiron(III) oxide. The last one is commonly called 'smithy scales' because it is the oxide formed when red hot iron is cooled in water, a practice common when metalsmiths make articles by shaping hot metals. This oxide, if very thin, can act as a protective coating preventing corrosion of iron. Fishhooks are treated in this way to coat them with this protective oxide.

Reaction of metals with metal oxides

This type of reaction is an obvious 'competition' between two metal atoms for oxygen atoms. The more reactive metal atoms will remove the oxygen from the less reactive metal oxide. This results in a transfer of oxygen from the less reactive metal oxide to the more reactive metal. The rule is that the more reactive metal always takes the oxygen away from the less reactive metal oxide:

magnesium	+ copper(II) oxide	→	copper	+ magnesium oxide
$Mg(s)$	+ $CuO(s)$	→	$Cu(s)$	+ $MgO(s)$
more reactive metal	+ less reactive metal oxide	→	less reactive metal	+ more reactive metal oxide

Reaction of metals with metal salts (displacements)

Metal salts react in the same way as oxides with other metals. **Heating** a reactive metal with the solid or molten salt of a less reactive metal results in the formation of the less reactive metal and a salt of the more reactive metal, e.g.

iron	+ copper(II) bromide	→	copper	+ iron(II) bromide
$Fe(s)$	+ $CuBr_2(l)$	→	$Cu(s)$	+ $FeBr_2(s)$
more reactive metal	+ bromide of less reactive metal	→	less reactive metal	+ bromide of more reactive metal

However, because many metal salts are soluble in water, the reaction with a metal can be more easily carried out by mixing the metal with the salt **solution.** Usually no heat is needed. The products are also easily separated from each other by simple **filtration.** The technique may vary from dipping a piece of clean metal foil into a solution of a metal salt, to stirring a metal powder into the metal salt solution.

There is always an energy change in these 'displacement' reactions and stirring with a thermometer or feeling the bottom of the reaction vessel will show that the temperature has risen—the reactions are **exothermic.**

Testing the reactions of several metals with their salts

We would place a small piece of each metal into separate solutions of the salts of each of the metals. An easier way is to place some of each salt solution on a clock glass and insert thin slivers of each metal into the solution as shown in the diagram (Fig. 17.2). If a reaction has occurred, a deposit will appear on the metal. This means that the metal of the sliver has displaced the metal element in the salt from its solution. For example, a sliver of zinc, placed in a solution of copper(II) sulphate, will become coated with a brown deposit. The deposit is copper. Copper has been displaced from copper(II) sulphate by the more reactive zinc:

$Zn(s)$	+	$CuSO_4(aq)$	→	$Cu(s)$	+	$ZnSO_4(aq)$
zinc	+	copper(II) sulphate solution	→	copper	+	zinc sulphate solution
grey metal		blue solution		brown metal		colourless solution

Fig. 17.2

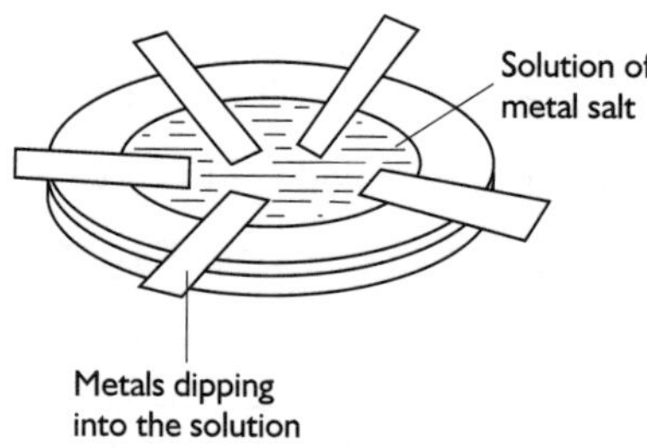

During the reaction the colour of the solution will change from blue to colourless if there is enough zinc to react with all the copper sulphate present.

It is found that the metals higher in the reactivity series displace the metals lower down from their salts (chlorides, nitrates, sulphates, etc.). The results of such a series of reactions would be as shown in Table 17.1.

Table 17.1

Metal	Salts of: Mg	Zn	Pb	Cu	Conclusion
Magnesium	×	✓	✓	✓	Mg most reactive—displaces 3 metals in this experiment
Zinc	×	×	✓	✓	
Lead	×	×	×	✓	
Copper	×	×	×	×	Copper least reactive—displaces no metals

× = no displacement, ✓ = displaced metal.

The stability of metal compounds to heat

Many metal compounds **decompose** on heating. The temperature at which the decomposition occurs depends on the reactivity of the metal in the compound.

The effect of heat on some metal compounds is summarized in Table 17.2.

There is a clear connection between the reactivity and products of decomposition. **Compounds** of the most reactive elements decompose less easily than similar compounds of the least reactive elements. Example reactions are:

- **Copper(II) hydroxide** and **copper(II) carbonate** decompose on heating:

$Cu(OH)_2(s)$	→	$CuO(s)$	+	$H_2O(g)$
copper(II) hydroxide	→	copper(II) oxide	+	water
$CuCO_3(s)$	→	$CuO(s)$	+	$CO_2(g)$
copper(II) carbonate	→	copper(II) oxide	+	carbon dioxide

- The **hydroxides** and **carbonates** of sodium will *not* decompose on heating.

Table 17.2

Metal	Hydroxide	Nitrate	Carbonate
Potassium, Sodium	None	Nitrite + oxygen	None
Calcium, Magnesium, Aluminium, Zinc, Lead, Copper	Form oxide and water	Form oxide and nitrogen dioxide and oxygen	Form oxide and carbon dioxide
Silver, Gold, Platinum	Form metal, oxygen and water	Form metal, oxygen and nitrogen dioxide	Form metal, oxygen and carbon dioxide

Reduction of metal oxides

By a more reactive metal

Removal of oxygen from metal oxides is the commonest method of obtaining the metal. The reduction of a metal oxide can be carried out by any metal **more reactive** than the metal contained in the oxide. For instance, sodium could be used to obtain iron from iron oxide ore. This process is not carried out in practice because:

(a) sodium is not available in sufficient quantities to produce all the iron required; and
(b) it would make the iron produced very expensive—more expensive than sodium.

The reduction of metal oxides by a more reactive metal is, however, used in industry. **Chromium oxides** and **manganese oxides** are reduced by aluminium to obtain the metals:

$$Cr_2O_3(s) + 2Al(s) \rightarrow 2Cr(s) + Al_2O_3(s)$$

chromium(III) oxide + aluminium → chromium + aluminium oxide

This is an example of the **thermit process** (Fig. 17.3) and you may have seen it demonstrated in a laboratory using iron(III) oxide and aluminium:

$$Fe_2O_3(s) + 2Al(s) \rightarrow 2Fe(s) + Al_2O_3(s)$$

iron(III) oxide + aluminium → iron + aluminium oxide

By including carbon and hydrogen in the reactivity series of metals, it is possible to see that these two non-metallic elements can reduce many metal oxides to metals.

Fig. 17.3 The thermit reaction

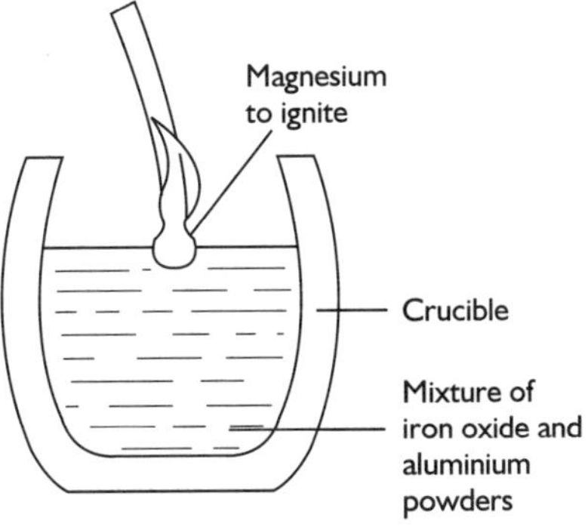

By hydrogen as a reducing agent

Hydrogen will reduce oxides of metals **lower than iron** in the reactivity series to the metal and water, e.g.

$$CuO(s) + H_2(g) \rightarrow Cu(s) + H_2O(l)$$

copper(II)oxide + hydrogen → copper + water

The metal oxide must be heated in a stream of hydrogen (Fig. 17.4).

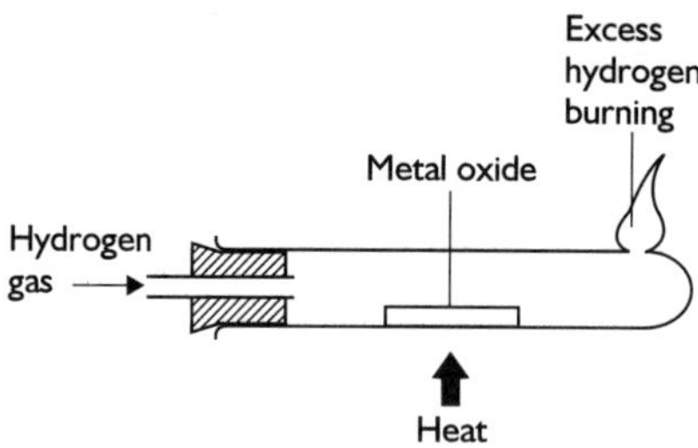

Fig. 17.4 Reduction of metal oxides

Aluminium and metals above it in the reactivity series cannot be formed by this type of reduction. Hydrogen will not reduce oxides of metals higher than iron. This fact places hydrogen between zinc and iron in the reactivity series.

By carbon as a reducing agent
Carbon will reduce oxides of metals **lower down in the reactivity series than aluminium** to the metal and carbon dioxide. Zinc and iron oxides, however, **just below aluminium,** need higher temperatures than can usually be obtained in a bunsen flame:

copper(II) oxide + carbon → carbon dioxide + copper

$$2CuO(s) + C(s) \rightarrow CO_2(g) + 2Cu(s)$$

lead(II) oxide + carbon → carbon dioxide + lead

$$2PbO(s) + C(s) \rightarrow CO_2(g) + 2Pb(l)$$

The oxides must be heated with powdered carbon. Lead forms as a liquid at the temperature of the reduction.

Table 17.3 also serves as a summary of the reactions of the metals.

Table 17.3 Reaction of the reactivity series metals

	Reaction of metals with:		
Metals	Water	Acids	Oxides and salts
Potassium Sodium Calcium	Rapid reaction with cold water giving hydrogen and a hydroxide	Violent reaction to form H_2 and the metal salt	Each metal will DISPLACE any of
Magnesium Aluminium Zinc	React with steam but not with cold water to give the oxide and hydrogen	React with decreasing vigour to form H_2 and the metal salt of the acid	the METALS below it in the TABLE from
Iron	Reversible reaction		their
Lead Copper Silver	**No reaction** with water or steam	**No reaction** with dilute acids to form hydrogen	OXIDES or from
Gold Platinum	**No reaction** with any substance except 'aqua regia'		their SALT SOLUTIONS

The reason why some metals are more reactive than others is their greater tendency to form **ions.** The most reactive metals, the alkali metals, have a greater tendency to form ions than less reactive metals. Gold and platinum, the least reactive of all metals, have hardly any tendency to form ions at all.

When metals are combined, the particles present in their compounds are ions. For metals, the process of combining is one of **formation of ions from atoms.**

Metal **atoms** form **ions** by loss of electrons. Metal **ions** form **atoms** by gain of electrons. Both of these types of process occur in a displacement reaction.

So, for the displacement of copper from any copper compound by magnesium we can write:

$$Cu^{2+} \quad + \quad Mg \quad \rightarrow \quad Mg^{2+} \quad + \quad Cu$$

copper ions + magnesium atoms → magnesium ions + copper atoms

$$\text{magnesium atoms} \xrightarrow{\text{oxidation}} \text{magnesium ions}$$

$$\text{copper ions} \xrightarrow{\text{reduction}} \text{copper atoms}$$

There are copper ions in solid copper oxide and in aqueous copper sulphate. Magnesium **reduces** these copper ions to atoms and magnesium atoms are themselves **oxidized** to magnesium ions.

The higher in the reactivity series, the greater the tendency of the atoms of a metal to give up electrons to form ions and the lower the tendency of those ions to accept electrons to form atoms. The atoms of elements lower in the series have little tendency to give up electrons to form ions but their ions have a greater tendency to accept electrons to form atoms (Table 17.4).

Table 17.4

Element	Atoms → ions	Ions → atoms
Potassium Sodium Lithium Calcium Magnesium Aluminium	Greatest tendency at the top of the series	Smallest tendency at the top of the series
CARBON Zinc Iron Tin Lead	↓	↓
HYDROGEN Copper Silver Gold Platinum	Smallest tendency at the bottom of the series	Greatest tendency at the bottom of the series

Corrosion of metals—rusting and anodizing

Metals corrode because they react with oxygen to give oxides. The most common example is the rusting of iron. Rusting is an oxidation process; the iron gains oxygen and loses electrons to form iron ions. However, water plays an important part in rusting.

To show the effects of oxygen and water on rusting
Set up the experiments shown in Fig. 17.5.

The nail in tube 1 which contains air but no water does NOT rust.
The nail in tube 2 which contains water but no air does NOT rust.
The nail in tube 3 which contains both air and water DOES rust.

Hence we can conclude that both air (oxygen) and water are necessary for rusting to take place.

Iron and steel rust readily in the presence of water and oxygen. The process is speeded up by the presence of acids in polluted air. Prevention takes several forms:

Fig. 17.5

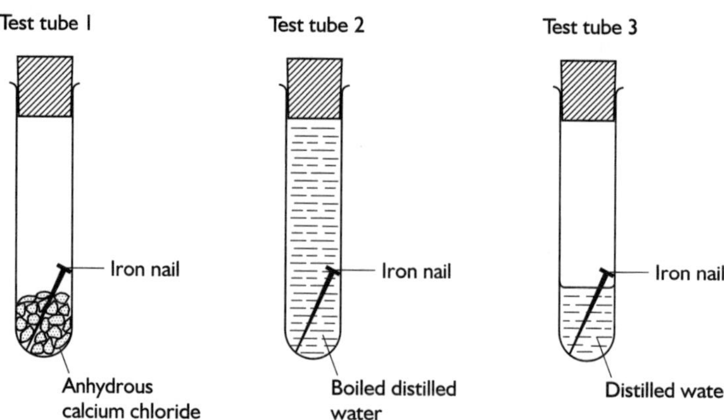

Covering up the surface to exclude air or water or both This is done by

- painting—cars, household machinery;
- metal plating—chromium or nickel or zinc (galvanizing) or silver (cutlery);
- plastic coating—dishwasher crockery racks, underground pipelines.

Sacrificial anode protection This is done in under water pipes and oil rigs in the North Sea. The pipe is attached by conducting wires to large lumps of zinc or magnesium at intervals. Zinc and magnesium are more reactive than iron and dissolve slowly. The reaction is

$$Zn(s) \rightarrow Zn^{2+}(aq) + 2e^-$$

or

$$Mg(s) \rightarrow Mg^{2+}(aq) + 2e^-$$

The electrons released in the reaction travel through the wire into the iron pipe where they build up, preventing the rusting reaction from occurring. In effect they *reverse* the reaction below.

$$\underset{\text{iron pipe}}{Fe(s)} \underset{\text{protection}}{\overset{\text{rusting}}{\rightleftharpoons}} \underset{\text{rust on iron pipe}}{Fe^{3+}(aq)} + \underset{\text{from zinc or magnesium}}{3e^-}$$

In the process, the zinc or magnesium dissolves (hence the sacrifice) and must be replaced from time to time. This is cheaper than replacing the pipeline!

Anodizing

Aluminium does not corrode because the oxide layer formed is very stable and is held firmly to the surface of the metal. This makes aluminium appear to be unreactive, whereas, if the oxide layer is removed, aluminium is very reactive. It is possible to increase the thickness of this film by anodizing.

'NEAB and London'

Anodizing is the electrolytic process of coating objects made of aluminium with a very thin **oxide film** to protect the metal from corrosion and dulling of the surface shine. To ensure a very thin film of oxide the oxidation is carried out by electrolysis using the aluminium object as the **anode**. The electrolyte is usually dilute sulphuric acid which, it will be remembered, gives oxygen at the anode on electrolysis. Under the correct conditions the oxygen reacts with the surface of the aluminium and coats it with a thin, invisible, but protective coating of aluminium oxide.

At the anode(+)

$$2Al(s) + 6OH^-(aq) \rightarrow \underset{\text{coating on aluminium}}{Al_2O_3(s)} + 3H_2O(l) + 6e^-$$

At the cathode(−)

$$6H^+(a) + 6e^- \rightarrow 3H_2(g)$$

Anodized aluminium can also be dyed, the oxide coating absorbing colour which cannot be washed out in normal use.

Preparation and properties of some non-metals and their compounds

Hydrogen

Hydrogen is prepared by reacting a fairly reactive metal such as zinc with a dilute acid such as sulphuric acid (Fig. 17.6).

Fig. 17.6 Preparation of hydrogen

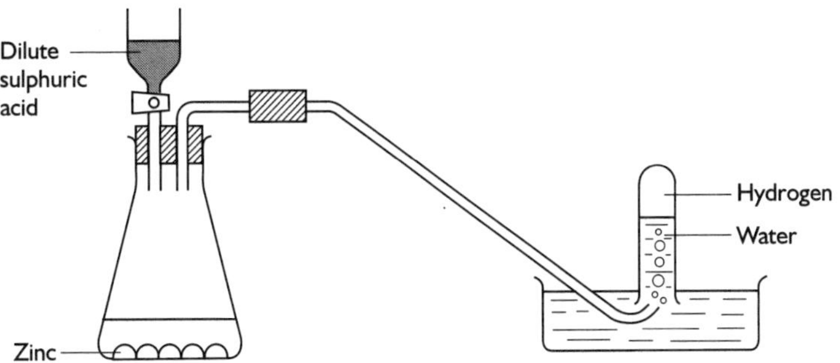

zinc + sulphuric acid → hydrogen + zinc sulphate

$$Zn(s) + H_2SO_4(aq) \rightarrow H_2(g) + ZnSO_4(aq)$$

This reaction is very slow. Copper acts as a catalyst for this reaction. A small amount of copper(II) sulphate is added to the zinc/sulphuric acid mixture. Zinc displaces copper, and this catalyses the reaction.

Sodium cannot be used to prepare hydrogen by this method because it is too reactive; and copper cannot be used because it is too unreactive.

Dilute nitric acid, concentrated nitric acid and concentrated sulphuric acid cannot be used because they are oxidizing agents and they would oxidize hydrogen to water.

Hydrogen can also be made when a very reactive metal such as sodium reacts with water:

sodium + water → hydrogen + sodium hydroxide

$$2Na(s) + 2H_2O(l) \rightarrow H_2(g) + 2NaOH(aq)$$

Hydrogen is formed when various aqueous solutions are electrolysed such as sulphuric acid, sodium hydroxide and magnesium nitrate. Hydrogen ions are discharged at the negative electrode:

hydrogen ions + electrons → hydrogen

$$2H^+(aq) + 2e^- \rightarrow H_2(g)$$

Properties of hydrogen

Hydrogen is a colourless gas. It has no smell. It is less dense than air. (It is the least dense of all gases.) It does not dissolve in water and therefore it has no effect on damp indicator paper. It is not poisonous.

Hydrogen burns with a squeaky pop in air or oxygen. This is used as a test for hydrogen:

hydrogen + oxygen → water

$$2H_2(g) + O_2(g) \rightarrow 2H_2O(l)$$

Hydrogen does not support the burning of a splint.

Hydrogen as a reducing agent

Hydrogen is a powerful **reducing agent.** It reduces the oxides of metals low in the reactivity series to the metal:

Fig. 17.7

H $\overset{\times}{\cdot}$ H H—H

copper(II) oxide + hydrogen → copper + water

$$CuO(s) + H_2(g) \rightarrow Cu(s) + H_2O(l)$$

Hydrogen reduces chlorine to hydrogen chloride, nitrogen to ammonia, and sulphur to hydrogen sulphide.

Hydrogen is a typical diatomic covalent molecule (Fig. 17.7). It is a gas which is insoluble in water. It does not conduct electricity.

Carbon

Apart from burning, carbon is unreactive under normal conditions. It does not dissolve in any of the common solvents. It does not react with dilute acids or with dilute alkalis.

Carbon burns in a plentiful supply of air or oxygen to form carbon dioxide:

carbon + oxygen → carbon dioxide

$$C(s) + O_2(g) \rightarrow CO_2(g)$$

This reaction is highly **exothermic.** This is the source of heat from carbon fuels.

If a limited supply of air or oxygen is used, the poisonous gas carbon monoxide is formed:

carbon + oxygen → carbon monoxide

$$2C(s) + O_2(g) \rightarrow 2CO(g)$$

This reaction is also exothermic.

Carbon monoxide is a very poisonous gas. It combines with haemoglobin in the blood to form **carboxyhaemoglobin.** This compound is about two hundred times more stable than the compound formed with oxygen, **oxyhaemoglobin.** Carboxyhaemoglobin cannot carry oxygen around the body, and the victim dies from lack of oxygen.

Carbon monoxide is an **atmospheric pollutant.** It is formed in the manufacture of iron and steel, in the paper industry and in petroleum refineries. It is formed during the incomplete combustion of carbon-containing compounds such as petrol, diesel, coal and cigarettes. Large quantities of carbon monoxide are formed when there are forest fires. Fortunately, there are many soil microorganisms using their enzyme catalysts to convert carbon monoxide into carbon dioxide, therefore keeping the percentage of carbon monoxide in the atmosphere low.

Carbon dioxide

About 0.033% by volume of the air is carbon dioxide. This value is kept constant by the equilibrium between its removal from the air by photosynthesis and dissolving in water, and its replacement by respiration and combustion of carbon-containing compounds. Carbon dioxide is also formed in the manufacture of alcohol and in the manufacture of lime.

There is a fear that, with the large-scale cutting down of forests and with the sea becoming saturated with carbon dioxide, there will be a build up of carbon dioxide in the atmosphere. This may lead to an increase in temperature, commonly known as the **greenhouse** effect.

Preparation of carbon dioxide

Carbon dioxide is usually prepared by the reaction between a dilute acid and a metal carbonate or hydrogencarbonate. The usual reactants are calcium carbonate (in the form of marble chips) and dilute hydrochloric acid:

calcium carbonate + hydrochloric acid → carbon dioxide + water + calcium chloride

$$CaCO_3(s) + 2HCl(aq) \rightarrow CO_2(g) + H_2O(l) + CaCl_2(aq)$$

Note that dilute sulphuric acid cannot be used in place of hydrochloric acid in this reaction. It reacts with calcium carbonate to form an insoluble layer of calcium sulphate. This prevents any further reaction.

Properties of carbon dioxide

Carbon dioxide is a colourless, odourless gas. It turns directly into a solid at −78 °C. Solid carbon dioxide is known as '**dry ice**'. Carbon dioxide is denser than air and fairly soluble in water to form a weak acid called **carbonic acid**. Carbon dioxide does not burn and it does not support burning.

Carbon dioxide as an oxidizing agent

Magnesium is a metal high in the reactivity series. Magnesium burns strongly enough in carbon dioxide to break carbon—oxygen bonds and hence continues to burn in the oxygen released.

carbon dioxide + magnesium → carbon + magnesium oxide

$$CO_2(g) + 2Mg(s) \rightarrow C(s) + 2MgO(s)$$

In this reaction carbon dioxide acts as an oxidizing reagent. It also acts as an oxidizing reagent in the blast furnace, where it oxidizes carbon to carbon monoxide:

carbon + carbon dioxide → carbon monoxide

$$C(s) + CO_2(g) \rightarrow 2CO(g)$$

Carbon dioxide reacts with water to form carbonic acid. This is a weak acid. It has a pH of about 5 or 6. Carbonic acid readily decomposes into water and carbon dioxide.

The reaction is reversible:

carbon dioxide + water ⇌ carbonic acid

$$CO_2(g) + H_2O(l) \rightleftharpoons H_2CO_3(aq)$$

Carbon dioxide reacts with alkalis to form either the carbonate or, with excess carbon dioxide, to form the hydrogencarbonate.

When carbon dioxide is passed into a solution of calcium hydroxide in water (lime-water), a white precipitate of calcium carbonate is formed. This is used as a test for carbon dioxide:

carbon dioxide + calcium hydroxide → calcium carbonate + water

$$CO_2(g) + Ca(OH)_2(aq) \rightarrow CaCO_3(s) + H_2O(l)$$

If carbon dioxide is passed, in excess, into this mixture, the white precipitate first formed disappears because soluble calcium hydrogencarbonate is formed:

carbon dioxide + calcium carbonate + water → calcium hydrogencarbonate

$$CO_2(g) + CaCO_3(s) + H_2O(l) \rightarrow Ca(HCO_3)_2(aq)$$

Preparation of oxygen

Oxygen is prepared by adding a catalyst, such as manganese(IV) oxide, to hydrogen peroxide. The catalyst makes the hydrogen peroxide break down at room temperature (Fig. 17.8).

hydrogen peroxide → oxygen + water

$$2H_2O_2(l) \rightarrow O_2(g) + 2H_2O(l)$$

Oxygen is obtained industrially from the atmosphere. Air is filtered to remove dust and other particles and dried to remove water vapour. Air is then cooled under pressure and it turns into a liquid. Liquid air is fractionally distilled. Nitrogen boils off first because it has the

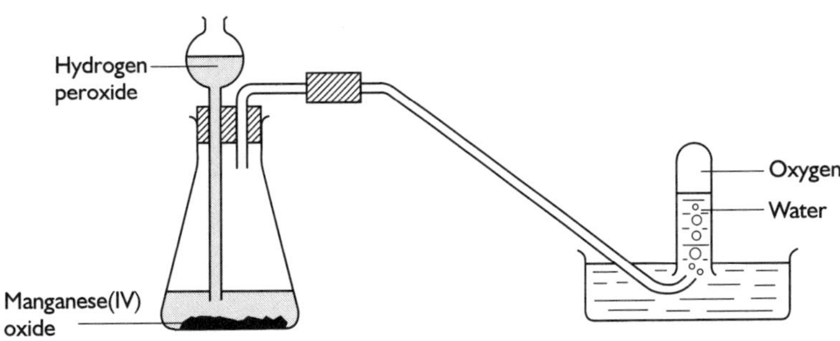

Fig. 17.8 Preparation of oxygen

lowest boiling point and then oxygen. Argon and other noble gases are also obtained by this process.

Oxygen is formed by the electrolysis of certain aqueous solutions, e.g. sulphuric acid, sodium hydroxide and magnesium sulphate. Hydroxyl ions are discharged at the positive electrode:

hydroxyl ions − electrons → oxygen + water

$$4OH^-(aq) - 4e^- \rightarrow O_2(g) + 2H_2O(l)$$

Fig. 17.9

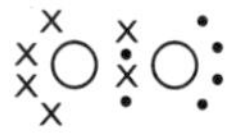

Oxygen is a typical covalent, diatomic molecule (Fig. 17.9). It is a gas and only slightly soluble in water. It does not conduct electricity.

Properties of oxygen

Oxygen is a colourless gas. It has no smell. It is slightly denser than air. It dissolves slightly in water. (In fact, oxygen is more soluble in water than nitrogen.) Fish breathe oxygen that is dissolved in water. Oxygen has no effect on damp pH paper. It is not poisonous. Oxygen does not burn.

Oxygen relights a glowing splint. This is used as a test for oxygen.

Chemical properties of oxygen

- Most elements react with oxygen to form oxides.
- Metals react to form **basic** oxides. These oxides are ionic and have high melting points.
- Non-metals react to form **acidic** oxides. These usually have very low melting points. Many non-metallic oxides are gases that are soluble in water to form acids.
- Some oxides react with both acids and bases. These are called **amphoteric** oxides. These oxides have both basic and acidic properties. Some examples of amphoteric oxides are aluminium oxide, lead(II) oxide and zinc oxide.
- There are also **neutral** non-metallic oxides, e.g. water (H_2O), carbon monoxide (CO) and nitrogen(II) oxide (NO).
- All reactions involving oxygen are **exothermic**.

Respiration

Carbohydrates in our bodies are oxidized by oxygen that we breathe in to form carbon dioxide and water. Some of the energy produced helps to keep us warm. A well-known carbohydrate that we eat is sugar:

sugar (glucose) + oxygen → carbon dioxide + water

$$C_6H_{12}O_6(aq) + 6O_2(g) \rightarrow 6CO_2(g) + 6H_2O(l)$$

This reaction is very slow when it occurs in our bodies; however, the same amount of energy is given out when sugar burns. The energy given out can easily be measured and is known as the **calorific value** of sugar. Most brands of packaged food have the calorific value stated on the packet—this is very useful information for people on diets.

Burning

Fig. 17.10 The triangle of fire

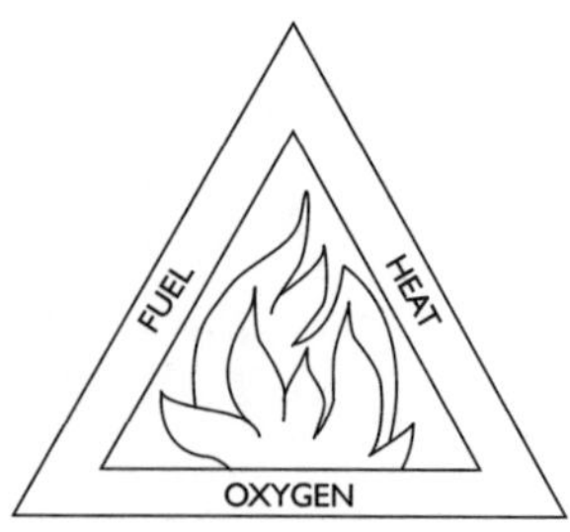

When we talk about **burning**, we are usually referring to the burning of fuels to produce heat and light. Before burning can start, three things are needed: fuel, heat and oxygen (Fig. 17.10). If any one of these is missing burning stops. If you have to put out a fire there are three things that you should do.

(1) Turn off the supply of fuel. This would mean that you would turn off the gas, oil or petrol tap.
(2) Lower the temperature by covering the flame with foam or water. **Water must not be used on petrol and oil fires because these substances float on water, causing the fire to spread out.**
(3) Cut off the supply of oxygen by covering the fire with sand, a blanket or foam.

- Water is often used to put out fires because it lowers the temperature of the fire. The heat turns water to steam and the presence of steam removes the air supply.
- Carbon dioxide is also used to put out fires. It does not support burning and it is denser than air. It therefore helps to keep away the air supply.
- If you see someone with their clothes on fire, you should wrap them in a blanket or carpet.
- If you are in a fire in a building and it is too difficult for you to put it out, you should shout 'fire', get everyone out of the building, close all doors and windows and 'phone for the emergency services.
- If a chip pan catches fire in your kitchen, the quickest action would probably be to cover the pan with a damp towel.

Oxides

Oxides are of three types: metallic, non-metallic and metalloid. These have different, distinguishing properties as is shown in Table 17.5.

Table 17.5

Property	Metal oxides	Non-metal oxides	Metalloid oxides
Acid/base nature	Bases or alkalis	Acidic or neutral	Amphoteric—both acidic and basic
Structure	Ionic	Molecular/covalent	Ionic
Examples	Na_2O, CuO, MgO	CO_2, SO_2, NO_2, H_2O	Al_2O_3, PbO

Sulphur

Sulphur is element 16 in the periodic table. It is a yellow, solid, non-metallic element. It has no smell or taste. It is insoluble in water but soluble in many organic liquids such as toluene and xylene. Because of the amount of sulphur used and the wide variety of processes that use it, it is one of the five basic raw materials of the chemical industry. The others are salt, limestone, coal and oil.

Its properties are typical of those of non-metals generally. It is a non-conductor of both heat and electricity, it is brittle and has a low density and a low melting point.

Sulphur occurs as native sulphur (pure sulphur) in volcanoes, in metal sulphides such as iron sulphide and zinc sulphide, and in natural gas and crude oil. The presence of sulphur in these last two chemicals causes wide pollution problems. When these fuels are burnt, sulphur dioxide is formed which escapes into the atmosphere.

Sulphur dioxide

Sulphur dioxide is formed by burning sulphur in air or oxygen:

$$S(s) + O_2(g) \rightarrow SO_2(g)$$

sulphur + oxygen → sulphur dioxide

Sulphur dioxide can act as both an oxidizing agent and a reducing agent. It oxidizes hydrogen sulphide to sulphur and reduces acidified potassium dichromate(VI) solution to chromium(III) sulphate. The solution changes in colour from orange to green:

sulphur dioxide + hydrogen sulphide → sulphur + water

$$SO_2(g) + 2H_2S(g) \rightarrow 3S(s) + 2H_2O(l)$$

potassium dichromate(VI) + sulphur dioxide + sulphuric acid → chromium(III) sulphate + potassium sulphate + water

$$K_2Cr_2O_7(aq) + 3SO_2(g) + H_2SO_4(aq) \rightarrow Cr_2(SO_4)_3(aq) + K_2SO_4(aq) + H_2O(l)$$

When it reacts with water, sulphur dioxide forms sulphurous acid:

$$H_2O(l) + SO_2(g) \rightarrow H_2SO_3(aq)$$

water + sulphur dioxide → sulphurous acid

Sulphurous acid is easily oxidized by air to sulphuric acid. In this way sulphur dioxide pollution of the atmosphere eventually produces 'acid rain', i.e. rain containing sulphuric acid.

The toxic nature of sulphur dioxide on humans at low concentrations causes breathing difficulties. The London 'smogs' (smoke plus fog) of the 1950s were believed to have killed many thousands of old and young people who suffered from asthma. At the time the sulphur dioxide concentration was as much as twenty times the yearly average. Since then the Clean Air Act of 1956 has forced a reduction in pollution from this gas.

Power station emissions

Pollution from power stations affects mainly those areas that are in the path of the gas as it is carried by the wind. It has been shown that this process can carry the gas many hundreds of miles and it is now accepted that much pollution is carried to Scandinavian countries by the prevailing south-westerly winds common in Britain. The gas attacks plants, stonework and metal causing damage to vegetation and corrosion to stone and metal structures.

Nitrogen

Nitrogen is a typical covalent, diatomic molecule (Fig. 17.11). It is a gas and only slightly soluble in water. It does not conduct electricity.

The 'triple' covalent bond in the nitrogen molecule is very strong and accounts for the lack of reactivity of nitrogen. One of the main uses of nitrogen is in the Haber–Bosch process for the manufacture of ammonia.

Fig. 17.11

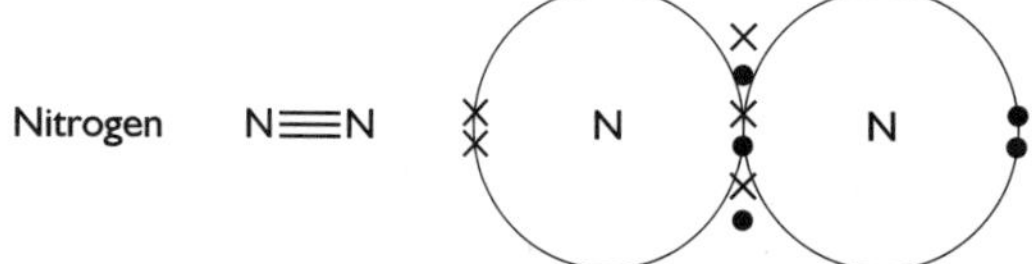

Ammonia

Ammonia is a colourless, pungent smelling, alkaline gas that is less dense than air. Apart from its smell, the other tests to confirm that ammonia is present is that it is the only common gas that turns damp universal indicator paper blue and it reacts with hydrogen chloride to give a 'white smoke' of ammonium chloride.

Ammonia is very soluble in water, producing a solution with a pH of about 10:

ammonia + water → ammonium ions + hydroxyl ions

$$NH_3(g) + H_2O(l) \rightarrow NH_4^+(aq) + OH^-(aq)$$

Ammonia solution is used in **qualitative analysis** to identify metal ions.

Ammonia is a base and reacts with acids to form ammonium salts:

ammonia + nitric acid → ammonium nitrate

$$NH_3(g) + HNO_3(aq) \rightarrow NH_4NO_3(aq)$$

Ammonium nitrate is used as a fertilizer.

You should be able to write equations for the reaction between ammonia and hydrogen chloride and the reaction between ammonia and sulphuric acid.

Chlorine

Chlorine is made by oxidizing concentrated hydrochloric acid with either manganese(IV) oxide or potassium manganate(VII); the latter reactions requires no heat.

hydrochloric acid + oxidizing agent → chlorine + water

$$2HCl(aq) + [O](aq\ or\ s) \rightarrow Cl_2(g) + H_2O(l)$$

Chlorine is a fairly typical covalent, diatomic molecule (see Fig. 17.12).

It is a pale green gas, has a choking smell, is denser than air, does not burn or support burning and is fairly soluble in water. It is very poisonous.

The test for chlorine is that it turns damp universal indicator paper red and then bleaches the paper.

Fig. 17.12

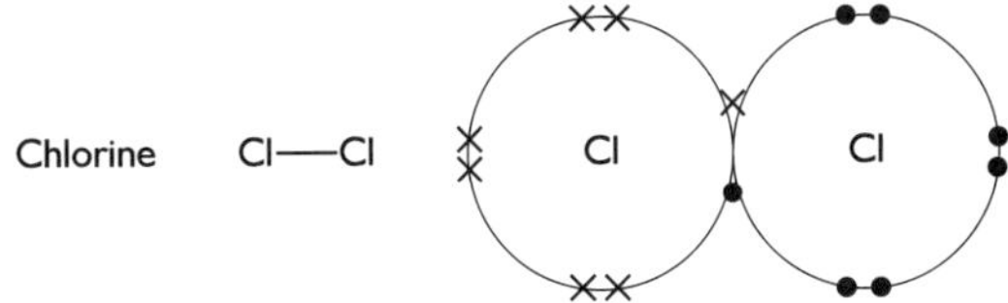

Reactions of chlorine

Hydrogen

Hydrogen reacts with chlorine to form hydrogen chloride:

hydrogen + chlorine → hydrogen chloride

$$H_2(g) + Cl_2(g) \rightarrow 2HCl(g)$$

When hydrogen burns in chlorine, the green colour of chlorine slowly disappears. The gas formed fumes in moist air and turns damp indicator paper red. When all the chlorine has reacted, the flame goes out because hydrogen chloride does not support burning (Fig. 17.13).

Fig. 17.13

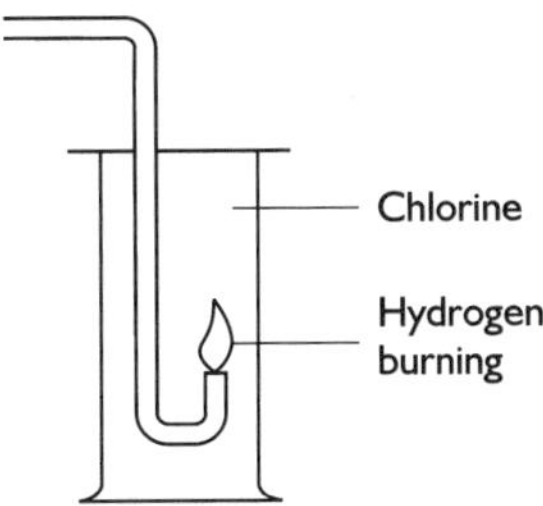

Iron and iron compounds

Chlorine oxidizes heated iron to iron(III) chloride and solutions of iron(II) compounds to iron(III) compounds:

iron + chlorine → iron(III) chloride

$$2Fe(s) + 3Cl_2(g) \rightarrow 2FeCl_3(s)$$

iron(II) compounds + chlorine → iron(III) compounds + chloride ions

$$2Fe^{2+}(aq) + Cl_2(g) \rightarrow 2Fe^{3+}(aq) + 2Cl^-(aq)$$

Displacement reactions
Chlorine is more reactive than bromine and iodine and thus it will displace these elements from solutions of their salts.

potassium bromide + chlorine → bromine + potassium chloride

$$2KBr(aq) + Cl_2(g) \rightarrow Br_2(aq) + 2KCl(aq)$$

potassium iodide + chlorine → iodine + potassium chloride

$$2KI(aq) + Cl_2(g) \rightarrow I_2(aq) + 2KCl(aq)$$

There are also examples of oxidizing reactions. Also note that bromine and iodine are diatomic.

Sodium hydroxide solution
When chlorine is passed into a cold solution of sodium hydroxide, a mixture of sodium chloride and sodium chlorate(I) is formed:

sodium hydroxide + chlorine → sodium chloride + sodium chlorate(I) + water

$$2NaOH(aq) + Cl_2(g) \rightarrow NaCl(aq) + NaClO(aq) + H_2O(l)$$

Hydrogen chloride

Hydrogen chloride is formed when concentrated sulphuric acid is added to solid sodium chloride:

sodium chloride + sulphuric acid → hydrogen chloride + sodium hydrogensulphate

$$NaCl(s) + H_2SO_4(l) \rightarrow HCl(g) + NaHSO_4(s)$$

Hydrogen chloride is very soluble in water because it reacts with water to form hydrochloric acid:

hydrogen chloride + water → hydrochloric acid

$$HCl(g) + H_2O(l) \rightarrow H_3O^+(aq) + Cl^-(aq)$$

Hydrogen chloride reacts with ammonia to form ammonium chloride:

hydrogen chloride + ammonia → ammonium chloride

$$HCl(g) + NH_3(g) \rightarrow NH_4Cl(s)$$

This last reaction is used as a test for hydrogen chloride. Hydrogen chloride fumes in moist air and gives a white 'smoke' of ammonium chloride when it reacts with ammonia gas.

Reactivity series of non-metals

We have seen that chlorine is more reactive than bromine and bromine is more reactive than iodine by displacement reactions. If chlorine is bubbled into water and the mixture left standing, oxygen will be formed:

chlorine + water → oxygen + hydrochloric acid

$$2Cl_2(g) + 2H_2O(l) \rightarrow O_2(g) + 4HCl(aq)$$

Chlorine is more reactive than oxygen. However, bromine and iodine do not react with water to give oxygen.

If chlorine or bromine or iodine are added to a solution of sodium sulphide, a white precipitate is formed showing that these elements are more reactive than sulphur:

iodine + sodium sulphide → sulphur + sodium iodide

$$I_2(aq) + Na_2S(aq) \rightarrow S(s) + 2NaI(aq)$$

You should be able to write the equations for the reactions between chlorine and sodium sulphide and for the reaction between bromine and sodium sulphide.

The reactivity series for some of the non-metals is:

Most reactive
chlorine
oxygen
bromine
iodine
sulphur
Least reactive

Noble gases

Helium, neon and argon are **noble gases**. Their molecules consist of a single atom—they are said to be **monatomic**. These gases are almost totally unreactive. They are sometimes referred to as **inert gases** because they do not react.

Tests to identify gases

You should try and use the mnemonic COWSLIPS for the property of gases:

Colour; Odour (smell); Weight (density); Supports burning; Litmus; Inflammable (does it burn?); Poisonous; Solubility (is it soluble in water?). These, together with special tests, will help you to identify gases (Table 17.6).

Table 17.6

Gas	Colour	Odour	Weight (density)	Supports burning	Litmus (damp)	Inflammable	Poisonous	Solubility (in water)
Ammonia	Colourless	Pungent—take care	Less dense than air	No	Blue	No	Yes	Very soluble
If you cannot *smell* ammonia it is *not* present.								
Confirmatory test: It gives a white smoke with hydrogen chloride.								
Carbon dioxide	Colourless	No smell	Denser than air	No	Slightly acidic	No	No	Soluble
Confirmatory test: Bubble the gas into lime water—it gives a white precipitate of calcium carbonate.								
Hydrogen	Colourless	No smell	Less dense than air	No	No effect	Burns with a 'pop'	No	Not soluble
Confirmatory test: It is the only gas that burns with a 'pop'.								
Hydrogen chloride	Fumes in moist air	Sharp—take care	Denser than air	No	Red	No	Yes	Very soluble
Confirmatory test: It gives a white smoke with ammonia gas.								
Oxygen	Colourless	No smell	About same as air	No	No effect	Relights a glowing splint	No	Slightly
Confirmatory test: It is the only gas that relights a glowing splint.								

Uses of non-metals

The uses of some non-metals are listed in Table 17.7.

Table 17.7 Uses of some non-metals

Non-metal element	Use
Argon	Lighting and welding
Carbon	Decolorizing 'brown' sugar; removing smells (kitchens and shoes!)
Chlorine	Bleach for cotton, linen and wood pulp; manufacture of hydrogen chloride and PVC; disinfectants; water sterilization
Helium	Filling balloons; breathing mixture for divers
Hydrogen	Filling balloons; manufacture of ammonia, hydrogen chloride and margarine
Iodine	Making antiseptics
Neon	Lighting
Nitrogen	Liquid nitrogen as coolant; food packaging; manufacture of ammonia
Oxygen	Steelmaking; oxygen tents in hospitals
Sulphur	Fungicide; vulcanizing rubber; manufacture of sulphuric acid

Uses of compounds

The uses of various compounds are listed in Table 17.8.

Table 17.8 Uses of compounds

Compound	Use
Ammonia	Manufacture of fertilizers, nitric acid and nylon
Ammonium carbonate	Smelling salts
Ammonium nitrate	Fertilizer
Aluminium hydroxide	Antacid
Calcium compounds	Important in the body for teeth and bones
Calcium carbonate	Manufacture of calcium oxide (quicklime), calcium hydroxide (slaked lime), cement and glass; blackboard chalk; in blast furnaces to remove slag
Calcium hydroxide	Neutralizing acidic soil; manufacture of mortar
Calcium oxide	Neutralizing acid soil
Calcium sulphate	Plaster of Paris; blackboard chalk; white line road markings
Carbon dioxide	Fire extinguishers; carbonated water; dry ice
Nitric acid	Manufacture of fertilizers and explosives
Silver halides	Making photographic film and photographic paper
Sodium chloride	De-icing roads; food industry
Sodium hydrogencarbonate	Cooking; antacid
Sodium hydroxide	Manufacture of soap, paper and ceramics
Sulphur dioxide	Bleach; preservative/sterilizing agent; fungicide
Sulphuric acid	Car batteries; manufacture of detergents, soaps, fertilizers, plastics, fibres, pigments and paints

Allotropy

Allotropy is the existence of more than one form of an element in the same physical state. The different forms are known as **allotropes.** The allotropes of carbon are **diamond** and **graphite.**

'Allotropes'
'Do not confuse allotropes with isotopes.'

Comparing diamond with graphite

Diamond and graphite can be shown to be pure forms of carbon by completely burning equal masses of each in oxygen. They both give the **same amount** of carbon dioxide as the **only** product:

carbon + oxygen → carbon dioxide

$C(s) + O_2(g) \rightarrow CO_2(g)$

As we see in Table 17.9, diamond and graphite are very different and the different arrangement of the carbon atoms in the two allotropes explains these differences.

Table 17.9

Properties of diamond	Properties of graphite
Hardest known natural substance (Mohs' scale = 10)	Relatively soft substance (Mohs' scale = 3)
Does not conduct electricity	Conducts electricity
Good conductor of heat (explains why diamonds feel cold)	Poor conductor of heat
Density 3.5 g cm^{-3}	Density 2.2 g cm^{-3}
Colourless, transparent solid	Dark grey solid

The 'large' distance between the layers in graphite explains why its density is less than that of diamond.

Both allotropes have macromolecular structures and hence they have high melting points and boiling points. (Graphite in fact **sublimes** at 4200 °C.)

In diamond (Fig. 17.14) each carbon atom is joined to four other carbon atoms by strong single, covalent bonds, producing a giant lattice in three dimensions. This giant atomic structure is the reason for the hardness of diamond. All the outer electrons of the carbon atoms are being used for bonding and therefore there are no free electrons to move through the structure, so diamond does not conduct electricity.

'Practise drawing the structures of diamond and graphite'

In graphite (Fig. 17.15), each carbon atom is joined to only three other carbon atoms by strong single, covalent bonds. This produces a giant lattice in two dimensions. The remaining electrons from the atoms are **delocalized** between the layers. Since the forces between these layers in the graphite structure are relatively weak, the layers can slide over one another. This explains why graphite can be used as a dry lubricant. The presence of free electrons between the layers allows graphite to conduct electricity.

Fig. 17.14 Diamond

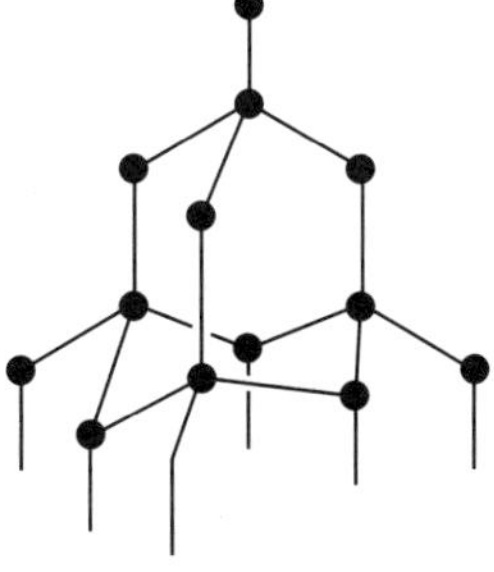

Fig. 17.15 Graphite

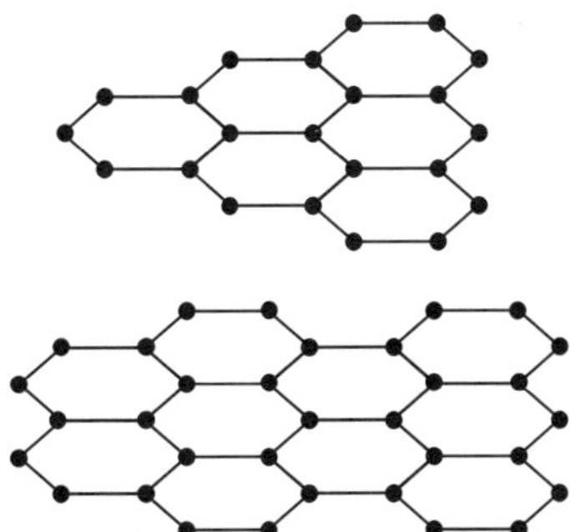

Uses of diamonds

Diamonds, because they are rare, are valued as gemstones and because they are hard they are used as tips for drills and in saws and other cutting tools. Synthetic diamonds are made from graphite using high temperatures and high pressures. These artificial diamonds are only used in industry; they have no value as gemstones.

Uses of graphite

Graphite, because it is a conductor of electricity and relatively unreactive, is used to make electrodes, e.g. for use in dry cells and the manufacture of aluminium.

'One of the disadvantages of graphite as an electrode is that it reacts with oxygen (to form carbon dioxide)'

- Because graphite is slippery, it is used as a dry lubricant, particularly when oil cannot be used
- Graphite is used in pencils because the layers slide off.
- Graphite is also used to make graphite fibres which are used to reinforce metals.
- There is a great demand for both diamonds and graphite. Synthetic graphite can be made by purifying coal.

Allotropes of sulphur

Sulphur occurs in two different crystalline forms—rhombic or alpha sulphur and monoclinic or beta sulphur. They are made up of **the same S_8 molecules arranged differently in the two crystal structures.** The molecules of rhombic sulphur are more tightly packed than those of the monoclinic allotrope, giving densities of $2.07\,g\,cm^{-3}$ and $1.96\,g\,cm^{-3}$ respectively. The different packing of the molecules gives the two allotropes different melting points also. Rhombic sulphur melts at 113 °C and monoclinic sulphur at 119 °C. However, the rhombic form normally converts to the monoclinic form on heating to 96°C or above, making the melting point of rhombic sulphur difficult to measure in the normal way.

If liquid sulphur is poured into cold water, another form of sulphur, called *plastic sulphur*, is formed. It is like yellow chewing gum.

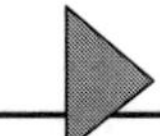

EXAMINATION QUESTIONS

Question 1(F) Fill in the gaps in the following table (Table 17.10): *[10]*

Table 17.10

Chemical	Property	Use
Chlorine	Sterilizing	
	Less dense than air, unreactive	Airships
Carbon	Reducing agent	
	Contains nitrogen	Fertilizer
Calcium oxide		
		Extinguishing fires
	Decomposed by light to its elements	

Question 2(F) The corrosion of iron is called *rusting*.

(a) Explain the meaning of the word *corrosion*. *[1]*

(b) Look at the rusting experiment shown below (Fig. 17.16).

Fig. 17.16

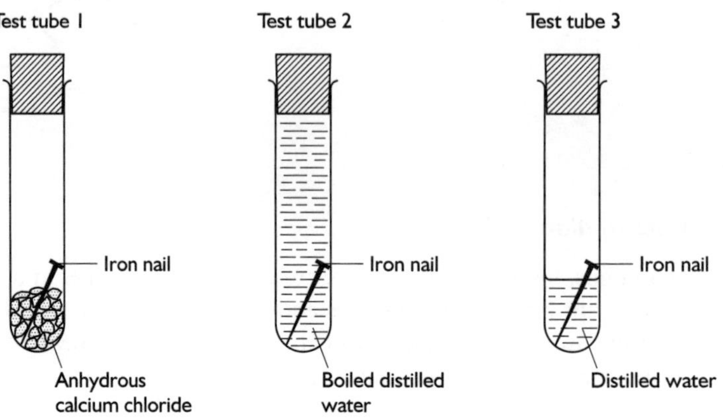

Complete the following sentences.
(i) The nail in test tube 1 does *not* rust because ______________________
(ii) The nail in test tube 2 does *not* rust because ______________________
(iii) The nail in test tube 3 *does* rust because ______________________ *[3]*

(c) Give three ways to stop a nail from rusting. *[3]*

Question 3(F)

Five metals were tested to see which would react in different metal nitrate solutions. The table below (Table 17.11) shows the results. A tick (✓) means that a reaction took place and a (x) means that a reaction did not take place.

Table 17.11

	Copper nitrate	Zinc nitrate	Nickel nitrate	Magnesium nitrate	Silver nitrate
Copper		x	x	x	✓
Zinc	✓		✓	x	✓
Nickel	✓	x		x	✓
Magnesium	✓	✓	✓		✓
Silver	x	x	x	x	

(a) The shaded areas represent experiments that were not carried out. Why was it not necessary to carry out these reactions? *[1]*
(b) Put the metals in order of reactivity, with the most reactive metal first. *[3]*
(c) Give one reason how could you tell that a chemical reaction had taken place? *[1]*
(d) Complete the following word equation:

nickel + silver nitrate → . . . . + ... *[1]*

(e) Which reaction would give the greatest rise in temperature? *[1]*

Question 4(F)

Look at the following list of substances:

argon
calcium
calcium oxide
chlorine
limestone
sulphur

From the list, choose one which is:

(a) a metal; *[1]*
(b) about 1 per cent of the atmosphere; *[1]*
(c) used to make cement; *[1]*
(d) used as a bleaching agent; *[1]*
(e) an element that forms allotropes; *[1]*
(f) a form of calcium carbonate. *[1]*

Question 5(F)

Identify the substances described below.

(a) Greenish-yellow gas; book on safety says 'very harmful gas which can cause skin damage on contact and severe lung damage if breathed in'.
Substance is . . . . *[1]*
(b) Colourless liquid which conducts electricity; turns pH paper red; reacts with silver nitrate solution forming a dense white precipitate.
Substance is . . . . *[2]*

Question 6(H)

(a) Describe a test for hydrogen and give the result of the test. *[2]*
(b) Describe a test for oxygen and give the result of the test. *[2]*
(c) Water is formed when hydrogen reacts with oxygen. Describe a simple test for the presence of water and give the result of the test. *[2]*
(d) Write a balanced chemical equation for the burning of hydrogen in oxygen to form water. *[2]*
(e) The burning of hydrogen in oxygen is an example of redox. What two other types of chemical reaction does this show? *[2]*
(f) A mixture of liquid hydrogen and liquid oxygen is sometimes used as a space fuel. Explain why this fuel produces no pollution. *[1]*

Question 7(H)

The following list is a reactivity order for a number of metals. You will not have met all of these metals; but use your knowledge of the reactivity series to answer the questions that follow.

potassium; lithium; magnesium; zinc; iron; tin; copper; gold
most reactive **least reactive**

(a) Why does gold occur as the element gold in the Earth's crust but magnesium always occur in compounds? *[2]*
(b) Suggest a method for the manufacture of each of the following metals: (i) potassium from potassium chloride; (ii) tin from tin oxide. *[1]*
(c) Bronze is an alloy of tin and copper. Why do you think the bronze age came before the iron age? *[2]*
(d) Tin cans are in fact iron cans coated with tin. Explain *why* iron cans are coated with tin. *[2]*
(e) Suggest what you would observe if a piece of lithium was added to cold water. *[2]*
(f) Lithium is in the same group of the Periodic Table as potassium and sodium; write a balanced symbol equation for the reaction of lithium with water, including state symbols. *[2]*
(g) (i) Suggest the compound that is removed from the surface of a magnesium ribbon when it is cleaned. *[1]*
(ii) What would you observe if an excess of clean magnesium ribbon was added to copper sulphate solution? *[3]*
(iii) Write an ionic equation for this reaction. *[2]*
(iv) Why is this reaction a redox reaction? *[4]*

Question 8(H)

(a) Draw a labelled diagram to show how you would prepare and collect several test tubes of hydrogen in the laboratory. Label all the apparatus and reagents. *[5]*
(b) Write a symbol equation for the reaction, including state symbols. *[2]*
(c) How would you test the gas you have collected to show that it was hydrogen? *[2]*
(d) Hydrogen is a reducing agent. Write balanced symbol equations to show hydrogen reducing (i) a metal oxide; (ii) an alkene; (iii) a non-metal (not oxygen). *[6]*
(e) Give two large-scale uses of hydrogen. *[2]*

Question 9(H)

(a) Why are the following elements unreactive?
(i) neon *[2]*
(ii) aluminium *[3]*
(iii) nitrogen *[2]*
(b) Why are the following compounds unreactive?
(i) ethane *[1]*
(ii) barium sulphate *[1]*
(c) Why is ethene very reactive? *[1]*

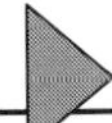

OUTLINE ANSWERS

Question 1 See Table 17.12.

Table 17.12

Chemical	Property	Use
Chlorine	Sterilizing	*Purifying water*
Helium	Less dense than air, unreactive	Airships
Carbon	Reducing agent	*Manufacture of iron*
Ammonium nitrate	Contains nitrogen	Fertilizer
Calcium oxide	*Basic oxide*	*Neutralizing acidic soil*
Carbon dioxide	*Does not support burning*	Extinguishing fires
Silver bromide or silver iodide	Decomposed by light to its elements	*Photography*

Question 2
(a) The process by which materials are eaten away.
(b) (i) There is no water present; (ii) there is no air present; (iii) both air and water are present.
(c) Painting; galvanizing; attaching a more reactive metal such as magnesium.

Question 3
(a) Metals cannot displace their own metal from their own compounds.
(b) Magnesium; zinc; nickel; copper; silver.
(c) A deposit of a metal will be formed either in the test tube or on the metal surface.
(d) Nickel nitrate + silver.
(e) Magnesium with silver nitrate.

Question 4 (a) calcium; (b) argon; (c) calcium oxide; (d) chlorine; (e) sulphur; (f) limestone.

Question 5 (a) chlorine; (b) hydrochloric acid.

Question 6
(a) Burns with a 'pop'.
(b) Relights a glowing splint.
(c) Turns anhydrous copper sulphate from white to blue.
(d) $2H_2(g) + O_2(g) \rightarrow 2H_2O(l)$.
(e) Synthesis; exothermic.
(f) The product water is not a pollutant.

Question 7
(a) Gold is very unreactive; magnesium is very reactive.
(b) (i) Electrolysis of molten KCl; (ii) reduction with carbon or carbon monoxide.
(c) Tin and copper occur naturally; iron has to be manufactured.
(d) To form a protective unreactive coating.
(e) React quickly to give hydrogen gas; metal might catch fire; alkaline solution (lithium hydroxide) formed.
(f) $2Li(s) + 2H_2O(l) \rightarrow 2LiOH(aq) + H_2(g)$.
(g) (i) Magnesium oxide.
(ii) Brown precipitate of copper; solution goes from blue to colourless.
(iii) $Mg(s) + Cu^{2+}(aq) \rightarrow Mg^{2+}(aq) + Cu(s)$.
(iv) Magnesium is oxidized to magnesium ions and copper ions are reduced to copper.

Question 8
(a) See Chapter 17, Fig. 17.6.
(b) $Zn(s) + H_2SO_4(aq) \rightarrow H_2(g) + ZnSO_4(aq)$.
(c) Burns with a 'pop'.
(d) (i) $CuO(s) + H_2(g) \rightarrow Cu(s) + H_2O(l)$.
(ii) $C_2H_4(g) + H_2(g) \rightarrow C_2H_6(g)$.
(iii) $N_2(g) + 3H_2(g) \rightarrow 2NH_3(g)$.
(e) Making ammonia; making margarine.

 **Question 9**

(a) (i) Noble gas; has a complete outer ring of 8 electrons.
(ii) Forms stable, unreactive oxide coating.
(iii) Has triple bond between atoms, which is hard to break.

(b) (i) Saturated.
(ii) Insoluble in water and very stable.

(c) Unsaturated and can therefore undergo addition reactions.

STUDENT ANSWER WITH EXAMINER'S COMMENTS

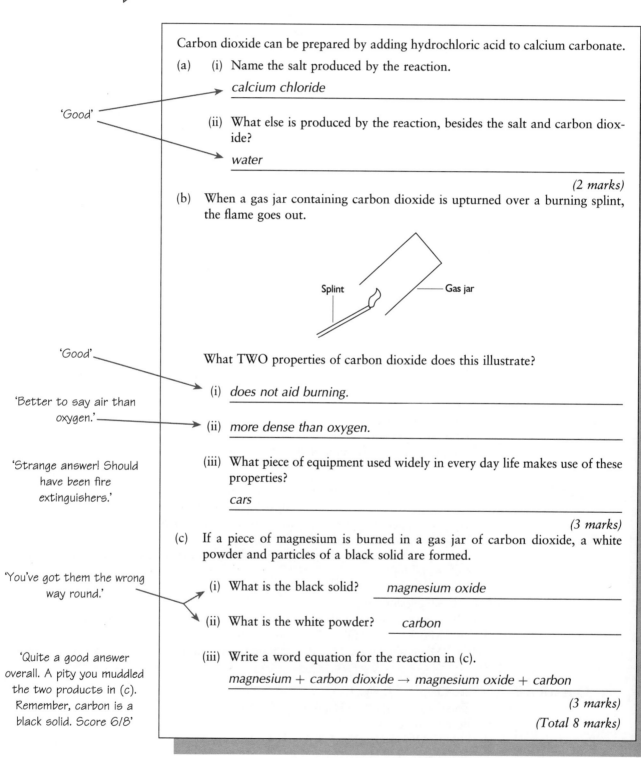

Carbon dioxide can be prepared by adding hydrochloric acid to calcium carbonate.

(a) (i) Name the salt produced by the reaction.

calcium chloride

'Good'

(ii) What else is produced by the reaction, besides the salt and carbon dioxide?

water

(2 marks)

(b) When a gas jar containing carbon dioxide is upturned over a burning splint, the flame goes out.

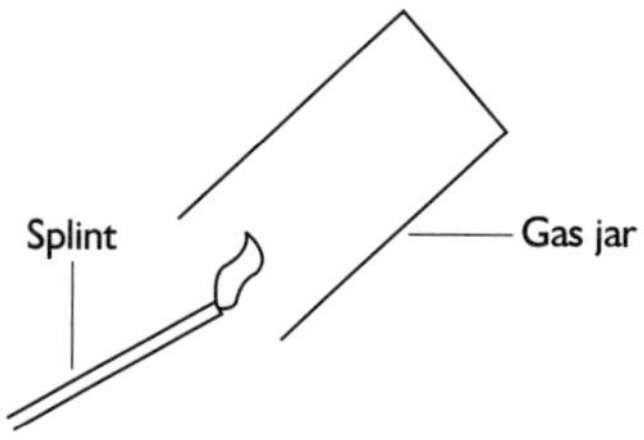

What TWO properties of carbon dioxide does this illustrate?

'Good'.

(i) *does not aid burning.*

'Better to say air than oxygen.'

(ii) *more dense than oxygen.*

'Strange answer! Should have been fire extinguishers.'

(iii) What piece of equipment used widely in every day life makes use of these properties?

cars

(3 marks)

(c) If a piece of magnesium is burned in a gas jar of carbon dioxide, a white powder and particles of a black solid are formed.

'You've got them the wrong way round.'

(i) What is the black solid? *magnesium oxide*

(ii) What is the white powder? *carbon*

(iii) Write a word equation for the reaction in (c).

magnesium + carbon dioxide → magnesium oxide + carbon

(3 marks)

(Total 8 marks)

'Quite a good answer overall. A pity you muddled the two products in (c). Remember, carbon is a black solid. Score 6/8'

SUMMARY

Use this list to help with your revision. Tick off the points as you learn them.

- ▷ The essential chemical difference between a metal and a non-metal is that **a metal forms positive ions by losing electrons and a non-metal forms ions by gaining electrons**.
- ▷ Chemical differences between metals and non-metals are:

Property	Metals	Non-metals
Oxides	Basic	Acidic
Bonding in chloride	Ionic	Covalent
Redox	Reducing agents	Oxidizing agents
With acids	Give hydrogen	No reaction

- ▷ Some metals are more reactive than others and a **reactivity series** for metals can be produced; the **alkali metals** are the most **reactive metals;** the **noble metals** such as gold and silver are the **least reactive.**
- ▷ The reactivity series can be determined by the following reactions:
  with water;
  with dilute acids;
  displacement reactions;
  action of heat on compounds such as nitrate, carbonate and hydroxides.
- ▷ Non-metals have the following general properties:
  - ▷ Their oxides are acidic.
  - ▷ Their chlorides are covalent.
  - ▷ They tend to be oxidizing agents.
  - ▷ In general they do not react with acids.
- ▷ Both water and oxygen are necessary for iron to rust.
- ▷ Rusting can be prevented either by coating the iron with a material or by sacrificial anode protection.
- ▷ Aluminium does not rust because it has a protective oxide coating—the coating can be increased by anodizing.
- ▷ You must learn how to recognize the following gases:

ammonia	smell, and turns damp universal indicator paper blue
carbon dioxide	turns lime-water cloudy
hydrogen	burns with a 'pop'
hydrogen chloride	fumes in moist air and turns damp universal paper red
oxygen	relights a glowing splint

- ▷ Make sure you know the use of the metals, non-metals and compounds for the syllabus you are studying.
- ▷ Allotropy is the existence of more than one form of an element in the same physical state.
- ▷ Carbon has two allotropes—graphite and diamond.
- ▷ Sulphur has two allotropes—rhombic and monoclinic.

Chapter

18 How fast? How far? Energetics

GETTING STARTED

How fast? Chemical equations tell you nothing about how fast a chemical reaction takes place. The speed of a reaction has to be found out by experiment.

Chemical reactions take place at different speeds. Some reactions, such as precipitation reactions, are very fast. Other reactions, such as ripening of fruit, rusting and fermentation, are slow reactions.

If an industrial reaction is too slow the process may become uneconomical.

Various factors effect the rate of a reaction such as whether the solid reactants are lumps or powder, temperature, concentration, catalysts and light. You will have noticed that milk turns sour much more quickly if kept in warm conditions than if kept in a refrigerator. Thinly sliced bread also goes stale much more quickly than a loaf of bread. Optimum conditions have to be chosen to ensure that the reaction does not occur too slowly and, at the same time, gives a good yield of the products.

The use of enzymes in making various foodstuffs is very important in industry.

How far? Some reactions go to completion. They are like baking a cake. Once the cake has cooked (reacted) it is impossible to get back the ingredients such as flour, eggs and milk. The thermal decomposition of sodium nitrate is an example of a reaction that is *not* reversible:

sodium nitrate → sodium nitrite + oxygen

$$2NaNO_3(s) \rightarrow 2NaNO_2(s) + O_2(g)$$

TOPIC CHART

LONDON	MEG	NEAB	SEG	NICCEA	WJEC	TOPIC	STUDY	REVISION 1	REVISION 2
✓	✓	✓	✓	✓	✓	Factors affecting the rate (speed) of a reaction			
✓	✓	✓	✓	✓		Collision theory of reactions			
✓	✓	✓	✓	✓	✓	Measuring rates of reactions			
✓	✓	✓	✓		✓	Reactions involving enzymes			
✓	✓	✓	✓			Reversible reactions			
✓	✓	✓				Dynamic equilibrium			
		✓				Le Chatelier's principle			
✓	✓	✓	✓		✓	Manufacture of ammonia			
✓	✓	✓	✓	✓	✓	Energy changes in chemical reactions			
✓	✓	✓	✓	✓	✓	Exothermic and endothermic reactions			
	✓	✓	✓			Energy level diagrams			
		✓	✓	✓		Activation energy of a reaction			
✓	✓	✓	✓	✓	✓	Fuels			
✓						Measuring the heat given out by burning fuel			

Many reactions can be reversed. A reversible change is a change that can be reversed by changing the conditions. Ice can be melted to water when warmed, but ice is reformed when the water is cooled below 0 °C.

Energetics. When chemical reactions occur there is usually a change of **energy**.

Exothermic reactions are those giving out heat energy. The convention used is to give the energy change a negative sign (to show that the products contain less energy than the reactants). Heat change is represented by ΔH. Thus a negative ΔH means that energy is released. All combustion reactions are exothermic.

Endothermic reactions are those taking in heat energy. Heat change is represented by a positive ΔH. The positive sign indicates that the products contain more energy than the reactants.

Activation energy is the energy required by the reactants to loosen the bonds to enable them to form new bonds in the products. It is the minimum energy needed, on collision, for molecules to react.

Energy is required to break bonds and energy is released when bonds are made.

WHAT YOU NEED TO KNOW

Factors affecting the rate (speed) of a reaction

The speed of a chemical reaction can be changed by:

- altering the size of the particles—the smaller the particles the faster the rate of reaction;
- altering the concentration of the reactants—the more concentrated the reactants the faster the rate of reaction; in the case of gases, increasing the pressure increases the rate of reaction;
- altering the temperature—for chemical reactions, the higher the temperature the faster the rate of reaction, but for reactions involving enzymes there is an optimum temperature;
- using catalysts—a substance that increases the rate of a reaction is called a **catalyst**; a substance that slows down the rate of reaction is called an **inhibitor**;
- using light—a small number of reactions go faster in the presence of light.

The rate of a reaction is followed by measuring either the rate of formation of a product or the rate of disappearance of a reactant. For the reaction

sodium thiosulphate + hydrochloric acid → sodium chloride + sulphur + sulphur dioxide + water

$$Na_2S_2O_3(aq) + 2HCl(aq) \rightarrow 2NaCl(aq) + S(s) + SO_2(g) + H_2O(l)$$

we could measure the rate of formation of sulphur or the rate that sulphur dioxide gas is given off or the rate at which hydrochloric acid is used up.

Normally the amount of product formed or reactant used up is measured at fixed intervals of time. Thus the time is plotted on the x-axis and amount on the y-axis. The slope of the graph gives a measure of the rate of reaction (see Fig. 18.1). Reaction A is faster than reaction B at time t.

Fig. 18.1

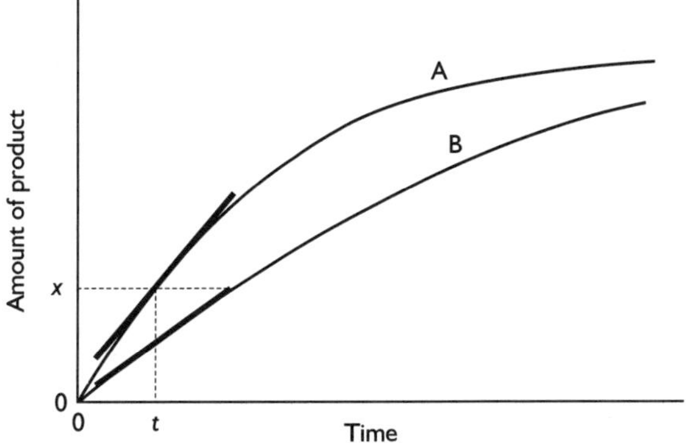

Collision theory of reactions

The increase in the rate of a chemical reaction can be explained by the **collision theory**. In order for particles to react they must collide, and they must also have sufficient energy to react.

- **If the size of the solid reactant is decreased, there is more surface area available for reacting and so the speed of the reaction increases.**
  This is why powdered calcium carbonate reacts far more quickly than lumps of calcium carbonate (marble chips). This also explains why there is a danger of explosions in flour mills. The very fine flour can easily catch fire, and a very fast reaction occurs which causes an explosion. A similar problem occurs in coal mines, where there can be a build up of coal dust and combustible gases. Bacterial spoilage of food is much quicker if the surface area of food is increased as in minced meat, meat pies, and thin sliced meats. Most food poisoning by bacterial growth occurs in these products.
- **When a solution becomes more concentrated, the number of particles present in the solution increases.**
  The more particles there are, the greater the number of collisions, and therefore the rate of the reaction increases. Gases can be concentrated by increasing the pressure. This squeezes more particles into a given volume. This is one reason why reactions between gases in industrial processes are usually carried out at higher than normal pressures.
- **Increasing the temperature increases the speed of the particles.**
  The faster the particles move, the greater the number of collisions, and therefore the rate of the reaction increases. A 10 °C rise in temperature almost doubles the rate of most reactions. One way you may have at home of speeding up the cooking of vegetables is a pressure cooker. A pressure cooker enables water to boil at a higher temperature, and this increases the rate of cooking.
- **Using a catalyst speeds up the reaction.**
  Solid catalysts bring reactants together on their surface so that they can react. For example, in the manufacture of sulphuric acid by the Contact process, the solid vanadium(V) oxide catalyst brings together the molecules of oxygen and sulphur dioxide on its surface so that they can react together to form sulphur trioxide.

Catalysts

A catalyst also speeds up a reaction by providing an alternative, lower energy route for the reactants to take in becoming products. This is shown on the energy profile (Fig. 18.2).

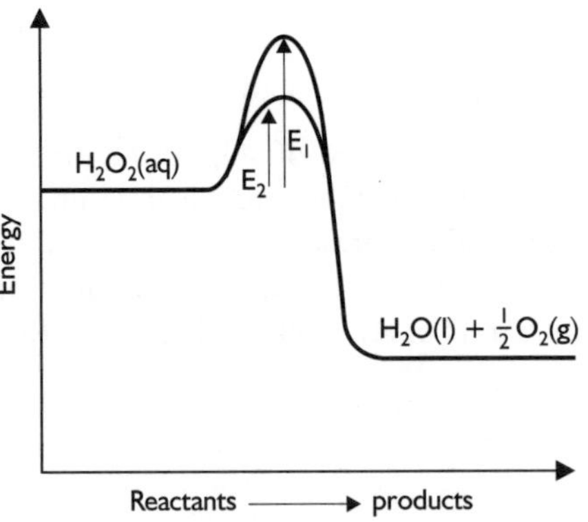

Fig. 18.2 Energy profile for the decomposition of aqueous hydrogen peroxide with a manganese(IV) oxide catalyst. E_1 = activation energy without catalyst. E_2 = activation energy with catalyst

In this reaction, the hydrogen peroxide molecules react with the manganese(IV) oxide catalyst to form water and oxygen, which leave the catalyst, which can now react with more oxide, and so on. The catalyst reacts with the reactants but is reformed as the products are created. The equation for the example shown could more accurately be given as

$$MnO_2(s) + H_2O_2(aq) \rightarrow MnO_2(s) + H_2O(l) + \tfrac{1}{2}O_2(g)$$

because this shows that the catalyst is a **reactant** and that it is also a product, i.e. it is reformed after reacting and so is not used up. Chemical equations do not usually show formulae which occur on both sides of the equation, so the formula of a catalyst is usually left out and the equation becomes

$$H_2O_2(aq) \rightarrow H_2O(l) + \tfrac{1}{2}O_2(g)$$

A catalyst speeds up a chemical reaction but is itself unchanged at the end of the reaction.

A catalyst can

- make a reaction occur faster at a given temperature, or
- make a reaction go quickly at a much reduced temperature.

The above reaction is faster at room temperature with the catalyst than without it. It is also faster at room temperature with the catalyst than at 100 °C without the catalyst.

Measuring rates of reactions

In most reactions the rate of reaction changes with time. In the following examples we will either measure the rate at which a reactant disappears or the rate at which a product appears. You should be able to work out for yourself which one is being measured.

The effect of particle size on the rate (speed) of reaction

The reaction between magnesium and hydrochloric acid

Place 50 cm^3 of 2 mol dm^{-3} hydrochloric acid into a beaker and add 10 cm of magnesium ribbon; at the same time start a stop-watch. Make a note of how long it takes for the magnesium to react completely. Repeat the experiment using magnesium powder in place of magnesium ribbon (ensure you have the same mass of powder as of ribbon). You will find that the magnesium powder reacts in a far shorter time than the ribbon.

magnesium + hydrochloric acid → hydrogen + magnesium chloride

$$Mg(s) + 2HCl(aq) \rightarrow H_2(g) + MgCl_2(aq)$$

The reaction between marble chips and hydrochloric acid

Place about 40 cm^3 of 2 mol dm^{-3} hydrochloric acid (an excess) in a conical flask on a top pan balance and place a piece of cotton wool in the neck of the flask. (The cotton wool prevents the acid from splashing on to the pan.) Add 6 g of marble chips (see Fig. 18.3).

Fig. 18.3

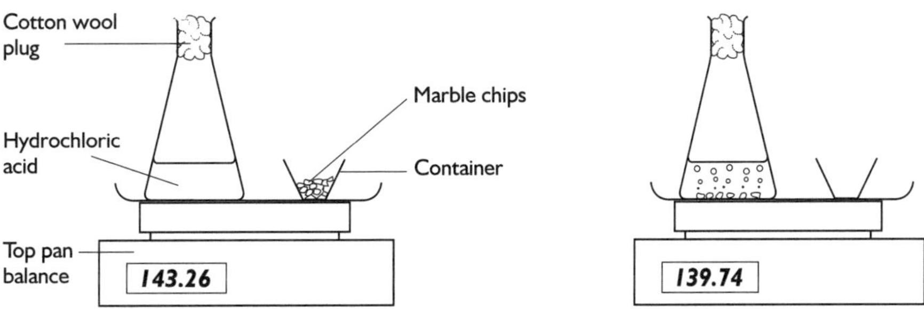

Note the total mass and immediately start the stop-watch. Note the mass every 30 seconds. Plot a graph of mass on the vertical scale against time on the horizontal scale.

Repeat the experiment using 6 g of smaller marble chips and take the same measurements. Draw the graph on the same axis. Your graph should be similar to that shown in Fig. 18.4.

calcium carbonate + hydrochloric acid → calcium chloride + water + carbon dioxide

$$CaCO_3(s) + 2HCl(aq) \rightarrow CaCl_2(aq) + H_2O(l) + CO_2(g)$$

The loss in mass is due to carbon dioxide being given off.

Fig. 18.4

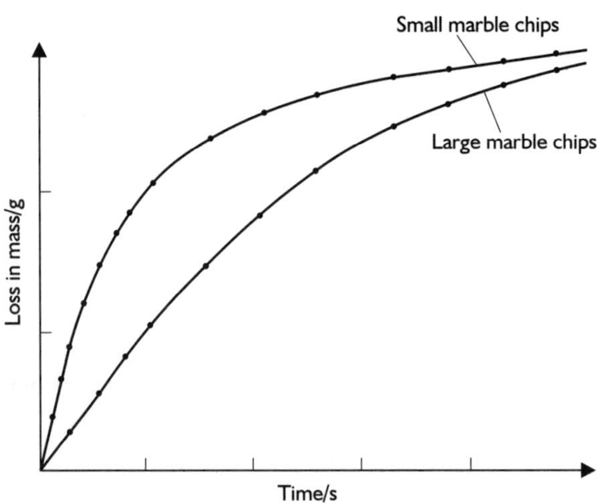

The effect of concentration on the rate of reaction

The reaction between magnesium and hydrochloric acid

Place 50 cm^3 of 2 mol dm^{-3} hydrochloric acid into a beaker and add 3 cm of magnesium ribbon, at the same time start a stop-watch. Make a note of how long it takes for the magnesium to react completely. Repeat the experiment using 25 cm^3 of 2 mol dm^{-3} hydrochloric acid mixed with 25 cm^3 of water. You will find that the magnesium reacts in a far shorter time in the more concentrated acid.

magnesium + hydrochloric acid → hydrogen + magnesium chloride

$$Mg(s) + 2HCl(aq) \rightarrow H_2(g) + MgCl_2(aq)$$

The reaction between marble chips and hydrochloric acid

Add about 20 cm^3 of 2 mol dm^{-3} of hydrochloric acid to 20 cm^3 of water (still an excess) (see Fig. 18.3) and to this solution add 6 g of marble chips. Note the total mass and immediately start the stop-watch. Note the mass every 30 seconds. Plot a graph of mass on the vertical scale against time on the horizontal scale.

Compare your result with that obtained earlier with 40 cm^3 of 2 mol dm^{-3} hydrochloric acid. Your graph should be similar to that shown in Fig. 18.5.

Fig. 18.5

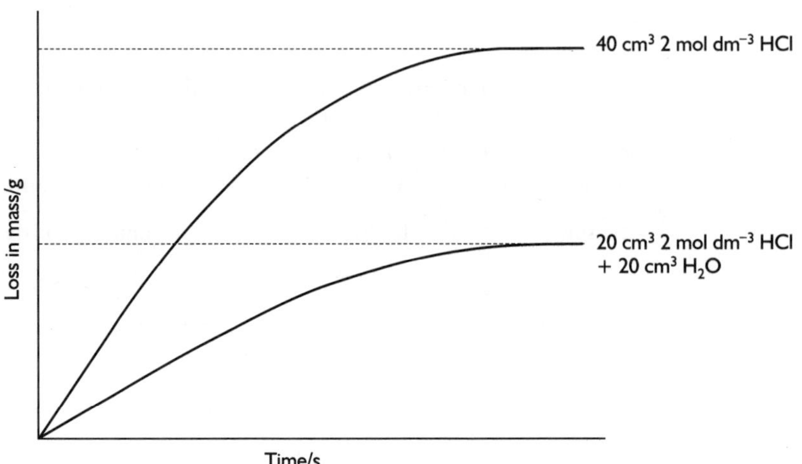

The reaction between sodium thiosulphate and hydrochloric acid

When dilute hydrochloric acid is added to sodium thiosulphate solution, a fine deposit of sulphur is formed. The sulphur makes the solution cloudy. As more and more sulphur is formed, the solution becomes more and more cloudy. Soon it is impossible to see through the solution (see Fig. 18.6).

$$\text{sodium thiosulphate} + \text{hydrochloric acid} \rightarrow \text{sodium chloride} + \text{water} + \text{sulphur dioxide} + \text{sulphur}$$

$$Na_2S_2O_3(aq) + 2HCl(aq) \rightarrow 2NaCl(aq) + H_2O(l) + SO_2(g) + S(s)$$

Fig. 18.6

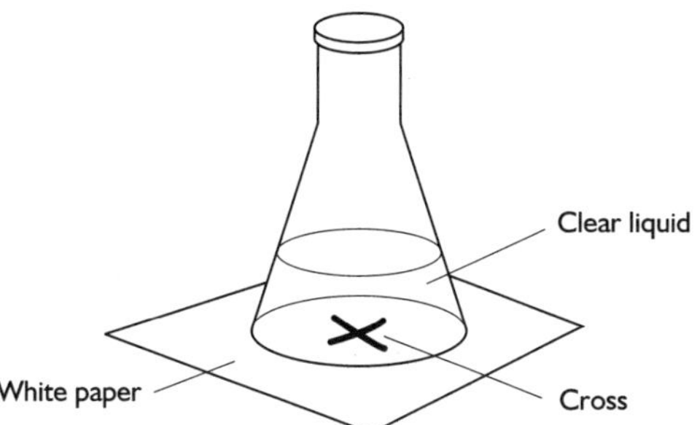

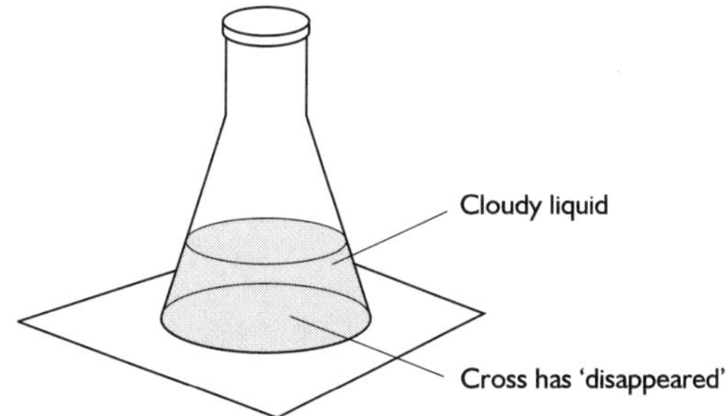

The cloudiness can be used to measure the speed of the reaction. Mark a cross on a piece of paper and stand a beaker on the cross. Measure 30 cm^3 of 0.16 mol dm^{-3} sodium thiosulphate into the beaker and mix with 20 cm^3 of water. Add 5 cm^3 of 2 mol dm^{-3} hydrochloric acid and start the clock. Stop the clock as soon as the cross cannot be seen.

Repeat the experiment using different volumes of the sodium thiosulphate solution, but each time make the total volume up to 50 cm^3 by adding water.

Your results should be similar to those shown in the graph in Fig. 18.7.

Fig. 18.7

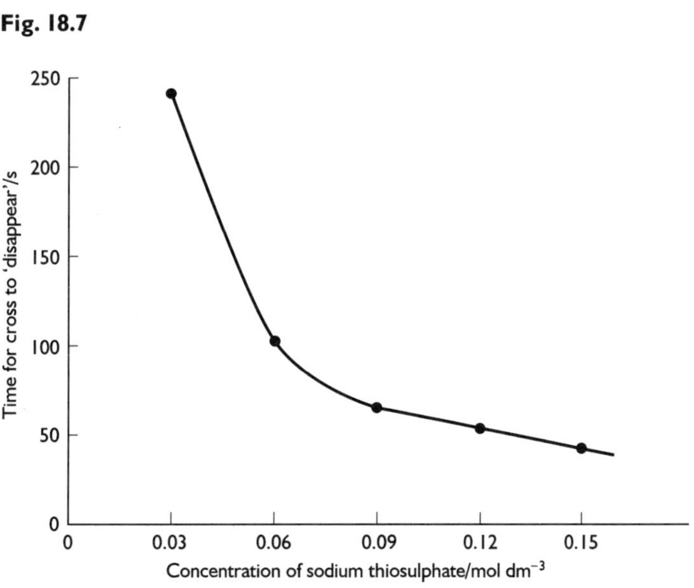

(**Note** that sulphur dioxide is a product of this reaction. Some of you, particularly if you are an asthma sufferer, will be affected by this gas, so **take care**.)

The effect of temperature on the rate of reaction

This is most readily studied by the reaction between sodium thiosulphate and hydrochloric acid. The weakest solution used in the experiment investigating the effect of concentration is used each time. The experiment is carried out at room temperature and at 30 °C, 40 °C, 50 °C, 60 °C and 70 °C. Your graph should be similar to that shown in Fig. 18.8.

The graph shows that the higher the temperature the faster the rate of reaction.

Fig. 18.8

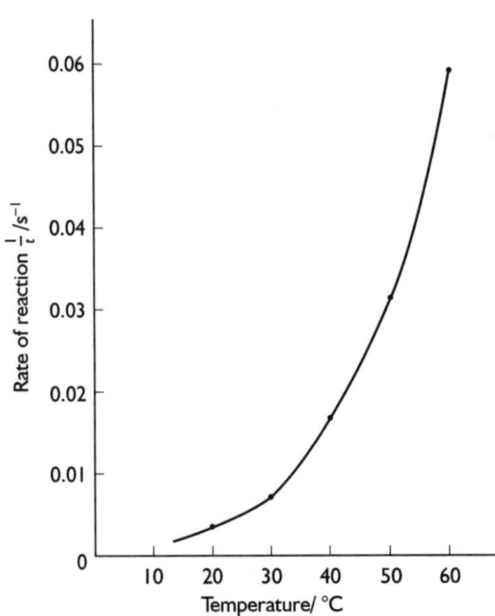

The effect of catalysts

The apparatus shown in Fig. 18.9 can be used to show how catalysts speed up a reaction. Weigh out exactly 1 g of manganese(IV) oxide. Pour 50 cm^3 of water into the conical flask and add 10 cm^3 of '10 volume' hydrogen peroxide. Add the manganese(IV) oxide to the conical flask and quickly cork. The volume of oxygen given off is measured at regular intervals. (The gas can be shown to be oxygen because it will re-light a glowing splint.) The graph you obtain should look like that shown in Fig. 18.10.

To prove that manganese(IV) oxide is really a catalyst in this reaction, you will have to show that:

- it does speed up the rate of reaction (hydrogen peroxide is relatively stable at room temperature);

Fig. 18.9

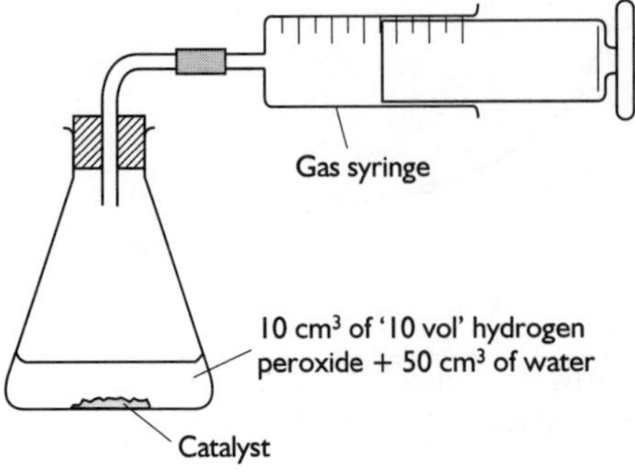

Fig. 18.10

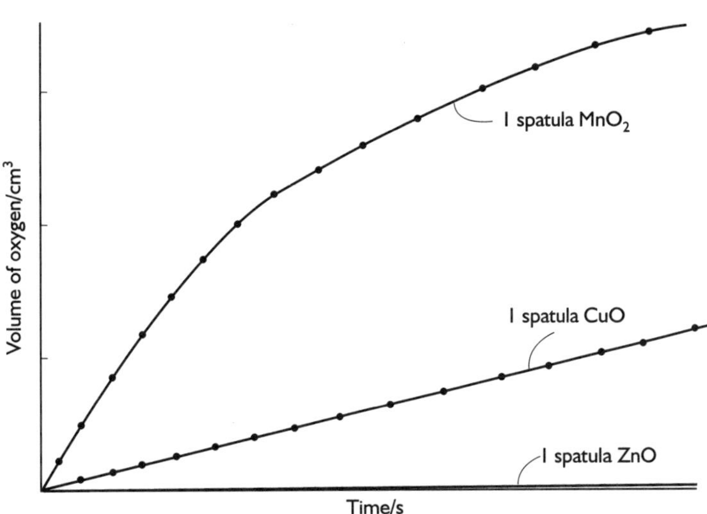

- the substance left in the flask is still manganese(IV) oxide;
- the mass of the catalyst is unchanged.

The experiment can be tried with oxides of other transition metals such as copper(II) oxide and iron(III) oxide. Compounds of transition metals are usually very good catalysts. Lead(IV) oxide also catalyses the decomposition of hydrogen peroxide:

hydrogen peroxide → oxygen + water

$$2H_2O_2(aq) \rightarrow O_2(g) + 2H_2O(l)$$

In all the above reactions, the slope of the graph tells you the rate of the reaction; the steeper the slope the faster the rate of the reaction. When the reaction has finished, the slope is horizontal.

Note that the rate can be measured either by the loss of reactants or by the rate of formation of a product. In the reaction between magnesium and hydrochloric acid we measured how long it took the magnesium to react; but in the reaction between marble chips and hydrochloric acid we measured the rate of formation of carbon dioxide.

Reactions involving enzymes

Yogurt and cheese are prepared from milk. When making yogurt, the milk is boiled to make it concentrated and to kill off unwanted micro-organisms. An enzyme is added to the concentrated milk kept at room temperature. It is kept under sterilized conditions for about 12 hours and yogurt is formed. New batches of yogurt are made by adding small amounts of previously made yogurt. The enzyme converts the sugar in milk (lactose) to lactic acid.

The older style detergents caused a great deal of pollution. They were not very soluble in water and they were not biodegradable, i.e. once put into water they remained and caused a great deal of foam. Modern detergents contain enzymes called proteases, making them soluble and biodegradable so that they form harmless products. Proteases break down protein materials such as grass, sweat, blood, gravy, egg and other food stains. Some people are allergic to certain brands of washing powder, particularly those containing enzymes. If you get a rash when using a certain type of washing powder, stop using it.

Fermentation to produce alcohol in beers and wines also depends on enzymes. Sugar is converted into ethanol at room temperature. It is interesting to note that the concentration of alcohol made by this method does not exceed about 7%. At about this concentration the enzyme in yeast is denatured.

Bread making depends upon the use of enzymes. Yeast is added to the mixture of flour, water and sodium chloride (common salt) and left at room temperature. Carbon dioxide is given off and this causes the bread to rise.

The effect of acids and temperature on enzymes can be seen in the graphs in Fig. 18.11. Enzymes only function between a certain range of pH and certain temperatures.

Fig. 18.11

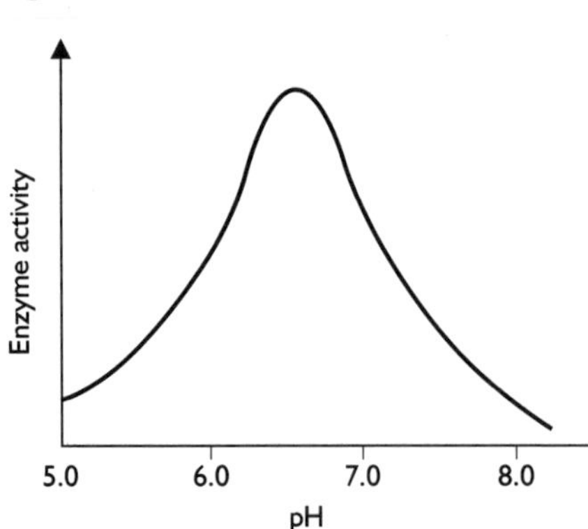

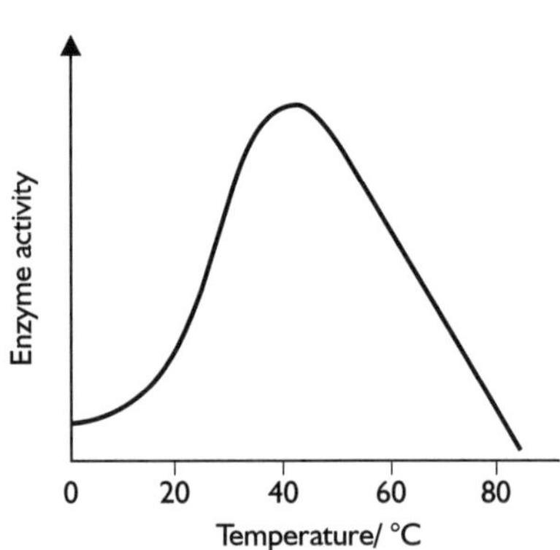

Enzymes are used more and more in industry for other manufacturing processes, including the tenderizing of meat and making soft-centred chocolates.

Reversible reactions

Many chemical reactions can be **reversed**. The industrial processes of extracting metals from their oxide ores is, in effect, the chemist's way of reversing the reactions which occur in nature. Iron that was present on the surface of the Earth when its crust formed, has been oxidized to iron(III) oxide by chemical attack from oxygen in the presence of water by rusting in fact. This oxide is found widely distributed in rocks and gives the brown colour to sand, clay and sandstone. We now reverse that process to make use of the metal. The same is true of other metals.

Thermal dissociation of ammonium chloride

The thermal dissociation of ammonium chloride is an example of a reversible reaction. When ammonium chloride is heated it breaks down into ammonia and hydrogen chloride. However, these two gases react together to give ammonium chloride. If you heat ammonium chloride gently in a test tube you will see a white solid form near the top of the test tube. If you continue to heat the ammonium chloride and hold a piece of damp universal indicator paper at the mouth of the test tube, the paper will first turn blue and then red. This is because ammonia diffuses faster than ammonium chloride and turns the indicator paper blue, followed by hydrogen chloride gas which turns the paper red.

ammonium chloride $\rightleftharpoons$ ammonia + hydrogen chloride

$$NH_4Cl(s) \rightleftharpoons NH_3(g) + HCl(g)$$

Remember that although this reaction goes from a solid to a gas and back to a solid, the reaction is thermal dissociation and not sublimation. In sublimation, no new substances are formed as intermediate products.

(This reaction is also used as a test for either ammonia or hydrogen chloride. If you can smell ammonia given off, the gas turns damp litmus paper blue and the gas gives a white smoke with hydrogen chloride, then the gas must be ammonia. Similarly, if an acidic gas is given off that fumes in moist air and gives a white smoke with ammonia, then the gas is hydrogen chloride.)

The thermal dissociation of copper(II) sulphate crystals

The thermal dissociation of hydrated copper(II) sulphate crystals to anhydrous copper(II) sulphate and water is also a reversible reaction. When hydrated copper(II) sulphate crystals are heated gently, the colour changes from blue to white as anhydrous copper(II) sulphate is formed. If water is added to anhydrous copper(II) sulphate, the white solid goes blue as hydrated copper(II) sulphate is formed.

hydrated copper(II) sulphate $\rightleftharpoons$ anhydrous copper(II) sulphate + water

$$CuSO_4.5H_2O(s) \rightleftharpoons CuSO_4(s) + 5H_2O(l)$$

blue white

This reaction can be used to show the *presence* of water. To show that a liquid *is* water you would have to measure its melting point (0 °C) and its boiling point (100 °C).)

Dynamic equilibrium

Physical equilibrium

The simplest example of an equilibrium process is the evaporation and condensation of water. We know that water evaporates to form water vapour at room temperature. We also know that it will evaporate faster at 100 °C. We further know that water vapour will condense back to water and that this occurs faster at room temperature than at 100 °C. What happens if we keep water in a closed vessel at a temperature between room temperature and 100 °C? Both processes occur at the same time and a balance is achieved when the amounts of water in the liquid and vapour states no longer change. **Evaporation is occurring as fast as condensation.** We show this as

$$\text{water} \underset{\text{evaporation}}{\overset{\text{condensation}}{\rightleftarrows}} \text{water vapour}$$

$$H_2O(l) \rightleftarrows H_2O(g)$$

In this **equilibrium** the rate of evaporation of the water equals the rate of condensation of the vapour. Although the two processes continue for ever, they do so at the same rate, so we detect no change in the proportions of vapour and liquid in the *closed vessel*. If the vessel was not closed, the vapour molecules could escape more easily than the liquid molecules; there would be less vapour to condense to liquid and so the speed of condensation would go down while the speed of evaporation would stay the same. This would eventually result in the water evaporating away completely. Equilibrium requires a closed vessel in this example.

Chemical equilibrium

The reaction between iodine monochloride and chlorine

Your teacher might demonstrate to you the reaction between iodine and chlorine to form iodine trichloride. When chlorine is passed into a U-tube containing iodine, a brown liquid is formed, iodine monochloride:

iodine + chlorine → iodine monochloride

$$I_2(s) + Cl_2(g) \rightarrow 2ICl(l)$$

If more chlorine is passed through the U-tube, a yellow solid, iodine trichloride, is formed:

iodine monochloride + chlorine ⇌ iodine trichloride

$$ICl(l) + Cl_2(g) \rightleftharpoons ICl_3(s)$$

brown   yellow

The reaction is reversible.

If the U-tube is turned upside down, chlorine falls out because it is a dense gas (heavier than air) and the brown liquid reforms. If chlorine is then passed through again, the yellow solid reappears.

The procedure is summarized in Fig. 18.12.

The reaction between bismuth chloride and water

If water is added to a solution of bismuth(III) chloride in concentrated hydrochloric acid, a white precipitate of bismuth(III) oxychloride is formed. If concentrated hydrochloric acid is added to the mixture, the solution goes clear again. The reaction is reversible:

bismuth(III) chloride + water ⇌ bismuth(III) oxychloride + hydrochloric acid

$$BiCl_3(aq) + H_2O(l) \rightleftharpoons BiOCl(s) + 2HCl(aq)$$

colourless   white precipitate

Fig. 18.12

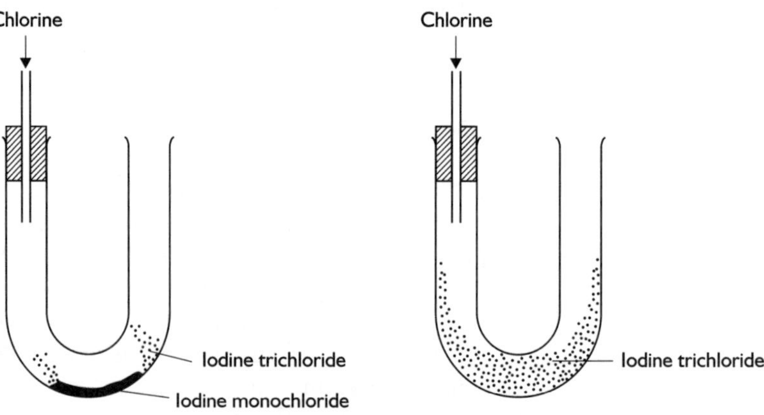

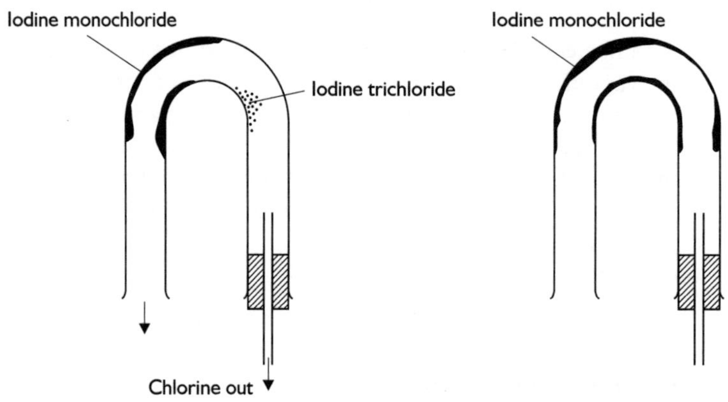

The reaction between potassium chromate(VI) and sulphuric acid

Potassium chromate(VI) is an orange solution. If sulphuric acid is added to the mixture, it goes yellow because potassium dichromate(VI) solution is formed. If sodium hydroxide is added to the yellow solution of potassium dichromate, it returns to orange. The reaction is reversible:

$$\text{chromate(VI) ions} + \text{acid} \rightleftharpoons \text{dichromate(VI) ions} + \text{water}$$

$$\underset{\text{yellow}}{2CrO_4^{2-}(aq)} + 2H^+(aq) \rightleftharpoons \underset{\text{orange}}{Cr_2O_7^{2-}(aq)} + H_2O(l)$$

Litmus solution

An example of a reversible reaction you will have met frequently is the action of acids and alkalis on litmus solution. When an acid is added the indicator turns red, and when an alkali is added the solution turns blue. When the indicator is in water the solution is mauve—mid-way between both colours.

Because some reactions go in both directions, a position can be reached where the speed (or rate) of the forward reaction is equal to the speed of the reverse reaction. At this point the reaction is said to be in a state of **dynamic equilibrium**. Looking at one of the above reactions, this point is reached when the rate of formation of the dichromate(VI) ions equals the rate of formation of the chromate(VI) ions.

Le Chatelier's principle

The effects of changing conditions on an equilibrium can be predicted using **Le Chatelier's principle**. The principle states that:

If an equilibrium is disturbed by changing the conditions such as temperature, pressure or concentration, the equilibrium will shift to counteract the change, and a new equilibrium will be established.

In the reaction between iodine monochloride and chlorine to form iodine trichloride, we can predict by applying Le Chatelier's principle that adding excess chlorine will make the reaction move in the direction to form more iodine trichloride. If, on the other hand, chlorine is removed by turning the U-tube upside down, more chlorine will be formed by the decomposition of iodine trichloride.

In the reaction between bismuth(III) chloride and water, the addition of more water will make the equilibrium move in the direction of making bismuth(III) oxychloride forming a white precipitate. If concentrated hydrochloric acid (it contains very little water) is added, the equilibrium will use up the acid by forming bismuth(III) chloride, the white precipitate will disappear and the solution will go colourless.

Remember that a catalyst does not alter the position of an equilibrium reaction; it cannot give you more of the product. However, a catalyst does speed up the rate of attaining equilibrium.

Manufacture of ammonia

An example of the application of Le Chatelier's principle is shown in the manufacture of ammonia by the Haber process. The reaction is exothermic in the forward direction and so endothermic in reverse.

$$N_2(g) + 3H_2(g) \underset{\text{endothermic reaction}}{\overset{\text{exothermic reaction}}{\rightleftarrows}} 2NH_3(g)$$

The $\leftrightarrows$ sign indicates that the chemical reaction is 'going both ways' at the same time. That is, nitrogen and hydrogen molecules are reacting together to form ammonia molecules at the same time as ammonia molecules are decomposing into nitrogen and hydrogen molecules. At equilibrium, these two opposing processes are happening at the same speed and the **equilibrium mixture** contains a constant proportion of each substance.

Effect of temperature change

An increase in temperature will cause equilibrium to be established more quickly. However, because this is an exothermic change, if the temperature of the equilibrium mixture is raised, the reaction which takes in heat is favoured. The reverse reaction takes in heat so the equilibrium mixture becomes less concentrated in ammonia molecules and more concentrated in hydrogen and nitrogen molecules. We see that increased temperature moves the position of equilibrium to the left. For high yield therefore, the reaction should be carried out at as *low a temperature as possible*. This is not done in practice because the reaction would become very slow.

Effect of pressure change

Changing the pressure of a gas changes it concentration. We increase concentrations of gases by increasing their pressure—squeezing more molecules into the same space. Increased pressure therefore means increased reaction speed and equilibrium is established faster. However, as with temperature change, the effect may not be the same on the forward and backward reactions. The effect depends on the change in the number of molecules in the reaction mixture as the reaction proceeds. In the synthesis of ammonia, four molecules of reactants becomes two molecules of products. This decrease in molecules represents a decrease in volume. **Increased pressure favours the reaction by which there is a decrease in volume.** The opposite is true of a decrease in pressure. In ammonia synthesis, high pressures are used to give high yields of ammonia.

Effect of removing the ammonia

If the ammonia is removed by either dissolving it in water or liquefying the ammonia under pressure, more nitrogen and hydrogen will combine to form ammonia. (The unreacted nitrogen and hydrogen are recycled.)

Table 18.1 shows the effects of changing conditions on the position of equilibrium. In summary:

Exothermic reaction + temperature rise = decreased yield of product
Endothermic reaction + temperature rise = increased yield of product
Molecules decrease on reaction + pressure rise = increased yield of product
Molecules increase on reaction + pressure rise = decreased yield of product

Table 18.1 The effects of conditions on the position of equilibrium

Variable	Reaction type	Effect on position of equilibrium	Example/industrial process
Temperature increase	Exothermic	Moves to left—less product forms	Contact process for sulphuric acid production
Temperature decrease		Moves to right—more product forms	$2SO_2 + O_2 \rightleftharpoons 2SO_3$ $\Delta H = -186$ kJ
Temperature increase	Endothermic	Moves to right—more product forms	Production of steam from water
Temperature decrease		Moves to left—less product forms	$H_2O(l) \rightleftharpoons H_2O(g)$ $\Delta H = 40.6$ kJ
Pressure increase	Decrease in molecules left to right	Moves to right—more product forms	Haber process for ammonia production
Pressure decrease		Moves to left—less product forms	$N_2 + 3H_2 \rightleftharpoons 2NH_3$ 4 moles 2 moles
Pressure increase	Increase in molecules left to right	Moves to left—less product forms	$2O_3 \rightleftharpoons 3O_2$ 2moles 3moles
Pressure decrease		Moves to right—more product forms	

Energy changes in chemical reactions

When chemical reactions occur there is often a change of temperature. For example, if you placed a thermometer in sodium hydroxide solution and added hydrochloric acid a little at a time you would notice that there would be a steady rise in the temperature until all the sodium hydroxide had reacted.

You may have carried out the following experiments and know that there are temperature changes in each reaction:

- dissolving (e.g. making a solution of potassium nitrate in water);
- displacement reactions (e.g. of one metal by another, such as adding zinc to copper(II) sulphate solution);
- precipitation reactions (e.g. adding sodium carbonate solution to barium sulphate solution);
- reactions between acids and carbonates (e.g. adding hydrochloric acid to calcium carbonate).

Exothermic and endothermic reactions

Exothermic reactions

Reactions that give out heat energy are said to be **exothermic**.

The following reactions are examples of exothermic reactions:

- reacting sodium hydroxide solution with hydrochloric acid
- adding concentrated sulphuric acid to water (Your teacher might demonstrate this experiment to you. You will realize, once you have seen this experiment, why you must always add concentrated sulphuric acid to water and *not* water to concentrated sulphuric acid!)
- adding drops of water to anhydrous copper(II) sulphate.

All combustion reactions are exothermic.

Endothermic reactions

Reactions that take in heat energy are said to be **endothermic.**

The following reactions are examples of endothermic reactions:

- dissolving potassium chloride in water;
- reacting barium hydroxide solution with ammonium thiocyanate solution (your teacher might demonstrate this reaction to you).

Photosynthesis is a well-known example of an endothermic reaction. Carbon dioxide from the air and water from the soil react in the presence of sunlight and a catalyst of chlorophyll to form sugar and oxygen. The products of photosynthesis can be burnt as fuels, producing a large amount of heat energy together with carbon dioxide and water. Products formed from photosynthesis are often known as 'bottled' sunshine because they store energy obtained from the sun.

Energy level diagrams

Bond breaking and bond making

When bonds between atoms are broken, energy is taken in. When new bonds form between atoms, energy is given out. The overall energy change of a reaction is due to the difference between these two quantities.

When hydrogen reacts with chlorine the reaction gives out heat—the mixture explodes! The energy given out when covalent bonds form between hydrogen and chlorine atoms is greater than the energy taken in to break the covalent bonds in hydrogen molecules and chlorine molecules (Table 18.2). This is shown in Fig. 18.13 and is an example of an exothermic reaction.

When ozone is formed in the stratosphere (the ozone layer), ultraviolet light gives energy to oxygen molecules, O_2, to convert them into ozone molecules, O_3. This is shown in Fig. 18.14 and is an example of an endothermic reaction. The energy given out when bonds between atoms in diatomic oxygen break is greater than the energy given out when bonds form to produce the ozone molecule.

Table 18.2

Bond	Covalent bond energies/kJ per mole of bonds
H—H	436
Cl—Cl	242
H—Cl	431

The bond energy is the energy, in kJ, needed to break 1 mole of the covalent bond specified

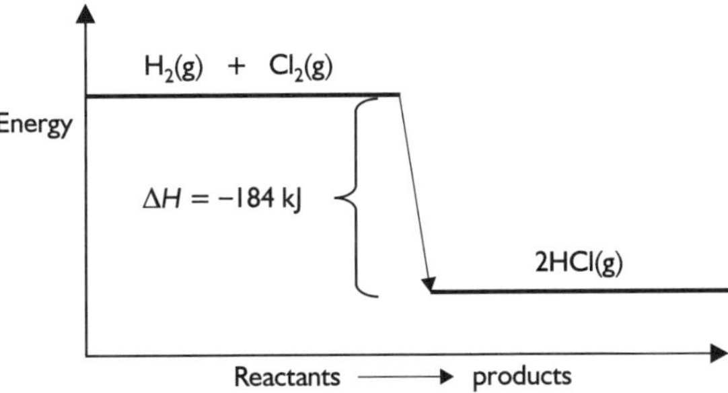

Fig. 18.13 Energy level diagram for the reaction of hydrogen and chlorine to form hydrogen chloride

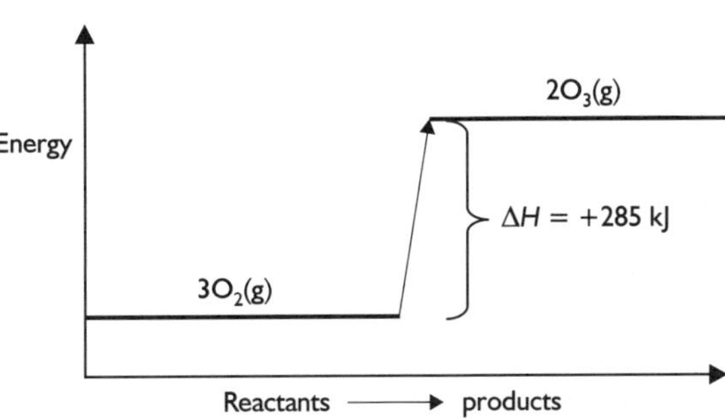

Fig. 18.14 Energy level diagram for the conversion of oxygen into ozone in the ozone layer

Bond energies

To study the energy diagram above in more detail we need to find the energies of the bonds involved. A data book will give the following information about bond energies (see Table 18.2).

Applied to the equation for the reaction of hydrogen with chlorine, we have

$H_2(g)$	+	$Cl_2(g)$	$\rightarrow$	$2HCl(g)$
Energy needed to break 1 mole of H—H bonds = 436 kJ		Energy needed to break 1 mole of Cl—Cl bonds = 242 kJ		Energy given out on making 2 moles of H—Cl bonds = 2×431 kJ

Total energy to be added to break the bonds in 1 mole of hydrogen and 1 mole of chlorine = $436 + 242 = 678$ kJ

Total energy given out in the formation of 2 moles of bonds in hydrogen chloride = $2 \times 431 = 862$ kJ

We see that more energy is given out in making the bond of the products than was taken in to break the bonds in the reactants. This leaves a surplus of energy, 184 kilojoules, given out. The reaction is exothermic. So the calculated value for the energy change of the above reaction is $\Delta H = -184$ kJ per mole of reaction.

The significance of bond energies

Bond energies tell us the strength of covalent bonds in covalently bonded elements and compounds.

The table of bond energies (Table 18.3) shows that

(i) not all bonds are equal in strength;
(ii) the strength of a bond can explain the reactivity, or lack of it, in substances.

For example, the very strong bonds in nitrogen molecules would lead us to predict that nitrogen would not be very reactive—a prediction confirmed by observation. Alternatively, the bonds between chlorine atoms are rather weak by comparison and chlorine would be expected to be much more reactive than nitrogen—which it is.

Table 18.3

Bond	Bond energy/kJ per mole of bonds
O=O	497
N≡N	945
H—O	464
C=O	800
C—F	452
C—Cl	339

Bond energies in calculations

We have earlier calculated the energy change for a simple chemical reaction involving only the making and breaking of covalent bonds.

Boiling a substance

Let us now consider a common misconception at this level of study—that boiling a substance splits the substance into its elements. A little thought will tell us that this is not what we observe. If it *were* so, the kitchen at home would soon fill with an explosive mixture of hydrogen and oxygen simply as a result of boiling water! We can show that this is not likely using bond energies. The reactions we are comparing are

$H_2O(l) \rightarrow H_2O(g)$ vaporization of water

and

$H_2O(g) \rightarrow H_2(g) + \frac{1}{2}O_2(g)$ decomposing water into its elements.

The energy to carry out the vaporization is the heat of vaporization of water, $\Delta H = +40.6\,\text{kJ mole}^{-1}$. To calculate the energy needed to convert 1 mole of water vapour into hydrogen and oxygen gases, we can use bond energy data (Fig. 18.15).

The energy change for the whole decomposition is the overall energy change for this reaction 928 kJ taken in less 684.5 given out = +243.5 kJ.

We see now that vaporizing 1 mole of water (18 g) requires an input of 40.6 kJ, whereas to decompose the same quantity requires 243.5 kJ, more than five times as much energy. This comparison is shown in the energy level diagrams (Fig. 18.16).

Fig. 18.15

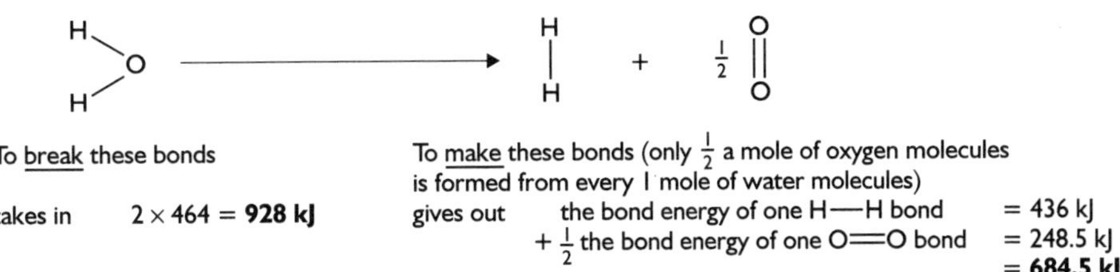

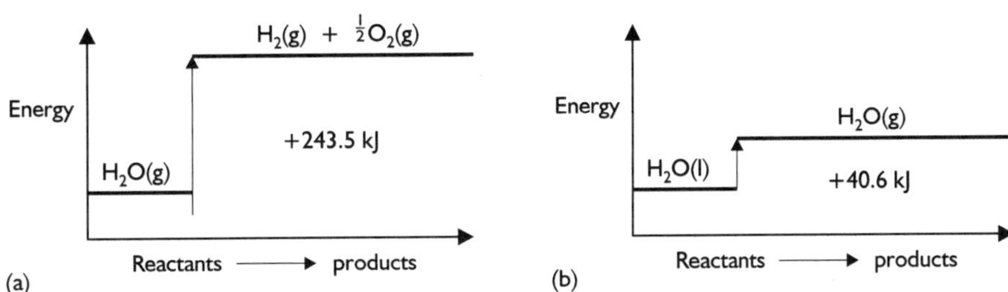

Fig. 18.16 Energy level diagrams. (a) Energy change for decomposition of 1 mole of water into its elements. (b) Energy change for vaporization of 1 mole of water

Unreactive chlorofluorocarbons, CFCs

The reason why chlorofluorocarbons (CFCs) are so unreactive in our atmosphere is related to the strength of the C—F and the C—Cl bonds they contain. Table 18.3 shows that the C—F bond is especially strong at 452 kJ mole^{-1}.

Activation energy of a reaction

Most reactions will not start unless they are supplied with energy. A match must be heated by friction before it will ignite; light energy must be shone onto a mixture of hydrogen and chlorine before it will form hydrogen chloride as in the reaction discussed earlier.

Energy must be added to reactants to loosen the bonds before reaction with the formation of new bonds takes place. This energy 'activates' the molecules and so is called the activation energy. The following energy level diagram shows the activation energy. This type of diagram is called an **energy profile** (Fig. 18.17).

The energy profile diagram shows that to react, a mixture of hydrogen and chlorine requires energy to be added. This can be done by shining UV light on the mixture. The

Fig. 18.17 Energy profile for the reaction of hydrogen with chlorine in UV light

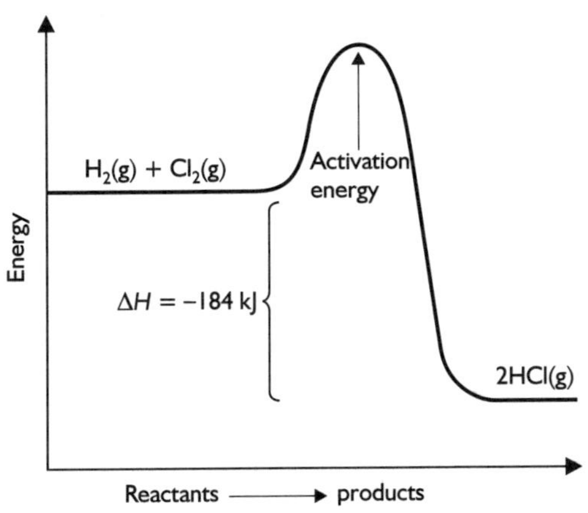

energy of the reactants is raised to the top of the 'hill' where the bonds are 'looser' and there they react to form the products. As calculated earlier, the bonds in the products are stronger than those in the reactants, resulting in hydrogen chloride formation and excess energy being given out in the form of heat. The overall energy change is still the difference in energy between the reactants and products despite the input of activation energy—as can be seen from the diagram.

The exothermic nature of most chemical reactions suggests that we can make use of a chemical reaction to heat our homes. This we do by burning fuels—an oxidation process usually called combustion.

Fuels

Fuels give out energy when they burn in oxygen or in air. Fuels usually contain carbon and hydrogen and the products of combustion are carbon dioxide and water, together with lots of energy. Coal is mainly carbon and it burns in an excess of air to give carbon dioxide:

carbon + oxygen → carbon dioxide

$$C(s) + O_2(g) \rightarrow CO_2(g)$$

North Sea gas (natural gas) is mainly methane. It burns in an excess of air to give carbon dioxide and water:

methane + oxygen → carbon dioxide + water

$$CH_4(g) + 2O_2(g) \rightarrow CO_2(g) + 2H_2O(l)$$

If a limited amount of air is used, the poisonous gas carbon monoxide is formed in both cases. This is why it is important that you keep a room well-ventilated when fuels are burning.

With so many different fuels to choose from, we would, if possible, choose the one that gives most heat energy per unit of cost to ourselves. This is not, however, the only consideration. It may not always be possible to obtain the cheapest fuel, or to use it if it is available. The cheapest fuel may be dirty to use or just inconvenient. Consider all the available energy sources, electricity, coal, oil, natural gas, wood and bottled gas. Make a list of the advantages and disadvantages of each for use in your own home. The results of your analysis must be compared with the relative costs of these sources—roughly in order of cost for the same heat output (most expensive first)—electricity > oil > bottled gas > natural gas > coal > wood. However, the order will vary a little depending on the area in which you live; wood is cheaper in the countryside, where there are trees, than in areas where there are no trees.

Measuring the heat energy given out by burning fuel

To make the comparison referred to above, we need a method of finding the heat output per unit weight of a fuel. We do this in a calorimeter.

The principle of the method is that heat energy can be measured if it is made to heat water. It is known that

4.2 kilojoules of energy will raise the temperature of 1 kilogram of water by 1 °C; therefore, energy in kJ = mass of water in kg × 4.2 × temperature rise in °C

As a laboratory investigation, the following would be an acceptable way of comparing the heat output of different fuels.

The investigation

The apparatus is set up as shown in Fig. 18.18. The tin container holds, say, 500 g (half a kilogram) of water.

(i) The fuel, in its container, is weighed (w_1).
(ii) The temperature of the water in the can is measured (T_1).
(iii) The container of fuel is placed under the can of water and lit.
(iv) The water is stirred as the burning fuel heats it.

Fig. 18.18

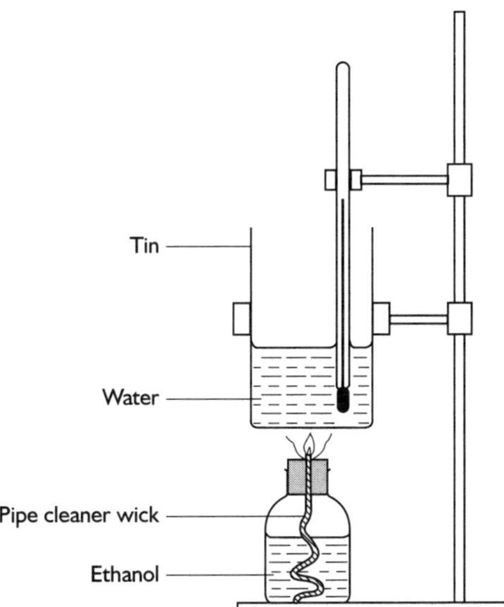

(v) When the temperature of the water has risen by just under 10 °C the flame is put out by excluding air.
(vi) The highest temperature of the water is taken (T_2).*
(vii) The fuel container is reweighed (w_2).

*The temperature may rise a little further because heat still in the bottom of the can continues to warm it after the flame has been extinguished.

Calculating the energy value of the fuel

Two quantities are needed to assess the fuel.

(i) the energy given out, which is measured by the amount that enters the water;
(ii) the mass of fuel burnt which is $w_1 - w_2$.

The energy value is now found by dividing energy by mass burnt to give an answer in kilojoules per gram of fuel burnt (Table 18.4).

Table 18.4

Energy in water/kJ	Mass of fuel burnt/g	Energy/kJ g^{-1}
$0.5 \times 4.2 \times 10 = 21$ kilojoules	$w_1 - w_2$	$\frac{21}{w_1 - w_2}$

Evaluating the results

It is evident that this cannot be an accurate method of determining the energy value. There are obvious areas of inaccuracy. You may see them if you answer the following questions:

(i) Does all the heat from the burning fuel go into the water?
(ii) If not, where does the rest go?
(iii) Has the temperature rise been accurately measured?
(iv) Has the mass of fuel burnt been accurately measured?

You are now in a position to suggest how the investigation could be improved.

EXAMINATION QUESTIONS

Question 1(F) The graph below (Fig. 18.19) shows the total volume of hydrogen produced in the reaction of magnesium ribbon with excess dilute hydrochloric acid over a period of time.

Fig. 18.19

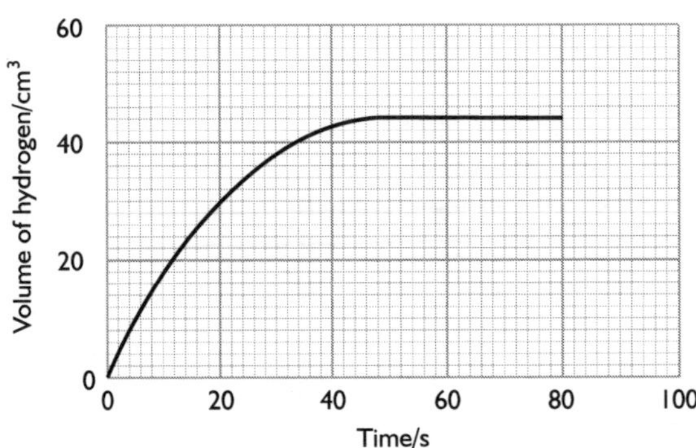

(a) What volume of hydrogen has been produced after 15 seconds? . . . . cm^3 *[1]*

(b) How long does it take to produce 28 cm^3 of hydrogen? . . . . seconds *[1]*

(c) Use the graph to work out the volume of hydrogen produced after 100 seconds . . .

. . . .cm^3 *[1]*

(d) Sketch *on the graph* the results you would expect to obtain if the same mass of magnesium was treated with more concentrated acid. *[2]*

(SEG)

Question 2(F) Oxygen can be made by adding manganese(IV) oxide to hydrogen peroxide (H_2O_2). Manganese(IV) oxide increases the speed of the reaction but it remains chemically unchanged at the end of the reaction.

(a) Suggest the name of the other product of this reaction. *[1]*

(b) What is the test for oxygen gas? *[1]*

(c) What name is given to a chemical like manganese(IV) oxide that speeds up the rate of a reaction, but remains chemically unchanged at the end of the reaction? *[1]*

(d) Explain why each of the following would speed up the reaction:
  (i) increasing the temperature;
  (ii) increasing the concentration of the hydrogen peroxide;
  (iii) using powdered manganese(IV) oxide instead of lumps of manganese(IV) oxide. *[3]*

Question 3(F) Hydrogen is usually prepared in the laboratory by collecting the gas given off when zinc reacts with sulphuric acid. This reaction was investigated using the apparatus shown (Fig. 18.20).

In a first experiment, the acid was added to the zinc and the volume of hydrogen was noted every 15 s. In a second experiment, five drops of copper sulphate solution were added to the zinc before the addition of the sulphuric acid, but otherwise the experiment was the same. The results obtained were plotted graphically and are shown on the next page (Fig. 18.21).

(a) What can you tell from the different curves resulting from the two experiments? *[1]*

(b) Suggest a possible explanation for the difference between the graphs. *[2]*

(c) Describe an experiment which you would use to see whether or not your suggested explanation in (b) is correct. *[4]*

Fig. 18.20

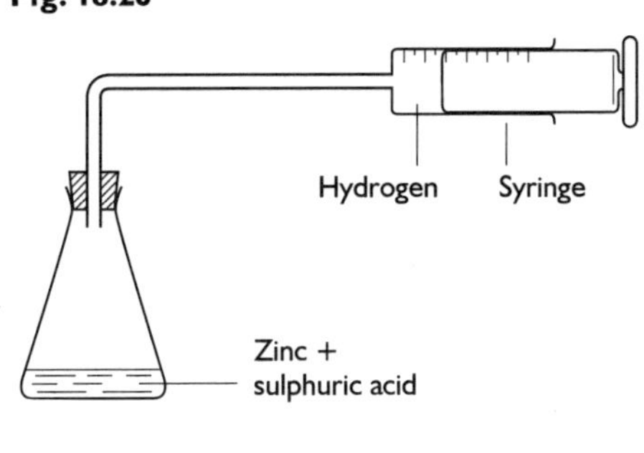

Fig. 18.21

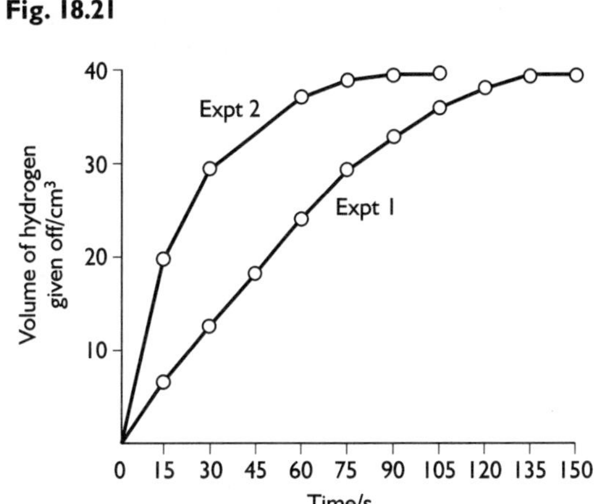

(d) Outline two other experiments to investigate more fully the reaction between zinc and sulphuric acid, and indicate the results that you would expect. *[6]*

Question 4(H)

The table below (Table 18.5) shows the total amount of hydrogen formed when magnesium reacts with hydrochloric acid at 20 °C.

Table 18.5

Time/s	0	20	40	60	80	100	120	140	160
Volume of hydrogen/cm^3	0	7	21	36	51	66	70	72	72

(a) Plot a graph of these results. *[2]*
(b) There is no suitable catalyst for this reaction to speed it up. Suggest two ways in which you could increase the rate of this reaction. *[2]*
(c) Suggest why the rate of reaction slows down near the end of the reaction. *[2]*
(d) Write a balanced chemical equation for this reaction. *[2]*

Question 5(H)

(a) Balance the equation for the formation of ammonia:

$$N_2(g) + H_2(g) \rightleftharpoons NH_3 \quad [1]$$

(b) What does the sign $\rightleftharpoons$ mean? *[1]*
(c) The rate of formation of ammonia can be increased by increasing the pressure. Explain why this happens in terms of the collision theory. *[2]*
(d) Name a suitable catalyst to speed up this reaction. *[1]*
(e) Why does a catalyst make the manufacture of ammonia more economical? *[3]*

Question 6(H)

When covalent elements or compounds react together, bonds are broken and new bonds are formed. Using the ideas of bond breaking and bond forming explain the following:

(a) The reaction between hydrogen and chlorine is exothermic. *[1]*
(b) Hydrogen and oxygen do not react together at room temperature. *[2]*
(c) The reaction $2NH_3(g) \rightarrow N_2(g) + 3H_2(g)$ is endothermic. *[3]*
(d) (i) Using the idea of spectator ions, explain why the reaction between sodium hydroxide and hydrochloric acid is exothermic. *[2]*
(ii) Why would you expect the energy change to be almost the same when 1 mole of any strong acid reacts with 1 mole of any strong alkali? *[2]*

Question 7(H) An equilibrium mixture is formed when iron(II) ions are added to silver ions. The equation for the equilibrium is

$$Fe^{2+}(aq) + Ag^{+}(aq) \rightleftharpoons Ag(s) + Fe^{3+}(aq)$$

(a) What is meant by 'dynamic equilibrium'? *[2]*
(b) What ions are present in solution at equilibrium? *[2]*
(c) What would you see if you added more $Fe^{2+}(aq)$ ions? *[2]*
(d) What would happen to the silver precipitate if more $Fe^{3+}(aq)$ ions were added? *[1]*
(e) $Ag^{+}(aq)$ ions can be removed by precipitation. Name a chemical that could be added and state the name of the silver solid formed. *[2]*

OUTLINE ANSWERS

Question 1
(a) 24 cm^3; (b) 18 seconds; (c) 44 cm^3.
(d) The curve would be steeper (because the acid is more concentrated) but the *same* volume of hydrogen would be given off (because excess acid was used in each case).

Question 2
(a) Water.
(b) Relights a glowing splint.
(c) Catalyst.
(d) (i) Particles move more quickly and therefore collide more often.
(ii) More particles are present and therefore collide more often.
(iii) It increases the surface area of the catalyst.

Question 3
(a) The reaction in experiment 2 was faster.
(b) Copper(II) sulphate (in fact copper) acts as a catalyst in experiment 2.
(c) Add powdered copper to the reacting mixture in place of copper sulphate. If the rate of the reaction increases, then copper does act as a catalyst for this reaction.
(d) (i) Repeat the experiment using *same mass* of finely divided zinc; reaction will be faster. (ii) Repeat the experiment but increase the concentration of the sulphuric acid; reaction will be faster.

Question 4
(a) Your graph should look like the graph of volume of carbon dioxide given off against time drawn in Fig. 18.4.
(b) Use magnesium powder; increase concentration of hydrochloric acid.
(c) The concentration of hydrochloric acid has decreased because some has reacted with the magnesium.
(d) $Mg(s) + 2HCl(aq) \rightarrow MgCl_2(aq) + H_2(g)$.

Question 5
(a) $N_2(g) + 3H_2(g) \rightleftharpoons 2NH_3(g)$.
(b) Reversible reaction.
(c) Increased pressure pushes particles closer together; they therefore collide more often, thus increasing the rate of the reaction.
(d) Iron.
(e) The reaction can take place at a much lower temperature, saving expensive energy costs.

Question 6
(a) The energy required to break H—H bonds and Cl—Cl bonds is less than the energy given out when H—Cl bonds are formed.
(b) The molecules do not have sufficient (activation) energy to react.
(c) The energy required to break the N—H bonds in ammonia is greater than the energy liberated when H—H bonds and N≡N bonds are formed.
(d) Writing the equation in terms of ions we get

$$H^+(aq) + Cl^-(aq) + Na^+(aq) + OH^-(aq) \rightarrow Na^+(aq) + Cl^-(aq) + H_2O(l)$$

Thus the only reaction taking place is $H^+(aq) + OH^-(aq) \rightarrow H_2O(l)$; i.e. bonds are formed which is an exothermic process.

(ii) For *any* strong acid reacting with any strong alkali, the reaction taking place will be $H^+(aq) + OH^-(aq) \rightarrow H_2O(l)$. Thus if the same amount and strength of acid and alkali is used each time, we would expect the energy change to be about the same.

Question 7

(a) The rate of the forward reaction equals the rate of the reverse reaction.
(b) $Fe^{2+}(aq)$, $Fe^{3+}(aq)$ and $Ag^+(aq)$.
(c) The solution would change from green to brown (from iron(II) ions to iron(III) ions).
(d) It would slowly disappear as the equilibrium shifts towards the left.
(e) Sodium chloride; silver chloride.

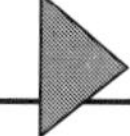

STUDENT ANSWER WITH EXAMINER'S COMMENTS

Excess of calcium carbonate was added to a known volume of dilute hydrochloric acid and a gas was produced. The volume of gas produced was recorded every ten seconds and the results are shown below.

Table 18.6

Time/s	10	20	30	40	50	60	70	80	90	100
Total volume/cm^3	130	225	300	360	410	480	490	500	500	500

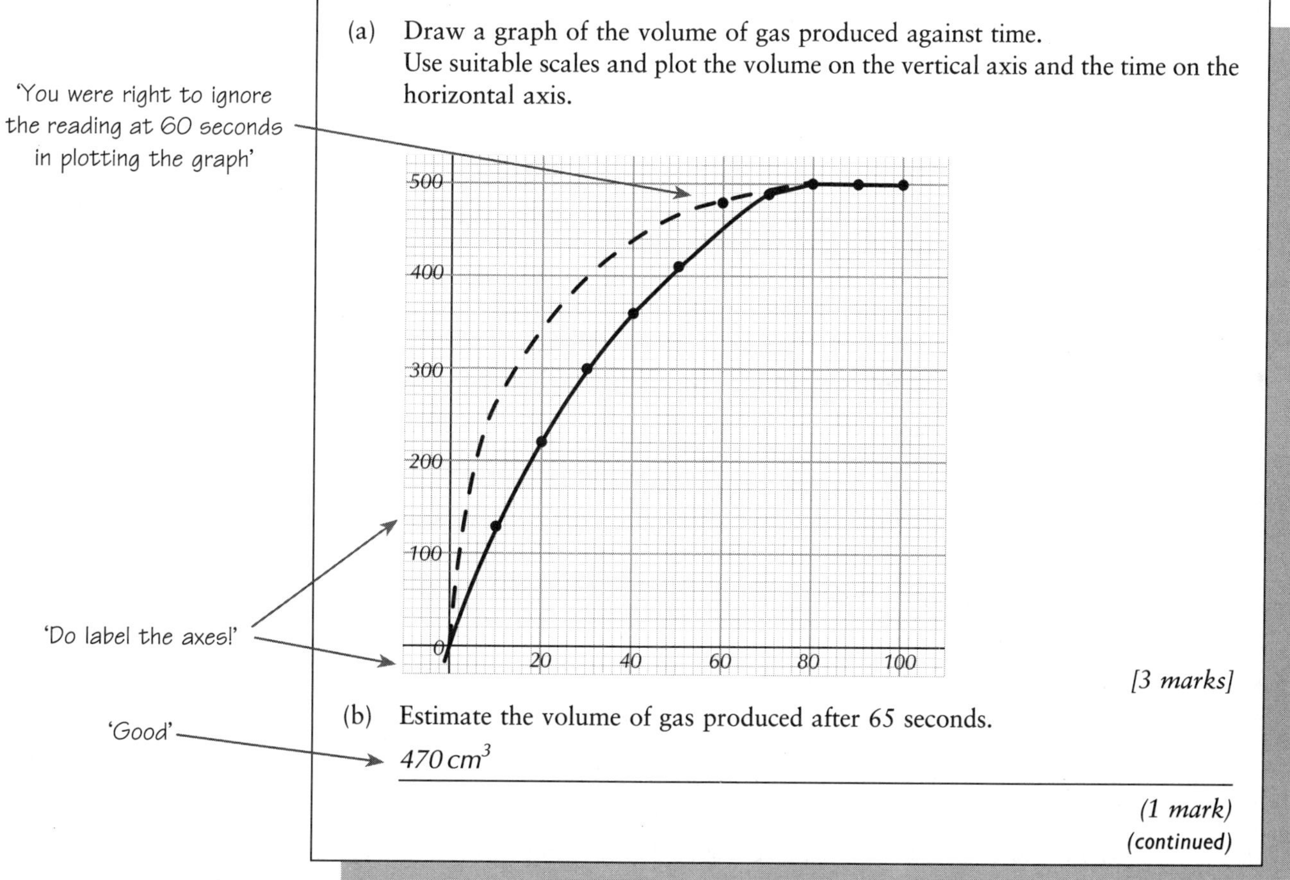

(a) Draw a graph of the volume of gas produced against time. Use suitable scales and plot the volume on the vertical axis and the time on the horizontal axis.

[3 marks]

(b) Estimate the volume of gas produced after 65 seconds.

470 cm^3

(1 mark)

(continued)

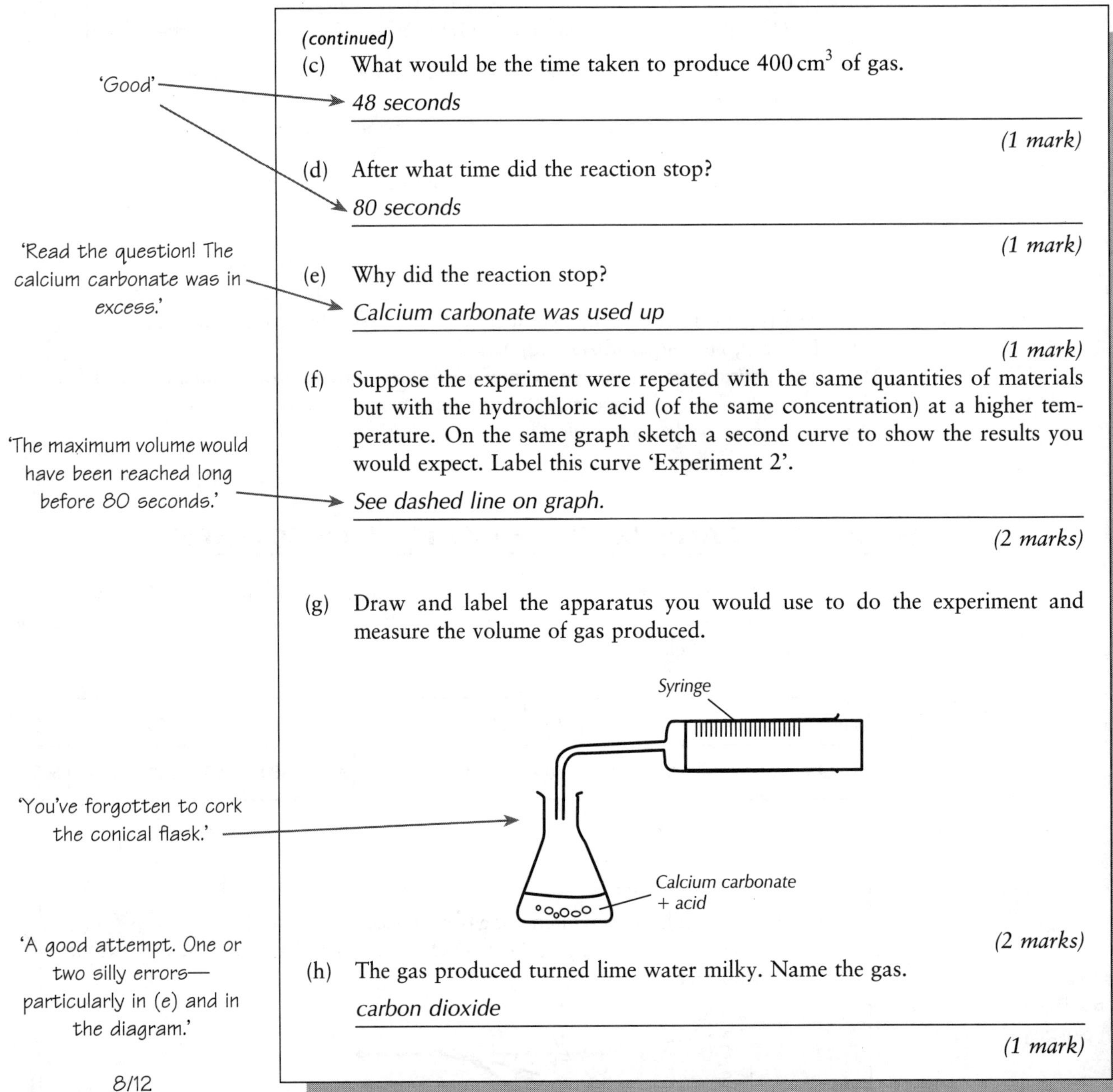

(continued)

(c) What would be the time taken to produce 400 cm^3 of gas.

48 seconds

(1 mark)

(d) After what time did the reaction stop?

80 seconds

(1 mark)

'Good'

(e) Why did the reaction stop?

Calcium carbonate was used up

(1 mark)

'Read the question! The calcium carbonate was in excess.'

(f) Suppose the experiment were repeated with the same quantities of materials but with the hydrochloric acid (of the same concentration) at a higher temperature. On the same graph sketch a second curve to show the results you would expect. Label this curve 'Experiment 2'.

See dashed line on graph.

(2 marks)

'The maximum volume would have been reached long before 80 seconds.'

(g) Draw and label the apparatus you would use to do the experiment and measure the volume of gas produced.

'You've forgotten to cork the conical flask.'

(2 marks)

(h) The gas produced turned lime water milky. Name the gas.

carbon dioxide

(1 mark)

'A good attempt. One or two silly errors— particularly in (e) and in the diagram.'

8/12

SUMMARY

Use this list to help with your revision. Tick off the points as you learn them.

- ▷ The speed (rate) of a reaction increases:
  - ▷ if the temperature is increased;
  - ▷ if the concentration of dissolved reactants is increased;
  - ▷ if the pressure of reacting gases is increased;
  - ▷ if solid reactants are in smaller pieces;
  - ▷ in the presence of light.
- ▷ A catalyst increases the rate of a reaction, but it is not used up in the reaction.
- ▷ Transition metal compounds are good catalysts:
  - ▷ Iron is used in the Haber process for the manufacture of ammonia.
  - ▷ Vanadium(V) oxide is used in the Contact process for the manufacture of sulphuric acid.
  - ▷ Manganese(IV) oxide is used in the decomposition of hydrogen peroxide.

(continued)

(continued)

- The rate of a chemical reaction can be followed by measuring
  (i) the rate of formation of products;
  (ii) the rate at which the reactants are used up.
- Chemical reactions occur when particles collide with one another and have sufficient energy to react (activation energy).
- Increasing the temperature increases the speed of particles and the energy content of particles.
- Enzymes are biological catalysts produced within living organisms; they are used to manufacture a wide range of materials including bread, alcohol and yogurt.
- Enzymes are very sensitive to temperature and pH.
- A reversible change is a change that can be reversed by altering the conditions.
- Changes of state are physical reversible reactions.
- The thermal *dissociation* of ammonia is an example of a reversible reaction. (Thermal *decomposition* is when a chemical is broken down by heat and the products cannot recombine to form the original chemical.)
- The presence of water can be shown by adding the liquid to anhydrous copper(II) sulphate—the white solid turns blue as hydrated copper(II) sulphate is formed—or by adding anhydrous cobalt chloride paper, when the colour change is from blue to pink.
- When the speed (or rate) of the forward reaction is equal to the speed of the reverse reaction, then the reaction is said to be in a state of dynamic equilibrium.
- Le Chatelier's principle states that
  If an equilibrium is disturbed by changing the conditions such as temperature, pressure or concentration, the equilibrium will shift to counteract the change, and a new equilibrium will be established.
- The conditions for the manufacture of ammonia by the Haber process are high pressure, low temperature, iron catalyst and removal of the ammonia as it is formed (either by dissolving it in water or by liquefying the ammonia).
- A catalyst does not alter the position of an equilibrium reaction but it does speed up the rate of attaining equilibrium.
- There is usually a change in temperature when a reaction occurs.
- Exothermic reactions are reactions that give out energy.
- Endothermic reactions are reactions that take in energy.
- All combustion reactions are exothermic.
- Photosynthesis is an endothermic reaction.
- Energy is required to break bonds.
- Energy is given out when bonds are formed.
- The difference between the energy required to break bonds and the energy given out when bonds are formed is called the heat of reaction.
- If more energy is given out than taken in, the reaction is exothermic.
- If less energy is given out than taken in, the reaction is endothermic.
- In order for chemicals to react they must:
  - collide;
  - have sufficient energy to react (activation energy);
  - be correctly orientated.

Chapter

19

Data

GETTING STARTED

Many GCSE questions need data. This data is given either in the question or in the form of a booklet. In the remainder of this chapter there is some data that you will find useful and at the end of the chapter there are questions based on data interpretation.

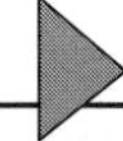

TOPIC CHART

LONDON	MEG	NEAB	NICCEA	SEG	WJEC	TOPIC	STUDY	REVISION 1	REVISION 2
✓	✓	✓	✓	✓	✓	Reactivity series of metals			
✓	✓	✓	✓	✓	✓	Common ions			
✓	✓	✓	✓	✓	✓	Organic compounds			
✓	✓	✓	✓	✓	✓	Properties of elements			
✓	✓	✓	✓	✓	✓	Properties of common compounds			
✓	✓	✓	✓	✓	✓	Properties of gases			
✓	✓	✓	✓	✓	✓	Testing for gases			

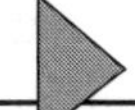

WHAT YOU NEED TO KNOW

Reactivity series of metals

The following list gives the order of **reactivity of metals**, with the most reactive metal first and least reactive metal last:

potassium sodium calcium magnesium aluminium carbon

zinc iron lead hydrogen copper silver

More reactive metals can displace less reactive metals from their salts or their oxides. Thus iron will displace copper from copper(II) sulphate. Two non-metals, carbon and hydrogen, have been included in this list. It is important to realize that at very high temperatures these non-metals would be higher in the list. Thus hydrogen will reduce zinc oxide at very high temperatures.

Common ions

The symbols of the common ions are given in the list below. For **metal ions** it should be noted that the charge on the ion is **positive** and is equal to its **group number**. Hence sodium has a charge of +1, magnesium +2 and aluminium +3. For **non-metals** the charge is **negative** and is equal to eight (8) – (minus) the group number. The charge on the chloride ion is −1 (i.e. 8 − 7); for the oxide ion −2 (8 − 6); and for the nitride ion −3 (8 − 5). The formulae of compounds can be worked out using these charges. A compound must be neutrally charged and therefore the number of positive charges must be equal to the number of negative charges. The formula of copper(II) oxide is CuO (two positive charges on the copper ion and two negative charges on the oxide ion). The formula of magnesium chloride is $MgCl_2$. Magnesium has two positive charges and therefore two negative charges are needed to make the charges equal.

Table 19.1

Positive ions	Name	Negative ions	Name
Ag^+	Silver	Br^-	Bromide
Al^{3+}	Aluminium	Cl^-	Chloride
Ba^{2+}	Barium	CO_3^{2-}	Carbonate
Ca^{2+}	Calcium	F^-	Fluoride
Cu^{2+}	Copper(II)	HCO_3^-	Hydrogencarbonate
Fe^{2+}	Iron(II)	HSO_4^-	Hydrogensulphate
Fe^{3+}	Iron(III)	I^-	Iodide
H^+	Hydrogen	N^{3-}	Nitride
K^+	Potassium	NO_3^-	Nitrate
Mg^{2+}	Magnesium	O^{2-}	Oxide
Na^+	Sodium	OH^-	Hydroxide
NH_4^+	Ammonium	S^{2-}	Sulphide
Pb^{2+}	Lead(II)	SO_3^{2-}	Sulphite
Zn^{2+}	Zinc	SO_4^{2-}	Sulphate

Organic compounds

Organic compounds are arranged in homologous series. The names of the first few members in each series are given together with their melting points and boiling points.

Gases

For a substance to be a gas, at room temperature, its melting point and boiling point must be below room temperature, say 20 °C. Thus some gases in Table 19.2 are methane, ethene and butene.

Table 19.2

Series	Name	Formula	M.p./°C	B.p./°C
Alkanes	Methane	CH_4	−183	−162
	Ethane	C_2H_6	−172	−89
	Propane	C_3H_8	−187	−42
	Butane	C_4H_{10}	−135	−0.5
	Pentane	C_5H_{12}	−130	36
Alkenes	Ethene	C_2H_4	−169	−102
	Propene	C_3H_6	−185	−48
	Butene	C_4H_8	−185	−7
Alcohols	Methanol	CH_3OH	−97	65
	Ethanol	C_2H_5OH	−114	78
	Propanol	C_3H_7OH	−126	97
Acids	Methanoic acid	HCO_2H	9	101
	Ethanoic acid	CH_3CO_2H	17	118

Liquids

For a substance to be a liquid, at room temperature, its melting point must be below room temperature and its boiling point above room temperature. Among the liquids in the above list are pentane, methanol and methanoic acid.

Solids

For a substance to be a solid, at room temperature, its melting point and boiling point must be above room temperature. There are no solids in the above list, at normal room temperature, though below 17 °C, ethanoic acid becomes a solid.

Properties of common elements

In Table 19.3 the melting points and boiling points of some elements are listed together with their ability to conduct electricity. Only two elements are liquids at room temperature and pressure; they are bromine and mercury. You will also notice that all metals are good conductors of electricity.

Properties of common compounds

In Table 19.4 the melting points and boiling points of some compounds are listed, together with an indication whether they conduct when molten. You will notice that all metal compounds conduct electricity when molten.

Properties of gases

The properties of gases can be studied using the mnemonic COWSLIPS—Colour; Odour; Weight; Solubility; Litmus; Inflammability; Poisonous; Supports burning.

Colour

The following gases are coloured:

chlorine	green
hydrogen chloride	colourless but fumes in moist air
iodine vapour	purple
nitrogen(IV) oxide	brown

Odour (smell)

chlorine	pungent
sulphur dioxide	choking
ammonia	makes eyes water
hydrogen chloride	pungent, leaves a sour taste in mouth

Table 19.3

Element	Relative atomic mass	Conductor of electricity	M.p./°C	B.p./°C
Aluminium	27	Yes	660	2450
Argon	40	No	−189	−186
Bromine	80	No	−7	−58
Calcium	40	Yes	845	1490
Carbon	12			
diamond		No	3550	4830
graphite		Yes	3730 sublimes	
Chlorine	35.5	No	−101	−34
Copper	64	Yes	1083	2600
Helium	4	No	−270	−269
Hydrogen	1	No	−259	−253
Iodine	127	No	114	184
Iron	56	Yes	1540	2900
Lead	207	Yes	330	1750
Magnesium	24	Yes	650	1100
Mercury	210	Yes	−39	357
Neon	20	No	−248	−246
Nitrogen	14	No	−210	−196
Oxygen	16	No	−218	−183
Potassium	39	Yes	63	760
Silicon	28	No	1410	2360
Sodium	23	Yes	98	880
Sulphur	32	No	119	445
Zinc	65	Yes	419	907

Table 19.4

'Substances that decompose easily do not have a melting point or a boiling point'

Compound	Relative molecular mass	Conduct when molten	M.p./°C	B.p./°C
Ammonia	17	No	−78	−34
Carbon dioxide	44	No	−111	−78
Calcium carbonate	100	Decomposes when heated		
Calcium oxide	56	Yes	2600	2850
Copper(II) chloride	135	Yes	620	990
Copper(II) sulphate	160	Decomposes when heated		
Glucose	180	No	146	Decomposes
Hydrogen chloride	36.5	No	−114	−85
Lead(II) chloride	278	Yes	501	950
Silicon dioxide	58.5	Yes	801	1413
Water	18	No	0	100

Weight/density

To work out whether a gas is denser or less dense than air, calculate its relative molecular mass (M_r); if it is less than 30, it is less dense than air; if it is greater than 30, it is denser than air.

Hydrogen, methane and ammonia are less dense than air.
Nitrogen, oxygen and carbon monoxide have approximately the same density as air.
Carbon dioxide, chlorine and hydrogen chloride are denser than air.

Solubility

'Acid solutions have an excess of H_3O^+ ions and alkaline solutions an excess of OH^- ions.'

Hydrogen chloride and ammonia are very soluble in water.
They both react with water, e.g.:

$$HCl + H_2O \rightarrow H_3O^+ + Cl^-$$

$$NH_3 + H_2O \rightarrow NH_4^+ + OH^-$$

Chlorine and carbon dioxide are fairly soluble in water:

$$Cl_2 + H_2O \rightarrow HClO + HCl$$

$$CO_2 + H_2O \rightarrow H_2CO_3$$

Hydrogen, carbon monoxide, oxygen and nitrogen are 'insoluble' in water.

Litmus (or universal indicator paper) response

All the gases that dissolve well in water change the colour of damp litmus paper, and of universal indicator (UI) paper.

Those that form acids turn blue litmus and UI paper red, i.e. hydrogen chloride and sulphur dioxide.

Chlorine turns litmus and (UI paper) red, then bleaches it (also does this to UI paper). Carbon dioxide only just changes the colour of litmus (turns UI paper orange). Ammonia turns damp red litmus paper blue (turns UI paper blue/green).

Flammability

The following gases burn:

Hydrogen with a 'pop'.
Carbon monoxide with a blue flame.
Hydrocarbons: the higher the percentage of carbon in the hydrocarbon, the more yellow and smokier the flame.

Poisonous

All gases that smell are poisonous but not all poisonous gases smell! Carbon monoxide, for instance, has no smell but is very poisonous.

Thus, chlorine, hydrogen chloride, ammonia, sulphur dioxide and hydrogen sulphide are poisonous.

Supporting burning

Only oxygen of the frequently met gases supports burning—the rest put out a burning splint.

Testing for gases

Before you start testing for gases, make sure that you have the following apparatus and chemicals at hand:

Bunsen (alight), splints, UI or litmus papers, delivery tube, lime-water, potassium dichromate(VI) paper, concentrated hydrochloric acid, silver nitrate solution, cobalt chloride paper.

The following tips will help when testing a powder:

(1) If you have added hydrochloric acid and a gas is **immediately given off**, you should test for **carbon dioxide**. If the powder looks metallic, test for **hydrogen**.
(2) If you have added **sodium hydroxide** or **sodium carbonate** and heated the solution, you should test for **ammonia** and not for acidic gases.
(3) You should **test in the order**: colour, smell, splint (glowing then burning), pH and then special tests (tests which identify a single gas).
(4) Some colours may be difficult to see, e.g. that of chlorine.

Table 19.5

Colour	Smell	Splint	Litmus or UI paper	Special test	Gas
Green/yellow	Pungent	Put out	Red then bleached		Chlorine
Colourless but fumes in moist air	Pungent	Put out	Red	Test with silver nitrate gives white precipitate	Hydrogen chloride
Colourless	Choking	Put out	Red	Turns potassium dichromate(VI) green	Sulphur dioxide
Colourless	None	Burns with a 'pop'	None		Hydrogen
Colourless	None	Burns with a blue flame	None	Burnt gas turns lime-water milky	Carbon monoxide
Colourless	Perhaps	Burns with a blue/yellow flame	None	Burnt gas turns lime-water milky	Hydrocarbons
Colourless	None	Relights glowing splint	None		Oxygen
Colourless	None	Put out	Faint red	Turns lime-water cloudy	Carbon dioxide
Colourless	Pungent	Put out	Blue	White smoke with hydrogen chloride	Ammonia
(If you cannot smell ammonia, it is not present.)					
Colourless liquid forms on cold part of test tube	None	Put out	None	Turns cobalt chloride pink	Water vapour
Colourless	None	Put out	None	None	Nitrogen

(5) If you cannot **smell** ammonia gas, it is not being given off.
(6) Make sure the litmus paper (or UI paper) is **damp**.
(7) All acidic gases give a white smoke with ammonia.
(8) All gases that **smell** are **poisonous.**
(9) If a **colourless liquid** forms near the top of the test tube, it is most likely to be **water**.

Other useful information

Atomic number — The number of protons in the nucleus of an atom

Avogadro's constant — The number of particles in a mole. Its value is 6×10^{23} particles per mole

Faraday constant — The electrical charge on one mole of electrons. Its value is 96 500 coulombs per mole

Isomers — Compounds with the same molecular formula but different structural formulae

Isotopes — Atoms with the same atomic number but different mass numbers

Mass number — The number of protons plus neutrons in the nucleus of an atom

Molar volume — The volume of one mole of gas at room temperature and pressure. Its value is 24 dm^3 (litres)

The mole — Number of moles = mass of element divided by relative atomic mass (A_r)

Relative atomic mass The relative mass of an atom on a scale on which an atom of carbon-12 is 12.00

Relative formula mass The sum of the relative atomic masses in a formula on a scale on which an atom of carbon-12 is 12.00

QUESTIONS ON DATA

Questions 1–4

Use the data in Table 19.1 to help you to answer the following questions using the A to D given below:

A: 1
B: 2
C: 3
D: 4

1. The value of the positive charge on a calcium ion.
2. The number of atoms joined together to make a nitrate ion.
3. The number of magnesium ions in the formula of magnesium hydrogencarbonate.
4. The number of sulphate ions in the formula of aluminium sulphate. (NEAB)

Questions 5–9

Select from the table (Table 19.6) the letter which represents the substance described in the question.

Table 19.6

Substance	Melting point/°C	Electrical conductivity		Result of heating in air or oxygen
		Solid	Molten	
A	770	Non-conductor	Good	No change
B	98	Good	Good	Burns forming a white solid
C	114	Non-conductor	Non-conductor	Burns forming a gas
D	31	Non-conductor	Non-conductor	Burns forming a gas and water
E	1 080	Good	Good	Substance becomes coated with a black powder

Each letter may be used once, more than once, or not at all.

5. A non-metallic element.
6. A covalent compound.
7. An ionic compound.
8. A substance which could be copper.
9. A substance which could be a hydrocarbon.

Questions 10–12

Match the properties lettered A to E (Table 19.7) with the gases given in questions 10 to 12 (p. 312). Each letter may be used once, more than once, or not at all.

Table 19.7

	Density	Effect of a burning splint	Solubility in water
A	Less than air	Goes out immediately	Not soluble
B	Same as air	Goes out immediately	Slightly soluble
C	Less than air	Gas burns	Not soluble
D	Greater than air	Goes out immediately	Moderately soluble
E	Same as air	Splint burns more brightly	Slightly soluble

Fig. 19.1 Periodic table of elements

1	2											3	4	5	6	7	0
							1 H Hydrogen 1										4 He Helium 2
7 Li Lithium 3	9 Be Beryllium 4											11 B Boron 5	12 C Carbon 6	14 N Nitrogen 7	16 O Oxygen 8	19 F Fluorine 9	20 Ne Neon 10
23 Na Sodium 11	24 Mg Magnesium 12											27 Al Aluminium 13	28 Si Silicon 14	31 P Phosphorus 15	32 S Sulphur 16	35.5 Cl Chlorine 17	40 Ar Argon 18
39 K Potassium 19	40 Ca Calcium 20	45 Sc Scandium 21	48 Ti Titanium 22	51 V Vanadium 23	52 Cr Chromium 24	55 Mn Manganese 25	56 Fe Iron 26	59 Co Cobalt 27	59 Ni Nickel 28	63.5 Cu Copper 29	65 Zn Zinc 30	70 Ga Gallium 31	73 Ge Germanium 32	75 As Arsenic 33	79 Se Selenium 34	80 Br Bromine 35	84 Kr Krypton 36
85 Rb Rubidium 37	88 Sr Strontium 38	89 Y Yttrium 39	91 Zr Zirconium 40	93 Nb Niobium 41	96 Mo Molybdenum 42	Tc Technetium 43	101 Ru Ruthenium 44	103 Rh Rhodium 45	106 Pd Palladium 46	108 Ag Silver 47	112 Cd Cadmium 48	115 In Indium 49	119 Sn Tin 50	122 Sb Antimony 51	128 Te Tellurium 52	127 I Iodine 53	131 Xe Xenon 54
133 Cs Caesium 55	137 Ba Barium 56	139 La Lanthanum 57	178 Hf Hafnium 72	181 Ta Tantalum 73	184 W Tungsten 74	186 Re Rhenium 75	190 Os Osmium 76	192 Ir Iridium 77	195 Pt Platinum 78	197 Au Gold 79	201 Hg Mercury 80	204 Tl Thallium 81	207 Pb Lead 82	209 Bi Bismuth 83	Po Polonium 84	At Astatine 85	222 Rn Radon 86
Fr Francium 87	226 Ra Radium 88	227 Ac Actinium 89															

140 Ce Cerium 58	141 Pr Praseodymium 59	144 Nd Neodymium 60	Pm Promethium 61	150 Sm Samarium 62	152 Eu Europium 63	157 Gd Gadolinium 64	159 Tb Terbium 65	162 Dy Dysprosium 66	165 Ho Holmium 67	167 Er Erbium 68	169 Tm Thulium 69	173 Yb Ytterbium 70	175 Lu Lutetium 71
232 Th Thorium 90	231 Pa Protactinium 91	238 U Uranium 92	Np Neptunium 93	Pu Plutonium 94	Am Americium 95	Cm Curium 96	Bk Berkelium 97	Cf Californium 98	Es Einsteinium 99	Fm Fermium 100	Md Mendelevium 101	No Nobelium 102	Lr Lowrencium 103

·58 – 57 Lanthanum series
†90 – 103 Actinium series

Elements for which no relative atomic mass is shown are not naturally occurring.

10. Oxygen
11. Carbon dioxide
12. Hydrogen

Question 13

Table 19.8 contains information about five compounds, A, B, C, D, and E.

Table 19.8

Compound	A	B	C	D	E
Melting point/°C	319	801	−115	−78	−117
Boiling point/°C	1 390	1 413	−85	−33	78
pH of solution in water	14	7	1	11	7

From the compounds A to E select

(a) a liquid;
(b) a salt;
(c) an alkaline gas;
(d) a compound which could be formed by adding sodium to water;
(e) two compounds which would react with each other. *[5]*

Table 19.9

Substance	Melting point °C	Boiling point °C	Electrical conductivity of	
			Pure solid	Solution with water
A	−40	150	Nil	Insoluble
B	1 083	2 600	Good	Insoluble
C	−112	−84	Nil	Good
D	801	1 450	Nil	Good
E	92	190	Nil	Insoluble
F	12	74	Nil	Nil

Question 14

(a) Using the table (Table 19.9) write the letter of:
(i) a solid at room temperature (20 °C);__________ *[1]*
(ii) a gas at room temperature (20 °C);__________ *[1]*
(iii) a metal;__________ *[1]*
(iv) a covalent liquid;__________ *[1]*
(v) an ionic solid;__________ *[1]*
(vi) a liquid at room temperature which has the smallest temperature range between its melting point and boiling point.__________ *[1]*
(b) Substance E in the table was prepared by pupils in a school laboratory and the melting points of the samples were found to be between 88 and 90 °C. Give an explanation of this fact. [3 lines] *[1]*

Question 15

Use the following data (Table 19.10) to answer the questions below.

(a) If the highest temperature reached by a Bunsen burner flame is 850 °C, which of the substances could be melted by this flame? [1 line] *[1]*
(b) Suggest why the melting point of magnesium carbonate cannot be measured. [2 lines] *[1]*
(c) The apparatus in Fig. 19.2 was used to investigate the reaction of hydrogen with copper(II) oxide and lead(II) oxide. One of the reasons why lead(II) oxide is placed in a 'boat' is because it reacts with glass. Suggest another reason for placing lead(II) oxide in a 'boat'. *[2]*

Table 19.10

Substance	Melting point/°C	Boiling point/°C
Copper	1 083	2 582
Copper(II) oxide	1 328	over 3 000
Lead	330	1 750
Lead(II) oxide	886	1 472
Magnesium carbonate	–	–
Sodium hydroxide	319	1 390

Fig. 19.2

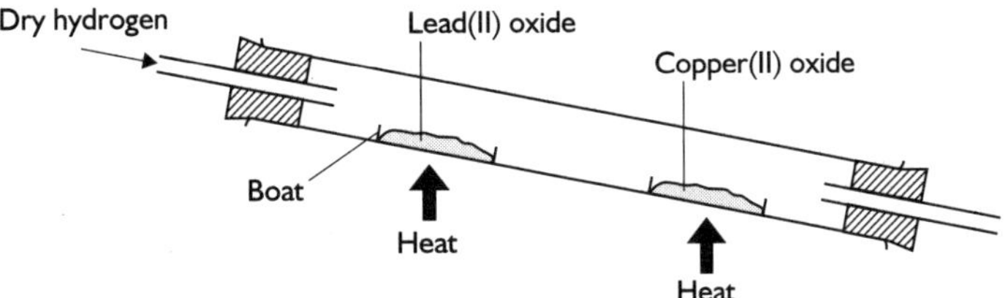

OUTLINE ANSWERS

Questions 1–4

1. If you found Table 19.1 you would have found the ions with their charges at the top right-hand side of each symbol. Answer to this questions is 2+, key B.
2. Nitrate ion has 1 nitrogen atom and 3 oxygen atoms hence the total number of atoms is 4, key D.
3. A–Mg HCO_3.
4. C–Al_2 $(SO_4)_3$.

Questions 5–9

For questions 5 to 9 you will need to remember that:

(i) Non-metallic elements (except carbon in the form of graphite) do not conduct when solid or molten.
(ii) Metallic elements conduct when solid and when molten.
(iii) Ionic compounds do not conduct when solid but do conduct when molten.
(iv) Covalent compounds do not conduct when solid or when molten.
(v) Hydrocarbons burn to form carbon dioxide and water.

5. Key C—must be a non-metal; possibly sulphur.
6. Because it is a compound at least *two* substances must be formed when it is burnt. A covalent compound does not conduct electricity, hence key is D.
7. A.
8. E (black coating is copper(II) oxide).
9. D (hydrocarbons contain hydrogen and carbon only and burn to form carbon dioxide and water).

Questions 10–12

You would find it helpful to refer to 'Properties of Gases', p. 306.

Question 13

(a) For a substance to be a liquid at room temperature its boiling point must be above room temperature (20 °C) and its melting point below room temperature. Hence the answer is E.

The answers to parts (b) to (e) are in Table 19.4, but the following tips will help you:

(b) a salt is usually neutral when dissolved in water and has a high melting point and boiling point. Answer, B.

(c) The melting point and boiling point of a gas are below room temperature. An alkaline solution has a pH greater than 7. Answer, D.
(d) Work out the compound formed. Is this a covalent or an ionic compound? Is this compound acid or alkaline? Answer, A.
(e) This is a difficult question! However, acids react with alkalis. Answer, C and D or C and A.

Question 14 (a) (i) either B, D or E; (ii) C; (iii) B; (iv) A or F; (v) D; (vi) F.
(b) The sample was not pure. (Pure substances have a sharp melting point. If they contain impurities then melting occurs over a **range** of temperatures and **lower** than for the pure substance.)

Question 15 (a) Lead and sodium hydroxide.
(b) Magnesium carbonate decomposes into magnesium oxide and carbon dioxide, hence its melting point cannot be measured.
(c) Lead would be formed and this would melt, run back down the tube and block the exit tube, preventing excess hydrogen from escaping.

STUDENT ANSWERS WITH EXAMINER'S COMMENTS

In the table below are some data concerning a number of well-known elements and compounds. (The letters are not the symbols for these substances.)

Substance	A	B	C	D	E	F
Melting point/°C	98	685	1 083	0	119	114
Boiling point/°C	890	1 322	2 600	100	444	183
Heat of vaporization/kJ mol^{-1}	89		305	41		42
Electrical conductivity: when solid	Good	Nil	Good	Nil	Nil	Nil
when molten	Good	Good	Good	Poor	Nil	Nil
when in aqueous solution	Reacts with water	Good	Not soluble	Poor	Not soluble	Not soluble

(a) Which substance is water? *D*

State one piece of evidence you used in making this choice.

Melting point 0 °C

(1 mark)

(continued)

(continued)

(b) State two pieces of evidence you would use to support the suggestion that substance C is a metal.

Good conductor of electricity and it does not dissolve in water

'Many compounds do not dissolve. Very high melting point is the best second reason.'

(1 mark)

(c) Substance B is dissolved in water, and substance F is dissolved in sodium hydroxide solution. When both solutions are electrolysed in separate electrolysis cells, they form dark brown solutions at the anodes. On heating, both dark brown solutions give a purple vapour. Name the element which is common to B and F.

Iodine

(1 mark)

(d) One of the substances B and F readily changes to this purple vapour when heated. State which one is more likely to do this and write a brief explanation to support your choice.

B, because it conducts when it is molten.

'F is covalent (molecular) and would easily turn into a vapour, B is ionic and would not vaporise readily.'

(1 mark)

(e) The graph below shows the data for three elements. Add to this the values for A, D and F from the table of data, and use the graph to obtain an estimated value for the heat needed to vaporize one mole of substance E.

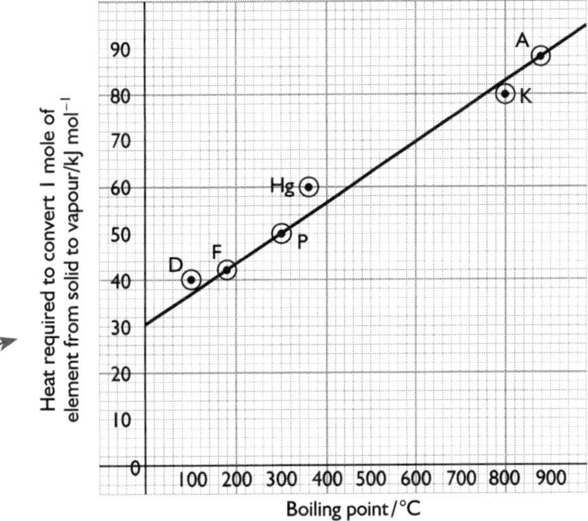

'Good plotting and a nicely drawn line of best fit'

The estimated value for E is *60 kJ/mol*

(3 marks)

(f) When 0.01 mole of the substance C (which is a metal) was added to an excess of silver nitrate solution, $AgNO_3(aq)$, a deposit of silver metal was formed which, after filtering off, washing and drying, was found to weigh 2.16 g.

(i) Calculate the number of moles of silver formed. (Relative atomic mass: Ag = 108)

$\frac{108}{2.16} = 50$

'You've divided this the wrong way up!'

(1 mark)

(ii) What is the charge on C? *+1*

(1 mark)

(iii) Using C as the symbol for the metal, write the ionic equation for the reaction between C and the $Ag^+(aq)$ ions in the silver nitrate solution, including the state symbols.

$C + Ag^+ \rightarrow C^+ + Ag$

(1 mark)

(LEAG) *(Total 10 marks)*

'You must revise the mole topic more carefully. Score 5/10. In (f) part (i) the answer is 2.16/108 = 0.02, the charge on C is 2+ and the ionic equation is $C(s) + 2Ag^+(aq) \rightarrow C^{2+}(aq) + 2Ag(s)$'

Index

Longman - for all your study guide needs

Addison Wesley Longman publishes a wide range of curriculum-related books to help you with your studies. If you have enjoyed using this book and have found it useful, you can now order others directly from us - simply follow the ordering instructions below.

Don't forget to tell your fellow students about *Longman Study Guides* - they might find them useful too!

HOW TO ORDER

A full list of titles is given overleaf. Decide which title(s) you require and then order in one of the following ways:

by post
Fill in the quantity alongside the title(s) you require, select your method of payment, complete your name and address details and return your completed order form and payment to:
Addison Wesley Longman Ltd
PO BOX 88
Harlow
Essex CM19 5SR

by phone
Call our Customer Information Centre on 01279 623923 to place your order, quoting mail number: HESG1

by fax
complete the order form overleaf and fill in your name and address details and method of payment, and fax it to us on 01279 414130.

by e-mail
E-mail your order to us on awlhe.orders@awl.co.uk listing title(s) and quantity required and providing full name and address details as requested here. Please quote mail number: HESG1. Please do not send credit card details by e-mail.

Mail no: HESG1

Your Name ____

Your Address ______________________________________

____

Postcode __________________ Telephone ______________________

Method of payment

☐ I enclose a cheque or a P/O for £ ______ made payable to Addison Wesley Longman Ltd
☐ Please charge my Visa/Access/AMEX/Diners Club card

Number __________________________ Expiry Date _____________

Signature _________________________ Date _________________

(please ensure that the address given above is the same as for your credit card)

Prices and other details are correct at time of going to press but may change without notice. All orders are subject to status.

☐ *Please tick this box if you would like a complete listing of York Notes Literature Guides (suitable for GCSE and A-level English students)*

LONGMAN

Addison Wesley Longman

LONGMAN HOMEWORK HANDBOOKS (KEY STAGE 3)

£7.99 each unless otherwise stated

	QTY *(0582)*		
1	_____	29330 8	English (KS3)
2	_____	29331 6	French (KS3)
3	_____	30423 7	French pack*(KS3) (£12.99)
4	_____	30425 3	French cassette (KS3) (£6.00)
5	_____	29329 4	German (KS3)
6	_____	30427 X	German pack*(KS3) (£12.99)
7	_____	30428 8	German cassette (KS3) (£6.00)
8	_____	29328 6	Mathematics (KS3)
9	_____	29327 8	Science (KS3)

LONGMAN GCSE STUDY GUIDES

£9.99 each unless otherwise stated

10	_____	30481 4	Biology
11	_____	31538 7	Business Studies
12	_____	30482 2	Chemistry
13	_____	31539 5	Economics
14	_____	30484 9	English
15	_____	30483 0	English Literature
16	_____	30485 7	French
17	_____	03839 1	French pack* (£14.99)
18	_____	03836 7	French cassette (£6.00)
19	_____	30486 5	Geography
20	_____	30487 3	German
21	_____	03837 5	German pack* (£14.99)
22	_____	03838 3	German cassette (£6.00)
23	_____	30495 4	Higher Level Mathematics
24	_____	30494 6	Information Technology (£10.99)
25	_____	30496 2	Mathematics
26	_____	30497 0	Music
27	_____	31540 9	Physics
28	_____	28700 6	Psychology
29	_____	31542 5	Religious Studies
30	_____	30498 9	Science (£10.99)
31	_____	22651 1	Sociology
32	_____	22652 X	Spanish
33	_____	24509 5	Spanish pack* (£14.99)
34	_____	24511 7	Spanish cassette (£6.00)
35	_____	23771 8	Technology
36	_____	30545 4	World History

LONGMAN GCSE EXAM PRACTICE KITS

37	_____	30381 8	Biology £4.99)
38	_____	30383 4	Business Studies (£4.99)
39	_____	31191 8	English (£4.99)
40	_____	30384 2	Geography (£4.99)
41	_____	30385 0	Mathematics (£4.99)
42	_____	30379 6	Physics (£4.99)
43	_____	30380 X	Science (£5.99)

LONGMAN GCSE REFERENCE GUIDES *£6.99 each*

44	_____	05788 4	Biology
45	_____	05790 6	Chemistry
46	_____	05072 3	English
47	_____	05077 4	French
48	_____	05074 X	Mathematics
49	_____	05794 9	Physics
50	_____	05076 6	Science

GCSE SURVIVAL GUIDE *£2.95*

51	_____	05078 2

_____**YORK NOTES LITERATURE GUIDES** *(see overleaf)*

LONGMAN A-LEVEL STUDY GUIDES

£9.99 each unless otherwise stated

52	_____	22569 8	Accounting (£10.99)
53	_____	31545 X	Biology
54	_____	31652 9	Business Studies
55	_____	31546 8	Chemistry
56	_____	05782 5	Computer Science
57	_____	27688 8	Economics (£10.99)
58	_____	31656 1	English
59	_____	05784 1	French
60	_____	24495 1	French pack* (£14.99)
61	_____	24497 8	French cassette (£6.00)
62	_____	05173 8	Geography
63	_____	31654 5	German
64	_____	24498 6	German pack* (£14.99)
65	_____	24508 7	German cassette (£6.00)
66	_____	28702 2	Government and Politics (£10.99)
67	_____	31549 2	Law (£10.99)
68	_____	31550 6	Mathematics (£10.99)
69	_____	31551 4	Modern History
70	_____	27690 X	Physics
71	_____	31655 3	Psychology
72	_____	27691 8	Sociology

LONGMAN A-LEVEL EXAM PRACTICE KITS *£6.99 each*

73	_____	30386 9	Biology
74	_____	30387 7	Business Studies
75	_____	30388 5	Chemistry
76	_____	30389 3	Mathematics
77	_____	30390 7	Psychology
78	_____	30382 6	Sociology

LONGMAN A-LEVEL REFERENCE GUIDES *£6.99 each*

79	_____	06394 9	Biology
80	_____	06390 6	Chemistry
81	_____	06396 5	English
82	_____	06398 1	Mathematics
83	_____	06392 2	Physics (£7.99)

LONGMAN HANDBOOKS *£7.99 each*

84	_____	09965 X	Botany
85	_____	08810 0	Chemistry

LONGMAN PARENT'S AND STUDENTS' GUIDES

£2.99 each

86	_____	29971 3	Longman Parent's Guide to Pre-school Choices and Nursery Education
87	_____	29975 6	Longman Parent's Guide to Key Stage 1 of the National Curriculum
88	_____	29974 8	Longman Parent's Guide to Key Stage 2 of the National Curriculum
89	_____	29973 X	Longman Parent's Guide to Key Stage 3 of the National Curriculum
90	_____	29972 1	Longman Parent's Guide to GCSE and Key Stage 4 of the National Curriculum
91	_____	29978 0	Longman A-level Survival Guide
92	_____	29969 1	Longman Students' Guide to Vocational Education
93	_____	29970 5	Longman Students' Guide to Returning Learning
to			
94	_____	29976 4	Longman Students' Guide to Higher Education

** pack = book and cassette*